AN ELEMENTARY TREATISE

ON THE

DIFFERENTIAL CALCULUS

WITH APPLICATIONS AND NUMEROUS EXAMPLES

BY

JOSEPH EDWARDS, M.A.

FORMERLY FELLOW OF SIDNEY SUSSEX COLLEGE, CAMBRIDGE

MACMILLAN AND CO., LIMITED
ST. MARTIN'S STREET, LONDON
1918

GLASGOW : PRINTED AT THE UNIVERSITY PRESS
BY ROBERT MACLEHOSE AND CO. LTD.

PREFACE TO THE SECOND EDITION.

In issuing a second edition of the present volume it has been found desirable to enlarge it considerably beyond its original limits. The necessity for this has arisen partly from the increased requirements of the class of students for whom the book was originally written, and partly from the expressed opinion of many teachers that its sphere of usefulness might be thereby extended.

Chapters have been added on Maxima and Minima of Several Independent Variables, on Elimination, on Lagrange's and Laplace's Theorems, on Changing the Independent Variable, and one giving a short account of the principal properties of the best-known curves, which may be convenient for reference. A number of isolated theorems and processes, which do not find a convenient place elsewhere, have been put into a separate chapter entitled Miscellaneous Theorems. Considerable additions have been made to some of the original articles, and others have been rewritten.

Many additional sets of easy examples, specially illustrative of the theorems and methods proved or explained in the immediately preceding bookwork, have been inserted, in the hope that a selection from these will firmly fix in the mind of the student the leading principles and processes to be adopted in their solution before attacking the generally more difficult problems at the ends of the chapters.

In a text-book of this character there will not be found much that is new or original, the object being to present to the student as succinct an account as possible of the most important results and methods which are up to the present time known, and to afford sufficient scope for practice in their use.

To attain this object many treatises on this and allied subjects have been consulted, and my acknowledgments of assistance are therefore due to many authors. More particularly I am indebted for much information to the admirable works of Cramer, Gregory, De Morgan, l'Abbé Moigno, Serret, Frenet, Bertrand, Frost, Todhunter, Williamson, and Salmon, whose labours have done so much to develop and extend the principles and applications of the subject.

I have consulted a large number of university and college examination papers set in Oxford, Cambridge, London, and elsewhere, and many of the examples given have been extracted from them. Such papers clearly define the extent of knowledge expected from students by the large body of distinguished scholars who from time to time are engaged in conducting these examinations, and the present work has been constructed to meet these requirements as far as possible.

My thanks are due to several friends and correspondents who have kindly sent me valuable suggestions and lists of errata occurring in the first edition.

JOSEPH EDWARDS.

80 CAMBRIDGE GARDENS,
   NORTH KENSINGTON, W.
     February, 1892.

THIRD EDITION.

IN this edition several errors have been eliminated, and a few additional articles inserted in Chapter XX. on Roulettes and on the Numbers of Bernoulli and Euler.

JOSEPH EDWARDS.

January, 1896.

CONTENTS.

PRINCIPLES AND PROCESSES OF THE
DIFFERENTIAL CALCULUS.

CHAPTER I.

DEFINITIONS. LIMITS.

CHAPTER II.

FUNDAMENTAL PROPOSITIONS.

CHAPTER III.

STANDARD FORMS.

CHAPTER IV.

Successive Differentiation

CHAPTER V.

Expansions.

CHAPTER VI.

Partial Differentiation.

APPLICATIONS TO PLANE CURVES.

CHAPTER VII.

TANGENTS AND NORMALS.

CHAPTER VIII.

ASYMPTOTES.

CHAPTER IX.

SINGULAR POINTS.

CHAPTER X.

CURVATURE.

CHAPTER XI.

ENVELOPES.

CHAPTER XII.

Curve Tracing.

CHAPTER XIII.

On Some Well-Known Curves.

APPLICATION TO THE EVALUATION OF
SINGULAR FORMS, MAXIMA AND MINIMA VALUES, ETC.

CHAPTER XIV.
UNDETERMINED FORMS.

CHAPTER XV.
MAXIMA AND MINIMA—ONE INDEPENDENT VARIABLE.

CHAPTER XVI.
MAXIMA AND MINIMA—SEVERAL INDEPENDENT VARIABLES.

CHAPTER XVII.

ELIMINATION.

CHAPTER XVIII.

EXPANSIONS (Continued from Chapter V.).

CHAPTER XIX.

CHANGE OF THE INDEPENDENT VARIABLE.

CHAPTER XX.

MISCELLANEOUS THEOREMS.

PRINCIPLES AND PROCESSES OF THE
DIFFERENTIAL CALCULUS

CHAPTER I.

DEFINITIONS. LIMITS.

1. Primary Object of the Differential Calculus.

When increasing or decreasing quantities are made the subject of mathematical investigation, it frequently becomes necessary to estimate their rates of growth. The primary object of the Differential Calculus is to describe an instrument for the measurement of such rates and to frame rules for its formation and use.

2. The whole machinery of the Differential Calculus will be completed in the first six chapters, and the student should make himself as proficient as possible in its manipulation. The remaining chapters simply consist of various applications of the methods and formulae here established.

3. We commence with an explanation of several technical terms which are of frequent occurrence in this subject, and with the meanings of which the student should be familiar from the outset.

4. Constants and Variables.

A CONSTANT *is a quantity which, during any set of mathematical operations, retains the same value.*

A VARIABLE *is a quantity which, during any set of mathematical operations, does not retain the same value, but is capable of assuming different values.*

Ex. The area of any triangle on a given base and between given parallels is a constant quantity ; so also the base, the distance between the parallel lines, the sum of the angles of the triangle are constant quantities. But the separate angles, the sides, the position of the vertex are variables.

It has become conventional to make use of the letters a, b, c, ..., a, β, γ, ..., from the beginning of the alphabet to denote constants; and to retain later letters, such as u, v, w, x, y, z, and the Greek letters ξ, η, ζ, for variables.

5. Dependent and Independent Variables.

An INDEPENDENT VARIABLE *is one which may take up any arbitrary value that may be assigned to it.*

A DEPENDENT VARIABLE *is one which assumes its value in consequence of some second variable or system of variables taking up any set of arbitrary values that may be assigned to them.*

6. Functions.

When one quantity depends upon another or upon a system of others, so that it assumes a definite value when a system of definite values is given to the others, it is called a FUNCTION *of those others.*

The function itself is a *dependent* variable, and the variables to which values are given are *independent* variables.

The usual notation to express that one variable y is a function of another x is

$$y = f(x), \text{ or } y = F(x), \text{ or } y = \phi(x);$$

the letters $f(\ )$, $F(\ )$, $\phi(\ )$, $\chi(\ )$, ... being generally retained to represent functions of arbitrary or unknown form. Occasionally the brackets are dispensed with when no confusion can thereby arise. Thus fx will sometimes be written for $f(x)$. If u be an arbitrary or unknown function of several variables x, y, z, we may express the fact by the equation

$$u = f(x, y, z).$$

Ex. In any triangle, two of whose sides are x and y and the included angle θ, we have $\Delta = \frac{1}{2}xy \sin \theta$ to express the area. Here Δ is the *dependent* variable, and is a *function* of known form—of x, y, and θ, which are the *independent* variables.

7. It will be seen that we could write the same equation in other forms,

$$e.g., \qquad\qquad \sin \theta = \frac{2\Delta}{xy},$$

which may be regarded as an expression for $\sin \theta$ in terms of the area and two sides; so that now $\sin\theta$ may be regarded as the *dependent* variable, while Δ, x, y, are *independent* variables.

And it is clear that if there be one equation between four variables, as above, it is sufficient to determine one in terms of the other three, so that *any one variable may be regarded as dependent and the others as independent.*

This may be extended. For, if there be one equation between n variables, it will suffice to find one of them in terms of the remaining $(n-1)$, so that *any one variable can be considered dependent and the remaining $(n-1)$ independent.*

And, further, if there be r equations connecting n variables (n being greater than r) they will be enough to determine r of the variables in terms of the other $n-r$ variables, so that *any r of the variables can be considered dependent, while the remaining $(n-r)$ are independent.*

8. Explicit and Implicit Functions.

A function is said to be EXPLICIT *when expressed directly in terms of the independent variable or variables.*

For example, if $\quad z=x^2$, or $z=r\sin\theta$, or $z=x^2y$,

or $\quad z=a^y e^x \log x + (a+x)^n:$

z is expressed *directly* in terms of the independent variables, and is therefore in each of the above cases said to be an *explicit* function of those variables.

But, *if the function be not expressed directly in terms of the independent variable (or variables) the function is said to be* IMPLICIT.

If, for example, $\quad ax^2+yx-b=0;$

or $\quad x^2y^2=(a^2-y^2)(b+y)^2;$

y in each case is said to be an implicit function of x.

Sometimes, however, we can solve the equation for y: *e.g.*, the first equation we can write as $y=\dfrac{b-ax^2}{x}$, and in this form y is said to be an explicit function of x.

It appears then that if the equation connecting the variables be solved for the dependent variable, that variable is reduced from being an implicit to being an explicit function of the remaining variable or variables. Such solution is not, however, always possible or convenient.

9. Species of Known Functions.

Functions which are made up of powers of variables and constants connected by the signs $+ - \times \div$ are classed as *algebraic* functions. If radical signs or fractional indices occur in the function, it is said to be *irrational*; if not, *rational*.

All other functions are classed as *transcendental* functions.

Of transcendental functions, sines, cosines, tangents, etc., are called *trigonometrical* or *circular* functions.

Functions such as $\sin^{-1}x$, $\tan^{-1}x$, etc., are called *inverse trigonometrical* functions.

Functions such as e^x, a^{x^2}, in which the variable occurs in the index, are called *exponential* functions.

While if logarithms are involved, as for instance in $\log_e x$ or $\log_{10}(a+bx)$, etc., the function is called *logarithmic*.

Besides the above we have the *hyperbolic* functions, $\sinh x$, $\cosh x$, etc., of which a short description follows in Art. 23.

10. Limit of a Function.

DEF. *When a function can be made to approach continually to equality with some fixed value so as to differ from it by less than any assignable quantity, however small, by making the independent variable (or variables) approach some assigned value (or values), that fixed value is called the* LIMIT *of the function for the value (or values) of the variable (or variables) referred to.*

11. Illustrations.

Ex. 1. If an equilateral polygon be inscribed in any closed curve, and the sides of the polygon be decreased indefinitely and at the same time increased in number indefinitely, the polygon continually approximates to the form of the curve, *and ultimately differs from it in area by less than any assignable magnitude,* and the curve is said to be the *limit* of the polygon inscribed in it.

Ex. 2. The limit of $\dfrac{2x+3}{x+1}$ when x is indefinitely diminished is 3. For the difference between $\dfrac{2x+3}{x+1}$ and 3 is $\dfrac{x}{x+1}$; and by diminishing x indefinitely $\dfrac{x}{x+1}$ can be made less than any assignable quantity however small. Hence it is said that the limit of $\dfrac{2x+3}{x+1}$ when x is indefinitely diminished is 3.

The expression can also be written $\dfrac{2+\dfrac{3}{x}}{1+\dfrac{1}{x}}$, which shows that if x be increased indefinitely it can be made to continually approach and *to differ by less than any assignable quantity* from 2, which is therefore its limit in that case.

Ex. 3. *The limits of some quantities are zero, e.g.,*

$$\left.\begin{array}{r} ax^2 + bx, \\ \sin x, \\ 1 - \cos x, \end{array}\right\} \text{when } x \text{ is zero,}$$

$$\left.\begin{array}{r} 1 - \sin x, \\ \cos x, \end{array}\right\} \text{when } x = \frac{\pi}{2}.$$

When the limit of a quantity is zero for any value or values of the independent variable or variables, the quantity is said to be a *vanishing quantity* for those values.

It is useful to adopt the notation $Lt_{x=a}$ to denote the words "*the limit when $x = a$ of.*"

Ex. 4. The sum of a *G.P.* of which the first term is a, common ratio r, and n the number of terms, is $a\dfrac{r^n - 1}{r - 1}$.

If $r < 1$, the sum to infinity is $\dfrac{a}{1-r}$. For the difference is $\dfrac{ar^n}{r-1}$; and since $Lt_{n=\infty}\dfrac{ar^n}{r-1} = 0$ (when $r < 1$), this difference is a *vanishing quantity*.

Ex. 5. We say $\cdot\dot{6} = \frac{2}{3}$, by which we mean that by taking enough sixes we can make $\cdot666\ldots$ *differ by as little as we please from* $\frac{2}{3}$.

Ex. 6. The DEFINITION OF A TANGENT is another example.

DEF. *Let PQ be a chord joining P, Q, two adjacent points on a curve. Let Q travel along the curve towards P and come so close as ultimately to coincide with P. Then the limiting position of PQ, viz. PT, is called the tangent at P.*

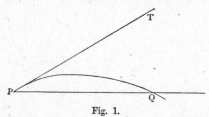

Fig. 1.

The angle QPT is a *vanishing quantity ;* for it can be made less than any assignable quantity by making Q move *along the curve* sufficiently close to P.

12. We proceed to state several important principles with regard to limits which are of frequent use :—

(1) The *limit of the sum* of a finite number of quantities is equal to the *sum of their limits*.

(2) The *limit of the product* of a finite number of quantities is *in general* equal to the *product of their limits*.

(3) The *limit of the ratio* of two quantities (*whose limits are not zero or infinite*) is equal to the *ratio of their limits*.

(4) The *limits of two quantities* (*whose limits are finite*) *are equal when the limit of their difference is zero*.

These statements are almost self-evident, and their formal proofs may be left as an elementary exercise for the student.

EXAMPLES.

1. If $u_1, u_2, \ldots$ be the varying quantities, prove
$$Lt(u_1 + u_2 + u_3 + \ldots) = Ltu_1 + Ltu_2 + \ldots.$$

[Let $v_1, v_2 \ldots$ be the respective limits of u_1, u_2, etc., and let $u_1 = v_1 + a_1$, $u_2 = v_2 + a_2$, etc., where $a_1, a_2, \ldots$ become less than any assignable quantities when the variables $u_1, u_2, \ldots$ approach their limits.

Then $u_1 + u_2 + \ldots = (v_1 + v_2 + \ldots) + (a_1 + a_2 + \ldots)$,
and if a be the greatest of the quantities $a_1, a_2 \ldots$ and n their number,
$$a_1 + a_2 + \ldots < na.$$
But by hypothesis $Lt a = 0$; and therefore if n be finite $Lt na = 0$,
whence $Lt(u_1 + u_2 + \ldots) = v_1 + v_2 + \ldots$
$$= Ltu_1 + Ltu_2 + \ldots].$$

2. Prove $Lt u_1 u_2 = Ltu_1 \cdot Ltu_2$
and $Lt(u_1 u_2 \ldots u_n) = Ltu_1 \cdot Ltu_2 \cdot Ltu_3 \ldots$;
pointing out any exceptions.

3. Prove $Lt \dfrac{u_1}{u_2} = \dfrac{Ltu_1}{Ltu_2}$; $Lt u^n = (Ltu)^n$; $Lt a^u = a^{Ltu}$; $Lt \log u = \log Ltu$;
pointing out any exceptions.

13. Indeterminate or Illusory Forms.

When a function involves the independent variable (or variables) in such a manner that, for a certain assigned value of that variable, its value *cannot be found by simply substituting* that value of the variable, the function is usually said to take an *indeterminate form* or to assume an *indeterminate value*.

14. The name *indeterminate*, though sanctioned by common use, is open to objection, inasmuch as it will be found that the true values of such forms *can in general be arrived at* by means of certain processes which we shall hereafter discuss at length in a special chapter; whereas it would seem to be implied in the name *indeterminate* that it would be *impossible*

to obtain the value of a function to which that name was applied. "Undetermined" or "Illusory Forms" appear to be better designations for such cases.

15. One of the commonest cases occurring is when the function takes the form of a fraction whose *Numerator and Denominator both vanish* for the assigned value of the variable.

The *limit of the ratio of two vanishing quantities may be zero, finite or infinite.*

Several other indeterminate forms are treated fully in Chapter XIII.

16. Two functions of the same independent variable are said to be *ultimately equal* when, as the independent variable approaches indefinitely near its assigned value, the *limit of their ratio is unity.*

Thus
$$Lt_{\theta=0} \frac{\sin \theta}{\theta} = 1 \; ;$$

and therefore, when an angle is indefinitely diminished, its sine and its circular measure are ultimately equal.

EXAMPLES.

1. Find the limit when $x = 0$ of $\frac{y}{x^2}$,

    (i.) When $y = mx.$

    (ii.) When $y = \frac{x^2}{a}.$

    (iii.) When $y = ax^2 + b.$

2. Find $Lt \frac{1+2x}{2+x}$, (i.) when $x = 0$; (ii.) when $x = \infty$.

3. Find $Lt_{x=0} \frac{y}{x}$, when $y^2 = 2ax - x^2$.

4. Find $Lt_{x=0} \frac{y}{x}$, when $\frac{x^2}{a^2} - \frac{y^2}{b^2} = x^3$.

5. Find $Lt_{x=0} \frac{\sqrt{1+x}-1}{x}$.

6. Find $Lt_{x=0} \frac{y^2}{x}$, when $y^2 = ax + bx^2 + cx^3$.

7. Find $Lt_{x=a} \frac{x^3 - a^3}{x - a}$.

8. Find $Lt \frac{ax^2 + bx}{bx^2 + ax}$, when (i.) $x = 0$; (ii.) $x = \infty$.

9. Find $Lt_{x=\infty} \sqrt{x}(\sqrt{x+1} - \sqrt{x})$.

10. Prove that $p - qx$ and $q - px$ tend to equality as x diminishes to zero, but yet that their limits are not equal.

11. The opposite angles of a quadrilateral inscribed in a circle are together equal to two right angles. What does this become when in the limit two angular points coincide?

12. Find the ultimate position of the point of intersection of the diagonals of a rhombus, when one of the angles diminishes indefinitely.

17. We now proceed to consider the limits of four very important undetermined forms.

18. I. The proofs of the well-known results

$$Lt_{\theta=0}\frac{\sin \theta}{\theta} = 1,$$

$$Lt_{\theta=0}\cos \theta = 1,$$

$$Lt_{\theta=0}\frac{\tan \theta}{\theta} = 1,$$

can be found in any standard book on Plane Trigonometry.

19. II. $$Lt_{x=1}\frac{x^n-1}{x-1} = n,$$

Let $x=1+z$. Then when x approaches the value unity z approaches zero, and we can therefore consider z to be less than 1, and therefore can apply the Binomial Theorem to expand $(1+z)^n$, whatever n may be.

Hence $$Lt_{x=1}\frac{x^n-1}{x-1} = Lt_{z=0}\frac{(1+z)^n-1}{z}$$

$$= Lt_{z=0}\frac{nz+\frac{n(n-1)}{2!}z^2+\dots}{z}$$

$$= Lt_{z=0}\left\{n+\frac{n(n-1)}{2!}z+\dots\right\}$$

$$= n.$$

20. III. $Lt_{x=\infty}\left(1+\frac{1}{x}\right)^x = e$, where e is the base of the Napierian system of logarithms. This number e is defined as the value of the series $1+1+\frac{1}{2!}+\frac{1}{3!}+\dots$ to ∞, and it may easily be shown to be $2.7182818\dots$

Since x is to be ultimately infinite, we may throughout consider $\frac{1}{x}$ to be less than unity, and may therefore apply the Binomial Theorem to the expansion of $\left(1+\frac{1}{x}\right)^x$. We thus obtain $\left(1+\dfrac{1}{x}\right)^x = 1 + x\dfrac{1}{x} + \dfrac{x(x-1)}{1 \cdot 2}\dfrac{1}{x^2} + \dfrac{x(x-1)(x-2)}{1 \cdot 2 \cdot 3}\dfrac{1}{x^3} + \cdots$

$$= 1 + 1 + \dfrac{1 - \dfrac{1}{x}}{2!} + \dfrac{\left(1 - \dfrac{1}{x}\right)\left(1 - \dfrac{2}{x}\right)}{3!} + \cdots$$

$$= 1 + 1 + \dfrac{1}{2!} + \dfrac{1}{3!} + \cdots$$

in the limit, when x is indefinitely increased.

COR. $\qquad Lt_{x=\infty}\left(1 + \dfrac{a}{x}\right)^x = Lt_{\frac{x}{a}=\infty}\left\{\left(1 + \dfrac{a}{x}\right)^{\frac{x}{a}}\right\}^a = e^a.$

21. IV. $\qquad Lt_{x=0}\dfrac{a^x - 1}{x} = \log_e a.$

Assume the expansion for a^x, viz. :

$$a^x = 1 + x\log_e a + \dfrac{x^2(\log_e a)^2}{2!} + \cdots$$

This is a convergent series, for the test fraction is $\dfrac{x \log_e a}{n}$, and can be made less than any assignable quantity by making n sufficiently large.

We have therefore

$$\dfrac{a^x - 1}{x} = \log_e a + \dfrac{x(\log_e a)^2}{2!} + \cdots$$

and the limit of the right-hand side, when x is indefinitely diminished, is clearly $\log_e a$.

22. The limit IV. can be deduced from III. thus :

Let $\qquad a^x - 1 = \dfrac{1}{y},$

then $\qquad a^x = 1 + \dfrac{1}{y},$

and therefore when x becomes zero y becomes infinite, and

$$x = \log_a\left(1 + \dfrac{1}{y}\right),$$

$\therefore \qquad Lt_{x=0}\dfrac{a^x - 1}{x} = Lt_{y=\infty}\dfrac{\dfrac{1}{y}}{\log_a\left(1 + \dfrac{1}{y}\right)}$

$$= Lt_{y=\infty}\dfrac{1}{y\log_a\left(1 + \dfrac{1}{y}\right)} = Lt_{y=\infty}\dfrac{1}{\log_a\left(1 + \dfrac{1}{y}\right)^y}$$

$$= \dfrac{1}{\log_a\left[Lt_{y=\infty}\left(1 + \dfrac{1}{y}\right)^y\right]} = \dfrac{1}{\log_a e} \qquad \text{[Art. 20]}.$$

$$= \log_e a.$$

Examples.

1. Prove $$Lt_{x=1}\frac{\log x}{x-1}=1.$$
[Put $x=1+y$.]

2. Prove $$Lt_{x=a}\frac{x^m-a^m}{x^n-a^n}=\frac{m}{n}a^{m-n}.$$

3. Prove $$Lt_{x=0}(1+ax)^{\frac{1}{x}}=e^a.$$

4. Prove $$Lt_{x=0}\frac{\sin mx}{\sin nx}=\frac{m}{n}.$$

5. Prove $$Lt_{x=0}\frac{a^x-1-x\log a}{x^2}=\tfrac{1}{2}(\log a)^2.$$

6. Prove $Lt_{x=1}\dfrac{x^n-1}{x-1}=n$ without assuming the Binomial theorem ; con-sidering the several cases, (i.) n a positive integer, (ii.) n a positive fraction, (iii.) n negative, (iv.) n incommensurable.

23. Hyperbolic Functions.

By analogy with the exponential values of the sine, cosine, tangent, etc., the exponential functions

$$\frac{e^\theta-e^{-\theta}}{2},\ \frac{e^\theta+e^{-\theta}}{2},\ \frac{e^\theta-e^{-\theta}}{e^\theta+e^{-\theta}},\ \text{etc.},$$

are respectively written

sinh θ, cosh θ, tanh θ, etc.,

and called the *hyperbolic sine, cosine, tangent*, etc., of θ, and as a class are styled *hyperbolic functions*.

Since $$\sin\theta=\frac{e^{\iota\theta}-e^{-\iota\theta}}{2\iota},\ \text{and}\ \cos\theta=\frac{e^{\iota\theta}+e^{-\iota\theta}}{2},$$

where $\iota=\sqrt{-1}$, it will be clear that

$$\sin\iota\theta=\iota\sinh\theta,$$
$$\cos\iota\theta=\cosh\theta,$$

and hence or from the definition

(1) $\tan\iota\theta=\iota\dfrac{\sinh\theta}{\cosh\theta}=\iota\tanh\theta$;

(2) $\cosh^2\theta-\sinh^2\theta=1$;

(3) $\sin(\theta+\iota\phi)=\sin\theta\cosh\phi+\iota\cos\theta\sinh\phi$;

with many other formulae analogous to, and easily deducible from, the common formulae of Trigonometry.

If $$x=\sinh\theta,$$
we have $$\theta=\sinh^{-1}x,$$
an *inverse hyperbolic* function of x analogous to the inverse trigonometrical function $\sin^{-1}x$.

This species of function however is merely logarithmic; for,

since $$x = \frac{e^\theta - e^{-\theta}}{2},$$

we have $$e^\theta = x + \sqrt{1 + x^2},$$

and $$\theta = \log_e(x + \sqrt{1 + x^2}),$$

while corresponding results hold for $\cosh^{-1}x$, $\tanh^{-1}x$, etc.

EXAMPLES.

1. Prove the following formulae—

(a) $$\operatorname{cosech}^2\theta = \coth^2\theta - 1 ;$$

(b) $$\sinh(\theta + \phi) = \sinh\theta\cosh\phi + \cosh\theta\sinh\phi ;$$

(c) $$\tanh(\theta + \phi) = \frac{\tanh\theta + \tanh\phi}{1 + \tanh\theta\tanh\phi} ;$$

(d) $$\sinh\theta + \sinh\phi = 2\sinh\frac{\theta + \phi}{2}\cosh\frac{\theta - \phi}{2}.$$

2. Show that the co-ordinates of any point on the rectangular hyperbola $x^2 - y^2 = a^2$ may be denoted by $a\cosh\theta$, $a\sinh\theta$.

3. Prove (a) $$\sinh^{-1}x = \tanh^{-1}\frac{x}{\sqrt{1 + x^2}} ;$$

(b) $$2\tanh^{-1}x = \log\frac{1 + x}{1 - x}.$$

4. If $x + \iota y = a\tan(u + \iota v)$, show that the curves $u = $ constant and $v = $ constant are circles whose radii are respectively $a\operatorname{cosec}2u$ and $a\operatorname{cosech}2v$ cutting each other orthogonally.

5. Show that $\sinh x$ and $\cosh x$ have an imaginary period $2\iota\pi$, and that $\tanh x$ has an imaginary period $\iota\pi$.

INFINITESIMALS.

24. All measurable quantities are estimated by the ratios which they bear to certain fixed but arbitrary units of their own kind. The whole measure of a quantity thus consists of two factors—the unit itself and an abstract number which represents the ratio of the measured quantity to the unit. The magnitude of the unit should be chosen as something comparable with the quantity to be measured, otherwise the abstract number which measures the ratio of the quantity to the unit will be too large or too small to lie within the limits of comprehension. For instance, the radius of the earth is conveniently estimated in *miles* (roughly 4,000); the moon's distance in *earth's radii* (about 60); the sun's distance in

moon's distances (about 400); the distance of Sirius in *sun's distances* (at least 200,000). Again, for such relatively small quantities as the wave-length of a particular kind of light, *one ten-millionth of an inch* is found to be a sufficiently large unit: the wave-length for light from the red end of the spectrum being about 266, that from the violet end 167 such units (Lloyd, "Wave Theory of Light," p. 18).

25. Any comparison of two quantities is equivalent to an estimate of how many times the one is contained in or contains the other; that is, the one quantity is estimated in terms of the other as a unit, and according as the number expressing their ratio is very large compared with unity or a very small fraction, the one is said to be very large or very small in comparison with the other. The *terms great and small are therefore purely relative.*

The standard of smallness is vague and arbitrary. An error of measurement which, centuries ago, would have been reckoned small would now be considered enormous. The accuracy of observation, and therefore the smallness of allowable errors of observation, increases with the continual improvement in the construction of instruments and methods of measurement.

26. **Orders of Smallness.**

If we conceive any magnitude A divided up into any large number of equal parts, say a billion (10^{12}), then each part $\dfrac{A}{10^{12}}$ is extremely small, and for all practical purposes negligible, in comparison with A. If this part be again subdivided into a billion equal parts, each $= \dfrac{A}{10^{24}}$, each of these last is extremely small in comparison with $\dfrac{A}{10^{12}}$, and so on. We thus obtain a series of magnitudes, $A,\ \dfrac{A}{10^{12}},\ \dfrac{A}{10^{24}},\ \dfrac{A}{10^{36}},\ \ldots$, each of which is excessively small in comparison with the one which precedes it, but very large compared with the one which follows it. This furnishes us with what we may designate *a scale of smallness.*

More generally, if we agree to consider any given fraction f as being small in comparison with unity, then fA will be small in comparison with A, and we may term the expressions fA, f^2A, f^3A, ..., *small quantities of the first, second, third, etc., orders;* and the numerical quantities f, f^2, f^3, ..., may be called *small fractions* of the first, second, third, etc., orders.

Thus, supposing A to be any given finite magnitude, any given fraction of A is at our choice to designate a small quantity of the first order in comparison with A. When this is chosen, any quantity which has to this small quantity of the first order a ratio which is a small fraction of the first order, is itself a small quantity of the second order. Similarly, any quantity whose ratio to a small quantity of the second order is a small fraction of the first order is a small quantity of the third order, and so on. So that generally, if a small quantity be such that its ratio to a small quantity of the pth order be a small fraction of the qth order, it is itself termed a small quantity of the $(p+q)^{\text{th}}$ order.

27. Infinitesimals.

If these small quantities Af, Af^2, Af^3, ..., be all quantities whose limits are zero, then supposing f *made smaller than any assignable quantity* by sufficiently increasing its denominator, these small quantities of the first, second, third, etc., orders are termed *infinitesimals of the first, second, third, etc., orders.*

From the nature of an infinitesimal it is clear that, *if any equation contain finite quantities and infinitesimals, the infinitesimals may be rejected.*

28. PROP. *In any equation between infinitesimals of different orders, none but those of the lowest order need be retained.*

Suppose, for instance the equation to be
$$A_1 + B_1 + C_1 + D_2 + E_2 + F_3 + \ldots = 0, \ldots\ldots\ldots \text{(i.)}$$
each letter denoting an infinitesimal of the order indicated by the suffix.

Then, dividing by A_1,
$$1 + \frac{B_1}{A_1} + \frac{C_1}{A_1} + \frac{D_2}{A_1} + \frac{E_2}{A_1} + \frac{F_3}{A_1} + \ldots = 0, \ldots\ldots\ldots\text{(ii.)}$$
the limiting ratios $\dfrac{B_1}{A_1}$ and $\dfrac{C_1}{A_1}$ are finite, while $\dfrac{D_2}{A_1}$, $\dfrac{E_2}{A_1}$, are in-

finitesimals of the first order, $\dfrac{F_3}{A_1}$ is an infinitesimal of the second order, and so on. Hence, by Art. 27, equation (ii.) may be replaced by

$$1 + \frac{B_1}{A_1} + \frac{C_1}{A_1} = 0,$$

and therefore equation (i.) by

$$A_1 + B_1 + C_1 = 0,$$

which proves the statement.

29. PROP. *In any equation connecting infinitesimals we may substitute for any one of the quantities involved any other which differs from it by a quantity of higher order.*

For if $\qquad A_1 + B_1 + C_1 + D_2 + \ldots = 0$

be the equation, and if $\qquad A_1 = F_1 + f_2,$

f_2 denoting an infinitesimal of higher order than F_1, we have

$$F_1 + B_1 + C_1 + f_2 + D_2 + \ldots = 0,$$

i.e., by the last proposition we may write

$$F_1 + B_1 + C_1 = 0,$$

which may therefore, if desirable, replace the equation

$$A_1 + B_1 + C_1 = 0.$$

30. **Illustrations.**

Since $\qquad\qquad \sin\theta = \theta - \dfrac{\theta^3}{3!} + \dfrac{\theta^5}{5!} - \ldots$

and $\qquad\qquad \cos\theta = 1 - \dfrac{\theta^2}{2!} + \dfrac{\theta^4}{4!} - \ldots$

$\sin\theta$, $1 - \cos\theta$, $\theta - \sin\theta$ are respectively of the first, second, and third orders of small quantities, when θ is of the first order; also, 1 may be written instead of $\cos\theta$ if second order quantities are to be rejected, and θ for $\sin\theta$ when cubes and higher powers are rejected.

31. Again, suppose AP the arc of a circle of centre O and radius a. Suppose the angle $AOP\ (=\theta)$ to be a small quantity of the first order. Let PN be the perpendicular from P upon OA and AQ the tangent at A, meeting OP produced in Q. Join P, A.

Then   arc $AP = a\theta$ and is of the first order,

$NP = a \sin \theta$ do.   do.,

$AQ = a \tan \theta$ do.   do.,

chord $AP = 2a \sin \dfrac{\theta}{2}$ do.   do.,

$NA = a(1 - \cos \theta)$ and is of the second order.

So that $OP - ON$ is a small quantity of the second order.

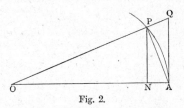

Fig. 2.

Again, arc AP — chord $AP = a\theta - 2a \sin \dfrac{\theta}{2}$

$$= a\theta - 2a\left(\frac{\theta}{2} - \frac{\theta^3}{8 \cdot 3!} + \cdots\right)$$

$$= \frac{a\theta^3}{4 \cdot 3!} - \text{etc.},$$

and is of the third order.

$PQ - NA = NA(\sec \theta - 1)$

$$= NA \cdot \frac{2 \sin^2 \dfrac{\theta}{2}}{\cos \theta}$$

$$= (\text{second order})(\text{second order})$$

$$= \text{fourth order of small quantities},$$

and similarly for others.

32. Such results may also be established *without the use of the series* for $\sin \theta$ and $\cos \theta$.

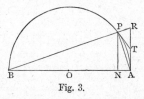

Fig. 3.

For example, let APB be a semicircle, P any point very near to A, so that the arc AP may be considered a small quantity of the first order.

Join AP, BP, and let BP produced cut the tangent at A in R, and let the tangent at P cut AR in T, and draw the perpendicular PN upon AB. T will be the middle point of AR, and $AT = TR = TP$.

(1) We may take it as *axiomatic* that the *length of the arc AP is intermediate between the chord AP and the sum of the tangents AT, TP*; *i.e.*, between chord AP and tangent AR. Hence chord AP, arc AP, tangent AR are in ascending order of magnitude, and therefore 1, $\dfrac{\text{arc } AP}{\text{chord } AP}$, $\dfrac{\text{tangent } AR}{\text{chord } AP}$ are in ascending order of magnitude.

Now,
$$Lt \frac{AR}{\text{chord } AP} = Lt \frac{BA}{BP} = 1,$$

whence
$$Lt \frac{\text{arc } AP}{\text{chord } AP} = 1,$$

and therefore, if arc AP be reckoned a small quantity of the first order, the chord AP and the tangent AR are also of the first order of smallness.

(2) Again, since $\dfrac{AN}{AP} = \dfrac{AP}{AB}$, and since AP is of the first order of smallness, AN is of the second order.

(3) Also $\dfrac{PR}{NA} = \dfrac{BP}{BN}$, which is ultimately a ratio of equality, and therefore PR is also of the second order.

(4) Similarly, since $AR - AP = \dfrac{AR^2 - AP^2}{AR + AP} = \dfrac{PR^2}{AR + AP}$, and since PR^2 is a small quantity of the fourth order, and $AR + AP$ is a small quantity of the first order, we see that $AR - AP$ is of the third order of small quantities.

And similarly for other quantities the order of smallness may be geometrically investigated.

33. *The base angles of a triangle being given to be small quantities of the first order, to find the order of the difference between the base and the sum of the sides.*

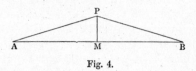

Fig. 4.

By what has gone before, (Art. 31) if APB be the triangle and PM the perpendicular on AB, $AP - AM$ and $BP - BM$ are both small quantities of the second order as compared with AB.

Hence $AP + PB - AB$ is of the second order compared with AB.

If AB itself be of the first order of small quantities, then $AP + PB - AB$ is *of the third order.*

34. *Degree of approximation in taking a small chord for a small arc in any curve.*

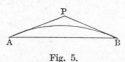

Fig. 5.

Let AB be an arc of a curve supposed continuous between A and B, and so small as to be concave at each point throughout its length to the foot of the perpendicular from that point upon the chord. Let AP, BP be the tangents at A and B. Then, when A and B are taken sufficiently near together, the chord AB and the angles at A and B may each be considered small quantities of at least the first order, and therefore, by what has gone before, $AP + PB - AB$ will be at least of the third order. Now we may take *as an axiom* that the *length of the arc AB is intermediate between the length of the chord AB and the sum of the tangents $AP, BP.$* Hence the difference of the arc AB and the chord AB, which is less than that between $AP + PB$ and the chord AB, must be at least *of the third order.*

EXAMPLES.

1. Show that, in the figure of Art. 31, the area of the segment bounded by the chord AP and the arc AP is of the third order of small quantities.

2. In the same figure, if PM be drawn perpendicular to AQ, show that the triangle PMQ is of the fifth order of smallness.

3. A straight line of constant length slides between two straight lines at right angles, viz., CAa, CbB; AB and ab are two positions of the line and P their point of intersection. Show that, in the limit, when the two positions coincide, we have

$$\frac{Aa}{Bb} = \frac{CB}{CA} \text{ and } \frac{PA}{PB} = \frac{CB^2}{CA^2}.$$

4. From a point T in a radius OA of a circle, produced, a tangent TP is drawn to the circle, touching it in P; PN is drawn perpen-

dicular to the radius OA. Show that, in the limit, when P moves up to A, $NA = AT$.

5. Tangents are drawn to a circular arc at its middle point and at its extremities. Show that the area of the triangle formed by the chord of the arc and the two tangents at the extremities is ultimately four times that of the triangle formed by the three tangents.

[FROST'S NEWTON.]

6. If, in the equation $\sin(\omega - \theta) = \sin \omega \cos a$, θ be very small, show that its approximate value is

$$2 \tan \omega \sin^2\frac{a}{2}\left(1 - \tan^2\omega \sin^2\frac{a}{2}\right). \qquad \text{[I. C. S.]}$$

7. If G be the centre of gravity of the arc PQ of any uniform curve, and if PT be the tangent at P, prove that, when PQ is indefinitely diminished, the angles GPT and QPT vanish in the ratio of 2 to 3. [I. C. S.]

8. If a side of a regular polygon be a small quantity of the first order in comparison with the radius of its inscribed circle, prove that the difference between the perimeter of the polygon and the circumference of the circle is a small quantity of the second order.

[I. C. S.]

9. Assuming the radius of the earth to be 4000 miles show that the difference between its circumference and the perimeter of a regular inscribed polygon of ten thousand sides is less than a yard.

10. Show that the curved surface of any belt of a sphere contained between parallel planes is equal to the surface of the corresponding belt of the circumscribing cylinder whose axis is perpendicular to the planes.

11. The sides of a triangle are 5 and 6 feet, and the included angle exceeds 60° by 10″. Calculating the third side for an angle of 60° find the correction to be applied for the extra 10″.

12. If a triangle be inscribed in a given circle prove that the algebraic sum of the small variations of its sides, each divided by the cosine of the angle opposite to it, is equal to zero. [MATH. TRIPOS.]

13. If x, y, z be the diagonals and the join of their mid-points in a quadrilateral whose sides are given, and ξ, η, ζ their respective increments when the quadrilateral receives a slight deformation, then will $\qquad x\xi + y\eta + 4z\zeta = 0.$

Also if the quadrilateral be a parallelogram

$$x\xi + y\eta = 0,$$

and if cyclic $\qquad\qquad y\xi + x\eta = 0.$

14. A person at a distance q from a tower of height p, observes that a flagpole upon the top of it subtends an angle θ at his eye. Neglecting his height show that if the observed angle be subject to a small error α, the corresponding error in the length of the pole has to the calculated length the ratio

$$q\alpha \operatorname{cosec} \theta/(q \cos \theta - p \sin \theta).$$

15. Prove that

$$\tan^{-1}\frac{\tan 2\theta + \tanh 2\phi}{\tan 2\theta - \tanh 2\phi} + \tan^{-1}\frac{\tan \theta - \tanh \phi}{\tan \theta + \tanh \phi}$$
$$= \tan^{-1}(\cot \theta \coth \phi). \qquad \text{[Math. Tripos, 1878.]}$$

16. If $x + \iota y = c \cos(\xi + \iota \eta)$, the curves $\eta = $ constant and $\xi = $ constant are confocal ellipses and hyperbolae respectively.

Prove that the square of the distance between the points (ξ, η), (ξ', η') is the same as the square of the distance between the corresponding points (ξ', η), (ξ, η'), viz.,

$$c^2\{\cosh(\eta + \eta') - \cos(\xi + \xi')\}\{\cosh(\eta - \eta') - \cos(\xi - \xi')\}.$$

Prove also that a bisector of the angle between these distances makes with the x-axis an angle $\tan^{-1}\dfrac{\tan\frac{1}{2}(\xi + \xi')}{\tanh\frac{1}{2}(\eta + \eta')}$. [London, 1887.]

17. If $\cos x \cosh u = 1$, x is called the Gudermannian of u and written gd u. [Cayley, Elliptic Functions.]

Prove

(a) $\quad \operatorname{gd} u = \tan^{-1}\sinh u = \sin^{-1}\tanh u.$

(b) $\quad \frac{1}{2} \operatorname{gd} u = \tan^{-1}\tanh \dfrac{u}{2}.$

(c) $\quad u = \log \tan\left(\dfrac{\pi}{4} + \tfrac{1}{2} \operatorname{gd} u\right).$

(d) $\quad \sin \operatorname{gd}(u + v) = \dfrac{\sin \operatorname{gd} u + \sin \operatorname{gd} v}{1 + \sin \operatorname{gd} u \sin \operatorname{gd} v}.$

18. Prove that $\quad \iota \operatorname{gd}\left(\dfrac{1}{\iota} \operatorname{gd} u\right) = u,$

and show that if $\qquad \operatorname{gd} u = a_1 u + a_3 u^3 + a_5 u^5 + \dots$

then will $\qquad \operatorname{gd}^{-1} u = a_1 u - a_3 u^3 + a_5 u^5 - \dots$

19. If $\quad f(x) = \dfrac{1}{1-x}$, prove $fff(x) = x.$

Also if $f(x) = a + bx$, prove that

$$f^r(x) = a\frac{b^r - 1}{b - 1} + b^r x.$$

20. If $\quad r = e^{-\frac{\pi a}{\beta}}$ and

$$f(x) = 2\{\ \sqrt[4]{r} \cosh \frac{\pi x}{2\beta} + \sqrt[4]{r^9}\cosh \frac{3\pi x}{2\beta} + \sqrt[4]{r^{25}}\cosh \frac{5\pi x}{2\beta} + \dots \text{ad inf.}\},$$

prove that $\qquad f(x + 2a) = \dfrac{1}{r}e^{\frac{\pi x}{\beta}} f(x)$ [Oxford.]

CHAPTER II.

FUNDAMENTAL PROPOSITIONS.

35. Direction of the Tangent of a Curve at a given point.

Let AB be an arc of a curve traced in the plane of the paper, OX a fixed straight line in the same plane. Let P, Q, be two

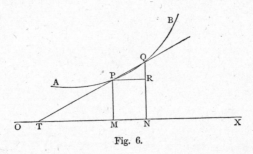

Fig. 6.

points on the curve; PM, QN, perpendiculars on OX, and PR the perpendicular from P on QN. Join P, Q, and let QP be produced to cut OX at T.

When Q, travelling along the curve, approaches indefinitely near to P, the chord QP becomes in the limit the tangent at P. QR and PR both ultimately vanish, but the limit of their ratio is in general finite; for $Lt\dfrac{RQ}{PR} = Lt \tan RPQ = Lt \tan XTP$

$= tangent\ of\ the\ angle\ which\ the\ tangent\ at$ P $to\ the\ curve$ $makes\ with$ OX.

Ex. 1. Consider the straight line whose equation is $y = mx + c$.
Let OX, OY, be the axes, and let the co-ordinates of P be x, y. Then, taking the general construction of the preceding article, the intercept $OA = c$, for $y = c$ when $x = 0$.

20

Draw AK parallel to OX to meet MP in K; then, from similar triangles,

$$\frac{RQ}{PR}=\frac{KP}{AK}=\frac{MP-OA}{OM}$$

$$=\frac{y-c}{x}=\frac{mx}{x}=m.$$

Hence $\tan XTP=\tan RPQ=m.$

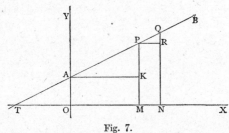

Fig. 7.

Ex. 2. Consider the parabola referred to its usual axes, viz., the axis of the parabola and the tangent at the vertex. With the same construction

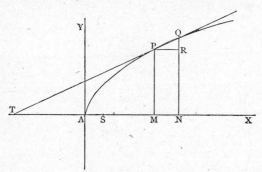

Fig. 8.

as before, we have $\qquad PM^2=4AS\,.\,AM,$

$$QN^2=4AS\,.\,AN,$$

$\therefore \qquad QN^2-PM^2=4AS(AN-AM)=4AS\,.\,PR.$

But $\qquad QN^2-PM^2=(QN-PM)(QN+PM)=RQ\,.\,(QN+PM),$

$\therefore \qquad RQ(QN+PM)=4AS\,.\,PR,$

whence $\qquad Lt\dfrac{RQ}{PR}=Lt\dfrac{4AS}{QN+PM}=\dfrac{4AS}{2PM}$

when Q comes to coincidence with P,

and therefore the limit of $\tan XTP$ is $\dfrac{2AS}{PM}.$

36. Equation of Tangent.

Let us now consider the general case in which the equation of the curve is $y=\phi(x)$.

Let the co-ordinates of the points P, Q, on the curve be (x, y) $(x+\delta x, y+\delta y)$ respectively, δx and δy being used to denote increments of the variables x and y.

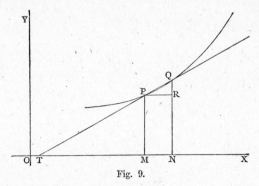

Fig. 9.

Then, the construction being as before,

$$OM = x,\ ON = x + \delta x,\ \text{therefore } PR = MN = \delta x;$$

also, $MP = y,\ NQ = y + \delta y,\ \text{therefore } RQ = \delta y.$

Again, since the point $x + \delta x,\ y + \delta y$, lies on the curve,

$$y + \delta y = \phi(x + \delta x),$$

whence $RQ = \delta y = \phi(x + \delta x) - \phi(x).$

Hence we can express $Lt\dfrac{RQ}{PR}$ as $Lt_{\delta x=0}\dfrac{\delta y}{\delta x}$ or $Lt_{\delta x=0}\dfrac{\phi(x + \delta x) - \phi(x)}{\delta x}.$

Hence, to draw the tangent at any point (x, y) on the curve $y = \phi(x)$, we must draw a line through that point, making with the axis of x an angle whose tangent is $Lt_{\delta x=0}\dfrac{\phi(x + \delta x) - \phi(x)}{\delta x}$;

and if this limit be called m, the equation of the tangent at $P(x, y)$ will be $Y - y = m(X - x),$
X, Y being the current co-ordinates of any point on the tangent; for the line represented by this equation goes through the point (x, y), and makes with the axis of x an angle whose tangent is m.

EXAMPLES.

Find the equation of the tangent at the point (x, y) on each of the following curves :—

1. $x^2 + y^2 = c^2.$

2. $\dfrac{x^2}{a^2} + \dfrac{y^2}{b^2} = 1.$

3. $y = c^x.$

4. $y = \log x.$

5. $y = \tan x.$

6. $y = \tan^{-1} x.$

37. DEF.—DIFFERENTIAL COEFFICIENT.

Let $\phi(x)$ denote any function of x, and $\phi(x+h)$ the same function of $x+h$; then $Lt_{h=0}\dfrac{\phi(x+h)-\phi(x)}{h}$ is called the FIRST DERIVED FUNCTION *or* DIFFERENTIAL COEFFICIENT *of $\phi(x)$ with respect to x.*

The operation of finding this limit is called *differentiating* $\phi(x)$.

After reading Chap. V., it will be obvious why the above expression is styled a "coefficient," for it is shown there to be one of a series of coefficients occurring in the expansion of $\phi(x+h)$ in powers of h.

The geometrical meaning of the above limit is indicated in the last article, where it is shown to be *the tangent of the angle ψ which the tangent at any definite point (x, y) on the curve $y=\phi(x)$ makes with the axis of x.*

38. We can now find the differential coefficient of any proposed function by investigating the value of the above limit; but it will be seen later on that, by means of certain rules and a knowledge of the differential coefficients of certain standard forms, we can always avoid the labour of an *ab initio* evaluation.

When such an investigation becomes necessary, it may sometimes be conducted very simply by pure geometry. It is however usual to treat the more complicated functions algebraically. Several examples are appended.

Ex. 1. To find *geometrically* the differential coefficient of sin x.

Let the angle $AOP=x$, $AOQ=x+h$, and let a circle with centre O and radius unity cut the lines OA, OP, OQ, in A, P, Q. Draw perpendiculars

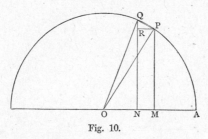

Fig. 10.

PM, QN, to OA, and PR to QN. Join PQ. Then
$$MP=\sin x,\quad NQ=\sin (x+h),$$
∴ $\quad \sin (x+h)-\sin x=RQ.$

Again, h=angle POQ=arc PQ, the radius being unity.
Hence

$$Lt_{h=0}\frac{\sin(x+h)-\sin x}{h}=Lt\frac{RQ}{\text{arc }PQ}=Lt\frac{RQ}{\text{chord }PQ}$$

(for chord PQ and arc PQ are equal in the limit)

$$=Lt\cos RQP=\cos OPR$$

(since in the limit QPO is a right angle)

$$=\cos AOP=\cos x.$$

In treating the trigonometrical functions by this method it is convenient to always arrange that the denominator of the ratio considered shall be unity.

Ex. 2. To find *geometrically* the differential coefficient of $\sin^{-1}x$.
In Fig. 10 let $A\widehat{O}P=\sin^{-1}x$,
and $A\widehat{O}Q=\sin^{-1}(x+h)$.
Then, with the same construction as before,

$$MP=x,\quad NQ=x+h,$$

therefore $RQ=h.$

Hence $\quad Lt_{h=0}\dfrac{\sin^{-1}(x+h)-\sin^{-1}x}{h}=Lt_{h=0}\dfrac{A\widehat{O}Q-A\widehat{O}P}{RQ}$

$$=Lt\frac{P\widehat{O}Q}{RQ}=Lt\frac{\text{chord }PQ}{RQ}=Lt\frac{1}{\cos RQP}=\frac{1}{\cos OPR}$$

$$=\frac{1}{\cos AOP}=\frac{1}{\sqrt{1-\sin^2AOP}}$$

$$=\frac{1}{\sqrt{1-x^2}}.$$

EXAMPLES.

Find in a similar manner the differential coefficients of

(1) $\tan x$.   (3) $\operatorname{cosec} x$.
(2) $\tan^{-1}x$.   (4) $\operatorname{cosec}^{-1}x$.

Ex. 3. Find from the definition the differential coefficient of $\dfrac{x^2}{a}$, where a is a constant.

Here $\phi(x)=\dfrac{x^2}{a}$,

$$\phi(x+h)=\frac{(x+h)^2}{a},$$

therefore $\quad Lt_{h=0}\dfrac{\phi(x+h)-\phi(x)}{h}=Lt_{h=0}\dfrac{(x+h)^2-x^2}{ha}$

$$=Lt_{h=0}\frac{2xh+h^2}{ha}=Lt_{h=0}\frac{(2x+h)}{a}$$

$$=\frac{2x}{a}.$$

The geometrical interpretation of this result is that, if a tangent be drawn to the parabola $ay = x^2$ at the point (x, y), it will be inclined to the axis of x at the angle $\tan^{-1}\dfrac{2x}{a}$.

Ex. 4. Find from the definition the differential coefficient of $\log \sin \dfrac{x}{a}$, where a is a constant.

Here $\phi(x) = \log \sin \dfrac{x}{a}$,

and
$$Lt_{h=0}\frac{\phi(x+h)-\phi(x)}{h} = Lt_{h=0}\frac{\log \sin\dfrac{x+h}{a} - \log \sin\dfrac{x}{a}}{h}$$

$$= Lt_{h=0}\frac{1}{h}\log\frac{\sin\dfrac{x}{a}\cos\dfrac{h}{a}+\cos\dfrac{x}{a}\sin\dfrac{h}{a}}{\sin\dfrac{x}{a}}$$

$$= Lt_{h=0}\frac{1}{h}\log\left(1+\frac{h}{a}\cot\frac{x}{a}-\text{higher powers of } h\right)$$

$$\left[\text{by substituting for } \sin\frac{h}{a} \text{ and } \cos\frac{h}{a} \text{ their expansions in powers of } \frac{h}{a}\right]$$

$$= Lt_{h=0}\frac{\dfrac{h}{a}\cot\dfrac{x}{a}-\text{higher powers of } h}{h}$$

[by expanding the logarithm]

$$= \frac{1}{a}\cot\frac{x}{a}.$$

Hence the tangent at any point on the curve $\dfrac{y}{a} = \log \sin \dfrac{x}{a}$ is inclined to the axis of x at an angle whose tangent is $\cot\dfrac{x}{a}$; that is at an angle $\dfrac{\pi}{2}-\dfrac{x}{a}$.

39. Notation.

The *result of the operation* expressed by $Lt_{h=0}\dfrac{\phi(x+h)-\phi(x)}{h}$ or by $Lt_{v=0}\dfrac{\delta y}{\delta x}$ is generally denoted by $\dfrac{d}{dx}y$ or $\dfrac{dy}{dx}$.

It will be well to note distinctly once for all that in the notation thus introduced, dx and dy, as here used, are *not separate small quantities* as δx and δy are, but that $\dfrac{d}{dx}$ is a *symbol of operation* which, when applied to y, denotes the result of *taking the limit of the ratio of the small quantities* δy, δx.

Sometimes $d_x y$ is used to denote the same thing; or, if $y = \phi(x)$, we often meet with the forms $\dfrac{d\phi(x)}{dx}$, $\dfrac{d\phi}{dx}$, $\phi'(x)$, ϕ_x, ϕ', or $\dot{\phi}$. Again, as the letters u, v, w, etc., are frequently used to denote functions of x, we shall consequently have the differential coefficient variously expressed, as $\dfrac{du}{dx}$, u', u_x, or $\dot{u}$, with a similar notation for those of v, w, etc.

40. Aspect of the Differential Coefficient as a Rate-Measurer. When a particle is in motion in a given manner the space described is a function of the time of describing it. We may consider the time as an independent variable, and the space described in that time as the dependent variable.

The rate of change of position of the particle is called its velocity.

If *uniform* the velocity is measured by the space described in one second; if *variable*, the velocity at any instant is measured by the space which would be described in one second if, for that second, the velocity remained unchanged.

Suppose a space s to have been described in time t with varying velocity, and an additional space δs to be described in the additional time δt. Let v_1 and v_2 be the greatest and least values of the velocity during the interval δt; then the spaces which would have been described with uniform velocities v_1, v_2, in time δt are $v_1 \delta t$ and $v_2 \delta t$, and are respectively greater and less than the actual space δs.

Hence v_1, $\dfrac{\delta s}{\delta t}$, and v_2 are in descending order of magnitude.

If then δt be diminished indefinitely, we have in the limit $v_1 = v_2 =$ the velocity at the instant considered, which is therefore represented by $Lt\dfrac{\delta s}{\delta t}$, i.e., by $\dfrac{ds}{dt}$.

41. It appears therefore that we may give another interpretation to a differential coefficient, viz., that $\dfrac{ds}{dt}$ means the *rate of increase of s in point of time*. Similarly $\dfrac{dx}{dt}$, $\dfrac{dy}{dt}$, mean the *rates of change* of x and y respectively in point of time and *measure the velocities*, resolved parallel to the axes, of a moving particle whose co-ordinates at the instant under consideration are x, y. If x and y be given functions of t, and therefore the path of the particle defined, and if δx, δy, δt, be simultaneous infinitesimal increments of x, y, t, then

$$\frac{dy}{dx} = Lt\frac{\delta y}{\delta x} = Lt\frac{\dfrac{\delta y}{\delta t}}{\dfrac{\delta x}{\delta t}} = \frac{\dfrac{dy}{dt}}{\dfrac{dx}{dt}}$$

and therefore represents *the ratio of the rate of change of y to that of x.* The rate of change of x is arbitrary, and if we choose it to be unit velocity, then $\dfrac{dy}{dx} = \dfrac{dy}{dt} =$ absolute rate of change of y.

42. Meaning of Sign of Differential Coefficient.

If x be increasing with t, the x-velocity is positive, whilst, if x be decreasing while t increases, that velocity is negative. Similarly for y.

Moreover, since $\dfrac{dy}{dx} = \dfrac{\dfrac{dy}{dt}}{\dfrac{dx}{dt}}$, $\dfrac{dy}{dx}$ is *positive when x and y increase or decrease together, but negative when one increases as the other decreases.*

This is obvious also from the geometrical interpretation of $\dfrac{dy}{dx}$. For, if x and y are *increasing together,* $\dfrac{dy}{dx}$ is the *tangent of an acute angle and therefore positive,* while if, as x increases y decreases, $\dfrac{dy}{dx}$ represents the *tangent of an obtuse angle and is negative.*

EXAMPLES.

Find from the definition the differential coefficient of y with respect to x in each of the following cases :

1. $y = x^3$.
2. $y = 2\sqrt{ax}$.
3. $y = \sqrt{a^2 + x^2}$.
4. $y = e^x$.
5. $y = e^{\sqrt{x}}$.
6. $y = a^{\sin x}$.
7. $y = a^{\log x}$.
8. $y = \tan^{-1} x^3$.
9. $y = \log \cos x$.
10. $y = \log \tan x$.
11. $y = x^x$.
12. $y = x^{\sin x}$.
13. $y = (\sin x)^x$.
14. $y = (\sin x)^{\sqrt{x}}$.

15. In the curve $y = ce^{\frac{x}{c}}$, if ψ be the angle which the tangent at any point makes with the axis of x, prove $y = c \tan \psi$.

16. In the curve $y = c \cosh \frac{x}{c}$, prove $y = c \sec \psi$.

17. In the curve $b^2 y = \frac{x^3}{3} - ax^2$ find the points at which the tangent is parallel to the axis of x.

[N.B.—This requires that $\tan \psi = 0$.]

18. Find at what points of the ellipse $\frac{x^2}{a^2} + \frac{y^2}{b^2} = 1$ the tangent cuts off equal intercepts from the axes.

[N.B.—This requires that $\tan \psi = \pm 1$.]

19. Prove that if a particle move so that the space described is proportional to the square of the time of description, the velocity will be proportional to the time, and the rate of increase of the velocity will be constant.

20. Show that if a particle move so that the space described is given by $s \propto \sin \mu t$, where μ is a constant, the rate of increase of the velocity is proportional to the distance of the particle measured along its path from a fixed position.

43. It will often be convenient in proving standard results to denote by a small letter the function of x considered, and by the corresponding capital the same function of $x + h$, e.g., if $u = \phi(x)$, then $U = \phi(x + h)$, or if $u = a^x$, then $U = a^{x+h}$.

Accordingly we shall have

$$\frac{du}{dx} = Lt_{h=0} \frac{U - u}{h},$$

$$\frac{dv}{dx} = Lt_{h=0} \frac{V - v}{h},$$

etc.

44. We now proceed to the consideration of several important propositions.

45. Prop. I. **The Differential Coefficient of any Constant is zero.**

This proposition will be obvious when we refer to the definition of a constant quantity. A constant is essentially a quantity of which there is no variation, so that if $y = c$, $\delta y =$ absolute zero, whatever may be the value of δx. Hence $\frac{\delta y}{\delta x} = 0$ and $\frac{dy}{dx} = 0$ when the limit is taken.

Or, geometrically; $y = c$ is the equation of a straight line parallel to the axis of x. This makes an angle zero with that axis, and therefore $\tan \psi$ or $\dfrac{dy}{dx} = 0$.

46. PROP. II. Product of Constant and Function.

The differential coefficient of a product of a constant and a function of x is equal to the product of the constant and the differential coefficient of the function, or, stated algebraically,

$$\frac{d}{dx}(cu) = c\frac{du}{dx}.$$

For, with the notation of Art. 43,

$$\frac{d}{dx}(cu) = Lt_{h=0}\frac{cU - cu}{h} = cLt_{h=0}\frac{U - u}{h}$$
$$= c\frac{du}{dx}.$$

47. PROP. III. Differential Coefficient of a Sum.

The differential coefficient of the sum of a set of functions of x is the sum of the differential coefficients of the several functions.

Let u, v, w, ..., be the functions of x, and y their sum.

Let U, V, W, ..., Y be what these expressions severally become when x is changed to $x+h$.

Then
$$y = u + v + w + \ldots$$
$$Y = U + V + W + \ldots,$$

and therefore
$$Y - y = (U - u) + (V - v) + (W - w) + \ldots;$$

dividing by h,
$$\frac{Y - y}{h} = \frac{U - u}{h} + \frac{V - v}{h} + \frac{W - w}{h} + \ldots$$

and taking the limit
$$\frac{dy}{dx} = \frac{du}{dx} + \frac{dv}{dx} + \frac{dw}{dx} + \ldots$$

If some of the connecting signs had been $-$ instead of $+$ a corresponding result would immediately follow, *e.g.*, if

$$y = u + v - w + \ldots$$

then
$$\frac{dy}{dx} = \frac{du}{dx} + \frac{dv}{dx} - \frac{dw}{dx} + \ldots$$

48. PROP. IV. The Differential Coefficient of the product of two functions is

$$(First\ Function) \times (Diff.\ Coeff.\ of\ Second)$$
$$+ (Second\ Function) \times (Diff.\ Coeff.\ of\ First),$$

or, stated algebraically,

$$\frac{d(uv)}{dx} = u\frac{dv}{dx} + v\frac{du}{dx}.$$

With the same notation as before, let

$$y = uv, \text{ and therefore } Y = UV;$$

whence

$$Y - y = UV - uv$$
$$= u(V - v) + V(U - u);$$

therefore

$$\frac{Y-y}{h} = u\frac{V-v}{h} + V\frac{U-u}{h},$$

and taking the limit

$$\frac{dy}{dx} = u\frac{dv}{dx} + v\frac{du}{dx}.$$

49. On division by uv the above result may be written

$$\frac{1}{y}\frac{dy}{dx} = \frac{1}{u}\frac{du}{dx} + \frac{1}{v}\frac{dv}{dx}.$$

Hence it is clear that the rule may be extended to products of more functions than two.

For example, if $y = uvw$; let $vw = z$, then $y = uz$.

Whence

$$\frac{1}{y}\frac{dy}{dx} = \frac{1}{u}\frac{du}{dx} + \frac{1}{z}\frac{dz}{dx},$$

but

$$\frac{1}{z}\frac{dz}{dx} = \frac{1}{v}\frac{dv}{dx} + \frac{1}{w}\frac{dw}{dx},$$

whence by substitution

$$\frac{1}{y}\frac{dy}{dx} = \frac{1}{u}\frac{du}{dx} + \frac{1}{v}\frac{dv}{dx} + \frac{1}{w}\frac{dw}{dx}.$$

Generally, if

$$y = uvwt\ldots$$

$$\frac{1}{y}\frac{dy}{dx} = \frac{1}{u}\frac{du}{dx} + \frac{1}{v}\frac{dv}{dx} + \frac{1}{w}\frac{dw}{dx} + \frac{1}{t}\frac{dt}{dx} + \ldots,$$

and if we multiply by $uvwt\ldots$ we obtain

$$\frac{dy}{dx} = (vwt\ldots)\frac{du}{dx} + (uwt\ldots)\frac{dv}{dx} + (uvt\ldots)\frac{dw}{dx} + \ldots,$$

i.e., *multiply the differential coefficient of each separate function by the product of all the remaining functions and add up all the results;* the sum will be the differential coefficient of the product of all the functions.

50. PROP. V. **The Differential Coefficient of a quotient of two functions is**

$$\frac{(\textit{Diff. Coeff. of Num}^r.)(\textit{Den}^r.) - (\textit{Diff. Coeff. of Den}^r.)(\textit{Num}^r.)}{\textit{Square of Denominator}}$$

or, stated algebraically,

$$\frac{d}{dx}\left(\frac{u}{v}\right) = \frac{\dfrac{du}{dx}v - \dfrac{dv}{dx}u}{v^2}.$$

With the same notation as before, let

$$y = \frac{u}{v}, \text{ and therefore } Y = \frac{U}{V},$$

whence

$$Y - y = \frac{U}{V} - \frac{u}{v}$$

$$= \frac{Uv - Vu}{Vv};$$

therefore

$$\frac{Y - y}{h} = \frac{\dfrac{U - u}{h}v - \dfrac{V - v}{h}u}{Vv},$$

and taking the limit

$$\frac{dy}{dx} = \frac{\dfrac{du}{dx}v - \dfrac{dv}{dx}u}{v^2}.$$

51. This proposition may also be deduced immediately from Prop. **IV.**, thus :

Let

$$y = \frac{u}{v} ;$$

i.e.,

$$u = vy ;$$

whence

$$\frac{du}{dx} = v\frac{dy}{dx} + y\frac{dv}{dx}$$

$$= v\frac{dy}{dx} + \frac{u}{v}\frac{dv}{dx} ;$$

and therefore

$$\frac{dy}{dx} = \frac{\dfrac{du}{dx} - \dfrac{u}{v}\dfrac{dv}{dx}}{v}$$

$$= \frac{\dfrac{du}{dx}\cdot v - \dfrac{dv}{dx}\cdot u}{v^2}.$$

EXAMPLES.

1. Deduce the result of Prop. II. from propositions I. and IV.

2. Deduce from Prop. V. that

$$\frac{d}{dx}\left(\frac{c}{u}\right) = -\frac{c}{u^2}\frac{du}{dx}.$$

3. Apply proposition IV. and the results of Art. 38 to show that

$$\frac{d}{dx}(x^2\sin x) = x^2\cos x + 2x\sin x.$$

4. Apply proposition V. to show that

$$\frac{d}{dx}\left(\frac{\sin x}{x^2}\right) = \frac{\cos x \cdot x - 2\sin x}{x^3}.$$

52. PROP. VI. **To find the Differential Coefficient of a Function of a Function.**

Let $u = f(v)$ ....(1)

and $v = F(x)$...............................(2)

Then, by elimination of v, we have a result which may be expressed as $u = \phi(x)$...............................(3)

Suppose the independent variable x to change to X in (2) and let a value of v *deduced from* (2) be V. Let this be substituted for v in (1), and let a value of u deduced from (1) be U. Then we have the following equations.

$$U = f(V) \ ....(4)$$

and $V = F(X)$...............................(5)

and *by the same process by which* (3) *was deduced from* (1) *and* (2) we obtain from (4) and (5)

$$U = \phi(X)...............................(6)$$

This result proves that if x be changed to X in *equation* (3), then *one of the values thence deduced for u will be U*, and therefore $Lt\dfrac{U-u}{X-x}$ when $X-x$ is diminished indefinitely is a value of the differential coefficient of u with respect to x, reckoned as a direct function of x as expressed in equation (3).

Now $$\frac{U-u}{X-x} = \frac{U-u}{V-v} \cdot \frac{V-v}{X-x}$$

and $Lt_{V-v=0}\dfrac{U-u}{V-v}$ is a value of the differential coefficient of u with respect to v *derived from equation* (1) and denoted by $\dfrac{du}{dv}$; also, $Lt_{X-x=0}\dfrac{V-v}{X-x}$ is a value of the differential coefficient of v with respect to x *derived from equation* (2) and denoted by $\dfrac{dv}{dx}$. We therefore have, when we proceed to the limit,

$$\frac{du}{dx} = \frac{du}{dv} \cdot \frac{dv}{dx},$$

a formula already established in a different manner and with different letters in Art. 41.

53. It is obvious that the above result may be extended. For, if $u = \phi(v)$, $v = \psi(w)$, $w = f(x)$, we have

$$\frac{du}{dx} = \frac{du}{dv} \cdot \frac{dv}{dx},$$

but

$$\frac{dv}{dx} = \frac{dv}{dw} \cdot \frac{dw}{dx};$$

and therefore

$$\frac{du}{dx} = \frac{du}{dv} \cdot \frac{dv}{dw} \cdot \frac{dw}{dx},$$

and a similar result holds however many functions there may be.

Ex. Let $u = b \sin v$, $v = \frac{1}{a}\sin^{-1}w$, $w = \frac{x^2}{a}$ that is,

$$u = b \sin\left(\frac{1}{a}\sin^{-1}\frac{x^2}{a}\right).$$

Then, by Ex. 1, Art. 38, $\dfrac{du}{dv} = b \cos v.$

Ex. 2, ibid. $\dfrac{dv}{dw} = \dfrac{1}{a}\,\dfrac{1}{\sqrt{1 - w^2}}.$

Ex. 3, ibid. $\dfrac{dw}{dx} = \dfrac{2x}{a}.$

Hence

$$\frac{du}{dx} = \frac{du}{dv} \cdot \frac{dv}{dw} \cdot \frac{dw}{dx} = b \cos v \cdot \frac{1}{a} \cdot \frac{1}{\sqrt{1 - w^2}} \cdot \frac{2x}{a}$$

$$= \frac{b}{a}\cos\left(\frac{1}{a}\sin^{-1}\frac{x^2}{a}\right) \cdot \frac{1}{\sqrt{1 - \dfrac{x^4}{a^2}}} \cdot \frac{2x}{a}.$$

The rule may be expressed thus:

$$\frac{d(1st\ Func.)}{dx} = \frac{d(1st\ Func.)}{d(2nd\ Func.)} \cdot \frac{d(2nd\ Func.)}{d(3rd\ Func.)} \cdots \frac{d(Last\ Func.)}{dx}$$

or if $\qquad u = \phi[\psi\{F(fx)\}],$

$$\frac{du}{dx} = \phi'[\psi\{F(fx)\}] \times \psi'\{F(fx)\} \times F'(fx) \times f'x.$$

54. There is a difficulty in Prop. VI. arising from the fact that for one value of x in (2) there may be *several values of* v, and for any value of v in (1) there may be *several values of* u. In fact the $f(v)$ and $F(x)$ may one or both be *many-valued functions* (such, for example, as $\sin^{-1}x$, which denotes any one of the series of angles whose sines are equal to x). But it is clear that the *same values of* u *and* x *will satisfy equation* (3) *as would simultaneously satisfy* (1) *and* (2), and that $Lt\dfrac{U - u}{X - x}$ when $X - x$ is indefinitely diminished is *one* value of the differential coefficient of u considered as a

function of x; and it is equally obvious that there may be a *series of such values* for $\dfrac{du}{dx}$, as also for $\dfrac{du}{dv}$ and for $\dfrac{dv}{dx}$, so that in the theorem enunciated and proved above, in Art. 52, a *proper selection of those values is assumed to be made.*

55. If in the theorem $\dfrac{du}{dx} = \dfrac{du}{dy} \cdot \dfrac{dy}{dx}$ (where y is written for v in the result of Art. 52) we suppose $u = x$, then

$$\frac{du}{dx} = \frac{dx}{dx} = Lt_{h=0} \frac{(x+h)-x}{h} = 1.$$

Hence we have $\dfrac{dy}{dx} \cdot \dfrac{dx}{dy} = 1,$

or $$\frac{dy}{dx} = \frac{1}{\dfrac{dx}{dy}}.$$

56. In this application of the general theorem of Prop. VI. y is assumed to be a function of x and consequently x is the *inverse function of y.* So that $\dfrac{dy}{dx}$ is the differential coefficient of y with respect to x when y is *considered as a function* of x, and $\dfrac{dx}{dy}$ is the differential coefficient of x with respect to y when x is considered as the *inverse function* of y:

e.g., if $\qquad y = \sin x$, then $x = \sin^{-1} y$,

$$\frac{dy}{dx} = \cos x \text{ (Ex. 1, Art. 38),}$$

and $$\frac{dx}{dy} = \frac{1}{\sqrt{1-y^2}} \text{ (Ex. 2, ibid.),}$$

and $\qquad \dfrac{dy}{dx} \cdot \dfrac{dx}{dy} = \cos x \cdot \dfrac{1}{\sqrt{1-y^2}} = \dfrac{\cos x}{\sqrt{1-\sin^2 x}} = 1.$

57. The same difficulty occurs in Arts. 55 and 56 as that discussed in Art. 54.

If $\qquad\qquad y = f(x)\ldots\ldots(1)$,

and this equation be supposed solved for x, the result will be of the form $\qquad\qquad x = F(y)\ldots\ldots(2)$.

Now, if x be changed to X in (1) and Y be a value deduced for y, then if Y be substituted for y in (2), X will be *one of the values* thence deduced for x.

Hence $Lt\dfrac{X-x}{Y-y}$ when $Y-y$ is indefinitely diminished is *a*
value of the differential coefficient of x with respect to y, as
derived from equation (2), while $Lt\dfrac{Y-y}{X-x}$ when $X-x$ is indefinitely diminished is *a* value of the differential coefficient of
y with respect to x as derived from equation (1). And since

$$\frac{Y-y}{X-x} \cdot \frac{X-x}{Y-y} = 1,$$

we have
$$\frac{dy}{dx} \cdot \frac{dx}{dy} = 1,$$

when the limit is taken, the *proper selection being made* of the
values deduced for $\dfrac{dy}{dx}$ and $\dfrac{dx}{dy}$.

58. This may be illustrated geometrically.
Let the curve $y = f(x)$ be drawn. Let the tangent to the

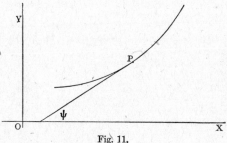

Fig. 11.

curve at the point P, (x, y), make an angle ψ with the axis of
x. Then, by Art. 37, $\dfrac{dy}{dx} = \tan \psi$; and in the same way it is
obvious that $\dfrac{dx}{dy} = \tan (90 - \psi) = \cot \psi$, so that

$$\frac{dy}{dx} \cdot \frac{dx}{dy} = \tan \psi \cdot \cot \psi = 1.$$

Suppose however that the ordinate through P cuts the curve
again at $P_1, P_2, P_3, \ldots$

Then, for a given value of x there are several values of y,
and therefore also for a given increase δx in the value of x
there may be several values of δy the increment of y. But if
it be carefully noted that the δy and δx chosen are to refer to

the *same branch of the curve at the same point* when we con-sider $\dfrac{dy}{dx}$ as when we consider $\dfrac{dx}{dy}$, then, under these circum-stances, these expressions are respectively the *tangent and*

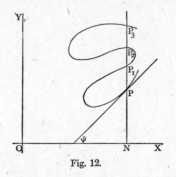

Fig. 12.

cotangent of the same angle, and therefore their product is unity.

We say *the same branch of the curve*, for it may happen that more than one branch of the curve passes through a given point

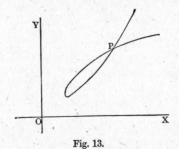

Fig. 13.

P, as in Fig. 13, and then there are two or more tangents at P and therefore two or more values of $\dfrac{dy}{dx}$ and $\dfrac{dx}{dy}$ at P. But the product of the $\dfrac{dy}{dx}$ and the $\dfrac{dx}{dy}$, which belong *to any the same branch through* P, is unity.

59. Differentiation of Inverse Functions.

When the differential coefficient of any function of x is found, that of the corresponding inverse function is easily deduced by means of the theorem of Art. 55.

For let $x = f(y)$, and therefore $y = f^{-1}(x)$; then

$$\frac{dx}{dy} = f'(y).$$

But

$$\frac{dy}{dx} = \frac{1}{\frac{dx}{dy}};$$

therefore

$$\frac{d}{dx} f^{-1}(x) = \frac{1}{f'(y)} = \frac{1}{f'\{f^{-1}(x)\}}.$$

EXAMPLES.

1. Differentiate by means of the definition and the foregoing rules:—

    (i.) $y = x \log \sin x.$

    (ii.) $y = x\sqrt{a^2 - x^2}.$

    (iii.) $y = \dfrac{c^2}{x} e^{\frac{x}{c}}.$

    (iv.) $y = \dfrac{a}{x}\sqrt{a^2 - x^2}.$

    (v.) $y = 2\sqrt{au}$, where $u = a^{\sin x}.$

    (vi.) $y = e^{\sqrt{u}}$, where $u = \log \sin v$, and $v = (\sin w)^w$, and $w = x^2.$

The results of any preceding examples may be assumed.

2. If $u_1, u_2, u_3, \ldots v_1, v_2, v_3, \ldots$ be functions of x, prove that

$$\frac{d}{dx} \frac{u_1 u_2 u_3 \ldots u_n}{v_1 v_2 v_3 \ldots v_n} = \frac{u_1 u_2 \ldots u_n}{v_1 v_2 \ldots v_n} \left\{ \sum_{r=1}^{r=n} \frac{1}{u_r} \frac{du_r}{dx} - \sum_{r=1}^{r=n} \frac{1}{v_r} \frac{dv_r}{dx} \right\}.$$

CHAPTER III.

STANDARD FORMS.

60. It is the object of the present Chapter to investigate and tabulate the results of differentiating the several standard forms referred to in Art. 38.

We shall always consider angles to be measured in circular measure, and all logarithms to be Napierian, unless the contrary is expressly stated.

It will be remembered that if $u = \phi(x)$, then, by the definition of a differential coefficient,

$$\frac{du}{dx} = Lt_{h=0}\frac{\phi(x+h) - \phi(x)}{h}.$$

61. Differential Coefficient of x^n.

If
$$u = \phi(x) = x^n,$$

then
$$\phi(x+h) = (x+h)^n,$$

and
$$\frac{du}{dx} = Lt_{h=0}\frac{(x+h)^n - x^n}{h}$$

$$= Lt_{h=0}x^n\frac{\left(1+\dfrac{h}{x}\right)^n - 1}{h}.$$

Now, since h is to be ultimately zero, we may consider $\dfrac{h}{x}$ to be less than unity, and we can therefore apply the Binomial Theorem to expand $\left(1+\dfrac{h}{x}\right)^n$, whatever be the value of n; hence

$$\frac{du}{dx} = Lt_{h=0}\frac{x^n}{h}\left\{n\frac{h}{x} + \frac{n(n-1)}{2!}\frac{h^2}{x^2} + \frac{n(n-1)(n-2)}{3!}\frac{h^3}{x^3} + \dots\right\}$$

$$= Lt_{h=0}nx^{n-1}\left\{1 + \frac{h}{x} \times (\text{a convergent series})\right\}$$

$$= nx^{n-1}.$$

62. If it be required to find the differential coefficient of x^n without the use of the Binomial Theorem we quote the result of Ex. 6 p. 10, viz. :

$$Lt_{y=1}\frac{y^n-1}{y-1}=n,$$

and proceed as follows :

$$\frac{dx^n}{dx}=Lt_{h=0}x^n\frac{\left(1+\frac{h}{x}\right)^n-1}{h}\quad\text{[as before]}$$

$$=Lt_{h=0}x^{n-1}\frac{\left(1+\frac{h}{x}\right)^n-1}{\left(1+\frac{h}{x}\right)-1}$$

$$=Lt_{y=1}x^{n-1}\frac{y^n-1}{y-1}\quad\left[\text{where }y=1+\frac{h}{x}\right]$$

$$=nx^{n-1}.$$

63. Differential Coefficient of a^x.

If $\qquad u=\phi(x)=a^x,$

$\qquad\qquad\phi(x+h)=a^{x+h},$

and $\qquad\dfrac{du}{dx}=Lt_{h=0}\dfrac{a^{x+h}-a^x}{h}$

$$=a^x Lt_{h=0}\frac{a^h-1}{h}$$

$$=a^x\log_e a. \quad\text{[Art. 21.]}$$

Cor. If $u=e^x,$ $\dfrac{du}{dx}=e^x\log_e e=e^x.$

64. Differential Coefficient of $\log_a x$.

If $\qquad u=\phi(x)=\log_a x,$

$\qquad\qquad\phi(x+h)=\log_a(x+h),$

and $\qquad\dfrac{du}{dx}=Lt_{h=0}\dfrac{\log_a(x+h)-\log_a x}{h}$

$$=Lt_{h=0}\frac{1}{h}\log_a\left(1+\frac{h}{x}\right).$$

Let $\dfrac{x}{h}=z,$ so that if $h=0,$ $z=\infty$; therefore

$$\frac{du}{dx}=Lt_{z=\infty}\frac{z}{x}\log_a\left(1+\frac{1}{z}\right)$$

$$=\frac{1}{x}Lt_{z=\infty}\log_a\left(1+\frac{1}{z}\right)^z$$

$$=\frac{1}{x}\log_a e \quad\text{[Art. 20.]}$$

Cor. If $u=\log_e x,$ $\dfrac{du}{dx}=\dfrac{1}{x}\log_e e=\dfrac{1}{x}.$

65. Differential Coefficient of sin x.

If
$$u = \phi(x) = \sin x,$$
$$\phi(x+h) = \sin(x+h),$$

and
$$\frac{du}{dx} = Lt_{h=0} \frac{\sin(x+h) - \sin x}{h}$$

$$= Lt_{h=0} \frac{2 \sin \frac{h}{2} \cos \left(x + \frac{h}{2}\right)}{h}$$

$$= Lt_{h=0} \frac{\sin \frac{h}{2}}{\frac{h}{2}} \cos \left(x + \frac{h}{2}\right)$$

$$= \cos x. \quad [\text{Art. 18.}]$$

66. Differential Coefficient of cos x.

If
$$u = \phi(x) = \cos x,$$
$$\phi(x+h) = \cos(x+h),$$

and
$$\frac{du}{dx} = Lt_{h=0} \frac{\cos(x+h) - \cos x}{h}$$

$$= -Lt_{h=0} \frac{2 \sin \frac{h}{2} \sin \left(x + \frac{h}{2}\right)}{h}$$

$$= -Lt_{h=0} \frac{\sin \frac{h}{2}}{\frac{h}{2}} \sin \left(x + \frac{h}{2}\right)$$

$$= -\sin x.$$

67. Differential Coefficient of tan x.

If
$$u = \phi(x) = \tan x,$$
$$\phi(x+h) = \tan(x+h),$$

and
$$\frac{du}{dx} = Lt_{h=0} \frac{\tan(x+h) - \tan x}{h}$$

$$= Lt_{h=0} \frac{\sin(x+h)\cos x - \cos(x+h)\sin x}{h \cos x \cos(x+h)}$$

$$= Lt_{h=0} \frac{\sin h}{h} \cdot \frac{1}{\cos x \cos(x+h)}$$

$$= \frac{1}{\cos^2 x} = \sec^2 x.$$

68. Differential Coefficient of cot x.

If
$$u = \phi(x) = \cot x,$$
$$\phi(x+h) = \cot(x+h),$$

and
$$\frac{du}{dx} = Lt_{h=0}\frac{\cot(x+h) - \cot x}{h}$$

$$= Lt_{h=0}\frac{\cos(x+h)\sin x - \cos x \sin(x+h)}{h \sin x . \sin(x+h)}$$

$$= -Lt_{h=0}\frac{\sin h}{h} \cdot \frac{1}{\sin x \sin(x+h)}$$

$$= -\frac{1}{\sin^2 x} = -\operatorname{cosec}^2 x.$$

69. Differential Coefficient of sec x.

If
$$u = \phi(x) = \sec x,$$

$$\phi(x+h) = \sec(x+h),$$

and
$$\frac{du}{dx} = Lt_{h=0}\frac{\sec(x+h) - \sec x}{h}$$

$$= Lt_{h=0}\frac{\cos x - \cos(x+h)}{h \cos x \cos(x+h)}$$

$$= Lt_{h=0}\frac{\sin \dfrac{h}{2}}{\dfrac{h}{2}} \cdot \frac{\sin\left(x+\dfrac{h}{2}\right)}{\cos x \cos(x+h)}$$

$$= \frac{\sin x}{\cos^2 x}.$$

70. Differential Coefficient of cosec x.

If
$$u = \phi(x) = \operatorname{cosec} x,$$

$$\phi(x+h) = \operatorname{cosec}(x+h),$$

and
$$\frac{du}{dx} = Lt_{h=0}\frac{\operatorname{cosec}(x+h) - \operatorname{cosec} x}{h}$$

$$= Lt_{h=0}\frac{\sin x - \sin(x+h)}{h \sin x \sin(x+h)}$$

$$= -Lt_{h=0}\frac{\sin \dfrac{h}{2}}{\dfrac{h}{2}} \frac{\cos\left(x+\dfrac{h}{2}\right)}{\sin x \sin(x+h)}$$

$$= -\frac{\cos x}{\sin^2 x}.$$

71. Inverse Trigonometrical Functions.

For the inverse trigonometrical functions it seems useful to recur to the notation of Art. 43, and to denote $\phi(x+h)$ by U.

72. Differential Coefficient of $\sin^{-1}x$.

If $\qquad u = \phi(x) = \sin^{-1}x,$

$\qquad\qquad U = \phi(x+h) = \sin^{-1}(x+h).$

Hence $\qquad x = \sin u$, and $x+h = \sin U$;

therefore $\qquad h = \sin U - \sin u,$

and $\qquad \dfrac{du}{dx} = Lt_{h=0}\dfrac{U-u}{h} = Lt_{U=u}\dfrac{U-u}{\sin U - \sin u}$

$$= Lt_{U=u}\left\{\frac{\dfrac{U-u}{2}}{\sin\dfrac{U-u}{2}}\right\}\frac{1}{\cos\dfrac{U+u}{2}}$$

$$= \frac{1}{\cos u} = \frac{1}{\sqrt{1-\sin^2 u}} = \frac{1}{\sqrt{1-x^2}}.$$

73. Differential Coefficient of $\cos^{-1}x$.

If $\qquad u = \phi(x) = \cos^{-1}x,$

$\qquad\qquad U = \phi(x+h) = \cos^{-1}(x+h).$

Hence $\qquad x = \cos u$, and $x+h = \cos U$;

therefore $\qquad h = \cos U - \cos u,$

and $\qquad \dfrac{du}{dx} = Lt_{h=0}\dfrac{U-u}{h} = Lt_{U=u}\dfrac{U-u}{\cos U - \cos u}$

$$= - Lt_{U=u}\left\{\frac{\dfrac{U-u}{2}}{\sin\dfrac{U-u}{2}}\right\}\frac{1}{\sin\dfrac{U+u}{2}}$$

$$= -\frac{1}{\sin u} = -\frac{1}{\sqrt{1-\cos^2 u}} = -\frac{1}{\sqrt{1-x^2}}.$$

74. Differential Coefficient of $\tan^{-1}x$.

If $\qquad u = \phi(x) = \tan^{-1}x,$

$\qquad\qquad U = \phi(x+h) = \tan^{-1}(x+h).$

Hence $\qquad x = \tan u$, and $x+h = \tan U$;

therefore $\qquad h = \tan U - \tan u,$

and $\qquad \dfrac{du}{dx} = Lt_{h=0}\dfrac{U-u}{h} = Lt_{U=u}\dfrac{U-u}{\tan U - \tan u}$

$$= Lt_{U=u}\frac{U-u}{\sin(U-u)}\cos U \cos u$$

$$= \cos^2 u = \frac{1}{\sec^2 u} = \frac{1}{1+\tan^2 u} = \frac{1}{1+x^2}.$$

75. Differential Coefficient of $\cot^{-1}x$.

If $\qquad u = \phi(x) = \cot^{-1}x,$

$\qquad\qquad U = \phi(x+h) = \cot^{-1}(x+h).$

Hence $\qquad x = \cot u,$ and $x+h = \cot U;$

therefore $\qquad h = \cot U - \cot u,$

and $\qquad \dfrac{du}{dx} = Lt_{h=0}\dfrac{U-u}{h} = Lt_{U=u}\dfrac{U-u}{\cot U - \cot u}$

$$= -Lt_{U=u}\dfrac{U-u}{\sin(U-u)}\sin U \sin u$$

$$= -\sin^2 u = -\dfrac{1}{\operatorname{cosec}^2 u} = -\dfrac{1}{1+\cot^2 u} = -\dfrac{1}{1+x^2}.$$

76. Differential Coefficient of $\sec^{-1}x$.

If $\qquad u = \phi(x) = \sec^{-1}x,$

$\qquad\qquad U = \phi(x+h) = \sec^{-1}(x+h).$

Hence $\qquad x = \sec u,$ and $x+h = \sec U;$

therefore $\qquad h = \sec U - \sec u,$

and $\qquad \dfrac{du}{dx} = Lt_{h=0}\dfrac{U-u}{h} = Lt_{U=u}\dfrac{U-u}{\sec U - \sec u}$

$$= Lt_{U=u}\dfrac{U-u}{\cos u - \cos U}\cos u \cos U$$

$$= Lt_{U=u}\left(\dfrac{\dfrac{U-u}{2}}{\sin\dfrac{U-u}{2}}\right)\dfrac{\cos u \cos U}{\sin\dfrac{U+u}{2}}$$

$$= \dfrac{\cos^2 u}{\sin u} = \dfrac{1}{\sec^2 u\sqrt{1-\cos^2 u}} = \dfrac{1}{x^2\sqrt{1-\dfrac{1}{x^2}}}$$

$$= \dfrac{1}{x\sqrt{x^2-1}}.$$

77. Differential Coefficient of $\operatorname{cosec}^{-1}x$.

If $\qquad u = \phi(x) = \operatorname{cosec}^{-1}x,$

$\qquad\qquad U = \phi(x+h) = \operatorname{cosec}^{-1}(x+h).$

Hence $\qquad x = \operatorname{cosec} u,$ and $x+h = \operatorname{cosec} U;$

therefore $\qquad h = \operatorname{cosec} U - \operatorname{cosec} u,$

and $\qquad \dfrac{du}{dx} = Lt_{h=0}\dfrac{U-u}{h} = Lt_{U=u}\dfrac{U-u}{\operatorname{cosec} U - \operatorname{cosec} u}$

$$= Lt_{U=u}\dfrac{U-u}{\sin u - \sin U}\sin u \sin U$$

$$= -Lt_{U=u}\left\{\frac{\dfrac{U-u}{2}}{\sin\dfrac{U-u}{2}}\right\}\frac{\sin u \sin U}{\cos\dfrac{U+u}{2}}$$

$$= -\frac{\sin^2 u}{\cos u} = -\frac{1}{\operatorname{cosec}^2 u \sqrt{1-\sin^2 u}}$$

$$= -\frac{1}{x^2\sqrt{1-\dfrac{1}{x^2}}} = -\frac{1}{x\sqrt{x^2-1}}.$$

78. From the importance of the results it has been thought preferable to deduce the differential coefficients of the inverse functions $\sin^{-1}x$ etc. immediately from the definition; but by aid of Prop. VI. of the preceding chapter we can simplify the proofs considerably.

Ex. (i.) If $u=\sin^{-1}x,$
we have $x=\sin u\,;$

whence $\dfrac{dx}{du}=\cos u\,;$

and therefore $\dfrac{du}{dx}=\dfrac{1}{\dfrac{dx}{du}}=\dfrac{1}{\cos u}=\dfrac{1}{\sqrt{1-\sin^2 u}}=\dfrac{1}{\sqrt{1-x^2}}\,;$

and since $\cos^{-1}x=\dfrac{\pi}{2}-\sin^{-1}x,$

we have $\dfrac{d\cos^{-1}x}{dx}=-\dfrac{1}{\sqrt{1-x^2}}.$

Ex. (ii.) If $u=\tan^{-1}x,$
we have $x=\tan u\,;$

whence $\dfrac{dx}{du}=\sec^2 u\,;$

and therefore $\dfrac{du}{dx}=\dfrac{1}{\sec^2 u}=\dfrac{1}{1+\tan^2 u}=\dfrac{1}{1+x^2}\,;$

and since $\cot^{-1}x=\dfrac{\pi}{2}-\tan^{-1}x,$

we have $\dfrac{d\cot^{-1}x}{dx}=-\dfrac{1}{1+x^2}.$

Ex. (iii.) If $u=\operatorname{vers}^{-1}x,$
we have $x=\operatorname{vers}u=1-\cos u\,;$

whence $\dfrac{dx}{du}=\sin u\,;$

and therefore $\dfrac{du}{dx}=\dfrac{1}{\sin u}=\dfrac{1}{\sqrt{1-\cos^2 u}}=\dfrac{1}{\sqrt{2x-x^2}}\,;$

whence also $\dfrac{d\operatorname{covers}^{-1}x}{dx}=-\dfrac{1}{\sqrt{2x-x^2}}.$

79. The Integral Calculus.

Suppose any expression in terms of x given; *can we find a function of which that expression is the differential coefficient?* The problem here suggested is inverse to that considered in the Differential Calculus. The discovery of such functions is the fundamental aim of the Integral Calculus. The function whose differential coefficient is the given expression is said to be the "integral" of that expression. For example, if $\phi'(x)$ be the differential coefficient of $\phi(x)$, $\phi(x)$ is said to be the integral of $\phi'(x)$. Moreover, since $\phi'(x)$ is also the differential coefficient of $\phi(x) + C$, C being any arbitrary constant disappearing upon differentiation, it is customary to state that the integral of $\phi'(x)$ is $\phi(x) + C$, C being any arbitrary constant.

The notation by which this is expressed is

$$\int \phi'(x)dx = \phi(x) + C,$$

$\int \phi'(x)dx$ being read "integral of $\phi'(x)$ with respect to x."

Thus we have seen

$$\frac{d}{dx}(\sin x) = \cos x,$$

$$\frac{d}{dx}(\tan^{-1}x) = \frac{1}{1+x^2},$$

$$\text{etc.,}$$

whence it follows immediately that

$$\int \cos x \, dx = \sin x,$$

$$\int \frac{1}{1+x^2} dx = \tan^{-1}x,$$

$$\text{etc.,}$$

where the arbitrary constant may be added in each case if desired.

80. We do not propose to enter upon any description of the various operations of the Integral Calculus, but it will be found that for integration we shall require to remember the same list of standard forms that is established in the present chapter and tabulated below, and it is advantageous to learn each formula here in its double aspect. We have therefore tabulated the standard forms for Differentiation and Integration together. Moreover, we shall find it convenient to be able to use the standard forms of integration in several of our subsequent articles.

TABLE OF RESULTS TO BE COMMITTED TO MEMORY.

$u = x^n.$ $\dfrac{du}{dx} = nx^{n-1}.$ $\int x^n dx$ $= \dfrac{x^{n+1}}{n+1}.$

$u = a^x.$ $\dfrac{du}{dx} = a^x \log_e a.$ $\int a^x dx$ $= \dfrac{a^x}{\log_e a}.$

$u = e^x.$ $\dfrac{du}{dx} = e^x.$ $\int e^x dx$ $= e^x.$

$u = \log_a x.$ $\dfrac{du}{dx} = \dfrac{1}{x} \log_a e.$ $\int \dfrac{dx}{x}$ $= \log_e x.$

$u = \log_e x.$ $\dfrac{du}{dx} = \dfrac{1}{x}.$ or $= \dfrac{\log_a x}{\log_a e}.$

$u = \sin x.$ $\dfrac{du}{dx} = \cos x.$ $\int \cos x\, dx$ $= \sin x.$

$u = \cos x.$ $\dfrac{du}{dx} = -\sin x.$ $\int \sin x\, dx$ $= -\cos x.$

$u = \tan x.$ $\dfrac{du}{dx} = \sec^2 x.$ $\int \sec^2 x\, dx$ $= \tan x.$

$u = \cot x.$ $\dfrac{du}{dx} = -\operatorname{cosec}^2 x.$ $\int \operatorname{cosec}^2 x\, dx$ $= -\cot x.$

$u = \sec x.$ $\dfrac{du}{dx} = \dfrac{\sin x}{\cos^2 x}.$ $\int \dfrac{\sin x}{\cos^2 x} dx$ $= \sec x.$

$u = \operatorname{cosec} x.$ $\dfrac{du}{dx} = -\dfrac{\cos x}{\sin^2 x}.$ $\int \dfrac{\cos x}{\sin^2 x} dx$ $= -\operatorname{cosec} x.$

$u = \sin^{-1} x.$ $\dfrac{du}{dx} = \dfrac{1}{\sqrt{1-x^2}}.$

$u = \cos^{-1} x.$ $\dfrac{du}{dx} = -\dfrac{1}{\sqrt{1-x^2}}.$ $\left.\right\}$ $\int \dfrac{dx}{\sqrt{1-x^2}}$ $= \sin^{-1} x,$ or $-\cos^{-1} x.$

$u = \tan^{-1} x.$ $\dfrac{du}{dx} = \dfrac{1}{1+x^2}.$

$u = \cot^{-1} x.$ $\dfrac{du}{dx} = -\dfrac{1}{1+x^2}.$ $\left.\right\}$ $\int \dfrac{dx}{1+x^2}$ $= \tan^{-1} x,$ or $-\cot^{-1} x.$

$u = \sec^{-1} x.$ $\dfrac{du}{dx} = \dfrac{1}{x\sqrt{x^2-1}}.$

$u = \operatorname{cosec}^{-1} x.$ $\dfrac{du}{dx} = -\dfrac{1}{x\sqrt{x^2-1}}.$ $\left.\right\}$ $\int \dfrac{dx}{x\sqrt{x^2-1}}$ $= \sec^{-1} x,$ or $-\operatorname{cosec}^{-1} x.$

$u = \operatorname{vers}^{-1} x.$ $\dfrac{du}{dx} = \dfrac{1}{\sqrt{2x-x^2}}.$

$u = \operatorname{covers}^{-1} x.$ $\dfrac{du}{dx} = -\dfrac{1}{\sqrt{2x-x^2}}.$ $\left.\right\}$ $\int \dfrac{dx}{\sqrt{2x-x^2}}$ $= \operatorname{vers}^{-1} x,$ or $-\operatorname{covers}^{-1} x.$

81. The Form u^v.

In functions of the form u^v, where both u and v are functions of x, it is generally advisable to *take logarithms* before proceeding to differentiate.

Let $\qquad\qquad y = u^v,$

then $\qquad\qquad \log_e y = v \log_e u ;$

therefore $\qquad \dfrac{1}{y}\dfrac{dy}{dx} = \dfrac{dv}{dx} \cdot \log_e u + v \cdot \dfrac{1}{u}\dfrac{du}{dx}$, Arts. 48, 52, 64.

or $\qquad\qquad \dfrac{dy}{dx} = u^v\left(\log_e u \cdot \dfrac{dv}{dx} + \dfrac{v}{u}\dfrac{du}{dx}\right).$

Three cases of this proposition present themselves.

I. If v *be a constant* and u a function of x, $\dfrac{dv}{dx} = 0$ and the above reduces to $\quad \dfrac{dy}{dx} = v \cdot u^{v-1}\dfrac{du}{dx},$
as might be expected from Arts. 52, 61.

II. If u *be a constant* and v a function of x, $\dfrac{du}{dx} = 0$ and the general form proved above reduces to

$$\dfrac{dy}{dx} = u^v \log_e u \cdot \dfrac{dv}{dx},$$

as might be expected from Arts. 52, 63.

III. If u and v be *both functions of x*, it appears that the general formula

$$\dfrac{dy}{dx} = u^v \log_e u \dfrac{dv}{dx} + v u^{v-1}\dfrac{du}{dx}$$

is the sum of the two special forms in I. and II., and therefore we may, instead of taking logarithms in any particular example, *consider first u constant and then v constant and add the results obtained on these suppositions.*

82. We shall presently (Art. 162) see further that if y be any complex function of x, then, in whatever way the various simple functions of which y is composed be connected together, the complete differential coefficient of y is the *algebraic sum of the differential coefficients obtained severally by considering all the functions but one to be constant.*

83. Hyperbolic Functions.

The differential coefficients of the direct and inverse hyperbolic functions are now appended as additional formulæ. Their verification is very simple and is left as an exercise. They will be found useful by the more advanced student by reason of their close analogy of form with the results tabulated above for the direct and inverse trigonometrical functions.

Results for Hyperbolic Functions.

$u = \sinh x = \dfrac{e^x - e^{-x}}{2}.$ $\qquad \dfrac{du}{dx} = \cosh x.$ $\qquad \int \cosh x\, dx \quad = \sinh x.$

$u = \cosh x = \dfrac{e^x + e^{-x}}{2}.$ $\qquad \dfrac{du}{dx} = \sinh x.$ $\qquad \int \sinh x\, dx \quad = \cosh x.$

$u = \tanh x = \dfrac{\sinh x}{\cosh x}.$ $\qquad \dfrac{du}{dx} = \operatorname{sech}^2 x.$ $\qquad \int \operatorname{sech}^2 x\, dx \quad = \tanh x.$

$u = \coth x = \dfrac{\cosh x}{\sinh x}.$ $\qquad \dfrac{du}{dx} = -\operatorname{cosech}^2 x.$ $\qquad \int \operatorname{cosech}^2 x\, dx = -\coth x.$

$u = \operatorname{sech} x = \dfrac{1}{\cosh x}.$ $\qquad \dfrac{du}{dx} = -\dfrac{\sinh x}{\cosh^2 x}.$ $\qquad \int \dfrac{\sinh x}{\cosh^2 x} dx \quad = -\operatorname{sech} x.$

$u = \operatorname{cosech} x = \dfrac{1}{\sinh x}.$ $\qquad \dfrac{du}{dx} = -\dfrac{\cosh x}{\sinh^2 x}.$ $\qquad \int \dfrac{\cosh x}{\sinh^2 x} dx = -\operatorname{cosech} x.$

$u = \sinh^{-1} x = \log(x + \sqrt{1 + x^2}).$ $\qquad \dfrac{du}{dx} = \dfrac{1}{\sqrt{1 + x^2}}.$ $\qquad \int \dfrac{dx}{\sqrt{1 + x^2}} = \sinh^{-1} x.$

$u = \cosh^{-1} x = \log(x + \sqrt{x^2 - 1}).$ $\qquad \dfrac{du}{dx} = \dfrac{1}{\sqrt{x^2 - 1}}.$ $\qquad \int \dfrac{dx}{\sqrt{x^2 - 1}} = \cosh^{-1} x.$

$u = \tanh^{-1} x = \tfrac{1}{2} \log \dfrac{1 + x}{1 - x}.$ $\qquad \dfrac{du}{dx} = \dfrac{1}{1 - x^2} (x < 1).$ $\qquad \int \dfrac{dx}{1 - x^2} = \tanh^{-1} x_{(x < 1)}.$

$u = \coth^{-1} x = \tfrac{1}{2} \log \dfrac{x + 1}{x - 1}.$ $\qquad \dfrac{du}{dx} = -\dfrac{1}{x^2 - 1} (x > 1).$ $\qquad \int \dfrac{dx}{x^2 - 1} = -\coth^{-1} x_{(x > 1)}.$

$u = \operatorname{sech}^{-1} x = \cosh^{-1} \dfrac{1}{x}.$ $\qquad \dfrac{du}{dx} = -\dfrac{1}{x \sqrt{1 - x^2}}.$ $\qquad \int \dfrac{dx}{x \sqrt{1 - x^2}} = -\operatorname{sech}^{-1} x.$

$u = \operatorname{cosech}^{-1} x = \sinh^{-1} \dfrac{1}{x}.$ $\qquad \dfrac{du}{dx} = -\dfrac{1}{x \sqrt{x^2 + 1}}.$ $\qquad \int \dfrac{dx}{x \sqrt{x^2 + 1}} = -\operatorname{cosech}^{-1} x.$

84. Transformations.

Algebraic or trigonometrical transformations are frequently useful to *shorten the work* of differentiation.

For instance, suppose $\qquad y = \tan^{-1} \dfrac{2x}{1 - x^2}.$

We observe that $\qquad y = 2 \tan^{-1} x\,;$

whence $\qquad \dfrac{dy}{dx} = \dfrac{2}{1 + x^2}.$

Again, suppose $\qquad y = \tan^{-1} \dfrac{1 + x}{1 - x}.$

Here $\qquad y = \tan^{-1} x + \tan^{-1} 1,$

and therefore $\qquad \dfrac{dy}{dx} = \dfrac{1}{1 + x^2}.$

As another example suppose

$$y = \tan^{-1}\frac{\sqrt{1+x^2} - \sqrt{1-x^2}}{\sqrt{1+x^2} + \sqrt{1-x^2}}.$$

Here

$$y = \frac{\pi}{4} - \tan^{-1}\sqrt{\frac{1-x^2}{1+x^2}}.$$

$$= \frac{\pi}{4} - \tfrac{1}{2}\cos^{-1}x^2 \; ;$$

therefore

$$\frac{dy}{dx} = \frac{x}{\sqrt{1-x^4}}.$$

85. Examples of Differentiation.

Ex. 1. Let $y = \sqrt{z}$, where z is a known function of x.

Here

$$y = z^{\frac{1}{2}},$$

and

$$\frac{dy}{dz} = \tfrac{1}{2}z^{-\frac{1}{2}} = \frac{1}{2\sqrt{z}},$$

whence

$$\frac{dy}{dx} = \frac{dy}{dz} \cdot \frac{dz}{dx}, \text{ (Art. 52)}$$

$$= \frac{1}{2\sqrt{z}} \cdot \frac{dz}{dx}.$$

This form *occurs so often that it will be found convenient to commit it to memory.*

Ex. 2. Let

$$y = e^{\sqrt{\cot x}}.$$

Let

$$\sqrt{\cot x} = z \text{ and } \cot x = p,$$

so that

$$y = e^z, \text{ where } z = \sqrt{p}.$$

Now

$$\frac{dy}{dz} = e^z. \quad \text{(Art. 63.)}$$

$$\frac{dz}{dp} = \frac{1}{2\sqrt{p}}. \quad \text{(Ex. 1 above.)}$$

$$\frac{dp}{dx} = -\operatorname{cosec}^2 x,$$

and (Art. 53)

$$\frac{dy}{dx} = \frac{dy}{dz} \cdot \frac{dz}{dp} \cdot \frac{dp}{dx} = -\operatorname{cosec}^2 x \cdot \frac{1}{2\sqrt{\cot x}} \cdot e^{\sqrt{\cot x}}.$$

With a little practice these actual substitutions can be avoided and the following is what passes in the mind :—

$$\frac{d(e^{\sqrt{\cot x}})}{dx} = \frac{d(e^{\sqrt{\cot x}})}{d(\sqrt{\cot x})} \cdot \frac{d(\sqrt{\cot x})}{d(\cot x)} \cdot \frac{d(\cot x)}{dx}$$

$$= e^{\sqrt{\cot x}} \cdot \frac{1}{2\sqrt{\cot x}} \cdot (-\operatorname{cosec}^2 x).$$

Ex. 3. Let

$$y = (\sin x)^{\log x}\cot\{e^x(a+bx)\}.$$

Taking logarithms

$$\log y = \log x \cdot \log \sin x + \log \cot\{e^x(a+bx)\}.$$

The differential coefficient of $\log y$ is $\dfrac{1}{y}\dfrac{dy}{dx}.$

Again, $\log x \cdot \log \sin x$ is a product, and when differentiated becomes

(Art. 48) $$\frac{1}{x}\log \sin x + \log x \cdot \frac{1}{\sin x} \cdot \cos x.$$

Also, $\log \cot\{e^x(a+bx)\}$ becomes when differentiated

$$\frac{1}{\cot\{e^x(a+bx)\}} \cdot [-\operatorname{cosec}^2\{e^x(a+bx)\}] \cdot \{e^x(a+bx)+be^x\};$$

$$\therefore \quad \frac{dy}{dx}=(\sin x)^{\log x} \cdot \cot\{e^x(a+bx)\}\left[\frac{1}{x}\log \sin x+\cot x \cdot \log x\right.$$

$$\left.-2e^x(a+b+bx)\operatorname{cosec} 2(e^x\overline{a+bx})\right].$$

When, as in the above example, logarithms are taken before differentiating, the compound process is called *Logarithmic Differentiation.* It is useful to adopt this method when variables occur in the index, or when the function to be differentiated consists of a product of several involved factors.

Ex. 4. Let

$$y=\sqrt{a^2-b^2\cos^2(\log x)}.$$

$$\frac{dy}{dx}=\frac{d\sqrt{a^2-b^2\cos^2(\log x)}}{d\{a^2-b^2\cos^2(\log x)\}}\times\frac{d\{a^2-b^2\cos^2(\log x)\}}{d\{\cos(\log x)\}}\times\frac{d\{\cos(\log x)\}}{d(\log x)}\times\frac{d(\log x)}{dx}$$

$$=\tfrac{1}{2}\{a^2-b^2\cos^2(\log x)\}^{-\frac{1}{2}}\times\{-2b^2\cos(\log x)\}\times\{-\sin(\log x)\}\times\frac{1}{x}$$

$$=\frac{b^2\sin 2(\log x)}{2x\sqrt{a^2-b^2\cos^2(\log x)}}.$$

Ex. 5. Differentiate x^5 with regard to x^2.

Let $$x^2=z.$$

Then $$\frac{dx^5}{dz}=\frac{dx^5}{dx}\cdot\frac{dx}{dz}=\frac{\dfrac{dx^5}{dx}}{\dfrac{dz}{dx}}=\frac{5x^4}{2x}$$

$$=\frac{5}{2}x^3.$$

Ex. 6. Given that $x^3+y^3=3axy$, find the value of $\dfrac{dy}{dx}$.

Here $$3x^2+3y^2\frac{dy}{dx}=3a\left(y+x\frac{dy}{dx}\right),$$

giving $$\frac{dy}{dx}=-\frac{x^2-ay}{y^2-ax}.$$

EXAMPLES.

Find $\dfrac{dy}{dx}$ in the following cases :

1. $y = \sqrt{x}$.

2. $y = \dfrac{1}{\sqrt{x}}$.

3. $y = \dfrac{a + bx}{c}$.

4. $y = x + \dfrac{1}{x}$.

5. $y = x + \dfrac{x^3}{3!} + \dfrac{x^5}{5!} + \dots$

6. $y = 1 + \dfrac{x^2}{2!} + \dfrac{x^4}{4!} + \dots$

7. $y = (a + bx^{\frac{3}{2}})/c\sqrt[4]{x^5}$.

8. $y = \sin(a + bx)$.

9. $y = \sin(a + bx^n)$.

10. $y = \sin\sqrt{x}$.

11. $y = \sqrt{\sin x}$.

12. $y = \sqrt{\sin\sqrt{x}}$.

13. $y = \sin^p x^q$.

14. $y = \sin^{-1} x^2$.

15. $y = (\sin^{-1}x)^2 - (\cos^{-1}x)^2$.

16. $y = \tan^{-1}(\log x)$.

17. $y = \sin x^\circ$.

18. $y = x \log x$.

19. $y = e^x \log x$.

20. $y = \sin(e^x) \log x$.

21. $y = \tan^{-1}(e^x) \log \cot x$.

22. $y = (x + a)^m (x + b)^n$.

23. $y = \dfrac{2 + x^2}{1 + x}$.

24. $y = \sqrt[n]{a + x}$.

25. $y = \sqrt[n]{a^2 + x^2}$.

26. $y = \sqrt{\cosh x}$.

27. $y = \log \cosh x$.

28. $y = \tan^{-1}(\tanh x)$.

29. $y = \mathrm{vers}^{-1} x^2$.

30. $y = \mathrm{vers}^{-1} \log(\cot x)$.

31. $y = \cot^{-1}(\mathrm{cosec}\, x)$.

32. $y = \sin^{-1} \dfrac{1}{\sqrt{1 + x^2}}$.

33. $y = \tan^{-1} \dfrac{1}{\sqrt{x^2 - 1}}$.

34. $y = \tan^{-1} \dfrac{\sqrt{x} - x}{1 + x^{\frac{3}{2}}}$.

35. $y = \sin^m x \cos^n x$.

36. $y = (\sin^{-1}x)^m (\cos^{-1}x)^n$.

37. $y = \sin(e^x \log x) \cdot \sqrt{1 - (\log x)^2}$.

38. $y = \sqrt{\dfrac{1 - x}{1 + x}}$.

39. $y = \dfrac{1 - x^2}{\sqrt{1 + x^2}}$.

40. $y = \dfrac{x\sqrt{x^2 - 4a^2}}{\sqrt{x^2 - a^2}}$.

41. $y = \sqrt{\dfrac{1 - x}{1 + x + x^2}}$.

42. $y = \log \dfrac{x^2 + x + 1}{x^2 - x + 1}$.

43. $y = \log \dfrac{x}{a^x}$.

44. $y = \cos^{-1}(1 - 2x^2)$.

45. $y = \left(\dfrac{x}{n}\right)^{nx}\left(1 + \log \dfrac{x}{n}\right)$.

46. $y = b \tan^{-1}\left(\dfrac{x}{a} \tan^{-1}\dfrac{x}{a}\right)$.

47. $y = \dfrac{x \cos^{-1} x}{\sqrt{1 - x^2}}$.

48. $y = \cos\left(a \sin^{-1}\dfrac{1}{x}\right)$.

49. $y = \sin^{-1}\dfrac{a + b \cos x}{b + a \cos x}$.

50. $y = e^{\tan^{-1}x} \log(\sec^2 x^3)$.

51. $y = e^{ax}\cos(b \tan^{-1}x)$.

52. $y = \tan^{-1}(a^{cx} \cdot x^2)$.

53. $y = \sec(\log_a \sqrt{a^2 + x^2})$.

54. $y = \tan^{-1}x + \tanh^{-1}x$.

55. $y = \tanh^{-1}\dfrac{3x + x^3}{1 + 3x^2} + \tan^{-1}\dfrac{3x - x^3}{1 - 3x^2}.$

56. $y = \log(\log x).$

57. $y = \log^n(x)$, where $\log^n$ means $\log \log \log \dots$
      (repeated n times).

58. $y = \dfrac{1}{\sqrt{b^2 - a^2}} \log \dfrac{\sqrt{b + a} + \sqrt{b - a}\tan \dfrac{x}{2}}{\sqrt{b + a} - \sqrt{b - a}\tan \dfrac{x}{2}}.$

59. $y = \sin^{-1}(x\sqrt{1 - x} - \sqrt{x}\sqrt{1 - x^2}).$

60. $y = \tan^{-1}\dfrac{4\sqrt{x}}{1 - 4x}.$

61. $y = \log\left\{ e^x\left(\dfrac{x - 2}{x + 2}\right)^{\frac{3}{4}} \right\}.$

62. $y = 10^{10^x}.$

63. $y = e^{e^x}.$

64. $y = e^{x^x}.$

65. $y = x^{e^x}.$

66. $y = x^{x^x}.$

67. $y = x^x + x^{\frac{1}{x}}.$

68. $y = (\sin x)^{\cos x} + (\cos x)^{\sin x}.$

69. $y = (\cot x)^{\cot x} + (\coth x)^{\coth x}.$

70. $y = \tan^{-1}(a^{cx}x^{\sin x})\dfrac{\sqrt{x}}{1 + x^{\frac{3}{2}}}.$

71. $y = \sin^{-1}\left(e^{\tan^{-1}x}\right).$

72. $y = \sqrt{\left(1 + \cos\dfrac{m}{x}\right)\left(1 - \sin\dfrac{m}{x}\right)}.$

73. $y = \tan^{-1}\sqrt{\sqrt{x} + \cos^{-1}x}.$

74. $y = \left(\dfrac{1 + \sqrt{x}}{1 + 2\sqrt{x}}\right)^{\sin e^{x^2}}.$

75. $y = (\cos x)^{\cot^2 x}.$

76. $y = (\cot^{-1}x)^{\frac{1}{x}}.$

77. $y = \left(1 + \dfrac{1}{x}\right)^x + x^{1 + \frac{1}{x}}.$

78. $y = b\tan^{-1}\left(\dfrac{x}{a} + \tan^{-1}\dfrac{y}{x}\right).$

79. $\tan y = e^{\cos^2 x}\sin x.$

80. $ax^2 + 2hxy + by^2 = 1.$

81. $e^y = \dfrac{(a + bx^n)^{\frac{1}{2}} - a^{\frac{1}{2}}}{(bx^n)^{\frac{1}{2}}}.$

82. $(\cos x)^y = (\sin y)^x.$

83. $x = e^{\tan^{-1}\frac{y - x^2}{x^2}}.$

84. $x = y\log xy.$

85. $y = x^y.$

86. $y = x^{y^x}.$

87. $y = x\log\dfrac{y}{a + bx}.$

88. $ax^2 + 2hxy + by^2 + 2gx + 2fy + c = 0.$

89. $x^m y^n = (x + y)^{m+n}.$

90. $y = e^{\tan^{-1}y}\log\sec^2 x^3.$

91. Differentiate $\log_{10}x$ with regard to x^2.

92. Differentiate $(x^2 + ax + a^2)^n \log\cot\dfrac{x}{2}$ with regard to
     $\tan^{-1}(a\cos bx).$

93. Differentiate $\log_e \left\{ \dfrac{a + b \tan \dfrac{x}{2}}{a - b \tan \dfrac{x}{2}} \right\}$ with regard to

$$\dfrac{1}{a^2\cos^2\dfrac{x}{2} - b^2\sin^2\dfrac{x}{2}}.$$

94. Differentiate $x^{\sin^{-1}x}$ with regard to $\sin^{-1}x$.

95. Differentiate $\tan^{-1}\dfrac{\sqrt{1 + x^2} - 1}{x}$ with regard to $\tan^{-1}x$.

96. Differentiate $\dfrac{\sqrt{1 + x^2} + \sqrt{1 - x^2}}{\sqrt{1 + x^2} - \sqrt{1 - x^2}}$ with regard to $\sqrt{1 - x^4}$.

97. Differentiate $\sec^{-1}\dfrac{1}{2x^2 - 1}$ with regard to $\sqrt{1 - x^2}$.

98. Differentiate $\tan^{-1}\dfrac{x}{\sqrt{1 - x^2}}$ with regard to $\sec^{-1}\dfrac{1}{2x^2 - 1}$.

99. Differentiate $\tan^{-1}\dfrac{2x}{1 - x^2}$ with regard to $\sin^{-1}\dfrac{2x}{1 + x^2}$.

100. Differentiate $x^n\log\tan^{-1}x$ with regard to $\dfrac{\sin\sqrt{x}}{x^{\frac{3}{2}}}$.

101. If $y = x^{x^{x^{\cdots\text{ to }\infty}}}$ prove $x\dfrac{dy}{dx} = \dfrac{y^2}{1 - y\log x}$.

102. If $y = \dfrac{x}{1 +}\dfrac{x}{1 +}\dfrac{x}{1 +}\dots$ to ∞, prove $\dfrac{dy}{dx} = \dfrac{1}{1 +}\dfrac{2x}{1 +}\dfrac{x}{1 +}\dfrac{x}{1 +}\dfrac{x}{1 +}\dots$

103. If $y = x + \dfrac{1}{x +}\dfrac{1}{x +}\dfrac{1}{x +}\dots$ to ∞, prove $\dfrac{dy}{dx} = \dfrac{1}{2} - \dfrac{x}{x +}\dfrac{1}{x +}\dfrac{1}{x +}\dots$

104. If $y = \dfrac{\sin x}{1 +}\dfrac{\cos x}{1 +}\dfrac{\sin x}{1 +}\dfrac{\cos x}{1 +}\dots$ to ∞,

prove $\dfrac{dy}{dx} = \dfrac{(1 + y)\cos x + y\sin x}{1 + 2y + \cos x - \sin x}$.

105. If $y = \sqrt{\sin x + \sqrt{\sin x + \sqrt{\sin x + \sqrt{\text{etc. to }\infty}}}}$,

prove $\dfrac{dy}{dx} = \dfrac{\cos x}{2y - 1}$.

106. If $S_n =$ the sum of a G. P. to n terms of which r is the common ratio, prove that

$$(r - 1)\dfrac{dS_n}{dr} = (n - 1)S_n - nS_{n-1}. \qquad \text{[Coll. Ex.]}$$

107. If $\dfrac{P}{Q} = a + \dfrac{1}{a_1} + \dfrac{1}{a_2} + \dfrac{1}{a_3} + \ldots + \dfrac{1}{x}$, prove $\dfrac{d}{dx}\left(\dfrac{P}{Q}\right) = \pm\dfrac{1}{Q^2}$.

[COLL. EX.]

108. Given $C = 1 + r\cos\theta + \dfrac{r^2\cos 2\theta}{2\,!} + \dfrac{r^3\cos 3\theta}{3\,!} + \ldots$

and $\qquad S = r\sin\theta + \dfrac{r^2\sin 2\theta}{2\,!} + \dfrac{r^3\sin 3\theta}{3\,!} + \ldots,$

show that

$$C\frac{dC}{dr} + S\frac{dS}{dr} = (C^2 + S^2)\cos\theta\,;$$

$$C\frac{dS}{dr} - S\frac{dC}{dr} = (C^2 + S^2)\sin\theta. \qquad \text{[COLL. EX.]}$$

109. If $y = \sec 4x$, prove that

$$\frac{dy}{dt} = \frac{16t(1 - t^4)}{(1 - 6t^2 + t^4)^2}, \text{ where } t = \tan x. \qquad \text{[COLL. EX.]}$$

110. If $y = e^{-x}\sec^{-1}(x\,\sqrt{z})$ and $z^4 + x^2 z = x^5$, find $\dfrac{dy}{dx}$ in terms of x and z. $\qquad$ [TRINITY SCHOL.]

111. Prove that if x be less than unity

$$\frac{1}{1+x} + \frac{2x}{1+x^2} + \frac{4x^3}{1+x^4} + \frac{8x^7}{1+x^8} + \ldots \text{ ad inf.} = \frac{1}{1-x}. \qquad \text{[COLL. EX.]}$$

112. Prove that if x be less than unity

$$\frac{1-2x}{1-x+x^2} + \frac{2x-4x^3}{1-x^2+x^4} + \frac{4x^3-8x^7}{1-x^4+x^8} + \ldots \text{ ad inf.} = \frac{1+2x}{1+x+x^2}.$$

113. Given Euler's Theorem that

$$Lt_{n=\infty}\cos\frac{x}{2}\cos\frac{x}{2^2}\cos\frac{x}{2^3}\ldots\cos\frac{x}{2^n} = \frac{\sin x}{x},$$

prove $\qquad \dfrac{1}{2}\tan\dfrac{x}{2} + \dfrac{1}{2^2}\tan\dfrac{x}{2^2} + \dfrac{1}{2^3}\tan\dfrac{x}{2^3} + \ldots \text{ ad inf.} = \dfrac{1}{x} - \cot x,$

and $\qquad \dfrac{1}{2^2}\sec^2\dfrac{x}{2} + \dfrac{1}{2^4}\sec^2\dfrac{x}{2^2} + \dfrac{1}{2^6}\sec^2\dfrac{x}{2^3} + \ldots \text{ ad inf.} = \operatorname{cosec}^2 x - \dfrac{1}{x^2}.$

114. Given the identity

$$(2\cos 2\theta - 1)(2\cos 2^2\theta - 1)\ldots(2\cos 2^n\theta - 1) = \frac{2\cos 2^{n+1}\theta + 1}{2\cos 2\theta + 1},$$

prove that $\displaystyle\sum_{r=1}^{r=n}\frac{2^r\sin 2^r\theta}{2\cos 2^r\theta - 1} = \frac{2^{n+1}\sin 2^{n+1}\theta}{2\cos 2^{n+1}\theta + 1} - \frac{2\sin 2\theta}{2\cos 2\theta + 1}.$

115. Given

$$\sin\phi\sin(2a + \phi)\sin(4a + \phi)\ldots\sin\{2(n-1)a + \phi\} = \frac{\sin n\phi}{2^{n-1}}$$

where $\qquad\qquad 2na = \pi$

prove that

$$\cot \phi + \cot(2a + \phi) + \cot(4a + \phi) + \ldots + \cot\{2(n-1)a + \phi\}$$
$$= n \cot n\phi,$$

and that $\cosec^2\phi + \cosec^2(2a + \phi) + \cosec^2(4a + \phi) + \ldots$
$$+ \cosec^2\{2(n-1)a + \phi\} = n^2\cosec^2 n\phi.$$

116. From the expression for $\sin \theta$ in factors prove

$$\theta \cot \theta = 1 + 2\theta^2 \sum_{n=1}^{n=\infty} \frac{1}{\theta^2 - n^2\pi^2},$$

and hence that $\pi \coth \pi = 1 + \dfrac{2}{1 + 1^2} + \dfrac{2}{1 + 2^2} + \dfrac{2}{1 + 3^2} + \ldots$ ad inf.,

and that $\qquad \dfrac{\pi}{2} \coth \dfrac{\pi}{2} = 1 + \dfrac{2}{1 + 2^2} + \dfrac{2}{1 + 4^2} + \dfrac{2}{1 + 6^2} + \ldots$ ad inf.

117. Prove $\qquad \dfrac{\tan \theta}{8\theta} = \sum_{n=1}^{n=\infty} \dfrac{1}{(2n-1)^2\pi^2 - 4\theta^2},$

and deduce $\qquad \dfrac{\pi}{8} \tanh \pi = \dfrac{1}{2^2 + 1^2} + \dfrac{1}{2^2 + 3^2} + \dfrac{1}{2^2 + 5^2} + \ldots$ ad inf.,

and $\qquad \dfrac{\pi}{4} \tanh \dfrac{\pi}{2} = \dfrac{1}{1 + 1^2} + \dfrac{1}{1 + 3^2} + \dfrac{1}{1 + 5^2} + \ldots$ ad inf.

118. Prove $\dfrac{x}{2} \coth x = \tfrac{1}{2} + x^2 \sum_{n=1}^{n=\infty} \dfrac{1}{x^2 + n^2\pi^2}.$

119. Prove that

$$\frac{nx^{n-1}}{x^n - a^n} = \frac{1}{x - a} + \frac{1}{x + a} + 2\sum_{r=1}^{r=\frac{n-2}{2}} \frac{x - a \cos \dfrac{2r\pi}{n}}{x^2 - 2ax \cos \dfrac{2r\pi}{n} + a^2},$$

if n be even,

but $\qquad = \dfrac{1}{x - a} + 2\sum_{r=1}^{r=\frac{n-1}{2}} \dfrac{x - a \cos \dfrac{2r\pi}{n}}{x^2 - 2ax \cos \dfrac{2r\pi}{n} + a^2},$

if n be odd.

120. Prove that

$$\frac{nx^{n-1}(x^n - a^n\cos \theta)}{x^{2n} - 2x^n a^n\cos \theta + a^{2n}} = \sum_{r=0}^{r=n-1} \frac{x - a \cos \dfrac{2r\pi + \theta}{n}}{x^2 - 2ax \cos \dfrac{2r\pi + \theta}{n} + a^2}.$$

121. Determine the coefficients $A_1, A_2 \ldots A_m$ so that

$$\frac{d}{dx}[\{x^m - A_1 x^{m-1} + A_2 x^{m-2} - \ldots + (-1)^m A_m\}e^x] = x^m e^x,$$

m being a positive integer. $\qquad\qquad$ [Univ. London, 1890.]

122. Writing $\operatorname{sg} u$ for $\operatorname{sin} \operatorname{gd} u$, etc., establish the following results—

(α) $\dfrac{d}{dx} \operatorname{gd} x = \operatorname{cg} x.$

(β) $\dfrac{d}{dx} \operatorname{sg} x = \operatorname{cg}^2 x.$

(γ) $\dfrac{d}{dx} \operatorname{tg} x = \dfrac{1}{\operatorname{cg} x}.$

123. The functions $x_1,\ x_2,\ x_3 \ldots x_n$ being defined by the equations
$$x_1 = \sqrt[p]{x\sqrt[q]{x}}, \quad x_{r+1} = \sqrt[p]{x\sqrt[q]{xx_r}},$$
find the differential coefficient of the function towards which x_n tends when n increases indefinitely.   [FRENET.]

124. If s_r denote the sum of the rth powers of the roots of the equation $x^n + p_1 x^{n-1} + p_2 x^{n-2} + \ldots + p_n = 0,$
prove that if the coefficients be expressed in terms of $s_1,\ s_2,\ s_3 \ldots s_n,$
then will $\dfrac{dp_{r+k}}{ds_r} = -\dfrac{p_k}{r}.$ [BRIOSCHI.]

125. Defining the Bessel's function of the nth order as
$$J_n(x) = \frac{x^n}{2^n n\,!}\left\{ 1 - \frac{x^2}{2(2n+2)} + \frac{x^4}{2.4(2n+2)(2n+4)} - \ldots \right\}$$
prove   (1) $\dfrac{d}{dx} J_0(x) = -J_1(x).$

(2) $2\dfrac{d}{dx} J_n(x) = J_{n-1}(x) - J_{n+1}(x).$

(3) $J_0 + J_1 - J_n - J_{n+1} = 2\sum_{r=1}^{r=n}\dfrac{d}{dx} J_r.$

CHAPTER IV.

SUCCESSIVE DIFFERENTIATION.

86. Repeated Operations.

The operation denoted by $\dfrac{d}{dx}$ is defined in Art. 37 without any reference to the form of the function operated upon, the only assumption made being that the function is a function of the same independent variable as that referred to in the operative symbol, viz. x. It is moreover clear that the result of the operation is also a function of x, and as such is itself capable of being operated upon by the same symbol. That is to say, if y be a function of x, $\dfrac{dy}{dx}$ is also a function of x, and therefore we can have $\dfrac{d}{dx}\left(\dfrac{dy}{dx}\right)$ as a true mathematical quantity. And further, it will be thus seen that the operation $\dfrac{d}{dx}$ may be performed upon any given function of x any number of times.

87. Notation.

The expression $\dfrac{d}{dx}\left(\dfrac{dy}{dx}\right)$ is generally abbreviated into $\left(\dfrac{d}{dx}\right)^2 y$ or $\dfrac{d^2 y}{dx^2}$, and is called the "*second derived function*" or "*second differential coefficient*" of y with respect to x. And, generally, if the operator $\dfrac{d}{dx}$ be applied n times, the result is denoted by $\left(\dfrac{d}{dx}\right)^n y$ or $\dfrac{d^n y}{dx^n}$, and is called the nth *derived function* or n^{th} *differential coefficient* of y with respect to x.

57

It will be convenient to denote the operative symbol $\dfrac{d}{dx}$ by D, which, in addition to being simpler to write, makes no assumption that the independent variable is *denoted by x*; and in many problems the independent variable is more conveniently denoted by some other letter. For example, in dynamical problems the time which has elapsed since a given epoch is frequently taken as the independent variable and is denoted by t, while the letters x, y, z, are reserved to denote the co-ordinates at that time of the point whose motion is considered.

It appears then that if we use indices to denote the number of times an operation has been performed, we may write

$$Dy = \frac{dy}{dx},$$

$$D \cdot Dy = D^2y = \frac{d^2y}{dx^2},$$

$$D \cdot D^2y = D^3y = \frac{d^3y}{dx^3},$$

$$\cdot \quad \cdot \quad \cdot \quad \cdot \quad \cdot \quad \cdot$$

$$D \cdot D^{n-1}y = D^ny = \frac{d^ny}{dx^n}.$$

88. Analogy between the operator $\dfrac{d}{dx}$ and symbols of quantity.

The index notation employed above to denote the number of times an operation is repeated is exactly analogous to the index notation used in algebra to denote powers of symbols of quantity.

If a be an algebraic quantity, the algebraical notation for $a \cdot a$ is a^2, and for $a \cdot a \cdot a$ is a^3, and so on; the index here denoting the number of factors each equal to a which are multiplied together. But, as defined above, there is no idea of multiplication in $D \cdot D$ or D^2, but a simple *repetition of an operation*. In the same way D^n has no *quantitative* meaning in itself, but represents an *operation* consisting of employing the process of differentiation n times. For example, the difference between such quantities as D^2y, $(Dy)^2$, and D^2y^2 should be carefully noted. The index in the first case has reference only to the *symbol of operation* " D," which is therefore to be applied twice to y.

In $(Dy)^2$ the index is a purely *quantitative one* used in the algebraical sense to denote the product $Dy \times Dy$.

While in D^2y^2 we are to understand that the *square of y is to be differentiated twice.*

That the ultimate results are different may be easily seen by taking any simple case,

e.g., if $\qquad\qquad y = x^2,$

then $\qquad\qquad Dy = 2x,$

and $\qquad\qquad D^2y = 2 \dots\dots\dots\dots\dots\dots\dots(1)$

Again $\qquad\qquad (Dy)^2 = 4x^2, \dots\dots\dots\dots\dots\dots(2)$

whilst $\qquad\qquad y^2 = x^4,$

and $\qquad\qquad Dy^2 = 4x^3,$

giving $\qquad\qquad D^2y^2 = 12x^2 \dots\dots\dots\dots\dots\dots(3)$

A comparison of the results (1), (2), (3), will at once satisfy the student of the truth of the above remarks.

89. The operator D satisfies the elementary rules of Algebra.

We will next consider how far the analogy goes between symbols of quantity and the symbol of operation which we have denoted by D.

The fundamental rules of algebra are three in number and are known as

     (1) The "*Distributive Law,*"

     (2) The "*Commutative Law,*" and

     (3) The "*Index Law.*"

These three laws form the basis of all subsequent algebraical formulae and investigations.

     (1) The *Distributive Law* is that denoted by

$$m(a+b+c+\dots) = ma+mb+mc+\dots$$

Now, in Chap. II., Prop. III., it is proved that

$$D(u+v+w+\dots) = Du+Dv+Dw+\dots,$$

so that the symbol D is *distributive* in its operation.

     (2) The *Commutative Law* in algebra is that expressed by

$$ab = ba.$$

Now, in Chap. II., Prop. II., it is proved that

$$Dcy = cDy,$$

so that the symbol D is *commutative with regard to constants.*

But it is clear that the positions of the D and the y cannot be interchanged; such an error would be similar to writing

θ sin instead of sin θ. So that, while D is commutative with regard to constants, *it is not so with regard to variables.*

(3) The *Index Law* in algebra is denoted by

$$a^m . a^n = a^{m+n},$$

m and n being supposed to be positive integers.

Now, to differentiate a result m times which has already been operated upon n times is clearly the same as differentiating $m+n$ times, *i.e.,* $D^m . D^n y = D^{m+n} y.$
So the operator $D^m . D^n$ is equivalent to the operator D^{m+n} where m and n are positive integers.

Hence the symbol D *obeys the Index Law* for a positive integral exponent.

To sum up then, the operative symbol D *satisfies all the elementary rules of combination of algebraical quantities, with the exception that it is not commutative with regard to variables.*

90. It follows from the above remarks that any rational algebraical identity has a corresponding symbolical operative analogue.

For example, $(m+a)(m+b) = m^2 + (a+b)m + ab,$
so also the operation $(D+a)(D+b)$ is exactly equivalent to the operation $D^2 + (a+b)D + ab.$

Similarly, to the identity

$$(m+a)^2 = m^2 + 2am + a^2$$

corresponds the equivalence of the operations $(D+a)^2$ and $D^2 + 2aD + a^2.$

91. It is clear that in cases like the above an *ab initio* proof may be given of the identity of the operations represented. For instance, suppose it be required to show that

$$(D+a)(D+b)y = [D^2 + (a+b)D + ab]y,$$

we have $(D+b)y = Dy + by,$

and $(D+a)(D+b)y = (D+a)(Dy+by)$
$$= D(Dy+by) + a(Dy+by)$$
$$= D^2 y + bDy + aDy + aby$$
$$= D^2 y + (a+b)Dy + aby$$
$$= [D^2 + (a+b)D + ab]y,$$

the result to be proved: and the process of proof is exactly the same as that employed in proving that

$$(m+a)(m+b) = m^2 + (a+b)m + ab.$$

However, such proofs are unnecessary after the remarks of Art. 89, for they simply repeat *in form* the proof of the corresponding algebraical theorem.

It will now be obvious, for instance, without further proof, that since

$$(m+a)^n = m^n + nam^{n-1} + \frac{n(n-1)}{1.2}a^2m^{n-2} + \ldots + a^n,$$

we shall also have

$$(D+a)^n y = \left(D^n + naD^{n-1} + \frac{n(n-1)}{1.2}a^2D^{n-2} + \ldots + a^n\right)y$$

$$= D^n y + naD^{n-1}y + \frac{n(n-1)}{1.2}a^2D^{n-2}y + \ldots + a^n y.$$

92. Notation.

The first derived function of y with respect to the independent variable is often denoted by y_1, y', or $\dot{y}$. This notation can be conveniently extended, and we shall often find it convenient to denote

$$Dy, D^2y, D^3y, \ldots D^n y$$

by

$$y_1, \quad y_2, \quad y_3, \quad \ldots y_n,$$

or by

$$y^{(1)}, \quad y^{(2)}, \quad y^{(3)}, \quad \ldots y^{(n)},$$

or by

$$y', \quad y'', \quad y''', \quad \text{etc.},$$

or by

$$\dot{y}, \quad \ddot{y}, \quad \dddot{y}, \quad \text{etc.}$$

It is clear however that the notation of dashes or dots as used in the last two systems is inconvenient for higher differential coefficients than the fourth or fifth by reason of the number of dashes or dots which it would be necessary to use. The bracketed index notation is a somewhat dangerous one, from the liability of confusion with an algebraical index. The suffix notation appears to be free from objection in cases where there can be no misunderstanding as to which is the independent variable.

93. Standard Results and Processes.

The nth differential coefficients of some functions are easy to find.

Ex. 1. If $y = e^{ax}$; $y_1 = ae^{ax}$; $y_2 = a^2e^{ax}$; $\ldots y_n = a^n e^{ax}$.

Cor. (i.) If $a = 1$

$$y = e^x, y_1 = e^x, \ldots y_n = e^x.$$

Cor. (ii.)　　$y = a^x = e^{x \log_e a}$;

$y_1 = (\log_e a) e^{x \log_e a} = (\log_e a) a^x$;

$y_2 = (\log_e a)^2 e^{x \log_e a} = (\log_e a)^2 a^x$;

etc. = etc.,

$y_n = (\log_e a)^n e^{x \log_e a} = (\log_e a)^n a^x$.

Ex. 2.　If　　$y = \log_e(x + a)$;

$$y_1 = \frac{1}{x+a}; \; y_2 = -\frac{1}{(x+a)^2}; \; y_3 = \frac{(-1)(-2)}{(x+a)^3};$$

$$y_n = \frac{(-1)(-2)(-3)\ldots(-n+1)}{(x+a)^n}$$

$$= \frac{(-1)^{n-1}(n-1)!}{(x+a)^n}.$$

Cor.　If　　$y = \dfrac{1}{x+a}$, $y_n = \dfrac{(-1)^n n!}{(x+a)^{n+1}}$.

Ex. 3.　If　　$y = \sin(ax + b)$;

$$y_1 = a \cos(ax+b) = a \sin\left(ax+b+\frac{\pi}{2}\right);$$

$$y_2 = a^2 \sin\left(ax+b+\frac{2\pi}{2}\right);$$

$$y_3 = a^3 \sin\left(ax+b+\frac{3\pi}{2}\right);$$

$$\ldots\ldots\ldots\ldots\ldots\ldots\ldots\ldots\ldots$$

$$y_n = a^n \sin\left(ax+b+\frac{n\pi}{2}\right).$$

Similarly, if　　$y = \cos(ax + b)$,

$$y_n = a^n \cos\left(ax+b+\frac{n\pi}{2}\right).$$

Cor.　If　　$a = 1$ and $b = 0$;

then, when　　$y = \sin x$, $y_n = \sin\left(x + \dfrac{n\pi}{2}\right)$;

and, when　　$y = \cos x$, $y_n = \cos\left(x + \dfrac{n\pi}{2}\right)$.

Ex. 4.　If　　$y = e^{ax} \sin(bx + c)$; [*]

$y_1 = a e^{ax} \sin(bx+c) + b e^{ax} \cos(bx+c)$.

Let　　$a = r \cos \phi$ and $b = r \sin \phi$,

so that　　$r^2 = a^2 + b^2$ and $\tan \phi = \dfrac{b}{a}$;

and therefore　$y_1 = r e^{ax} \sin(bx + c + \phi)$.

[*] Murphy, *Camb. Trans.* vol. V.

Similarly $\quad y_2 = r^2 e^{ax}\sin(bx+c+2\phi),$

$\dots\dots\dots\dots\dots\dots\dots\dots$

and finally $\quad y_n = r^n e^{ax}\sin(bx+c+n\phi)$

$$= (a^2+b^2)^{\frac{n}{2}} e^{ax}\sin\left(bx+c+n\tan^{-1}\frac{b}{a}\right).$$

Similarly, if $\quad y = e^{ax}\cos(bx+c),$

$$y_n = (a^2+b^2)^{\frac{n}{2}} e^{ax}\cos\left(bx+c+n\tan^{-1}\frac{b}{a}\right).$$

As the above results are frequently wanted, it will be well for the student to be able to obtain them immediately.

EXAMPLES.

1. Find the nth differential coefficient of $\cos^7 x \sin^3 x$.

We must first transform this expression trigonometrically.

Let $\qquad\qquad \cos x + \iota \sin x = y.$

Then by Trigonometry $2\cos x = y + \dfrac{1}{y}, \qquad 2\cos kx = y^k + \dfrac{1}{y^k}$

$$2\iota \sin x = y - \frac{1}{y}, \qquad 2\iota \sin kx = y^k - \frac{1}{y^k}.$$

Thus $\quad 2^7.2^3\iota^3\cos^7 x \sin^3 x = \left(y+\dfrac{1}{y}\right)^7\left(y-\dfrac{1}{y}\right)^3$

$$= \left(y^{10}-\frac{1}{y^{10}}\right)+4\left(y^8-\frac{1}{y^8}\right)+3\left(y^6-\frac{1}{y^6}\right)-8\left(y^4-\frac{1}{y^4}\right)-14\left(y^2-\frac{1}{y^2}\right)$$

$$= 2\iota \sin 10x + 8\iota \sin 8x + 6\iota \sin 6x - 16\iota \sin 4x - 28\iota \sin 2x.$$

Thus $\qquad\qquad 2^9\cos^7 x \sin^3 x$

$$= -\sin 10x - 4\sin 8x - 3\sin 6x + 8\sin 4x + 14\sin 2x,$$

and therefore $\qquad 2^9\dfrac{d^n}{dx^n}(\cos^7 x \sin^3 x)$

$$= -10^n\sin\left(10x+\frac{n\pi}{2}\right)-4.8^n\sin\left(8x+\frac{n\pi}{2}\right)-3.6^n\sin\left(6x+\frac{n\pi}{2}\right)$$

$$+8.4^n\sin\left(4x+\frac{n\pi}{2}\right)+14.2^n\sin\left(2x+\frac{n\pi}{2}\right).$$

Find y_n in the following cases :—

2. $y = \sin^3 x.$

3. $y = \sin^6 x.$

4. $y = \sin^2 x \cos^3 x.$

5. $y = \sin^4 x \cos^4 x.$

6. $y = \sin x \sin 2x \sin 3x.$

7. $y = e^{2x}\cos^2 x.$

8. $y = e^{ax}\sin^3 bx.$

9. $y = e^{3x}\sin^2 x \cos^3 x.$

94. Fractional expressions of the form $\dfrac{f(x)}{\phi(x)}$ (both functions being algebraic and rational) can be differentiated n times by first putting them into *partial fractions*. (See p. 72.)

Ex. 1.
$$y = \frac{x^2}{(x-a)(x-b)(x-c)} = \frac{a^2}{(a-b)(a-c)} \frac{1}{x-a}$$
$$+ \frac{b^2}{(b-c)(b-a)} \frac{1}{x-b} + \frac{c^2}{(c-a)(c-b)} \frac{1}{x-c},$$

(see note on partial fractions);

therefore
$$y_n = \frac{a^2}{(a-b)(a-c)} \frac{(-1)^n n!}{(x-a)^{n+1}} + \frac{b^2}{(b-c)(b-a)} \frac{(-1)^n n!}{(x-b)^{n+1}}$$
$$+ \frac{c^2}{(c-a)(c-b)} \frac{(-1)^n n!}{(x-c)^{n+1}}.$$

Ex. 2.
$$y = \frac{x^2}{(x-1)^2(x+2)}.$$

To put this into Partial Fractions let $x = 1 + z$;

then
$$y = \frac{1}{z^2} \cdot \frac{1 + 2z + z^2}{3 + z}$$
$$= \frac{1}{z^2}\left(\frac{1}{3} + \frac{5z}{9} + \frac{4}{9} \frac{z^2}{3+z}\right) \text{ by division}$$
$$= \frac{1}{3z^2} + \frac{5}{9z} + \frac{4}{9} \frac{1}{3+z}$$
$$= \frac{1}{3(x-1)^2} + \frac{5}{9(x-1)} + \frac{4}{9(x+2)}$$

whence
$$y_n = \frac{(n+1)!(-1)^n}{3(x-1)^{n+2}} + \frac{5n!(-1)^n}{9(x-1)^{n+1}}$$
$$+ \frac{4n!(-1)^n}{9(x+2)^{n+1}}.$$

EXAMPLES.

Find the nth differential coefficients of y with regard to x in the following cases :—

1. $y = \dfrac{x}{(x-a)(x-b)}.$

2. $y = \dfrac{1}{(3x-2)(x-3)}.$

3. $y = \dfrac{1}{x^2 - a^2}.$

4. $y = \dfrac{x^2}{(x-1)^3(x-2)}.$

95. When quadratic factors (which are not resolvable into real linear factors) occur in the denominator, it is often convenient to make use of Demoivre's Theorem.*

Ex. Let
$$y = \frac{1}{(x+a)^2 + b^2} = \frac{1}{\{(x+a)+\iota b\}\{(x+a)-\iota b\}}.$$

Then
$$y = \frac{1}{2\iota b}\left\{\frac{1}{x+a-\iota b} - \frac{1}{x+a+\iota b}\right\};$$

* Liouville, *Journal de l'Ecole Polytechnique.*

and $\qquad y_n = \dfrac{1}{2\iota b}(-1)^n n! \left\{ \dfrac{1}{(x+a-\iota b)^{n+1}} - \dfrac{1}{(x+a+\iota b)^{n+1}} \right\}.$

Let $\qquad x+a = r\cos\theta, \qquad$ and $\qquad b = r\sin\theta \,;$

whence $\qquad r^2 = (x+a)^2 + b^2,$ and $\tan\theta = \dfrac{b}{x+a}.$

Hence $\quad y_n = \dfrac{(-1)^n n!}{2\iota b r^{n+1}} \{ (\cos\theta - \iota\sin\theta)^{-n-1} - (\cos\theta + \iota\sin\theta)^{-n-1} \}$

$$= \dfrac{(-1)^n n!}{2\iota b r^{n+1}} \, 2\iota \sin(n+1)\theta$$

$$= \dfrac{(-1)^n n!}{b^{n+2}} \sin(n+1)\theta \sin^{n+1}\theta,$$

$$\text{where } \theta = \tan^{-1}\dfrac{b}{(x+a)}.$$

Cor. If $y = \tan^{-1}\dfrac{x+a}{b}$, $y_1 = \dfrac{b}{(x+a)^2+b^2}$,

and therefore $\quad y_n = \dfrac{(-1)^{n-1}(n-1)!}{b^n} \sin n\theta \sin^n\theta,$

$$\text{where } \tan\theta = \dfrac{b}{x+a} = \cot y,$$

$$\text{i.e.,} \qquad \theta = \dfrac{\pi}{2} - y.$$

EXAMPLES.

Find the nth differential coefficients of y with respect to x in the following cases.

1. $y = \dfrac{1}{x^2+a^2}.$

2. $y = \tan^{-1}\dfrac{x}{a}.$

3. $y = \dfrac{x}{x^2+a^2}.$

4. $y = \tanh^{-1}\dfrac{x}{a}.$

5. $y = \dfrac{1}{x^4-a^4}.$

6. $y = \dfrac{1}{(x^2+a^2)(x^2+b^2)}.$

7. $y = \sin^{-1}\dfrac{2x}{1+x^2}.$

8. $y = x\tan^{-1}x.$

9. $y = \tan^{-1}\dfrac{x\sin a}{1-x\cos a}.$

10. $y = \dfrac{x^2+2x}{x^3-1}.$

11. $y = \dfrac{x}{x^4+a^2x^2+a^4}.$

12. $y = \dfrac{2x^2+x+2}{x^4+x^3+2x^2+x+1}.$

E.D.C. $\qquad\qquad\qquad$ E

96. LEIBNITZ'S THEOREM.*

To find the nth differential coefficient of a product of two functions of x in terms of the differential coefficients of the separate functions.

It was proved in Chap. II., Prop. IV., that

$$\frac{d}{dx}(uv) = v\frac{du}{dx} + u\frac{dv}{dx}.$$

It appears from this formula that the operative symbol $\frac{d}{dx}$ or D may be considered as the sum of two operative symbols D_1 and D_2, such that D_1 only operates on u and differential coefficients of u, while D_2 operates solely upon v and differential coefficients of v. For with such symbols

$$D_1(uv) = v\frac{du}{dx},$$

and

$$D_2(uv) = u\frac{dv}{dx},$$

whence

$$D(uv) = v\frac{du}{dx} + u\frac{dv}{dx} = D_1(uv) + D_2(uv)$$

$$= (D_1 + D_2)uv.$$

We may therefore write for D the compound symbol

$$D_1 + D_2.$$

Now, since D_1 and D_2 are symbols which indicate differentiations, they each, like the original symbol D, *obey the distributive and index laws and are commutative with regard to constants and each other.* It therefore follows by formal analogy with the Binomial Theorem that the operations

$$(D_1 + D_2)^n$$

and

$$D_1{}^n + nD_1{}^{n-1}D_2 + \frac{n(n-1)}{1 \cdot 2}D_1{}^{n-2}D_2{}^2 + \ldots + D_2{}^n$$

are identical.

Now

$$D_1{}^n(uv) = v\frac{d^n u}{dx^n},$$

$$D_1{}^{n-1}D_2(uv) = D_1{}^{n-1}\left(u\frac{dv}{dx}\right) = \frac{dv}{dx} \cdot \frac{d^{n-1}u}{dx^{n-1}},$$

etc.

* *Commercium Epistolicum*, vol. i.

Hence

$$\frac{d^n(uv)}{dx^n} = D^n(uv) = (D_1 + D_2)^n(uv)$$

$$= \left\{ D_1{}^n + nD_1{}^{n-1}D_2 + \frac{n(n-1)}{1\cdot 2}D_1{}^{n-2}D_2{}^2 + \dots + D_2{}^n \right\}uv$$

$$= v\frac{d^n u}{dx^n} + n\frac{dv}{dx}\cdot\frac{d^{n-1}u}{dx^{n-1}} + \frac{n(n-1)}{1\cdot 2}\frac{d^2v}{dx^2}\cdot\frac{d^{n-2}u}{dx^{n-2}}$$

$$+ \dots + u\frac{d^n v}{dx^n};$$

a result which may be written

$$(uv)_n = u_n v + {}_nC_1 u_{n-1}v_1 + {}_nC_2 u_{n-2}v_2 + \dots + uv_n.$$

It appears therefore from this formula that if all the differential coefficients of u and v be known up to the nth, inclusive, the nth differential coefficient of the product may at once be written down.

97. Extension.

It will be also clear that this result admits of extension to the case of a product of several functions.

For instance, if $\qquad y = uvw,$

$$\frac{d}{dx}y = vw\frac{d}{dx}u + wu\frac{d}{dx}v + uv\frac{d}{dx}w,$$

which, agreeably with the above notation, may be written

$$Dy = (D_1 + D_2 + D_3)uvw;$$

so that $\qquad \dfrac{d^n}{dx^n}(uvw) = (D_1 + D_2 + D_3)^n uvw.$

This may be expanded by formal analogy with the Multinomial Theorem, giving a result which may be written

$$\frac{d^n}{dx^n}(uvw) = \sum \frac{n!}{r!\,s!\,t!}\frac{d^r u}{dx^r}\cdot\frac{d^s v}{dx^s}\cdot\frac{d^t w}{dx^t},$$

the summation being extended to all positive integral values of r, s, t inclusive of zero, which satisfy

$$r + s + t = n.$$

98. Inductive Proof of Leibnitz's Theorem.

From the importance of this theorem it is considered useful to add here an inductive proof.

[Lemma. If ${}_nC_r$ denote the number of combinations of n things r at a time, then will $\qquad {}_nC_r + {}_nC_{r+1} = {}_{n+1}C_{r+1}.$
This will form an easy exercise for the student.]

Let $y = uv$, and let suffixes denote differentiations with regard to x.
Then $y_1 = u_1 v + u v_1$,

$y_2 = u_2 v + 2 u_1 v_1 + u v_2$, by differentiation.

Assume generally that

$$y_n = u_n v + {}_n C_1 u_{n-1} v_1 + {}_n C_2 u_{n-2} v_2 + \ldots + {}_n C_r u_{n-r} v_r + {}_n C_{r+1} u_{n-r-1} v_{r+1}$$
$$+ \ldots + u v_n. \quad \ldots\ldots\ldots\ldots\ldots\ldots\ldots\ldots\ldots\ldots\ldots\ldots\ldots\ldots\ldots\ldots(a)$$

Therefore, differentiating,

$$y_{n+1} = u_{n+1} v + u_n v_1 \begin{Bmatrix} {}_n C_1 \\ +1 \end{Bmatrix} + u_{n-1} v_2 \begin{Bmatrix} {}_n C_2 \\ + {}_n C_1 \end{Bmatrix} + \ldots$$

$$+ u_{n-r} v_{r+1} \begin{Bmatrix} {}_n C_{r+1} \\ + {}_n C_r \end{Bmatrix} + \ldots + u v_{n+1}$$

$$= u_{n+1} v + {}_{n+1} C_1 u_n v_1 + {}_{n+1} C_2 u_{n-1} v_2 + {}_{n+1} C_3 u_{n-2} v_3 + \ldots$$
$$+ {}_{n+1} C_{r+1} u_{n-r} v_{r+1} + \ldots + u v_{n+1}, \text{ by the Lemma ;}$$

therefore if the law (a) hold for n differentiations it holds for $n+1$.

But it was proved to hold for two differentiations, and therefore it holds for three ; therefore for four ; and so on ; and therefore it is generally true, i.e.,

$$(uv)_n = u_n v + {}_n C_1 u_{n-1} v_1 + {}_n C_2 u_{n-2} v_2 + \ldots + {}_n C_r u_{n-r} v_r + \ldots + u v_n.$$

99. Applications.

Ex. 1. $y = x^3 \sin ax$.

$$y_n = x^3 a^n \sin\left(ax + \frac{n\pi}{2}\right) + n 3 x^2 a^{n-1} \sin\left(ax + \frac{n-1}{2}\pi\right)$$

$$+ \frac{n(n-1)}{2!} 3 \cdot 2 x a^{n-2} \sin\left(ax + \frac{n-2}{2}\pi\right)$$

$$+ \frac{n(n-1)(n-2)}{3!} 3 \cdot 2 \cdot 1 a^{n-3} \sin\left(ax + \frac{n-3}{2}\pi\right).$$

Ex. 2. Differentiate n times the equation

$$x^2 \frac{d^2 y}{dx^2} + x \frac{dy}{dx} + y = 0.$$

$$\frac{d^n}{dx^n}(x^2 y_2) = x^2 y_{n+2} + n \cdot 2x \cdot y_{n+1} + \frac{n(n-1)}{2!} 2 y_n,$$

$$\frac{d^n}{dx^n}(x y_1) = \qquad\qquad x y_{n+1} + \qquad\quad n y_n,$$

$$\frac{d^n y}{dx^n} = \qquad\qquad\qquad\qquad y_n ;$$

therefore by addition

$$x^2 y_{n+2} + (2n+1) x y_{n+1} + (n^2 + 1) y_n = 0,$$

or

$$x^2 \frac{d^{n+2} y}{dx^{n+2}} + (2n+1) x \frac{d^{n+1} y}{dx^{n+1}} + (n^2 + 1) \frac{d^n y}{dx^n} = 0.$$

Ex. 3. When the general value of y_n cannot be obtained we may sometimes find its value for $x = 0$ as follows.

Suppose $\qquad\qquad y = (\sinh^{-1} x)^2$.

Here $\qquad\qquad y_1 = 2 \sinh^{-1} x / \sqrt{1 + x^2} \ldots\ldots\ldots\ldots\ldots\ldots\ldots\ldots(1)$

therefore $\qquad (1 + x^2) y_1^2 = 4y$,

whence differentiating and dividing by $2 y_1$

$$(1 + x^2) y_2 + x y_1 = 2. \ldots\ldots\ldots\ldots\ldots\ldots\ldots\ldots\ldots\ldots\ldots\ldots(2)$$

Differentiating n times by Leibnitz's Theorem

$$(1+x^2)y_{n+2}+2nxy_{n+1}+n(n-1)y_n$$
$$+ \quad xy_{n+1}+ \qquad ny_n=0$$

or $\qquad (1+x^2)y_{n+2}+(2n+1)xy_{n+1}+n^2y_n=0.$

Putting $x=0$ we have $\qquad (y_{n+2})_0= -n^2(y_n)_0$ ....(3)

indicating by suffix zero the value attained upon the vanishing of x.

Now, when $x=0$ we have from the value of y and equations (1) and (2)

$$(y)_0=0, \quad (y_1)_0=0, \quad (y_2)_0=2.$$

Hence equation (3) gives

$$(y_3)_0=(y_5)_0=(y_7)_0=\ldots\ldots=(y_{2k+1})_0=0$$

and

$$(y_4)_0= -2^2 . 2,$$
$$(y_6)_0= \quad 4^2 . 2^2 . 2,$$
$$(y_8)_0= -6^2 . 4^2 . 2^2 . 2,$$

$$\text{etc.,}$$

$$(y_{2k})_0=(-1)^{k-1}2 . 2^2 . 4^2 . 6^2 \ldots\ldots(2k-2)^2$$
$$=(-1)^{k-1}2^{2k-1}\{(k-1)!\}^2.$$

EXAMPLES.

1. If $y=x^2e^{ax}$ find y_n.   3. If $y=x^na^x$ find y_n.

2. If $y=x^2\sin ax$ find y_n.   4. If $y=x^ne^{ax}\sin bx$ find y_n.

5. Prove that the differential equation

$$(1+x^2)y_2+xy_1=m^2y$$

is satisfied by $\qquad y=\sinh(m\sinh^{-1}x).$

Prove also that

$$(1+x^2)y_{n+2}+(2n+1)xy_{n+1}+(n^2-m^2)y_n=0,$$

and find the value of y_n when $x=0$.

100. Some Important Symbolic Operations.

It has been proved, Art. 93, that if r be a positive integer,

$$D^re^{ax}=a^re^{ax}.$$

Let us define the operation D^{-r} to be such that

$$D^rD^{-r}u=u.$$

Thus D^{-1} represents an integration (Art. 79). We shall suppose moreover that no arbitrary constants are added.

Now, since $\qquad D^ra^{-r}e^{ax}=e^{ax}=D^rD^{-r}e^{ax},$

it follows that $\qquad D^{-r}e^{ax}=a^{-r}e^{ax}.$

Hence it is now clear that

$$D^re^{ax}=a^re^{ax}$$

for all integral values of r *positive* or *negative*.

101. Let $f(z)$ be any function of z capable of expansion in integer powers of z, positive or negative ($=\Sigma A_rz^r$ say, A_r being independent of z).

Then
$$f(D)e^{ax} = (\Sigma A_r D^r)e^{ax}$$
$$= \Sigma(A_r D^r e^{ax})$$
$$= (\Sigma A_r a^r)e^{ax}$$
$$= f(a)e^{ax}.$$

102. Next let $y = e^{ax}X$, where X is any function of x.

Then since
$$D^r e^{ax} = a^r e^{ax},$$
we have by Leibnitz's Theorem
$$y_n = e^{ax}(a^n X + {}_nC_1 a^{n-1}DX + {}_nC_2 a^{n-2}D^2X + \ldots + D^nX),$$
which by analogy with the Binomial Theorem (Art. 91) may
be written
$$D^n e^{ax}X = e^{ax}(D+a)^n X,$$
n being a positive integer.

103. Now let
$$X = (D+a)^n Y,$$
so that we may write
$$Y = (D+a)^{-n}X.$$
Then
$$D^n e^{ax}Y = e^{ax}(D+a)^n Y \text{ (Art. 102)},$$
or
$$D^n e^{ax}(D+a)^{-n}X = e^{ax}X,$$
and therefore
$$D^{-n} e^{ax}X = e^{ax}(D+a)^{-n}X.$$
Hence in *all* cases for integral values of n *positive* or *negative*
$$D^n e^{ax}X = e^{ax}(D+a)^n X.$$

104. As in Art. 101 we shall have
$$f(D)e^{ax}X = \Sigma(A_r D^r)e^{ax}X$$
$$= \Sigma(A_r D^r e^{ax}X)$$
$$= e^{ax}\Sigma A_r(D+a)^r X$$
$$= e^{ax}f(D+a)X.$$

105. Again
$$D^2 {}_{\cos}^{\sin} mx = (-m^2){}_{\cos}^{\sin} mx,$$
and therefore
$$D^{2r} {}_{\cos}^{\sin} mx = (-m^2)^r {}_{\cos}^{\sin} mx.$$
Hence, as before (Arts. 101 and 104), it will follow that
$$f(D^2) {}_{\cos}^{\sin} mx = f(-m^2) {}_{\cos}^{\sin} mx.$$

Ex.
$$\int e^{ax}\sin bx \, dx$$
$$= D^{-1}e^{ax}\sin bx = e^{ax}(D+a)^{-1}\sin bx \text{ (Art. 103)}$$
$$= e^{ax}\frac{a-D}{a^2-D^2}\sin bx$$
$$= \frac{e^{ax}}{a^2+b^2}(a-D)\sin bx \text{ (Art. 105)}.$$
$$= e^{ax}\frac{a \sin bx - b \cos bx}{a^2+b^2}$$
$$= e^{ax}(a^2+b^2)^{-\frac{1}{2}}\sin\left(bx - \tan^{-1}\frac{b}{a}\right) \text{ (compare Ex. 4, Art. 93)}.$$

106. Successive Differentiation of $F(x^2)$.

[Lemma. If $_nA_{2k}=\dfrac{n(n-1)\ldots(n-2k+1)}{k!}$ it is an elementary exercise to show that

$$_nA_{2k}+2(n-2k+2)_nA_{2k-2}=_{n+1}A_{2k}.$$

This is left to the student.]

We shall establish inductively that

$$\frac{d^n}{dx^n}F(x^2)=\sum_{k=0}{}_nA_{2k}(2x)^{n-2k}F^{n-k}(x^2),$$

the series continuing until a zero coefficient occurs; $_nA_0$ being supposed unity, and indices of F denoting differentiations with regard to x^2.

For differentiating this, the coefficient of

$$(2x)^{n-2k+1}F^{n-k+1}(x^2)$$

is $_nA_{2k}+2(n-2k+2)_nA_{2k-2}$, i.e. $_{n+1}A_{2k}$,

by the lemma.

Hence we obtain

$$\frac{d^{n+1}}{dx^{n+1}}F(x^2)=\sum_{k=0}{}_{n+1}A_{2k}(2x)^{n+1-2k}F^{n+1-k}(x^2),$$

so that if the law holds for n differentiations it holds for $n+1$. Moreover, the law is obvious for one and for two differentiations. Hence it is true for any positive integral value of n.

Ex. If $F(x^2)=e^{ax^2}$, then since

$$F^r(x^2)=a^re^{ax^2},$$

we obtain

$$\left(\frac{d}{dx}\right)^n e^{ax^2}=$$

$$e^{ax^2}[a^n(2x)^n+\frac{n(n-1)}{1!}a^{n-1}(2x)^{n-2}+\frac{n(n-1)(n-2)(n-3)}{2!}a^{n-2}(2x)^{n-4}+\text{etc.}]$$

107. Successive Differentiation of $F(\sqrt{x})$.

[Lemma. If $_nB_{2k}=\dfrac{(n+k-1)(n+k-2)\ldots(n-k)}{k!}$ then will

$$_nB_{2k}+{}_nB_{2k-2}2(n+k-1)={}_{n+1}B_{2k}.$$

The verification is left to the student.]

We shall establish inductively that

$$\frac{d^n}{dx^n}F(\sqrt{x})=\sum_{k=0}{}_nB_{2k}(-1)^k\left(\frac{1}{2\sqrt{x}}\right)^{n+k}F^{n-k}(\sqrt{x}),$$

the summation continuing until a zero coefficient occurs; $_nB_0$ being supposed unity, and indices of F denoting differentiations with regard to $\sqrt{x}$.

For differentiating, the coefficient of

$$(-1)^k\left(\frac{1}{2\sqrt{x}}\right)^{n+k+1} F^{n-k+1}(\sqrt{x})$$

is
$$_nB_{2k}+2(n+k-1)_nB_{2k-2},$$

i.e. $_{n+1}B_{2k}$ by the lemma.

Hence we obtain

$$\frac{d^{n+1}}{dx^{n+1}}F(\sqrt{x})=\sum_{k=0}{}_{n+1}B_{2k}(-1)^k\left(\frac{1}{2\sqrt{x}}\right)^{n+1+k} F^{n+1-k}(\sqrt{x}),$$

so that if the law holds for n differentiations it holds for $n+1$. Moreover the law is obvious for one or two differentiations. Hence it is proved true for any positive integral value of n.

Ex. Prove that
$$\frac{d^n}{dx^n}(e^{a\sqrt{x}})=e^{a\sqrt{x}}\left(\frac{a}{2\sqrt{x}}\right)^n\sum_{r=0}^{r=n-1}\left\{(-1)^r\frac{(n+r-1)!}{r!(n-r-1)!}\frac{1}{(2a\sqrt{x})^r}\right\}$$

[MATH. TRIPOS, 1886.]

108. Function of a Function.

A general expression for the nth differential coefficient of a function of a function will be found in Chapter V.

109. NOTE ON PARTIAL FRACTIONS.

Since a number of examples on successive differentiation and on integration depend on the ability of the student to put certain fractional forms into partial fractions, we give the methods to be pursued in a short note.

Let $\dfrac{f(x)}{\phi(x)}$ be the fraction which is to be resolved into its partial fractions.

1. If $f(x)$ be not already of lower degree than the denominator, *we can divide out until the numerator of the remaining fraction is of lower degree:*

e.g.
$$\frac{x^2}{(x-1)(x-2)}=1+\frac{3x-2}{(x-1)(x-2)}.$$

Hence we shall consider only the case in which $f(x)$ is of lower degree than $\phi(x)$.

2. If $\phi(x)$ contain a single factor $(x-a)$, not repeated, we proceed thus: suppose
$$\phi(x)=(x-a)\psi(x),$$

and let
$$\frac{f(x)}{(x-a)\psi(x)}\equiv\frac{A}{x-a}+\frac{\chi(x)}{\psi(x)},$$

A being independent of x.

Hence
$$\frac{f(x)}{\psi(x)}\equiv A+(x-a)\frac{\chi(x)}{\psi(x)}.$$

This is an identity and therefore true for all values of the variable x; put $x=a$. Then, since $\psi(x)$ does not vanish when $x=a$ (for by hypothesis $\psi(x)$ does not contain $x-a$ as a factor), we have

$$A=\frac{f(a)}{\psi(a)}.$$

Hence the rule to find A is, "Put $x=a$ in every portion of the fraction except in the factor $x-a$ itself."

Ex.   (i.) $$\frac{x-c}{(x-a)(x-b)}=\frac{a-c}{a-b}\cdot\frac{1}{x-a}+\frac{b-c}{b-a}\cdot\frac{1}{x-b}.$$

Ex.   (ii.) $$\frac{x^2+px+q}{(x-a)(x-b)(x-c)}=\frac{a^2+pa+q}{(a-b)(a-c)}\frac{1}{x-a}+\frac{b^2+pb+q}{(b-c)(b-a)}\frac{1}{x-b}$$
$$+\frac{c^2+pc+q}{(c-a)(c-b)}\frac{1}{x-c}.$$

Ex.   (iii.) $$\frac{x}{(x-1)(x-2)(x-3)}=\frac{1}{2(x-1)}-\frac{2}{x-2}+\frac{3}{2(x-3)}.$$

Ex.   (iv.) $$\frac{x^2}{(x-a)(x-b)}.$$

Here the numerator not being of *lower degree than the denominator*, we divide the numerator by the denominator. The result will then be expressible in the form $1+\dfrac{A}{x-a}+\dfrac{B}{x-b}$, where A and B are found as before and are respectively $\dfrac{a^2}{a-b}$ and $\dfrac{b^2}{b-a}$.

3. Suppose the factor $(x-a)$ in the denominator to be repeated r times so that $\quad\phi(x)=(x-a)^r\psi(x).$

Put $\quad x-a=y.$

Then $\quad\dfrac{f(x)}{\phi(x)}=\dfrac{f(a+y)}{y^r\psi(a+y)},$

or expanding each function by any means in ascending powers of y,

$$=\frac{A_0+A_1y+A_2y^2+\dots}{y^r(B_0+B_1y+B_2y^2+\dots)}.$$

Divide out thus:—

$$B_0+B_1y+\dots\big|\,A_0+A_1y+\dots\,\big|\underline{C_0+C_1y+C_2y^2+\dots},$$
$$\text{etc.,}$$

and let the division be continued until y^r is a factor of the remainder

Let the remainder be $y^r\chi(y)$.

Hence the fraction $=\dfrac{C_0}{y^r}+\dfrac{C_1}{y^{r-1}}+\dfrac{C_2}{y^{r-2}}+\dots+\dfrac{C_{r-1}}{y}+\dfrac{\chi(y)}{\psi(a+y)}$

$$=\frac{C_0}{(x-a)^r}+\frac{C_1}{(x-a)^{r-1}}+\frac{C_2}{(x-a)^{r-2}}+\dots$$

$$+\frac{C_{r-1}}{x-a}+\frac{\chi(x-a)}{\psi(x)}.$$

Hence the partial fractions corresponding to the factor $(x-a)^r$ are determined by a long division sum.

Ex. Take $$\frac{x^2}{(x-1)^3(x+1)}.$$

Put $\quad x-1=y.$

Hence the fraction $= \dfrac{(1+y)^2}{y^3(2+y)}$.

$$2+y \overline{)}\ 1+2y+y^2 \left(\tfrac{1}{2}+\tfrac{3}{4}y+\tfrac{1}{8}y^2 - \tfrac{1}{8}\dfrac{y^3}{2+y}\right).$$

$$\underline{1+\tfrac{1}{2}y}$$

$$\tfrac{3}{2}y+y^2$$
$$\underline{\tfrac{3}{2}y+\tfrac{3}{4}y^2}$$

$$\tfrac{1}{4}y^2$$
$$\underline{\tfrac{1}{4}y^2+\tfrac{1}{8}y^3}$$

$$-\tfrac{1}{8}y^3$$

Therefore the fraction

$$=\frac{1}{2y^3}+\frac{3}{4y^2}+\frac{1}{8y}-\frac{1}{8(2+y)}$$

$$=\frac{1}{2(x-1)^3}+\frac{3}{4(x-1)^2}+\frac{1}{8(x-1)}-\frac{1}{8(x+1)}.$$

4. If a factor, such as x^2+ax+b, which is not resolvable into real linear factors occur in the denominator, the form of the corresponding partial fraction is $\dfrac{Ax+B}{x^2+ax+b}$. For instance, if the expression be

$$\frac{1}{(x-a)(x-b)^2(x^2+a^2)(x^2+b^2)^2}$$

the proper assumption for the form in partial fractions would be

$$\frac{A}{x-a}+\frac{B}{x-b}+\frac{C}{(x-b)^2}+\frac{Dx+E}{x^2+a^2}+\frac{Fx+G}{x^2+b^2}+\frac{Hx+K}{(x^2+b^2)^2},$$

where A, B, and C can be found according to the preceding methods, and on reduction to a common denominator we can, by equating coefficients of like powers in the two numerators, find the remaining letters D, E, F, G, H, K. Variations upon these methods will suggest themselves to the student.

EXAMPLES.

1. If $y=\tan^{-1}x^2$, find y_2.

2. If $y=x^2\log x$, find y_3.

3. If $y=xe^{ax}$, find y_3.

4. If $y=x^n$, find y_r, distinguishing the cases in which $r<$, $=$ or $>n$; supposing n to be a positive integer.

5. If $y=A\sin mx+B\cos mx$, prove that $y_2+m^2y=0$.

6. If $y=Ae^{mx}+Be^{-mx}$, prove that $y_2-m^2y=0$.

7. If $y=ax\sin x$, prove that $x^2y_2-2xy_1+(x^2+2)y=0$.

8. If $y=a\cos(\log x)$, prove that $x^2y_2+xy_1+y=0$.

9. If $y=ax^{n+1}+bx^{-n}$, prove that $x^2y_2=n(n+1)y$.

10. If $y^{-2}=1+2\sqrt{2}\cos 2x$, prove that $y_2=y(3y^2+1)(7y^2-1)$.

[OXFORD, 1889.]

11. If $y = x \log \dfrac{x}{a + bx}$, prove that $x^3 y_2 = (y - xy_1)^2$.

12. If $y = \sin x$ prove $4\dfrac{d^3 \cos^7 x}{dy^3} = 105 \sin 4x$. [OXFORD; 1890.]

13. Find the nth differential coefficient of
$$e^{ax}\{a^2 x^2 - 2nax + n(n + 1)\}.$$
[I. C. S.]

14. If $u = \sin nx + \cos nx$, show that
$$u_r = n^r \{1 + (-1)^r \sin 2nx\}^{\frac{1}{2}}.$$
[I. C. S.]

15. If $y = \sin^{-1}x$, prove that $(1 - x^2)y_2 - xy_1 = 0$; also that
$(1 - x^2)y_{n+2} - (2n + 1)xy_{n+1} - n^2 y_n = 0$.

16. If $y = A(x + \sqrt{x^2 + a^2})^n + B(x + \sqrt{x^2 + a^2})^{-n}$,
then will $(x^2 + a^2)y_{m+2} + (2m + 1)xy_{m+1} + (m^2 - n^2)y_m = 0$.

17. If $y^{\frac{1}{m}} + y^{-\frac{1}{m}} = 2x$, prove that
$$(x^2 - 1)y_{n+2} + (2n + 1)xy_{n+1} + (n^2 - m^2)y_n = 0.$$

18. If $y = e^{-x} \cos x$, prove that $y_4 + 4y = 0$.

19. If $y = \dfrac{x^2}{(x - a)(x - b)}$, find y_n.

20. If $y = \dfrac{1}{(x - 1)^3(x - 2)}$, find y_n.

21. If $y = (x^m - a^m)^{-1}$, find y_n, m being a positive integer.

22. If $y = x^n \log x$, find y_n.

23. If $y = (1 + x + x^2 + x^3)^{-1}$ and $\theta = \cot^{-1}x$, show that y_n is
$\frac{1}{2}(-1)^n n! \sin^{n+1}\theta\{\sin(n + 1)\theta - \cos(n + 1)\theta + (\sin \theta + \cos \theta)^{-n-1}\}$.
[MATH. TRIPOS.]

24. If $y = e^{\tan^{-1}x} = a_0 + a_1 x + a_2 x^2 + \dots$, show that
    (i.) $(1 + x^2)y_2 + (2x - 1)y_1 = 0$;
    (ii.) $(1 + x^2)y_{n+2} + \{2(n + 1)x - 1\}y_{n+1} + n(n + 1)y_n = 0$
    (iii.) $(n + 2)a_{n+2} + na_n = a_{n+1}$.
The last equation is to be found by substituting the series for y in equation (i.) and equating the coefficient of x^n to zero.

25. If $y = \sin(m \sin^{-1}x) = a_0 + a_1 x + a_2 x^2 + \dots$, show that
        (i.) $(1 - x^2)y_2 = xy_1 - m^2 y$;
        (ii.) $(1 - x^2)y_{n+2} - (2n + 1)xy_{n+1} - (n^2 - m^2)y_n = 0$;
and   (iii.) $(n + 1)(n + 2)a_{n+2} = (n^2 - m^2)a_n$.

26. If $e^{a \sin^{-1}x} = a_0 + a_1 x + a_2 x^2 + \dots$, prove
$$(n + 1)(n + 2)a_{n+2} = (n^2 + a^2)a_n.$$

27. If $(\sin^{-1}x)^2 = a_0 + a_1 x + a_2 x^2 + a_3 x^3 + \dots$, show that
$$(n + 1)(n + 2)a_{n+2} = n^2 a_n.$$

28. If u, v, w be functions of t, and if suffixes denote differentiations with regard to t, prove that

$$\frac{d}{dt}\begin{vmatrix} u_1, & v_1, & w_1 \\ u_2, & v_2, & w_2 \\ u_3, & v_3, & w_3 \end{vmatrix} = \begin{vmatrix} u_1, & v_1, & w_1 \\ u_2, & v_2, & w_2 \\ u_4, & v_4, & w_4 \end{vmatrix}.$$

[Coll. Exam.]

29. If $\dfrac{1}{e^x - 1}$ be differentiated i times, the denominator of the result will be $(e^x - 1)^{i+1}$, and the sum of the coefficients of the several powers of e^x in the numerator will be $(-1)^i 1 . 2 . 3 \dots i$.

[Caius Coll.]

30. Prove that

$$v\frac{d^n u}{dx^n} = \frac{d^n uv}{dx^n} - n\frac{d^{n-1}}{dx^{n-1}}\left(u\frac{dv}{dx}\right) + \frac{n(n-1)}{1 . 2}\frac{d^{n-2}}{dx^{n-2}}\left(u\frac{d^2 v}{dx^2}\right) - \dots + (-1)^n u\frac{d^n v}{dx^n}.$$

31. Show that if $x = \cot y$

$$\frac{d^n}{dx^n}\frac{x^n}{1+x^2} = n!\sin y\{\sin y - {}_nC_1\cos y\sin 2y + {}_nC_2\cos^2 y\sin 3y - \dots\}.$$

[Oxford, 1890.]

32. Prove that if $ac > b^2$

$$\frac{d^n}{dx^n}\frac{b+cx}{a+2bx+cx^2}$$
$$= (-1)^n n!\left(\frac{c}{a+2bx+cx^2}\right)^{\frac{n+1}{2}}\cos\left[(n+1)\tan^{-1}\frac{\sqrt{ac-b^2}}{b+cx}\right].$$

[London, 1890.]

33. Show that $\tan\left(y\dfrac{d}{dx}\right)\sin mx = \tanh my . \cos mx$;

[Oxford, 1888.]

also $\qquad \tan^{-1}\left(y\dfrac{d}{dx}\right)\sin mx = \tanh^{-1}my . \cos mx$;

and $\qquad \mathrm{gd}\left(y\dfrac{d}{dx}\right)\sin mx = \mathrm{gd}^{-1}(my)\cos mx.$

34. Prove $\qquad \left(\dfrac{d}{dx}\right)^r e^{ax}x^n = a^{r-n}x^{n-r}\left(\dfrac{d}{dx}\right)^n e^{ax}x^r.$

[Gregory's Examples.]

35. Prove that if $x + y = 1$

$$\frac{d^n}{dx^n}(x^n y^n) = n!\left(y^n - {}_nC_1^2 y^{n-1}x + {}_nC_2^2 y^{n-2}x^2 - \dots\right)$$

[Murphy, Electricity.]

36. Prove that

$$x\log x + x(\log x)^2 + \frac{1}{2!}\frac{d}{dx}\{x^2(\log x)^3\} + \frac{1}{3!}\left(\frac{d}{dx}\right)^2\{x^3(\log x)^4\}$$
$$+ \dots \text{ to } n+1 \text{ terms} = \frac{1}{(n+1)!}\left(\frac{d}{dx}\right)^n\{x^{n+1}(\log x)^{n+1}\}.$$

[Math. Tripos, 1889.]

37. Find the nth differential coefficients of $\sin x^2$ and $\cos x^2$.

38. Establish Rodrigues' Theorem* that if n be a positive integer

$$\sin nx = \frac{n}{1 \cdot 3 \cdot 5 \dots (2n-1)}\left(\frac{1}{\sin x}\frac{d}{dx}\right)^{n-1}(\sin x)^{2n-1}.$$

39. Prove that

$$\frac{d^n}{dx^n}\sin^{-1}x = \frac{1 \cdot 3 \cdot 5 \dots 2n-3}{2^{n-1}(1-x)^{n-1}(1-x^2)^{\frac{1}{2}}}\left[1 + \sum_{k=1}^{k=n-1}(-1)^k{}_{n-1}C_kT_k\right]$$

where $\qquad T_k = \dfrac{1 \cdot 3 \cdot 5 \dots (2k-1)}{(2n-3)(2n-5)\dots(2n-2k-1)}\left(\dfrac{1-x}{1+x}\right)^k.$

[FRENET.]

40. If $f(x) = a_0 + a_1x + a_2x^2 + \dots + a_r x^r + \dots$, prove that

$$1^n a_1 + 2^n a_2 + \dots + r^n a_r + \dots = \left[\left(x\frac{d}{dx}\right)^n f(x)\right]_{x=1}.$$

41. If $\phi(n)$ be a rational algebraic function of n, prove that

$$\phi(1)x + \phi(2)x^2 + \dots + \phi(n)x^n = \phi\left(x\frac{d}{dx}\right)x\frac{1-x^n}{1-x}.$$

42. If $f(x)$ can be expanded in positive integral powers of x, prove that

$$f(D)(uv) = u f(D)v + Du f'(D)v + \frac{D^2u}{2!}f''(D)v + \frac{D^3u}{3!}f'''(D)v + \dots.$$

43. Show that the Bessel's Function $J_n(x)$ (Ex. 125, Chap. III.) satisfies the differential equation

$$\frac{d^2u}{dx^2} + \frac{1}{x}\frac{du}{dx} + \left(1 - \frac{n^2}{x^2}\right)u = 0.$$

44. Prove that Legendre's function of the nth order, viz.,

$$P_n(x) = \frac{1}{2^n \cdot n!}\frac{d^n}{dx^n}(x^2-1)^n$$

satisfies the equation

$$\frac{d}{dx}\left\{(1-x^2)\frac{dP_n}{dx}\right\} + n(n+1)P_n = 0,$$

and may be expressed as

(a) $\dfrac{1}{2^n}\{u^n + {}_nC_1^2 u^{n-1}v + {}_nC_2^2 u^{n-2}v^2 + \dots + v^n\}$;

where $\qquad u \equiv x+1 \text{ and } v \equiv x-1$;

(β) $x^n + \dfrac{1}{2^2}{}^nC_2{}^2C_1 x^{n-2}(x^2-1) + \dfrac{1}{2^4}{}^nC_4{}^4C_2 x^{n-4}(x^2-1)^2$

$\qquad\qquad + \dfrac{1}{2^6}{}^nC_6{}^6C_3 x^{n-6}(x^2-1)^3 + \dots.$

---

* M. Frenet has pointed out (*Recueil d'Exercices*) that this result which is usually ascribed to Jacobi and known by his name (being given by him in *Crelle's Journal*) had been previously published by Rodrigues.

CHAPTER V.

EXPANSIONS.

110. The student will have already met with several expansions of given explicit functions in ascending integral powers of the independent variable; for example, those for $(x+a)^n$, e^x, $\log(1+x)$, $\tan^{-1}x$, $\sin x$, $\cos x$, which occur in ordinary Algebra and Trigonometry.

The principal methods of development in common use may be briefly classified as follows:

I. By purely Algebraical or Trigonometrical processes.

II. By Taylor's or Maclaurin's Theorems.

III. By Differentiation or Integration of a known series, or equivalent process.

IV. By the use of a differential equation.

These methods we proceed to explain and exemplify.

111. METHOD I. **Algebraic and Trigonometrical Methods.**

Ex. 1. Find the first three terms of the expansion of $\log \sec x$ in ascending powers of x.

By Trigonometry

$$\cos x = 1 - \frac{x^2}{2!} + \frac{x^4}{4!} - \frac{x^6}{6!} + \dots$$

Hence $\log \sec x = -\log \cos x = -\log(1-z)$,

where $$z = \frac{x^2}{2!} - \frac{x^4}{4!} + \frac{x^6}{6!} - \dots\;;$$

and expanding $\log(1-z)$ by the logarithmic theorem we obtain

$$\log \sec x = z + \frac{z^2}{2} + \frac{z^3}{3} + \dots$$

$$= \left[\frac{x^2}{2!} - \frac{x^4}{4!} + \frac{x^6}{6!} - \dots\right] + \frac{1}{2}\left[\frac{x^2}{2!} - \frac{x^4}{4!} + \dots\right]^2$$

$$+ \frac{1}{3}\left[\frac{x^2}{2!} - \dots\right]^3 \dots\dots$$

$$=\frac{x^2}{2}-\frac{x^4}{24}+\frac{x^6}{720}-\dots$$

$$+\frac{x^4}{8}-\frac{x^6}{48}+\dots$$

$$+\frac{x^6}{24}-\dots;$$

hence $\qquad \log \sec x = \frac{x^2}{2}+\frac{x^4}{12}+\frac{x^6}{45}\dots\dots$

Ex. 2. Expand $\cos^3 x$ in powers of x.

Since $\qquad 4\cos^3 x = \cos 3x + 3\cos x$

$$= 1 - \frac{3^2 x^2}{2!} + \frac{3^4 x^4}{4!} - \dots + (-1)^n \frac{3^{2n} x^{2n}}{(2n)!} + \dots$$

$$+ 3\left[1 - \frac{x^2}{2!} + \frac{x^4}{4!} - \dots + (-1)^n \frac{x^{2n}}{(2n)!} + \dots\right],$$

we obtain $\qquad \cos^3 x = \frac{1}{4}\Big\{(1+3)-(3^2+3)\frac{x^2}{2!}+(3^4+3)\frac{x^4}{4!}-\dots$

$$+(-1)^n(3^{2n}+3)\frac{x^{2n}}{(2n)!}+\dots\Big\}.$$

Similarly $\qquad \sin^3 x = \frac{1}{4}\Big\{(3^3-3)\frac{x^3}{3!}-(3^5-3)\frac{x^5}{5!}+(3^7-3)\frac{x^7}{7!}-\dots$

$$+(-1)^n\frac{3^{2n-1}-3}{(2n-1)!}x^{2n-1}-\dots\Big\}.$$

Ex. 3. Expand $\tan x$ in powers of x as far as the term involving x^5.

Since $\qquad \tan x = \dfrac{x-\dfrac{x^3}{3!}+\dfrac{x^5}{5!}-\dots}{1-\dfrac{x^2}{2!}+\dfrac{x^4}{4!}-\dots}$

we may by actual division show that

$$\tan x = x + \frac{x^3}{3} + \frac{2}{15}x^5 + \dots$$

Ex. 4. Expand $\frac{1}{2}\{\log(1+x)\}^2$ in powers of x.

Since $\qquad (1+x)^y \equiv e^{y\log(1+x)},$

we have, by expanding each side of this identity,

$$1+yx+\frac{y(y-1)}{2!}x^2+\frac{y(y-1)(y-2)}{3!}x^3+\frac{y(y-1)(y-2)(y-3)}{4!}x^4+\dots$$

$$\equiv 1+y\log(1+x)+\frac{y^2}{2!}\{\log(1+x)\}^2+\dots$$

Hence, equating coefficients of y^2,

$$\tfrac{1}{2}\{\log(1+x)\}^2=\frac{x^2}{2!}-\frac{1+2}{3!}x^3+\frac{1\cdot 2+2\cdot 3+3\cdot 1}{4!}x^4-\text{etc.},$$

a series which may be written in the form

$$\frac{x^2}{2}-(1+\tfrac{1}{2})\frac{x^3}{3}+(1+\tfrac{1}{2}+\tfrac{1}{3})\frac{x^4}{4}-(1+\tfrac{1}{2}+\tfrac{1}{3}+\tfrac{1}{4})\frac{x^5}{5}+\dots$$

EXAMPLES.

1. Prove $e^{x \sin x} = 1 + x^2 + \frac{1}{3}x^4 + \frac{1}{120}x^6 \ldots$

2. Prove $\cosh^n x = 1 + \frac{nx^2}{2!} + n(3n-2)\frac{x^4}{4!} \ldots$

3. Prove $\log \frac{\sin x}{x} = -\frac{x^2}{6} - \frac{x^4}{180} \ldots$

4. Prove $\log \frac{\sinh x}{x} = \frac{x^2}{6} - \frac{x^4}{180} \ldots$

5. Prove $\log x \cot x = -\frac{x^2}{3} - \frac{7}{90}x^4 \ldots$

6. Prove $\log \frac{\tan^{-1} x}{x} = -\frac{x^2}{3} + \frac{13}{90}x^4 - \frac{251}{5 \cdot 7 \cdot 9^2}x^6 \ldots$

7. Expand $\sinh^3 x$ and $\cosh^3 x$, giving the general term in each case.

8. Prove $\log(1 - x + x^2) = -x + \frac{x^2}{2} + \frac{2x^3}{3} + \frac{x^4}{4} - \frac{x^5}{5} - \frac{x^6}{3} - \frac{x^7}{7} + \frac{x^8}{8} \ldots$

9. Expand $\log(1 + x^3 e^x)$ as far as the term containing x^5.

10. Expand in powers of x,

     (a) $\tan^{-1}\dfrac{p - qx}{q + px}$.   (c) $\sin^{-1}\dfrac{2x}{1 + x^2}$.

     (b) $\tan^{-1}\dfrac{\sqrt{1 + x^2} - 1}{x}$.   (d) $\cos^{-1}\dfrac{x - x^{-1}}{x + x^{-1}}$.

11. Prove that

$$\frac{[\log(1 + x)]^r}{r!} = \frac{x^r}{r!} - {}_r P_1 \frac{x^{r+1}}{(r+1)!} + {}_{r+1}P_2 \frac{x^{r+2}}{(r+2)!} - {}_{r+2}P_3 \frac{x^{r+3}}{(r+3)!} + \ldots,$$

where ${}_r P_k$ denotes the sum of all products k at a time of the first r natural numbers.

112. Method II. Taylor's and Maclaurin's Theorems.

It has been discovered that the Binomial, Exponential, and other well-known expansions are all particular cases of one general theorem known as Taylor's Theorem, which has for its object the *expansion of $f(x + h)$ in ascending integral positive powers of h*, $f(x)$ being a function of x of *any form whatever*. It will be found that such an expansion is not always possible, but we reserve for later articles a rigorous discussion of the limitations of the theorem.

113. The theorem referred to is that *under certain circum-stances* $f(x + h) = f(x) + h f'(x) + \frac{h^2}{2!}f''(x) + \frac{h^3}{3!}f'''(x) + \ldots$

$$+ \frac{h^n}{n!}f^n(x) + \ldots \text{ to infinity,}$$

an expansion of $f(x + h)$ in powers of h.

This result was first published by Taylor in 1715, in his "Methodus Incrementorum Directa et Inversa." In 1717 Stirling pointed out another form of Taylor's Theorem, viz.,

$$f(x) = f(0) + xf'(0) + \frac{x^2}{2!}f''(0) + \frac{x^3}{3!}f'''(0) + \dots$$

$$+ \frac{x^n}{n!}f^n(0) + \dots \text{ to infinity,}$$

which is *easily deducible from Taylor's Series* by writing 0 for x and x for h; the meaning of $f^r(0)$ being that $f(x)$ is to be differentiated r times with respect to x, and then x is to be put equal to zero in the result.

The latter series gives a method of expanding any function of x in positive integral powers of x. Being a form of Taylor's Theorem it is subject to the same limitations. It is generally known as *Maclaurin's Theorem*, though its publication by Maclaurin was not made until twenty-five years after its first discovery by Stirling.

114. *Taylor's Theorem also deducible from Maclaurin's.*

It has been shown that Maclaurin's series is deducible from Taylor's form. Taylor's series is also deducible from Maclaurin's.

For, let $\qquad f(x) = F(x+y),$

then $\qquad f'(x) = F'(x+y),$ etc.,

so that $\qquad f(0) = F(y), f'(0) = F'(y), f''(0) = F''(y),$ etc.

Hence Maclaurin's Theorem

$$f(x) = f(0) + xf'(0) + \frac{x^2}{2!}f''(0) + \dots$$

becomes $\qquad F(y+x) = F(y) + xF'(y) + \frac{x^2}{2!}F''(y) + \dots,$

which is Taylor's form.

TAYLOR'S THEOREM.

115. PROP. To prove that, *if $f(x+h)$ can be expanded in a convergent series of positive integral powers of h, that expansion is*

$$f(x+h) = f(x) + hf'(x) + \frac{h^2}{2!}f''(x) + \dots \text{ to } \infty.$$

Put $x+h = X$; then since x and h are independent

$$\frac{dX}{dh} = 1.$$

Hence $$\frac{df(X)}{dh} = \frac{df(X)}{dX} \cdot \frac{dX}{dh} = f'(X).$$

Similarly $$\frac{d^2 f(X)}{dh^2} = f''(X), \text{ etc.}$$

Now, *assuming the possibility* of such an expansion, let

$$f(x+h) = A_0 + A_1 h + A_2 \frac{h^2}{2!} + A_3 \frac{h^3}{3!} + \dots, \quad \dots\dots\dots(1)$$

where A_0, A_1, A_2, ... are functions *of x alone, not containing h,* and are to be determined.

Differentiating with regard to h we have, by the preceding work, $$f'(x+h) = \frac{df(x+h)}{dh} = A_1 + A_2 h + A_3 \frac{h^2}{2!} + A_4 \frac{h^3}{3!} + \dots \quad \dots(2)$$

Differentiating again

$$f''(x+h) = \frac{df'(x+h)}{dh} = A_2 + A_3 h + A_4 \frac{h^2}{2!} + A_5 \frac{h^3}{3!} + \dots, \quad \dots\dots(3)$$

etc.

Put $h = 0$, and we have at once from (1), (2), (3), ...
$$A_0 = f(x), \ A_1 = f'(x), \ A_2 = f''(x), \text{ etc.}, \dots$$

Substituting these values in (1)

$$f(x+h) = f(x) + h f'(x) + \frac{h^2}{2!} f''(x) + \dots + \frac{h^r}{r!} f^r(x) + \dots$$

116. This theorem may be written

$$f(x+h) = \left\{ 1 + h\frac{d}{dx} + \frac{h^2}{2!}\left(\frac{d}{dx}\right)^2 + \frac{h^3}{3!}\left(\frac{d}{dx}\right)^3 + \dots \right\} f(x),$$

and by analogy of form with the exponential theorem the operator may be represented shortly by

$$e^{h\frac{d}{dx}} \text{ or } e^{hD}.$$

Thus $$f(x+h) = e^{hD} f(x).$$

STIRLING'S OR MACLAURIN'S THEOREM.

117. PROP. To prove that *if $f(x)$ can be expanded in a convergent series of positive integral powers of x, that expansion is*

$$f(x) = f(0) + x f'(0) + \frac{x^2}{2!} f''(0) + \frac{x^3}{3!} f'''(0) + \dots \text{ to } \infty.$$

Assuming the possibility of such an expansion, let

$$f(x) = A_0 + A_1 x + A_2 \frac{x^2}{2!} + A_3 \frac{x^3}{3!} + \dots, \quad \dots\dots\dots\dots\dots(1)$$

where A_0, A_1, A_2, ..., are constants to be determined, *not containing x*.

Then differentiating we have

$$f'(x) = A_1 + A_2 x + A_3\frac{x^2}{2!} + A_4\frac{x^3}{3!} + ... \quad ....(2)$$

$$f''(x) = A_2 + A_3 x + A_4\frac{x^2}{2!} + A_5\frac{x^3}{3!} + ... \quad ....(3)$$

etc.

Hence putting $x = 0$ in (1), (2), (3), ..., we have

$$A_0 = f(0),\ A_1 = f'(0),\ A_2 = f''(0),\ \text{etc.,} ...\ ;$$

and substituting these values in (1)

$$f(x) = f(0) + xf'(0) + \frac{x^2}{2!}f''(0) + \frac{x^3}{3!}f'''(0) + ... + \frac{x^r}{r!}f^r(0) + ...$$

118. It will be noticed that in the above proofs there is nothing to indicate in what cases the expansions assumed in the equations numbered (1) in Arts. 115, 117 are illegitimate, and we shall have to refer the student to Arts. 130 to 142 for a fuller and more rigorous discussion.

119. It is important before proceeding further, that the student should satisfy himself that the well-known expansions of such functions as $(x+h)^n$, e^x, $\sin x$, etc., are really all included in the general results of Arts. 115, 117.

For example, if $f(x) = x^n$, $f(x+h) = (x+h)^n$, $f'(x) = nx^{n-1}$, $f''(x) = n(n-1)x^{n-2}$, etc. Hence Taylor's Theorem,

$$f(x+h) = f(x) + hf'(x) + \frac{h^2}{2!}f''(x) + ...,$$

gives the binomial expansion

$$(x+h)^n = x^n + nhx^{n-1} + \frac{n(n-1)}{2!}h^2 x^{n-2} + ...$$

Again, suppose $f(x) = e^x$, then $f'(x) = e^x$, $f''(x) = e^x$, etc., therefore $f(0) = 1, f'(0) = 1, f''(0) = 1$, etc.
Hence Maclaurin's Theorem,

$$f(x) = f(0) + xf'(0) + \frac{x^2}{2!}f''(0) + ...,$$

gives $\qquad e^x = 1 + x + \frac{x^2}{2!} + \frac{x^3}{3!} + ...,$

the result known as the Exponential Theorem.

120. We append a few examples which admit of expansion, and to which therefore the results of Arts. 115, 117 apply.

EXAMPLES.

Prove the following results :—

1. $\sin x = x - \dfrac{x^3}{3!} + \dfrac{x^5}{5!} - \dots$.

2. $\log(1+x) = x - \dfrac{x^2}{2} + \dfrac{x^3}{3} - \dots$

3. $\tan^{-1}x = x - \dfrac{x^3}{3} + \dfrac{x^5}{5} - \dots$

4. $e^x \cos x = 1 + 2^{\frac{1}{2}}\cos\dfrac{\pi}{4}\cdot x + 2^{\frac{2}{2}}\cos\dfrac{2\pi}{4}\dfrac{x^2}{2!} + 2^{\frac{3}{2}}\cos\dfrac{3\pi}{4}\dfrac{x^3}{3!} + \dots$

$$+ 2^{\frac{n}{2}}\cos\dfrac{n\pi}{4}\dfrac{x^n}{n!} + \dots$$

5. $\cos x \cdot \cosh x = 1 - \dfrac{2^2 x^4}{4!} + \dfrac{2^4 x^8}{8!} - \dfrac{2^6 x^{12}}{12!} + \dots$

[OXFORD, 1888.]

6. $\log(1+e^x) = \log 2 + \frac{1}{2}x + \frac{1}{8}x^2 - \dfrac{x^4}{192}\dots$

7. $e^{\sin x} = 1 + x + \frac{1}{2}x^2 - \frac{1}{8}x^4 - \dots$

8. $\sin(x+h) = \sin x + h\cos x - \dfrac{h^2}{2!}\sin x - \dfrac{h^3}{3!}\cos x + \dots$

9. $\sin^{-1}(x+h) = \sin^{-1}x + \dfrac{h}{\sqrt{1-x^2}} + \dfrac{x}{(1-x^2)^{\frac{3}{2}}}\dfrac{h^2}{2!} + \dfrac{1+2x^2}{(1-x^2)^{\frac{5}{2}}}\dfrac{h^3}{3!} + \dots$

10. $\log\sin(x+h) = \log\sin x + h\cot x - \dfrac{h^2}{2}\operatorname{cosec}^2 x + \dfrac{h^3}{3}\dfrac{\cos x}{\sin^3 x} + \dots$

11. $\sec^{-1}(x+h) = \sec^{-1}x + \dfrac{h}{x\sqrt{x^2-1}} - \dfrac{2x^2-1}{x^2(x^2-1)^{\frac{3}{2}}}\dfrac{h^2}{2!} + \dots$

METHOD III.

121. *Expansion by Differentiation or Integration of a known series or equivalent process.*

The method of treatment is indicated in the following examples :

Ex. 1. *To expand $\tan^{-1}x$ in powers of x*, assuming x to be numerically less than unity. Gregorie's Series.*

Suppose $f(x) = \tan^{-1}x = a_0 + a_1 x + a_2 x^2 + a_3 x^3 + \dots,$

then $f'(x) = \dfrac{1}{1+x^2} = a_1 + 2a_2 x + 3a_3 x^2 + 4a_4 x^3 + \dots$;

also $(1+x^2)^{-1} = 1 - x^2 + x^4 - x^6 + \dots$.

Hence, comparing these expansions, we have

$$a_2 = a_4 = a_6 = a_8 = \dots = 0,$$

and $a_1 = 1,\ 3a_3 = -1,\ 5a_5 = 1,$ etc.

Also $a_0 = \tan^{-1}0 = n\pi$;

therefore $\tan^{-1}x = n\pi + x - \dfrac{x^3}{3} + \dfrac{x^5}{5} - \dfrac{x^7}{7} + \dots$

* Commercium Epistolicum, p. 98.

This result may be obtained immediately by integration of the series for $\dfrac{1}{1+x^2}$, viz.,

$$1 - x^2 + x^4 - x^6 + \dots,$$

the constant a_0 being determined as before.

Ex. 2. *To expand $\sin^{-1}x$.*

Suppose
$$f(x) = \sin^{-1}x = a_0 + a_1 x + a_2 x^2 + a_3 x^3 + \dots ;$$

therefore
$$f'(x) = \frac{1}{\sqrt{1-x^2}} = a_1 + 2a_2 x + 3a_3 x^2 + 4a_4 x^3 + \dots .$$

But
$$\frac{1}{\sqrt{1-x^2}} = 1 + \tfrac{1}{2}x^2 + \frac{1 \cdot 3}{2 \cdot 4}x^4 + \dots .$$

Hence, comparing these series, we have
$$a_2 = a_4 = a_6 = \dots = 0,$$

and
$$a_1 = 1, \quad 3a_3 = \tfrac{1}{2}, \quad 5a_5 = \frac{1 \cdot 3}{2 \cdot 4} \dots .$$

Also
$$a_0 = \sin^{-1}0 = n\pi.$$

Hence
$$\sin^{-1}x = n\pi + x + \frac{1}{2} \cdot \frac{x^3}{3} + \frac{1 \cdot 3}{2 \cdot 4}\frac{x^5}{5} + \frac{1 \cdot 3 \cdot 5}{2 \cdot 4 \cdot 6} \cdot \frac{x^7}{7} + \dots ;$$

and, as before, this might have been obtained immediately by integration of the expansion of $\dfrac{1}{\sqrt{1-x^2}}$.

Ex. 3. Again, if a known series be given, we can obtain others from it *by differentiation.*

For example, borrowing the series for $(\sin^{-1}x)^2$ established in Ex. 2 of the next Art., viz.—

$$\tfrac{1}{2}(\sin^{-1}x)^2 = \frac{x^2}{2} + \frac{2}{3}\frac{x^4}{4} + \frac{2 \cdot 4}{3 \cdot 5}\frac{x^6}{6} + \frac{2 \cdot 4 \cdot 6}{3 \cdot 5 \cdot 7}\frac{x^8}{8} + \dots ,$$

we obtain at once by differentiation

$$\frac{\sin^{-1}x}{\sqrt{1-x^2}} = x + \frac{2}{3}x^3 + \frac{2 \cdot 4}{3 \cdot 5}x^5 + \frac{2 \cdot 4 \cdot 6}{3 \cdot 5 \cdot 7}x^7 + \dots .$$

EXAMPLES.

1. Prove $\log(x + \sqrt{1+x^2}) \equiv \sinh^{-1}x = x - \dfrac{1}{2}\dfrac{x^3}{3} + \dfrac{1 \cdot 3}{2 \cdot 4} \cdot \dfrac{x^5}{5} - \dots .$

2. Prove $\tanh^{-1}x = x + \dfrac{x^3}{3} + \dfrac{x^5}{5} + \dots .$

Expand examples 3 to 9 in ascending integral powers of x.

3. $\tan^{-1}x + \tanh^{-1}x.$

4. $\tan^{-1}\dfrac{2x}{1-x^2} + \sinh^{-1}\dfrac{2x}{1-x^2}.$

5. $\tan^{-1}\dfrac{3x - x^3}{1-3x^2} + \tanh^{-1}\dfrac{3x + x^3}{1+3x^2}.$

6. $\tan^{-1}\dfrac{x}{\sqrt{1-x^2}}.$

7. $\sec^{-1}\dfrac{1}{1-2x^2}.$

8. $\sinh^{-1}(3x+4x^3).$

9. $\tan^{-1}\dfrac{\sqrt{1+x^2}-\sqrt{1-x^2}}{\sqrt{1+x^2}+\sqrt{1-x^2}}.$

10. Deduce from Ex. 3, Art. 121,

$$(1-x^2)^{\frac{1}{2}}\sin^{-1}x = x - \frac{x^3}{3} - \frac{2}{3}\frac{x^5}{5} - \frac{2.4}{3.5}\cdot\frac{x^7}{7} - \dots$$

And hence by putting $x=\sin\theta$, prove

$$\theta\cot\theta = 1 - \frac{\sin^2\theta}{3} - \frac{2}{3}\cdot\frac{\sin^4\theta}{5} - \frac{2.4}{3.5}\frac{\sin^6\theta}{7} - \dots$$

[QUARTERLY JOURNAL, vol. vi.]

11. Given that

$$\sin\log(1+x) = \frac{A_1}{1!}x + \frac{A_2}{2!}x^2 + \frac{A_3}{3!}x^3 + \dots + \frac{A_n}{n!}x^n + \dots$$

$$\cos\log(1+x) = 1 + \frac{B_1}{1!}x + \frac{B_2}{2!}x^2 + \frac{B_3}{3!}x^3 + \dots + \frac{B_n}{n!}x^n + \dots,$$

calculate the first eight coefficients of each expansion.

[MATH. TRIPOS, 1887.]

12. Prove that when x is between $-\dfrac{\pi}{2}$ and $+\dfrac{\pi}{2}$,

$$\frac{1}{1^3}\cos x - \frac{1}{3^3}\cos 3x + \frac{1}{5^3}\cos 5x - \dots \text{ to infinity} = \frac{\pi}{8}\left(\frac{\pi^2}{4} - x^2\right).$$

[MATH. TRIPOS, 1875.]

METHOD IV.—BY THE FORMATION OF A DIFFERENTIAL EQUATION.*

122. This method may often be employed with advantage. Assume a series for the expansion

$$(\text{say } a_0 + a_1 x + a_2 x^2 + \dots\dots).$$

Then form a differential equation in the way indicated in several of the examples in the preceding chapter. Substitute the series in the differential equation and equate the coefficients of like powers of x on each side of the equation. We shall thus obtain sufficient equations to find all the coefficients except one or two of the first which may be easily obtained from the values of $f(0)$ and $f'(0)$.

---

* Professor Williamson has pointed out that some historical interest attaches to this method, as having probably been employed by Newton in his expansion of $\sin(m\sin^{-1}x)$ and other expressions.

Ex. 1. To apply this method to the expansion of $(1+x)^n$.

Let $\qquad y=(1+x)^n=a_0+a_1x+a_2x^2+a_3x^3+\dots\ \dots\ \dots\dots\dots\dots$(1)

Then $\qquad y_1=n(1+x)^{n-1}$ or $(1+x)y_1=ny.$ $\dots\dots\dots\dots\dots$(2)

But $\qquad y_1=a_1+2a_2x+3a_3x^2+\dots\ \dots\dots\dots\dots\dots\dots\dots$(3)

Therefore substituting for (1) and (3) in the differential equation (2)

$$(1+x)(a_1+2a_2x+3a_3x^2+\dots)\equiv n(a_0+a_1x+a_2x^2+\dots.)$$

Hence, comparing coefficients

$$a_1=na_0,$$
$$2a_2+a_1=na_1,$$
$$3a_3+2a_2=na_2,\qquad \text{etc.,}$$

and by putting $\qquad x=0$ in equation (1),

$$a_0=1,$$

giving $\qquad a_1=n,$

$$a_2=\frac{n-1}{2}a_1=\frac{n(n-1)}{2!},$$

$$a_3=\frac{n-2}{3}a_2=\frac{n(n-1)(n-2)}{3!},\quad \text{etc.,}$$

$$a_r=\frac{n-r+1}{r}a_{r-1}=\frac{n(n-1)\dots(n-r+1)}{r!},$$

whence $\qquad (1+x)^n=1+nx+\dfrac{n(n-1)}{2!}x^2+\dots.$

Ex. 2. Let $y=f(x)=(\sin^{-1}x)^2.$

$$y_1=2\sin^{-1}x\ .\ \frac{1}{\sqrt{1-x^2}},$$

$\therefore\qquad (1-x^2)y_1^2=4y.$

Differentiating, and dividing by $2y_1$, we have

$(1-x^2)y_2=xy_1+2\dots\dots\dots\dots\dots\dots\dots\dots\dots\dots\dots\dots$(1)

Now, let $\qquad y=a_0+a_1x+a_2x^2+\dots+a_nx^n+a_{n+1}x^{n+1}+a_{n+2}x^{n+2}+\dots,$

therefore $\quad y_1=a_1+2a_2x+\dots+na_nx^{n-1}+(n+1)a_{n+1}x^n+(n+2)a_{n+2}x^{n+1}+\dots,$

and

$y_2=2a_2+\dots+n(n-1)a_nx^{n-2}+(n+1)na_{n+1}x^{n-1}+(n+2)(n+1)a_{n+2}x^n+\dots.$

Picking out the coefficient of x^n in the equation (*which may be done without actual substitution*) we have

$$(n+2)(n+1)a_{n+2}-n(n-1)a_n=na_n\ ;$$

therefore $\qquad a_{n+2}=\dfrac{n^2}{(n+1)(n+2)}a_n.$ $\quad\dots\dots\dots\dots$(2)

Now, $\qquad a_0=f(0)=(\sin^{-1}0)^2,$

and if we consider $\sin^{-1}x$ to be the *smallest positive angle* whose sine is x,

$$\sin^{-1}0=0.$$

Hence $\qquad a_0=0.$

Again, $\qquad a_1=f'(0)=2\sin^{-1}0\ .\ \dfrac{1}{\sqrt{1-0}}=0,$

and $\qquad a_2=\tfrac{1}{2}f''(0)=\tfrac{1}{2}\left(\dfrac{2}{1-0}+0\right)=1.$

Hence, from equation (2), a_3, a_5, a_7, ..., are each $=0$,

and
$$a_4 = \frac{2^2}{3 \cdot 4} \cdot a_2 = \frac{2^2}{3 \cdot 4} = \frac{2^2}{4!} 2,$$

$$a_6 = \frac{4^2}{5 \cdot 6} \cdot a_4 = \frac{2^2 \cdot 4^2}{3 \cdot 4 \cdot 5 \cdot 6} = \frac{2^2 \cdot 4^2}{6!} \cdot 2,$$

etc. $=$ etc.;

therefore $\quad (\sin^{-1}x)^2 = \frac{2x^2}{2!} + \frac{2^2}{4!} 2x^4 + \frac{2^2 \cdot 4^2}{6!} 2x^6 + \frac{2^2 \cdot 4^2 \cdot 6^2}{8!} 2x^8 + \ldots.$

A different method of proceeding is indicated in the following example.

Ex. 3. Let $\quad y = \sin(m \sin^{-1}x) = a_0 + a_1 x + a_2 \frac{x^2}{2!} + a_3 \frac{x^3}{3!} + \ldots \quad \ldots\ldots\ldots (1)$

Then $\qquad\qquad y_1 = \cos(m \sin^{-1}x) \dfrac{m}{\sqrt{1-x^2}},$

whence $\qquad (1-x^2)y_1^2 = m^2(1-y^2).$

Differentiating again, and dividing by $2y_1$, we have

$$(1-x^2)y_2 - xy_1 + m^2 y = 0. \quad \ldots\ldots\ldots\ldots\ldots\ldots\ldots (2)$$

Differentiating this n times by Leibnitz's Theorem

$$(1-x^2)y_{n+2} - (2n+1)xy_{n+1} + (m^2 - n^2)y_n = 0. \quad \ldots\ldots\ldots (3)$$

Now, $\qquad\qquad a_0 = (y)_{x=0} = \sin(m \sin^{-1}0) = 0,$

(assuming that $\sin^{-1}x$ is the smallest positive angle whose sine is x)

$$a_1 = (y_1)_{x=0} = m,$$
$$a_2 = (y_2)_{x=0} = 0,$$
$$\text{etc.}$$
$$a_n = (y_n)_{x=0}.$$

Hence, putting $x=0$ in equation (3),

$$a_{n+2} = -(m^2 - n^2)a_n.$$

Hence a_4, a_6, a_8, ..., each $=0$,

and
$$a_3 = -(m^2 - 1^2)a_1 = -m(m^2 - 1^2),$$
$$a_5 = -(m^2 - 3^2)a_3 = m(m^2 - 1^2)(m^2 - 3^2),$$
$$a_7 = -(m^2 - 5^2)a_5 = -m(m^2 - 1^2)(m^2 - 3^2)(m^2 - 5^2),$$
$$\text{etc.}$$

Whence

$$\sin(m \sin^{-1}x) = mx - \frac{m(m^2 - 1^2)}{3!} x^3 + \frac{m(m^2 - 1^2)(m^2 - 3^2)}{5!} x^5$$
$$- \frac{m(m^2 - 1^2)(m^2 - 3^2)(m^2 - 5^2)}{7!} x^7 + \ldots.$$

The corresponding series for $\cos(m \sin^{-1}x)$ is

$$\cos(m \sin^{-1}x) = 1 - \frac{m^2 x^2}{2!} + \frac{m^2(m^2 - 2^2)}{4!} x^4 - \frac{m^2(m^2 - 2^2)(m^2 - 4^2)}{6!} x^6 + \ldots.$$

If we write $x = \sin \theta$ these series become

$$\sin m\theta = m \sin \theta - \frac{m(m^2 - 1^2)}{3!} \sin^3\theta + \frac{m(m^2 - 1^2)(m^2 - 3^2)}{5!} \sin^5\theta - \text{etc.},$$

$$\cos m\theta = 1 - \frac{m^2}{2!} \sin^2\theta + \frac{m^2(m^2 - 2^2)}{4!} \sin^4\theta - \frac{m^2(m^2 - 2^2)(m^2 - 4^2)}{6!} \sin^6\theta + \text{etc.}$$

Ex. 4. Expressions of the form $(\tan^{-1}x)^p/p!$ may be easily expanded as follows :

Taking $\tan^{-1}x$ to lie between $\dfrac{\pi}{4}$ and $-\dfrac{\pi}{4}$ we have

$$\tan^{-1}x = x - \frac{x^3}{3} + \frac{x^5}{5} - \ldots.$$

We may therefore evidently assume expansions of the form

$$y \equiv (\tan^{-1}x)^p/p! = a_p x^p - a_{p+2}x^{p+2} + a_{p+4}x^{p+4} - \ldots$$
$$z \equiv (\tan^{-1}x)^{p-1}/(p-1)! = b_{p-1}x^{p-1} - b_{p+1}x^{p+1} + b_{p+3}x^{p+3} - \ldots.$$

Then $\qquad\qquad\qquad y_1 = z(1+x^2)^{-1},$

or $\qquad pa_p x^{p-1} - (p+2)a_{p+2}x^{p+1} + (p+4)a_{p+4}x^{p+3} - \ldots$

$$\equiv (1 - x^2 + x^4 - \ldots)(b_{p-1}x^{p-1} - b_{p+1}x^{p+1} + \ldots),$$

whence, equating coefficients,

$$pa_p = b_{p-1},$$
$$(p+2)a_{p+2} = b_{p-1} + b_{p+1},$$
$$(p+4)a_{p+4} = b_{p-1} + b_{p+1} + b_{p+3},$$
$$\text{etc.,}$$

and the law which connects the several coefficients is obvious.

Thus starting with Gregorie's Series we successively deduce

$$\frac{(\tan^{-1}x)^2}{2!} = \frac{x^2}{2} - \left(1 + \frac{1}{3}\right)\frac{x^4}{4} + \left(1 + \frac{1}{3} + \frac{1}{5}\right)\frac{x^6}{6} - \left(1 + \frac{1}{3} + \frac{1}{5} + \frac{1}{7}\right)\frac{x^8}{8} + \ldots$$

$$\frac{(\tan^{-1}x)^3}{3!} = \frac{1}{2}\frac{x^3}{3} - \left\{\frac{1}{2} + \frac{1}{4}\left(1 + \frac{1}{3}\right)\right\}\frac{x^5}{5} + \left\{\frac{1}{2} + \frac{1}{4}\left(1 + \frac{1}{3}\right) + \frac{1}{6}\left(1 + \frac{1}{3} + \frac{1}{5}\right)\right\}\frac{x^7}{7} - \ldots.$$

$$\text{etc.}$$

These results have been communicated to me by Professor Anglin of Queen's College, Cork.

EXAMPLES.

1. Apply this method to find the known expansions of
$$a^x, \ \log(1+x), \ \sin x, \ \tan^{-1}x.$$

2. If $y = \sin^{-1}x = a_0 + a_1x + a_2x^2 + a_3x^3 + \ldots,$

prove that $\qquad\qquad a_{n+2} = \dfrac{n^2}{(n+1)(n+2)}a_n,$

and in this manner deduce the expansion given in Ex. 2, Art. 121.

3. If $e^{a\sin^{-1}x} = a_0 + a_1x + a_2x^2 + a_3x^3 + \ldots,$ prove

(1) $a_{n+2} = \dfrac{n^2+a^2}{(n+1)(n+2)}a_n$;

(2) $e^{a\sin^{-1}x} = 1 + ax + \dfrac{a^2x^2}{2!} + \dfrac{a(a^2+1)}{3!}x^3 + \dfrac{a^2(a^2+2^2)}{4!}x^4$

$$+ \dfrac{a(a^2+1)(a^2+3^2)}{5!}x^5 + \ldots$$

(3) Deduce from (2), by expanding the left side according to the exponential theorem and equating the coefficients of a, a^2, ... the series for $\sin^{-1}x$, $(\sin^{-1}x)^2$, ..., and show that if in the development of $\dfrac{(\sin^{-1}x)^1}{1}$, viz.,

$$\frac{x^1}{1} + \frac{1}{2} \cdot \frac{x^3}{3} + \frac{1.3}{2.4} \cdot \frac{x^5}{5} + \dots .$$

every number which occurs be increased by unity, the result, viz.,

$$\frac{x^2}{2} + \frac{2}{3} \frac{x^4}{4} + \frac{2.4}{3.5} \cdot \frac{x^6}{6} + \dots$$

is equal to $\dfrac{(\sin^{-1}x)^2}{2}$.

4. Prove that if $\log_e y = \tan^{-1}x$.

$$(1+x^2)y_n = \{1 - 2(n-1)x\}y_{n-1} - (n-1)(n-2)y_{n-2},$$

and hence find the coefficient of x^5 in the expansion of y by Maclaurin's Theorem. [I. C. S. Exam.]

5. If

$$\frac{(\tan^{-1}x)^2}{2!} = \frac{a_2 x^2}{2} - \frac{a_4 x^4}{4} + \frac{a_6 x^6}{6} - \dots,$$

prove that

$$a_{2n} - a_{2n-2} = \frac{1}{2n-1}.$$

6. If y satisfy the equation $y_2 - m^2y = 0$, and if the first and second terms of its expansion be respectively $A + B$ and $(Am - Bm)x$, show that the general term is $\{A + (-1)^k B\}\dfrac{m^k x^k}{k!}$. Hence show that

$$y = Ae^{mx} + Be^{-mx}.$$

7. If y satisfy the differential equation

$$y_2 + 2ky_1 + (k^2 + b^2)y = 0,$$

and the first terms of the expansion of y are

$$1 - kx + \frac{k^2 - b^2}{2}x^2 + \dots$$

continue the expansion.

8. If

$$\sin^{-1}x = \sum_{n=1}^{n=\infty} \frac{b_n x^n}{n!} \text{ and } \frac{(\sin^{-1}x)^3}{3!} = \sum_{n=1}^{n=\infty} \frac{a_n x^n}{n!},$$

show that

$$a_{n+2} = n^2 a_n + b_n.$$

Hence establish the expansion

$$\frac{(\sin^{-1}x)^3}{3!} = \frac{1}{2} \cdot \frac{x^3}{3} + \frac{1.3}{2.4}\left(\frac{1}{1^2} + \frac{1}{3^2}\right)\frac{x^5}{5} + \frac{1.3.5}{2.4.6}\left(\frac{1}{1^2} + \frac{1}{3^2} + \frac{1}{5^2}\right)\frac{x^7}{7} + \dots.$$

9. Prove (a) $\dfrac{\sinh^{-1}x}{\sqrt{1+x^2}} = x - \dfrac{2}{3}x^3 + \dfrac{2.4}{3.5}x^5 - \dots.$

(b) $\dfrac{(\sinh^{-1}x)^2}{2!} = \dfrac{x^2}{2} - \dfrac{2}{3} \cdot \dfrac{x^4}{4} + \dfrac{2.4}{3.5} \dfrac{x^6}{6} - \dots.$

(c) $\log(1 + \sqrt{2}) = 1 - \dfrac{1}{2} \cdot \dfrac{1}{3} + \dfrac{1.3}{2.4} \cdot \dfrac{1}{5} - \dots.$

(d) $\dfrac{2}{\sqrt{3}}\log\left(\dfrac{1+\sqrt{3}}{\sqrt{2}}\right) = 1 - \dfrac{1}{3} + \dfrac{1.2}{3.5} - \dfrac{1.2.3}{3.5.7} + \dots.$ [Anglin.]

10. Establish the expansion

$$\frac{\pi^2}{8} = 1 + \frac{1}{2} \cdot \frac{1}{3} + \frac{1}{3} \cdot \frac{1.2}{3.5} + \frac{1}{4} \cdot \frac{1.2.3}{3.5.7} + \dots.$$ [Anglin.]

CONTINUITY.

123. DEF. A function ϕx is said to be *continuous* between any two values a, b of the independent variable involved if, as that variable is made to assume successively *all* intermediate values from a to b the function *does not suddenly change its value*, but is such that its Cartesian graph $[y = \phi x]$ can be described by the motion of a particle travelling *along it* from the point $(a, \phi a)$ to the point $(b, \phi b)$ without moving off the curve.

124. Trace the curve $y = \phi x$ between the ordinates $AL(x = a)$ and $BM(x = b)$. Then if we find that as x increases through some value, as ON (Fig. 14), the ordinate ϕx *suddenly changes* from NP to NQ without going through the intermediate values, the function is said to be discontinuous for the value $x = ON$ of the independent variable.

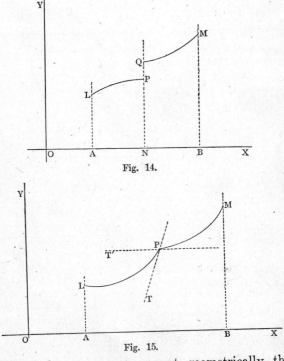

Fig. 14.

Fig. 15.

125. Similarly, we may represent geometrically the discontinuity of a differential coefficient. For $\dfrac{dy}{dx}$ represents the tangent of the angle which the tangent line to the curve makes with the axis of x. If, therefore, as the point P travels along the curve the tangent *suddenly changes its position* (as, for example, from PT to PT' in Fig. 15), *without going through the intermediate positions*, there is a discontinuity in the value of $\dfrac{dy}{dx}$.

126. PROP. *If any function of x, say ϕx, vanish when $x = a$ and when $x = b$ and is finite and continuous, as also its first differential coefficient $\phi' x$ between those values, then will $\phi' x$ vanish for at least one intermediate value.*

For if $\phi' x$ were always positive or always negative between $x = a$ and $x = b$, ϕx would be continually increasing or continually decreasing between those values (Art. 42) and therefore could not vanish for both $x = a$ and $x = b$, which would be contrary to the hypothesis. Hence $\phi' x$ must change sign and therefore vanish for some value of x intermediate between $x = a$ and $x = b$.

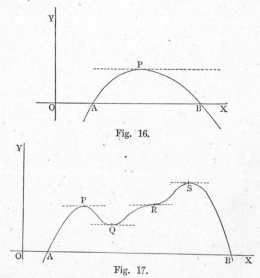

Fig. 16.

Fig. 17.

127. The same thing is obvious at once from a figure. For, suppose the curve $y = \phi x$ cuts the axis at A $(x = a,\ y = 0)$ and

B $(x = b,\ y = 0)$, then it is obvious (Fig. 16) that if the curve $y = \phi x$ and the inclination of its tangent be continuous between A and B, the tangent line must be *parallel to the axis of x* at some intermediate point P.

It is also clear that the tangent may be parallel to the axis of x at other points between A and B besides P as in Fig. 17, so that it does not follow that $\phi'x$ vanishes *only once* between two contiguous roots of $\phi x = 0$.

128. The same proposition is thus enunciated in books on Theory of Equations: "*A real root of the equation $\phi'x = 0$ lies between every adjacent two of the real roots of the equation $\phi x = 0$*"; and is known as Rolle's Theorem.

EXAMPLES.

1. Show that if a rational integral function of x vanish for n values between given limits, its first and second differential coefficients will vanish for at least $(n-1)$ and $(n-2)$ values of x respectively between the same limits. Illustrate these results geometrically.

[I. C. S. EXAM.]

2. Prove that no more than one root of an equation $f(x) = 0$ can lie between any adjacent two of the roots of the equation $f'(x) = 0$.

3. Show that the following expressions are positive for all positive values of x :

(i.) $(x-1)e^x + 1$;

(ii.) $(x-2)e^x + x + 2$;

(iii.) $(x-3)e^x + \dfrac{x^2}{2} + 2x + 3$;

(iv.) $x - \log(1+x)$.

[N.B.—By Art. 42, if $\dfrac{dy}{dx}$ be positive, y is increasing when x is increasing. Hence, if y be positive when $x = 0$, and if also $\dfrac{dy}{dx}$ be positive as x increases from 0 to ∞, it follows that y will be positive for all positive values of x.]

129. There is much difficulty in giving a rigorous direct proof of Taylor's Series, as might be expected from the highly general character of the result to be established. It is found easier to consider what is left after n terms of Taylor's Series have been taken from $f(x+h)$. *If the form of this remainder be such that it can be made smaller than any assignable quantity when sufficient terms of the series are taken, the*

difference between $f(x+h)$ and Taylor's Series for $f(x+h)$ will be indefinitely small, and under these circumstances we shall be able to assert the truth of the theorem.

130. Lagrange Formula for the remainder after the first n terms have been taken from Taylor's Series.

THEOREM.—If $f(z)$ and all its differential coefficients up to the nth inclusive be finite and continuous between the values $z=x$ and $z=x+h$ of the variable z then will

$$f(x+h)=f(x)+hf'(x)+\frac{h^2}{2!}f''(x)+\ldots$$
$$+\frac{h^{n-1}}{(n-1)!}f^{n-1}(x)+\frac{h^n}{n!}f^n(x+\theta h)$$

where θ is some positive proper fraction.

Let $\quad f(x+h)=f(x)+hf'(x)+\frac{h^2}{2!}f''(x)+\ldots$
$$+\frac{h^{n-1}}{(n-1)!}f^{n-1}(x)+\frac{h^n}{n!}R,\ \ldots\ldots\ldots\ldots\ldots(1)$$

R being some function of x and h, whose form remains to be discovered.

Consider the function

$$f(x+z)-f(x)-zf'(x)-\frac{z^2}{2!}f''(x)-\ldots-\frac{z^{n-1}}{(n-1)!}f^{n-1}(x)-\frac{z^n}{n!}R\equiv\phi(z),$$

say; then differentiating with regard to z (keeping x constant),

$$f'(x+z)\quad -f'(x)-zf''(x)-\ldots-\frac{z^{n-2}}{(n-2)!}f^{n-1}(x)-\frac{z^{n-1}}{(n-1)!}R\equiv\phi'(z),$$

$$f''(x+z)\quad\quad -f''(x)-\ldots-\frac{z^{n-3}}{(n-3)!}f^{n-1}(x)-\frac{z^{n-2}}{(n-2)!}R\equiv\phi''(z),$$

etc.,   etc.,   etc.

$$f^{n-1}(x+z)\quad\quad\quad -\quad\quad f^{n-1}(x)-\quad zR\equiv\phi^{n-1}(z),$$
$$f^n(x+z)\quad\quad\quad\quad\quad -\quad\quad\quad R\equiv\phi^n(z).$$

All the functions $\phi(z)$, $\phi'(z)\ldots$, $\phi^n(z)$ are finite and continuous between the values 0 and h of the variable z, and evidently $\phi(0)$, $\phi'(0)$, $\phi''(0)\ldots$, $\phi^{n-1}(0)$ are all zero. Also from equation (1) $\phi(h)=0$. Therefore by Art. 126,

$\quad\quad \phi'(z)=0$ for some value (h_1) of z between 0 and h,

$\therefore\quad \phi''(z)=0$ for some value (h_2) of z between 0 and h_1,

$\therefore\quad \phi'''(z)=0$ for some value (h_3) of z between 0 and h_2,

and so on; and finally

$\quad\quad \phi^n(z)=0$ for some value (h_n) of z between 0 and h_{n-1}.

Thus $\qquad\qquad f^n(x+h_n)-R=0.$

Now since $\qquad h_n < h_{n-1} < h_{n-2} \ldots < h_2 < h_1 < h,$

we may put $h_n = \theta h$ where θ is some positive proper fraction.

Thus $\qquad\qquad R = f^n(x+\theta h).$

Hence substituting in equation (1)

$$f(x+h) = f(x) + hf'(x) + \frac{h^2}{2!}f''(x) + \ldots$$
$$+ \frac{h^{n-1}}{(n-1)!}f^{n-1}(x) + \frac{h^n}{n!}f^n(x+\theta h)\ldots\ldots(2)$$

This method of establishing the result is a modification of one due to Mr. Homersham Cox (Camb. and Dublin Math. Journal).

131. If then the form of the function $f(x)$ be such that by making n sufficiently great the expression $\dfrac{h^n}{n!}f^n(x+\theta h)$ can be made less than any assignable quantity however small, we can make the true series for $f(x+h)$ *differ by as little as we please from Taylor's form*

$$f(x) + hf'(x) + \frac{h^2}{2!}f''(x) + \ldots \text{ to } \infty.$$

The above form of the remainder is due to Lagrange,[*] and the investigation is spoken of as *Lagrange's Theorem on the Limits of Taylor's Theorem.*

132. The corresponding Lagrange formula for the remainder after n terms of Maclaurin's Series is obtained by writing 0 for x and x for h and becomes $\dfrac{x^n}{n!}f^n(\theta x),$

thus giving

$$f(x) = f(0) + xf'(0) + \frac{x^2}{2!}f''(0) + \ldots + \frac{x^{n-1}}{(n-1)!}f^{n-1}(0) + \frac{x^n}{n!}f^n(\theta x).$$

133. The following investigations of an expression for the remainder are taken, with but few changes, from Bertrand's "Traité de Calcul Différentiel et Intégral."[†]

We shall assume that $f(z)$ and all its differential coefficients up to the nth inclusive are finite and continuous between the values x and $x+h$ of the variable z.

Let R denote the remainder after n terms of Taylor's series have been taken from $f(x+h)$; so that

$$f(x+h) = f(x) + hf'(x) + \frac{h^2}{2!}f''(x) + \ldots + \frac{h^{n-1}}{(n-1)!}f^{n-1}(x) + R \ldots\ldots(1)$$

Let $\quad x+h=X$, hence

$$f(X)-f(x)-\frac{X-x}{1!}f'(x)-\frac{(X-x)^2}{2!}f''(x)-\ldots-\frac{(X-x)^{n-1}}{(n-1)!}f^{n-1}(x)-R=0\ldots(2)$$

Put $R=\dfrac{(X-x)^n}{n!}P$, a form suggested by the remaining terms of Taylor's series. Consider the function formed by writing z instead of x throughout the left hand member of equation (2) *except in P*.

Let $\phi(z)\equiv$

$$f(X)-f(z)-\frac{X-z}{1!}f'(z)-\frac{(X-z)^2}{2!}f''(z)-\ldots-\frac{(X-z)^{n-1}}{(n-1)!}f^{n-1}(z)-\frac{(X-z)^n}{n!}P\ldots(3)$$

From equation (2) $\phi(x)=0$, and it is evident that $\phi(X)=0$.

Also $\phi(z)$ and $\phi'(z)$ are finite and continuous between these values of the variable z. Hence $\phi'(z)$ vanishes for some value of z intermediate between $z=x$ and $z=X=x+h$, say for $z=x+\theta h$ where θ is a positive proper fraction.

Differentiating equation (3) with respect to z

$$\phi'(z)\equiv-\frac{(X-z)^{n-1}}{(n-1)!}f^n(z)+\frac{(X-z)^{n-1}}{(n-1)!}P\ldots\ldots\ldots\ldots\ldots\ldots(4)$$

whence $P=f^n(z)$ for that value of z which makes $\phi'(z)$ vanish, *i.e.*

$$z=x+\theta h.$$

Hence $\qquad\qquad\qquad\qquad P=f^n(x+\theta h)$

and $\qquad\qquad\qquad\qquad R=\dfrac{h^n}{n!}f^n(x+\theta h)\ldots\ldots\ldots\ldots\ldots\ldots\ldots\ldots(5)$

134. A different form of the remainder is due to Cauchy.

In equation (2) put $R=(X-x)P$ and proceed as before, then, instead of equation (4), we shall have

$$\phi'(z)=-\frac{(X-z)^{n-1}}{(n-1)!}f^n(z)+P,$$

which vanishes as before for some value of z between $z=x$ and $z=X=x+h$, say for $z=x+\theta h$; whence

$$P=\frac{(1-\theta)^{n-1}h^{n-1}}{(n-1)!}f^n(x+\theta h),$$

and therefore $\qquad\qquad R=\dfrac{(1-\theta)^{n-1}h^n}{(n-1)!}f^n(x+\theta h).$

135. Another form is obtained by Schlömilch and Roche by assuming a slightly different form for R, viz.,

$$=\frac{(X-x)^{p+1}}{p+1}P.$$

This gives, instead of equation (4),

$$\phi'(z)=-\frac{(X-z)^{n-1}}{(n-1)!}f^n(z)+(X-z)^pP,$$

whence $\qquad\qquad P=\dfrac{(1-\theta)^{n-p-1}h^{n-p-1}}{(n-1)!}f^n(x+\theta h),$

and $\qquad\qquad R=\dfrac{(1-\theta)^{n-p-1}h^n}{(n-1)!\,(p+1)}f^n(x+\theta h).$

136. The last form includes those of Arts. 133, 134 as particular cases ; for putting $p+1=n$ it reduces to Lagrange's result, and putting $p=0$ it reduces to Cauchy's.

137. The corresponding forms of remainder for Maclaurin's Theorem are obtained by writing 0 for x and x for h, when the three expressions investigated above become respectively

$$\frac{x^n}{n!}f^n(\theta x), \quad \frac{(1-\theta)^{n-1}x^n}{(n-1)!}f^n(\theta x), \text{ and } \frac{(1-\theta)^{n-p-1}x^n}{(n-1)!(p+1)}f^n(\theta x).$$

138. The student should notice the special cases of equation (2), Art. 130, when $n = 1, 2, 3$, etc., viz.,

$$f(x+h) = f(x) + hf'(x+\theta_1 h),$$

$$f(x+h) = f(x) + hf'(x) + \frac{h^2}{2!}f''(x+\theta_2 h),$$

$$\text{etc. ;}$$

all that is known with respect to the θ in each case being that it is a *positive proper fraction*.

139. Geometrical Illustration.

It is easy to give a geometrical illustration of the equation

$$f(x+h) = f(x) + hf'(x+\theta h).$$

For let x, $f(x)$, be the co-ordinates of a point P on the curve $y = f(x)$, and let $x+h$, $f(x+h)$ be the co-ordinates of another point Q, also on the curve. And suppose the curve and the inclination of the tangent to the curve to the axis of x to be continuous and finite between P and Q; draw PM, QN perpendicular to OX and PL perpendicular to QN, then

$$\frac{f(x+h)-f(x)}{h} = \frac{NQ-MP}{MN} = \frac{LQ}{PL} = \tan LPQ.$$

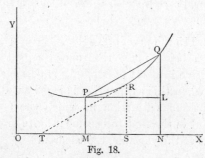

Fig. 18.

Also, $x+\theta h$ is the abscissa of some point R on the curve between P and Q, and $f'(x+\theta h)$ is the tangent of the angle which the tangent line to the curve at R makes with the axis of x. Hence the assertion that

$$\frac{f(x+h)-f(x)}{h} = f'(x+\theta h)$$

is equivalent to the obvious geometrical fact that *there must be a point R somewhere between P and Q at which the tangent to the curve is parallel to the chord PQ.*

140. Failure of Taylor's Theorem.

The cases in which Taylor's Theorem is said to fail are those in which it happens

(1) That $f(x)$, or one of its differential coefficients, *becomes infinite* between the values of the variable considered;

(2) Or that $f(x)$, or one of its differential coefficients, becomes *discontinuous* between the same values;

(3) Or that the remainder, $\dfrac{h^n}{n!}f^n(x+\theta h)$, *cannot be made to vanish in the limit* when n is taken sufficiently large, so that the series does not approach a finite limit.

Ex. If $\qquad\qquad f(x)=\sqrt{x}$,
$$f(x+h)=\sqrt{x+h},\, f'(x)=\frac{1}{2\sqrt{x}},\text{ etc.}$$
Hence Taylor's Theorem gives
$$f(x+h)=\sqrt{x+h}=\sqrt{x}+\frac{1}{2\sqrt{x}}h+\ldots.$$

If, however, we put $x=0$, $\dfrac{1}{2\sqrt{x}}$ becomes infinite, while $\sqrt{x+h}$ becomes $\sqrt{h}$.

Thus, as we might expect, we fail at the second term to expand $\sqrt{h}$ in a series of integral powers of h.

141. In Art. 115 the proof of Taylor's Theorem is not general, the assumption being made that a convergent expansion in ascending positive integral powers of x is possible. The above article shows when this assumption is legitimate.

For any continuous function in which the $(p+1)^{\text{th}}$ differential coefficient is the first to become infinite or discontinuous for the value x of the variable, the theorem
$$f(x+h)=f(x)+hf'(x)+\ldots+\frac{h^p}{p!}f^p(x+\theta h),$$
which involves no differential coefficients of higher order than the pth, is rigorously true, although Taylor's Theorem,
$$f(x+h)=f(x)+hf'(x)+\ldots+\frac{h^p}{p!}f^p(x)+\frac{h^{p+1}}{(p+1)!}f^{p+1}(x)+\ldots$$
fails to furnish us with an intelligible result.

Ex. If
$$f(x)=(x-a)^{\frac{5}{2}},$$

we have
$$f'(x)=\frac{5}{2}(x-a)^{\frac{3}{2}},$$

$$f''(x)=\frac{15}{4}(x-a)^{\frac{1}{2}},$$

$$f'''(x)=\frac{15}{8}\Big(\frac{1}{x-a}\Big)^{\frac{1}{2}}, \text{ etc.},$$

and Taylor's Theorem gives

$$(x+h-a)^{\frac{5}{2}}=(x-a)^{\frac{5}{2}}+\frac{5}{2}(x-a)^{\frac{3}{2}}h+\frac{15}{4}(x-a)^{\frac{1}{2}}\frac{h^2}{2!}+\frac{15}{8}\frac{1}{(x-a)^{\frac{1}{2}}}\frac{h^3}{3!}+\dots,$$

which fails at the fourth term when $x=a$.

But Equation 2 of Art. 130 gives the result

$$(x+h-a)^{\frac{5}{2}}=(x-a)^{\frac{5}{2}}+\frac{5}{2}(x-a)^{\frac{3}{2}}h+\frac{15}{4}\frac{h^2}{2!}(x+\theta h-a)^{\frac{1}{2}},$$

which, in the case when $x=a$, reduces to

$$h^{\frac{5}{2}}=\frac{15}{8}\theta^{\frac{1}{2}}h^{\frac{5}{2}},$$

or
$$\theta=\frac{64}{225},$$

and this obeys the only limitation necessary, viz., that θ should be a positive proper fraction.

142. The remarks made with respect to the failure of Taylor's Theorem obviously also apply to the particular form of it, Maclaurin's Theorem, so that Maclaurin's Theorem is said to fail when any of the expressions $f(0), f'(0), f''(0), \dots$ become *infinite*, or if there be a *discontinuity* in the function or any of its differential coefficients as x passes through the value zero, or if the remainder $\frac{x^n}{n!}f^n(\theta x)$ *does not become infinitely small* when n becomes infinitely large, for in this case the series is divergent and does not tend to any finite limit.

EXAMPLES.

1. Show for what values of x and at what differential coefficient Taylor's Theorem will fail if
$$f(x)=\frac{(x-a)^5(x-b)^{\frac{7}{2}}(x-c)^{\frac{9}{2}}}{(x-d)^{14}}.$$

2. Can $\log x$ or $\tan^{-1}\sqrt{\dfrac{x}{a}}$ be expanded by Maclaurin's Theorem in a series of ascending positive integral powers of x?

3. If $f(x)=e^{-\frac{1}{x}}$, how does Maclaurin's Theorem fail for an expansion in ascending powers of x? Is $f(x)$ continuous as x passes through zero?

4. If $f(x)=\dfrac{x}{1+e^{\frac{1}{x}}}$, show that there is a discontinuity in $\dfrac{df(x)}{dx}$ as x passes through zero.

143. **Examples of Expansions by Maclaurin's Theorem, with investigation of Remainder after n terms.**

1. Let $\quad\quad\quad f(x) = a^x,$

then $\quad\quad\quad f^n(x) = a^x (\log_e a)^n,$ and $f^n(0) = (\log_e a)^n.$

Hence the formula

$$f(x) = f(0) + x f'(0) + \frac{x^2}{2!} f''(0) + \dots + \frac{x^{n-1}}{(n-1)!} f^{n-1}(0) + \frac{x^n}{n!} f^n(\theta x)$$

gives

$$a^x = 1 + x \log_e a + \frac{x^2}{2!} (\log_e a)^2 + \dots + \frac{x^{n-1}}{(n-1)!} (\log_e a)^{n-1} + \frac{x^n}{n!} a^{\theta x} (\log_e a)^n.$$

Now $\dfrac{x^n a^{\theta x} (\log_e a)^n}{n!}$ can be made *smaller than any assignable quantity* by sufficiently increasing n; hence the remainder, after n terms of Maclaurin's Theorem have been taken, ultimately vanishes when n is taken very large, and therefore Maclaurin's Theorem is applicable and gives

$$a^x = 1 + x \log_e a + \frac{x^2}{2!} (\log_e a)^2 + \frac{x^3}{3!} (\log_e a)^3 + \dots \text{ to } \infty.$$

2. Let $\quad\quad\quad f(x) = \log(1+x),$

$$f'(x) = \frac{1}{1+x}, \quad f''(x) = (-1)\frac{1}{(1+x)^2}, \dots f^n(x) = (-1)^{n-1}\frac{(n-1)!}{(1+x)^n}.$$

Hence $\quad\quad f(0) = 0, f'(0) = 1, f''(0) = -1, f'''(0) = 2\dots,$

$$f^n(0) = (-1)^{n-1}(n-1)!.$$

And the Lagrange-formula for the remainder, after n terms of Maclaurin's Series have been subtracted from $f(x)$, viz. $\dfrac{x^n f^n(\theta x)}{n!}$, becomes

$$\frac{(-1)^{n-1}}{n} \cdot \left(\frac{x}{1+\theta x}\right)^n;$$

and if x be not greater than 1, and positive, $\dfrac{x}{1+\theta x}$ is a proper fraction, and therefore by making n sufficiently large the above remainder ultimately vanishes, and therefore Maclaurin's Theorem is applicable and gives

$$\log(1+x) = x - \frac{x^2}{2} + \frac{x^3}{3} - \frac{x^4}{4} + \dots \text{ to } \infty,$$

where x lies between 0 and 1 inclusive.

It appears that if we consider $f(x) = \log(1-x)$ the remainder is

$$-\frac{1}{n}\left(\frac{x}{1-\theta x}\right)^n.$$

In this form it is not clear that the limit of the remainder is zero. But if we choose for this example Cauchy's form of remainder, Art. 134, it reduces to

$$-\frac{1}{1-\theta}\left(\frac{x-\theta x}{1-\theta x}\right)^n;$$

and if x be positive and less than unity, $\dfrac{x-\theta x}{1-\theta x}$ is also less than unity, and therefore $\dfrac{1}{1-\theta}\left(\dfrac{x-\theta x}{1-\theta x}\right)^n$ can be made as small as we like by sufficiently increasing n. Hence Maclaurin's series is applicable and gives

$$\log(1-x) = -x - \frac{x^2}{2} - \frac{x^3}{3} - \frac{x^4}{4} - \dots \text{ to } \infty \,.$$

3. Prove $\sin ax = ax - \dfrac{a^3x^3}{3!} + \dfrac{a^5x^5}{5!} - \dots + \dfrac{a^nx^n}{n!} \sin \dfrac{n\pi}{2} + \dots$, and that the remainder after r terms may be expressed as

$$\frac{a^rx^r}{r!} \sin\left(a\theta x + \frac{r\pi}{2} \right).$$

4. Prove $\cos ax = 1 - \dfrac{a^2x^2}{2!} + \dfrac{a^4x^4}{4!} - \dots + \dfrac{a^nx^n}{n!} \cos \dfrac{n\pi}{2} + \dots$, and that the remainder after r terms may be expressed as

$$\frac{a^rx^r}{r!} \cos\left(a\theta x + \frac{r\pi}{2} \right).$$

5. Prove $(1-x)^{-n} = 1 + nx + \dfrac{n(n+1)}{2!}x^2 + \dots$

$$+ \frac{n(n+1)\dots(n+r-2)}{(r-1)!}x^{r-1}$$

$$+ \frac{n(n+1)\dots(n+r-1)}{r!} \frac{x^r}{(1-\theta x)^{n+r}}.$$

6. Expand and find the remainder after n terms of the expansion of $e^{ax}\cos bx$.

RESULTS.　　$1 + ax + \dfrac{a^2-b^2}{2!}x^2 + \dfrac{a(a^2-3b^2)}{3!}x^3 + \dots$

$$\text{Remainder} = \frac{(a^2+b^2)^{\frac{n}{2}}}{n!} x^n e^{a\theta x} \cos\left(b\theta x + n \tan^{-1}\frac{b}{a} \right).$$

144. The Rule of Proportional Parts.　　Interpolation.

Let us suppose that $f(x)$ is one of those functions (such as $\log \sin x$) whose values have been calculated and tabulated at small intervals h of the variable x, so that the values of $f(x)$, $f(x+h), f(x+2h)\dots$ may be taken when wanted from the tables to a certain number of decimal places. It is required to make an easy rule to obtain a close approximation for the hitherto uncalculated value of $f(x+k)$ where k lies between 0 and h.

We shall assume that h, and therefore k, is so small that its square may be rejected.

Then since

$$f(x+h) = f(x) + hf'(x) + \frac{h^2}{2!}f''(x) + \frac{h^3}{3!}f'''(x+\theta_1 h)\dots\dots(1)$$

and　　$$f(x+k) = f(x) + kf'(x) + \frac{k^2}{2!}f''(x) + \frac{k^3}{3!}f'''(x+\theta_2 k)\dots \dots(2)$$

we have on rejection of squares of h and k

$$\frac{f(x+k)-f(x)}{f(x+h)-f(x)}=\frac{k}{h}\dots\dots\dots\dots\dots\dots\dots(3)$$

which gives $f(x+k)$ in terms of the known quantities, h, k, $f(x)$, $f(x+h)$. This rule is known as the rule of Proportional Parts.

145. Insensibility and Irregularity.

It will be seen that if at any point of the tables $f'(x)$ is very small, the term $hf'(x)$ may be so small that the difference between the tabulated values of $f(x)$ and $f(x+h)$ is not perceptible within the number of decimal places to which the tables are calculated. In this case the difference $f(x+h)-f(x)$ is said to be *insensible* and the rule of proportional parts cannot be applied.

Again if, although h is small, $\dfrac{f''(x)}{f'(x)}$ is large at any point of the tables, the term $\dfrac{h^2 f''(x)}{2!}$ bears to the term $hf'(x)$ a ratio which is not necessarily small. In this case the term in h^2 cannot be rejected. There is then said to be *irregularity* in the tables and the rule of proportional parts does not hold.

Ex. Suppose $f(x)=\log \sin x.$

Then $\log \sin(x+h)=\log \sin x+h \cot x-\dfrac{h^2}{2!} \operatorname{cosec}^2 x\dots$

Now when x is very near $90°$, $\cot x$ is very small,

and when x is near $0°$ or $90°$, $\dfrac{\operatorname{cosec}^2 x}{2 \cot x}$, *i.e.* $\operatorname{cosec} 2x$ is very large.

Hence at the $90°$ end of the tables for $\log \sin x$ there is insensibility, whilst at either end of the tables there is irregularity.

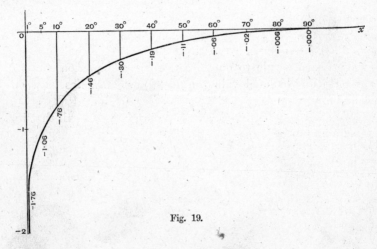

Fig. 19.

The accompanying graph of $\log \sin x$ for values of x lying between $x=0$ and $x=90°$ will illustrate the smallness of the differences when the angle is nearly a right angle, and the very rapidly increasing magnitude of the differences as the angle decreases to zero.

It will be seen that the geometrical meaning of Equation 3 of Art. 144, viz., "The Rule of Proportional Parts," is, that the portion of the curve between the two very adjacent points whose abscissae are x and $x+h$, may in general be regarded as *straight* in interpolation for the value of $f(x+k)$.

146. On the Value of θ in the Equation

$$f(x+h)=f(x)+hf'(x+\theta h).$$

Hitherto all that is known of θ is that it is some function of x and h, less than unity, and positive.

Let its expansion in powers of h be

$$\theta \equiv A_0+A_1h+A_2h^2+A_3h^3+\ldots$$

$A_0, A_1, A_2 \ldots$ being functions of x, to be determined.

Then expanding both sides of the equation

$$f(x+h)=f(x)+hf'(x+\theta h)$$

we have

$$fx+hf'x+\frac{h^2}{2!}f''x+\frac{h^3}{3!}f'''x+\frac{h^4}{4!}f''''x+\ldots$$

$$=fx+hf'x+\theta h^2f''x+\frac{\theta^2 h^3}{2!}f'''x+\frac{\theta^3 h^4}{3!}f''''x+\ldots$$

$$=fx+hf'x+A_0h^2f''x+\left(A_1f''x+\frac{A_0^2f'''x}{2!}\right)h^3$$

$$+\left(A_2f''x+A_1A_0f'''x+\frac{A_0^3f''''x}{6}\right)h^4+\ldots.$$

upon substituting for θ its equivalent series and collecting the several powers of h.

Hence equating coefficients

$$A_0f''x=\frac{f''x}{2!};$$

$$A_1f''x+\frac{A_0^2f'''x}{2}=\frac{f'''x}{6};$$

$$A_2f''x+A_1A_0f'''x+\frac{A_0^3f''''x}{6}=\frac{f''''x}{24}; \text{ etc.}$$

These equations give

$$A_0=\frac{1}{2},\ A_1=\frac{f'''x}{24f''x},$$

$$A_2=\frac{f''xf''''x-(f'''x)^2}{48(f''x)^2}, \text{ etc.,}$$

whence

$$\theta=\frac{1}{2}+h\cdot\frac{f'''x}{24f''x}+h^2\frac{f''xf''''x-(f'''x)^2}{48(f''x)^2}+\ldots$$

It appears therefore that the limiting value of θ, when h is indefinitely diminished is $\frac{1}{2}$; that is to say, the point R in Fig. 18 is in the limit half way between the ordinates of P and Q.

It should be noticed that if $f(x)$ be a rational quadratic function of x, $f''''x$ and all higher differential coefficients vanish. Hence for such a function $\theta = \frac{1}{2}$, and we have the equation

$$f(x+h) = f(x) + hf'\left(x + \frac{h}{2}\right)$$

as may at once be verified.

147. The nth Differential Coefficient of a function of a function.
Let $y = f(u)$ where $u = \phi(x)$.

Then will
$$\frac{1}{n!}\frac{d^n y}{dx^n} = \sum \frac{1}{r!}\,{}^n K_r f^r(u)$$

where ${}^n K_r \equiv$ the coefficient of h^n in $\{\phi(x+h) - \phi(x)\}^r$; and the summation extends to all positive integral values of r from $r = 1$ to $r = n$.

To prove this, suppose x increases to $x + h$; then $\phi(x)$ becomes $\phi(x+h)$ i.e., $\phi(x) + z$ where z is written for $\phi(x+h) - \phi(x)$ or

$$h\phi'(x) + \frac{h^2}{2!}\phi''(x) + \frac{h^3}{3!}\phi'''(x) + \cdots \quad \ldots\ldots\ldots\ldots(1)$$

Hence $f(u)$ becomes $f(u+z)$.

Thus $\qquad f\{\phi(x+h)\} \equiv f(u+z)$.

Expanding each side by Taylor's Theorem

$$y + h\frac{dy}{dx} + \frac{h^2}{2!}\frac{d^2 y}{dx^2} + \frac{h^3}{3!}\frac{d^3 y}{dx^3} + \cdots + \frac{h^n}{n!}\frac{d^n y}{dx^n} + \cdots$$

$$\equiv f(u) + zf'(u) + \frac{z^2}{2!}f''(u) + \cdots + \frac{z^n}{n!}f^n(u) + \cdots \quad \ldots\ldots(2)$$

Substituting the series (1) for z in the right hand member of equation (2) we obtain on equating coefficients of h^n

$$\frac{1}{n!}\frac{d^n y}{dx^n} = \text{coeff. } h^n \text{ in } \frac{1}{n!}[\phi(x+h) - \phi(x)]^n f^n(u)$$

$$+ \text{coeff. } h^n \text{ in } \frac{1}{(n-1)!}[\phi(x+h) - \phi(x)]^{n-1} f^{n-1}(u)$$

$$+ \text{coeff. } h^n \text{ in } \frac{1}{(n-2)!}[\phi(x+h) - \phi(x)]^{n-2} f^{n-2}(u)$$

$$+ \text{etc.},$$

i.e., $\qquad \dfrac{1}{n!}\dfrac{d^n y}{dx^n} = \sum \dfrac{1}{r!}\,{}^n K_r f^r(u)$

the result stated.

Ex. 1. Suppose $u = x^2$, and therefore $y = f(x^2)$.

Here $\qquad \phi(x+h) - \phi(x) = h(2x+h)$.

We thus have to pick out the coefficient of h^n from the series

$$\frac{h^n}{n!}(2x+h)^n f^n(x^2) + \frac{h^{n-1}}{(n-1)!}(2x+h)^{n-1}f^{n-1}(x^2) + \frac{h^{n-2}}{(n-2)!}(2x+h)^{n-2}f^{n-2}(x^2) + \dots$$

thus obtaining

$$\frac{d^n}{dx^n}f(x^2)$$

$$= (2x)^n f^n(x^2) + \frac{n(n-1)}{1!}(2x)^{n-2}f^{n-1}(x^2) + \frac{n(n-1)(n-2)(n-3)}{2!}(2x)^{n-4}f^{n-2}(x^2) + \dots$$

as inductively proved in Art. 106.

Ex. 2. If $u = a + bx + cx^2$ and $u_1 = b + 2cx$, prove that

$$\frac{d^r u^n}{dx^r} = n(n-1)\dots(n-r+1)u^{n-r}u_1^r$$

$$\left\{ 1 + \frac{r(r-1)}{1.(n-r+1)}\frac{cu}{u_1^2} + \frac{r(r-1)(r-2)(r-3)}{1.2.(n-r+1)(n-r+2)}\frac{c^2u^2}{u_1^4} + \dots \right\}.$$

$$[\text{LAGRANGE.}]$$

BERNOULLI'S NUMBERS.

148. *To expand* $u \equiv f(x) = \dfrac{x}{2}\dfrac{e^x+1}{e^x-1}$ *in powers of* x.

Let $\qquad u = f(x),$ and $u' = f(0),$

$\qquad\qquad u_1 = f'(x)$ and $u'_1 = f'(0),$

$\qquad\qquad u_2 = f''(x)$ and $u'_2 = f''(0),$

with a similar notation for higher differential coefficients. Then Maclaurin's Theorem gives

$$u = \frac{x}{2}\frac{e^x+1}{e^x-1} = u' + xu'_1 + \frac{x^2}{2!}u'_2 + \dots.$$

Changing the sign of x we see that the left hand member of this equation remains unaltered; hence we have

$$u = u' - xu'_1 + \frac{x^2}{2!}u'_2 - \dots,$$

and by subtraction

$$0 = 2xu'_1 + 2\frac{x^3}{3!}u'_3 + 2\frac{x^5}{5!}u'_5 + \dots,$$

whence, by equating to zero the coefficients of the several powers of x, we infer that $\qquad u'_1 = u'_3 = u'_5 = \dots = 0,$

so that the expansion contains no odd powers of x.*

Again, since $\qquad\qquad e^x u = u + \dfrac{x}{2} + x\dfrac{e^x}{2},$

we have, by differentiating,

$$e^x(u_1 + u) = u_1 + \frac{1}{2} + (x+1)\frac{e^x}{2},$$

$$e^x(u_2 + 2u_1 + u) = u_2 + (x+2)\frac{e^x}{2},$$

$$e^x(u_3 + 3u_2 + 3u_1 + u) = u_3 + (x+3)\frac{e^x}{2},$$

$$\text{etc.,}$$

* This artifice may often be advantageously employed.

and putting $x=0$ in these equations we obtain from the first, third, fifth, etc.,
$$u'=\tfrac{1}{2}+\tfrac{1}{2},$$
$$3u'_2+u'=\tfrac{3}{2},$$
$$5u'_4+10u'_2+u'=\tfrac{5}{2},$$
$$7u'_6+35u'_4+21u'_2+u'=\tfrac{7}{2},$$
$$\text{etc.,}$$

giving $u'=1$, $u'_2=\tfrac{1}{6}$, $u'_4=-\tfrac{1}{30}$, $u'_6=\tfrac{1}{42}$, $u'_8=-\tfrac{1}{30}$, etc.

Hence
$$\frac{x}{2}\frac{e^x+1}{e^x-1}=1+\frac{1}{6}\frac{x^2}{2!}-\frac{1}{30}\frac{x^4}{4!}+\frac{1}{42}\frac{x^6}{6!}-\frac{1}{30}\frac{x^8}{8!}+\dots$$

This series introduces a set of coefficients which are found of great importance in the higher branches of analysis. The series is frequently written in the form
$$\frac{x}{2}\frac{e^x+1}{e^x-1}\ \text{ or }\ \left(\frac{x}{e^x-1}+\frac{x}{2}\right)=1+B_1\frac{x^2}{2!}-B_3\frac{x^4}{4!}+B_5\frac{x^6}{6!}-B_7\frac{x^8}{8!}+\dots$$

and the numbers B_1, B_3, B_5, ..., which are calculated above are called Bernoulli's numbers, having been first discovered and used by James Bernoulli.[*]

The coefficients of this expansion were investigated as far as the term containing x^{32} by Rothe, and published in *Crelle's Journal*. Professor Adams has recently calculated thirty-one more.[†]

149. Many important expansions can be deduced from that of $\dfrac{x}{2}\dfrac{e^x+1}{e^x-1}$.

For example,
$$x\coth x=x\frac{e^x+e^{-x}}{e^x-e^{-x}}=x\frac{e^{2x}+1}{e^x-1}$$
$$=1+B_1\frac{2^2x^2}{2!}-B_3\frac{2^4x^4}{4!}+\dots$$

Writing ιx for x, $\iota x\coth\iota x$ becomes $x\cot x$, and we have
$$x\cot x=1-B_1\frac{2^2x^2}{2!}-B_3\frac{2^4x^4}{4!}-\dots$$

Again, $\tan x=\cot x-2\cot 2x$
$$=\frac{1}{x}-B_1\frac{2^2x}{2!}-B_3\frac{2^4x^3}{4!}-\dots-2\left[\frac{1}{2x}-B_1\frac{2^3x}{2!}-B_3\frac{2^7x^3}{4!}-\dots\right]$$
$$=B_1\frac{2^2(2^2-1)}{2!}x+B_3\frac{2^4(2^4-1)}{4!}x^3+\dots$$

EXAMPLES.

1. Find the first three terms of expansion in powers of x of $\log(1+\tan x)$.   RESULT. $x-\tfrac{1}{2}x^2+\tfrac{2}{3}x^3+\dots$

2. Expand as far as the term containing x^4 (1) $\log(1+\cos x)$ and (2) $\log(1+x\sin x)$.

RESULTS. $\begin{cases}(1)\ \log 2-\dfrac{x^2}{4}-\dfrac{x^4}{96}\dots\\[2mm](2)\ x^2-\dfrac{2}{3}x^4+\dots\end{cases}$

---

[*] *Ars Conjectandi*, p. 97.

[†] *Encyclopædia Britt.*: Infinitesimal Calc. *Proceedings of the British Assoc.*, 1877.

3. Prove $\log \cos x = -\dfrac{x^2}{2!} - 2\dfrac{x^4}{4!} - 16\dfrac{x^6}{6!} - 272\dfrac{x^8}{8!} \ldots$

4. Prove $e^{x \cos x} = 1 + x + \dfrac{x^2}{2} - \dfrac{x^3}{3} - \dfrac{11x^4}{24} - \dfrac{x^5}{5} \ldots$

5. Prove $e^{x \sec x} = 1 + x + \dfrac{1}{2}x^2 + \dfrac{2x^3}{3} \ldots$

6. Prove $\log \dfrac{xe^x}{e^x - 1} = \dfrac{x}{2} - \dfrac{x^2}{24} + \dfrac{x^4}{2880} \ldots$

7. Prove $\log \left\{ \log(1 + x)^{\frac{1}{x}} \right\} = -\dfrac{x}{2} + \dfrac{5x^2}{24} - \dfrac{x^3}{8} + \dfrac{251x^4}{2880} \ldots$

8. Prove $\log(1 + x + x^2 + x^3 + x^4) = x + \dfrac{x^2}{2} + \dfrac{x^3}{3} + \dfrac{x^4}{4} - \dfrac{4x^5}{5} + \dfrac{x^6}{6} + \ldots$

9. Prove $(1 + x)^x = 1 + x^2 - \frac{1}{2}x^3 + \frac{5}{6}x^4 - \frac{3}{4}x^5 \ldots$

10. If a_n be the coefficient of x^n in the expansion of $e^x \sin x$, show that

$$a_n - \frac{a_{n-1}}{1!} + \frac{a_{n-2}}{2!} - \frac{a_{n-3}}{3!} + \ldots = \frac{\sin \dfrac{n\pi}{2}}{n!}.$$

[I. C. S. Exam.]

11. From $y = (x + \sqrt{1 + x^2})^n$ obtain a linear differential equation with rational algebraic coefficients, and by means of it find the expansion of y in ascending powers of x.

12. From the relation $y = \dfrac{(1 + x)^{\frac{1}{2}}}{1 - x}$ obtain a linear differential equation with rational algebraic coefficients, and by means of it find the expansion of y in ascending powers of x.   [I. C. S. Exam]

13. If $\tan y = 1 + ax + bx^2$, expand y in powers of x as far as x^3.

[I. C. S. Exam.]

14. If A_0, A_1, etc., be the successive coefficients in the expansion of $y = e^{\cos mx + \sin mx}$, prove

$$A_{n+1} = \frac{m}{n+1} \left\{ A_n + \Sigma_1^n \frac{m^r}{r!} A_{n-r} \left(\cos \frac{r\pi}{2} - \sin \frac{r\pi}{2} \right) \right\}.$$

[I. C. S. Exam.]

15. If $a_n x^n + a_{n+1} x^{n+1} + a_{n+2} x^{n+2}$ be three consecutive terms of the expansion of $(1 - x^2)^{\frac{1}{2}} \sin^{-1} x$ in powers of x, prove that

$$a_{n+2} = \frac{n-1}{n+2} a_n;$$

also that all even terms vanish, and that the expansion is

$$x - \frac{1}{3}x^3 - \frac{2}{3 \cdot 5} \cdot x^5 - \frac{2 \cdot 4}{3 \cdot 5 \cdot 7} x^7 - \ldots$$

[Quarterly Journal].

16. If
$$x^2 + 2x = 2\log\left(c\,\frac{dx}{dy}\right)$$

and
$$y = a_0 + a_1 x + \frac{a_2}{2!}x^2 + \dots,$$

show that
$$a_{n+2} + a_{n+1} + na_n = 0. \qquad \text{[Oxford, 1888.]}$$

17. Prove
$$\frac{f(x+h)+f(x-h)}{2} = f(x) + \frac{h^2}{2!}f''(x) + \frac{h^4}{4!}f''''(x) + \dots$$

18. If
$$\theta = \log x,$$

prove that $\;u + x\dfrac{du}{dx} + \dfrac{x^2}{2!}\dfrac{d^2u}{dx^2} + \dots = u + \log 2 \cdot \dfrac{du}{d\theta} + \dfrac{(\log 2)^2}{2!}\dfrac{d^2u}{d\theta^2} + \dots$

19. Deduce from Taylor's Theorem, by putting $h = -x$, the series
$$f(x) = f(0) + xf'(x) - \frac{x^2}{2!}f''(x) + \frac{x^3}{3!}f'''(x) - \text{etc.} \qquad \text{[Bernoulli.]}$$

20. Prove
$$\tan^{-1}(x+h) = \tan^{-1}x + (h\sin\theta)\sin\theta - \frac{(h\sin\theta)^2}{2}\sin 2\theta$$
$$+ \frac{(h\sin\theta)^3}{3}\sin 3\theta - \frac{(h\sin\theta)^4}{4}\sin 4\theta + \text{etc.},$$

where
$$x = \cot\theta.$$

21. Verify the following deductions from Ex. 20 :—

(1) $\;\dfrac{\pi}{2} = \theta + \cos\theta \cdot \sin\theta + \dfrac{\cos^2\theta}{2}\sin 2\theta + \dfrac{\cos^3\theta}{3}\sin 3\theta + \dfrac{\cos^4\theta}{4}\sin 4\theta + \dots$

by putting $h = -x = -\cot\theta.$

(2) $\;\dfrac{\pi}{2} = \dfrac{\theta}{2} + \sin\theta + \tfrac{1}{2}\sin 2\theta + \tfrac{1}{3}\sin 3\theta + \tfrac{1}{4}\sin 4\theta + \dots$

by putting $h = -\sqrt{1+x^2} = -\dfrac{1}{\sin\theta}.$

(3) $\;\dfrac{\pi}{2} = \dfrac{\sin\theta}{\cos\theta} + \dfrac{1}{2}\cdot\dfrac{\sin 2\theta}{\cos^2\theta} + \dfrac{1}{3}\cdot\dfrac{\sin 3\theta}{\cos^3\theta} + \dfrac{1}{4}\cdot\dfrac{\sin 4\theta}{\cos^4\theta} + \dots$

by putting $h = -x - \dfrac{1}{x} = -\dfrac{1}{\sin\theta \cdot \cos\theta}.$ \qquad \text{[Euler.]}

22. If $\dfrac{f(x)}{F(x)}$ be a rational fraction in which the denominator has n factors, each equal to $x - a$, and the remaining factors are $x - h$, $x - k$, etc., so that $F(x) = (x-a)^n\phi(x)$ where
$$\phi(x) = (x-h)(x-k)\dots,$$

prove that
$$\frac{f(x)}{F(x)} = \frac{1}{(x-a)^n}\cdot\frac{f(a)}{\phi(a)} + \frac{1}{(x-a)^{n-1}}\frac{d}{da}\left\{\frac{f(a)}{\phi(a)}\right\}$$
$$+ \frac{1}{2!(x-a)^{n-2}}\frac{d^2}{da^2}\left\{\frac{f(a)}{\phi(a)}\right\} + \dots + \frac{H}{x-h} + \dots$$
$$= \frac{1}{(n-1)!}\frac{d^{n-1}}{da^{n-1}}\left\{\frac{f(a)}{\phi(a)(x-a)}\right\} + \frac{H}{x-h} + \dots$$

23. Establish the following approximations to the length of a circular arc :—

Let $\qquad$ C be the chord of the whole arc,

$\qquad H \qquad$ do. $\qquad$ half the arc,

$\qquad Q \qquad$ do. $\qquad$ quarter the arc.

(1) Arc $= \dfrac{8H - C}{3}$ nearly. $\qquad$ [HUYGHENS.]

(2) Arc $= \dfrac{C + 256Q - 40H}{45}$ nearly.

Examine the closeness of the approximation in each case.

24. Find by division the first six of Bernoulli's coefficients.

They are $\qquad \dfrac{1}{6}, \dfrac{1}{30}, \dfrac{1}{42}, \dfrac{1}{30}, \dfrac{5}{66}, \dfrac{691}{2730}.$

25. Prove by continuing the differentiations in Art. 148 that

$$\frac{1}{n+1} + \frac{1}{2} + \frac{n}{2!}B_1 - \frac{n(n-1)(n-2)}{4!}B_3 + \ldots = 1,$$

a formula from which the values of the coefficients $B_1, B_3 \ldots$ can be successively deduced by putting $n = 2, 4, 6$, etc. $\qquad$ [DE MOIVRE.]

26. Expand $\left(\dfrac{\theta}{\sin \theta}\right)^2$ in powers of θ.

[Differentiate expansion of cot θ, Art. 149.]

27. Prove $\dfrac{\theta}{\sin \theta} = 1 + 2(2-1)\dfrac{B_1}{2!}\theta^2 + 2(2^3 - 1)\dfrac{B_3}{4!}\theta^4 + \ldots$

[Use cosec $\theta = \cot \dfrac{\theta}{2} - \cot \theta$ and Art. 149.]

28. Prove $\tanh x = \dfrac{2^2(2^2 - 1)}{2!}B_1 x - \dfrac{2^4(2^4 - 1)}{4!}B_3 x^3 + \ldots$

29. By taking the logarithmic differential of the expression for $\sin \theta$ in factors and comparison of the expansion of the result with that of $\theta \cot \theta$ (Art. 149), show that

$$B_{2n-1} = \frac{2(2n)!}{(2\pi)^{2n}}\left\{1 + \frac{1}{2^{2n}} + \frac{1}{3^{2n}} + \ldots\right\}$$

$$= \frac{2(2n)!}{(2\pi)^{2n}} \frac{1}{\Pi\left(1 - \dfrac{1}{r^{2n}}\right)},$$

$\qquad$ [RAABE.]

where $\Pi\left(1 - \dfrac{1}{r^{2n}}\right)$ denotes the continued product of such factors as $1 - \dfrac{1}{r^{2n}}$ for all integral prime values of r from 2 to ∞.

30. Show that

$$\log \frac{\sinh x}{x} = B_1\frac{2^2 x^2}{2 \cdot 2!} - B_3\frac{2^4 x^4}{4 \cdot 4!} + B_5\frac{2^6 x^6}{6 \cdot 6!} - \ldots$$

31. Expand $\log \dfrac{\sin x}{x}$ and $\log \tan x$ by means of Bernoulli's numbers.

                                                                [CATALAN.]

32. Show that

$$\log \frac{\cosh x - \cos x}{x^2} + \Sigma 2^{n+1} \cos \frac{n\pi}{2} \frac{B_{2n-1}}{2n} \frac{x^{2n}}{(2n)!} = 0.$$

                                                 [MATH. TRIPOS, 1890.]

33. Expand $\sin(m \tan^{-1}x)(1 + x^2)^{\frac{m}{2}}$

in powers of x.

                                                                 [BERTRAND.]

34. Being given the two convergent series

$$y = a_0 + a_1 x + a_2 x^2 + \ldots + a_n x^n + \ldots$$
$$\log y = b_0 + b_1 x + b_2 x^2 + \ldots + b_n x^n + \ldots$$

prove $na_n = b_1 a_{n-1} + 2b_2 a_{n-2} + 3b_3 a_{n-3} + \ldots + nb_n a_0.$

35. Prove $\tan^{-1}x = \dfrac{x}{1 + x^2}\left\{1 + \dfrac{2}{3} \dfrac{x^2}{1 + x^2} + \dfrac{2 \cdot 4}{3 \cdot 5}\left(\dfrac{x^2}{1 + x^2}\right)^2 + \ldots\right\}$

                                                                      [FRENET.]

36. In the equation

$$f(x + h) = f(x) + hf'(x + \theta h),$$

if θ be expanded in powers of h, the first four terms will be

$$\theta = \frac{1}{2} + \frac{1}{24}\frac{f_3}{f_2}h + \frac{1}{48}\frac{f_2 f_4 - f_3^2}{f_2^2}h^2 + \frac{33f_5 f_2^2 - 90f_2 f_3 f_4 + 55f_3^3}{5760f_2^3}h^3 + \ldots$$

suffixes being used to denote differentiations.

37. In the equation

$$f(x + h) = f(x) + hf'(x) + \ldots + \frac{h^{n-1}}{(n-1)!}f^{n-1}(x + \theta h)$$

show that the limiting value of θ as h is indefinitely diminished is $\dfrac{1}{n}$.

38. If in a plane curve $y = f(x)$, V be the midpoint of a chord AB drawn parallel to the tangent at any point P (x, y), prove that when AB approaches indefinitely near to the tangent at P, the angle which PV makes with the axis of x approximates to $\tan^{-1}\left(p - \dfrac{3q^2}{r}\right)$, where p, q and r are respectively the first, second and third differential coefficients of y with regard to x.   [OXFORD, 1890.]

Show also that the angle which PV makes with the normal is ultimately $\tan^{-1}\left\{p - \dfrac{(1 + p^2)r}{3q^2}\right\}.*$ [OXFORD, 1886.]

---

* In a circle PV coincides with the normal. This angle therefore measures the deviation of the curve from the circular shape. Transon (Liouville, vol. VI.) calls the angle the "deviation." Dr. Salmon names it the "Aberrancy of Curvature" (see *Higher Plane Curves*, p. 356).

39. If $\qquad u = e^{e^x} = \Sigma a_n x^n,$

prove that $\quad a_{n+1} = \dfrac{1}{n+1}\left(a_n + a_{n-1} + \dfrac{a_{n-2}}{2!} + \dfrac{a_{n-3}}{3!} + \ldots + \dfrac{a_0}{n!}\right).$

[GREGORY'S EXAMPLES.]

40. Show that

$$\frac{1}{n!} \frac{d^n}{dx^n}[x^n(\log x)^n] = 1 + S_1 \log x + \frac{S_2}{2!}(\log x)^2 + \ldots + \frac{S_n}{n!}(\log x)^n$$

where $S_r \equiv$ the sum of the products r at a time of the first n natural numbers. [MURPHY.]

41. If $F(z)$ and $f(z)$ be two functions which are continuous and finite, as also their differential coefficients, between the values x and $x + h$ of the variable z, and if $f'(z)$ does not vanish between these limits, prove that

$$\frac{F(x+h) - F(x)}{f(x+h) - f(x)} = \frac{F'(x+\theta h)}{f'(x+\theta h)}$$

where θ is some positive proper fraction. [CAUCHY.]

CHAPTER VI.

PARTIAL DIFFERENTIATION.

150. Functions of several Independent Variables.

Our attention has hitherto been confined to methods for the differentiation of functions of a single independent variable. In the present chapter we propose to discuss the case in which several such variables occur. Such functions are common; for instance, the area of a triangle depends upon two variables, viz., the base and the altitude; while the volume of a rectangular box depends upon three, viz., its length, breadth, and depth; and it is plain that each of these variables may vary independently of the others.

151. Partial Differentiation.

If a differentiation of a function of several independent variables be performed with regard to any one of them just as if the others were constants, it is said to be a *partial differentiation*.

The symbols $\dfrac{\partial}{\partial x}$, $\dfrac{\partial}{\partial y}$, etc., are used to denote such differentiations, and the expressions $\dfrac{\partial u}{\partial x}$, $\dfrac{\partial u}{\partial y}$, etc., are called *partial differential coefficients* with regard to x, y, etc., respectively.

Thus if, for instance,

$$u = e^{xy} \sin z,$$

we have

$$\frac{\partial u}{\partial x} = y e^{xy} \sin z,$$

$$\frac{\partial u}{\partial y} = x e^{xy} \sin z,$$

$$\frac{\partial u}{\partial z} = e^{xy} \cos z.$$

112

152. Analytical Meaning.

The meanings of the differential coefficients thus formed are clear; for if we denote u by $f(x, y, z)$ the operation denoted by $\dfrac{\partial u}{\partial x}$ may be expressed as

$$Lt_{h=0} \frac{f(x+h,\ y,\ z) - f(x,\ y,\ z)}{h},$$

and similarly for $\dfrac{\partial u}{\partial y}$ or $\dfrac{\partial u}{\partial z}$.

These partial differential coefficients are often conveniently written u_x, u_y, u_z.

153. Geometrical Illustration.

It will throw additional light upon the subject of partial differentiation if we explain the geometrical meaning of the process for the case of two independent variables.

Let $PQRS$ be an elementary portion of the surface $z = f(x, y)$ cut off by the four planes

$$Y = y,\quad Y = y + \delta y\Big\}\ \text{[Capital letters representing}$$
$$X = x,\quad X = x + \delta x\Big\}\quad \text{current co-ordinates],}$$

so that the co-ordinates of the corners P, Q, R, S are

for P	$x,\ y,\ f(x,\ y)$,
for Q	$x+\delta x,\ y,\ f(x+\delta x,\ y)$,
for S	$x,\ y+\delta y,\ f(x,\ y+\delta y)$,
and for R	$x+\delta x,\ y+\delta y,\ f(x+\delta x,\ y+\delta y)$.

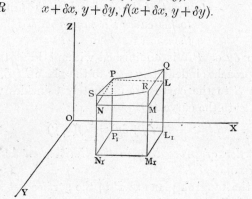

Fig. 20.

If $PLMN$ be a plane through P, parallel to the plane of xy, and cutting the ordinates of P, Q, R, S in P, L, M, N respectively, we have

E.D.C.   H

$$LQ = f(x + \delta x, y) - f(x, y),$$
$$NS = f(x, y + \delta y) - f(x, y),$$
$$MR = f(x + \delta x, y + \delta y) - f(x, y). \qquad \Bigg\} \dots\dots\dots(1)$$

Hence the partial differential coefficient $\dfrac{\partial z}{\partial x}$ obtained by *considering y a constant* is

$$= Lt_{\delta x = 0} \frac{f(x + \delta x, y) - f(x, y)}{\delta x} = Lt \frac{LQ}{PL} = Lt \tan LPQ \dots\dots(2)$$

= *tangent of the angle which the tangent at P to the curved section PQ (parallel to the plane xz) makes with a line drawn parallel to the axis of x.*

Similarly $\dfrac{\partial z}{\partial y}$, which is obtained on the supposition that x is constant

$$= Lt \tan NPS, \dots\dots\dots\dots\dots\dots\dots\dots(3)$$

= *tangent of the angle which the tangent at P to a section parallel to the plane of yz makes with a parallel to the axis of y.*

It further appears from the figure that

$$\frac{\partial}{\partial x} f(x, y + \delta y) = Lt_{\delta x = 0} \frac{f(x + \delta x, y + \delta y) - f(x, y + \delta y)}{\delta x}$$
$$= Lt_{NM = 0} \frac{MR - NS}{NM}$$

= *tangent of the angle which the tangent at S to the curve SR makes with a parallel to the x-axis.*

Now when δy or PN is diminished without limit the plane $NSRM$ approaches indefinitely near to the plane PQL, and the tangent at S to the curve SR ultimately coincides with the tangent at P to the curve PQ.

i.e. $\qquad Lt_{\delta y = 0} \dfrac{\partial}{\partial x} f(x, y + \delta y) = \dfrac{\partial}{\partial x} f(x, y)$

and the *order of proceeding to the limit when δx and δy vanish is immaterial.*

154. If the tangent plane at P to the surface cut LQ, MR, NS in Q', R', S' respectively,

$$LQ' = PL \tan LPQ = \frac{\partial z}{\partial x} . \delta x, \dots\dots\dots\dots(4)$$

$$NS' = PN \tan NPS = \frac{\partial z}{\partial y} . \delta y, \dots\dots\dots\dots(5)$$

Also the section made on the tangent plane by the four bounding planes of the element is a parallelogram, and the height of its centre above the plane $PLMN$ is given by $\frac{1}{2}MR'$ and also by $\frac{1}{2}(LQ'+NS')$, which proves that

$$MR' = LQ' + NS'$$

$$= \frac{\partial z}{\partial x}\delta x + \frac{\partial z}{\partial y}\delta y \quad \ldots\ldots\ldots\ldots\ldots\ldots\ldots\ldots(6)$$

The expressions proved in (4), (5), and (6) are *first approximations* to the lengths LQ, NS, and MR respectively, and differ from those lengths by small quantities of higher order than PL and PN, and which are therefore negligible in the limit when δx and δy are taken very small. The investigation of the total values of LQ, NS, MR must be postponed until we have investigated the extension of Taylor's Theorem to functions of several variables. (Art. 175.)

155. We may state the rule established in the preceding article (equation 6) thus :

In the limit, the total variation in z

= the variation due to the change in x

+ the variation due to the change in y,

supposing that as each variation is estimated the other quantity is regarded as constant.

This may be illustrated further.

Let P be any point (co-ordinates r, θ). Let a point travel from P to any contiguous position $Q(r+\delta r,\ \theta+\delta\theta)$ along any path whatever. Let x and $x+\delta x$ be the abscissæ of P and Q. Let P and Q be so close that δx, δr, $\delta\theta$ are infinitesimals of the first order, so that in comparison with them their squares, products, and higher powers may be disregarded.

Draw circular arcs whose centres are at the pole O and radii OQ and OP cutting OP at P' and OQ at Q' respectively.

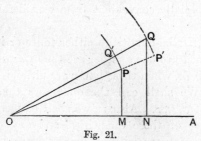

Fig. 21.

Then $PP'=\delta r$, $PQ'=r\delta\theta$, and to the first order

$$P'Q[=(r+\delta r)\delta\theta]=r\delta\theta,$$

chord $P'Q$ = arc $P'Q = r\delta\theta$.

Also the angle $QP'O$ differs from a right angle by an infinitesimal of the first order.

Hence to this order the projection of $P'Q$ on the initial line $= -P'Q \sin\theta$ $= -r\delta\theta \sin\theta$. Also projection of $PQ=$ algebraical sum of projections of PP', $P'Q$. Thus we have the following equation among first order infinitesimals, viz. :

$$\delta x = \delta r \cos\theta - r\delta\theta \sin\theta \dots\dots\dots\dots\dots\dots\dots\dots(1)$$

It should be noticed that the projection of PP', viz. $\delta r \cos\theta$, is the variation in x due to a change δr in the value of r, θ remaining constant; whilst the projection of $P'Q$ or of PQ' is the variation in x due to an increase $\delta\theta$ in the value of θ, r remaining constant.

Moreover, since $x = r \cos\theta$,

we have $\dfrac{\partial x}{\partial r} = \cos\theta, \ \dfrac{\partial x}{\partial\theta} = -r\sin\theta$;

so that equation (1) may be written

$$\delta x = \frac{\partial x}{\partial r}\delta r + \frac{\partial x}{\partial\theta}\delta\theta \ ;$$

verifying equation 6 of Art. 154 in this case.

EXAMPLES.

1. If $A = xy$, explain geometrically the equation

$$\delta A = \frac{\partial A}{\partial x}\delta x + \frac{\partial A}{\partial y}\delta y$$

by reference to the area of a rectangle whose sides x, y are allowed to increase to $x+\delta x$, $y+\delta y$; the increments being infinitesimals of the first order.

2. If $V = xyz$, show geometrically that

$$\delta V = \frac{\partial V}{\partial x}\delta x + \frac{\partial V}{\partial y}\delta y + \frac{\partial V}{\partial z}\delta z.$$

156. Differentials.

It is useful at this point to introduce a new notation, which will prove especially convenient from considerations of symmetry.

Let Dx, Dy, Dz be quantities either finite or infinitesimally small whose ratios to one another are the *same as the limiting ratios of* δx, δy, δz, when these latter are ultimately diminished indefinitely. We shall call the quantities thus defined the *differentials* of x, y, z. Also, as we shall be merely concerned with the ratios of these quantities, and any equation into which they may enter will be homogeneous in them, it is unnecessary to define them further or to obtain absolute values for them. The student is warned again (see Art. 39) that the differential coefficient $\dfrac{dy}{dx}$ is to be considered as the result of performing the operation represented by $\dfrac{d}{dx}$ upon y, an operation described in Art. 37. The dy and dx of the symbol $\dfrac{dy}{dx}$ cannot therefore be separated, and have separately no meaning, and hence have no connection with the differentials Dx and Dy as defined in the present article; but at the same time we have by definition

$$Dy : Dx = \text{Limit of the ratio } \delta y : \delta x$$
$$= Lt \frac{\delta y}{\delta x} : 1$$
$$= \frac{dy}{dx} : 1,$$

and therefore $\qquad Dy = \dfrac{dy}{dx} Dx,$

and $\qquad \dfrac{Dy}{Dx}$ (which is a fraction)

$$= \frac{dy}{dx} \text{ (which is the result of the process}$$
$$\text{of Art. 37).}$$

We have used a capital in the differentials Dx, Dy, Dz for the purpose of explanation, and to avoid any confusion between the notation for differentials and for differential coefficients; but when once understood there is no necessity for the continuance of the capital letter, and it is usual in the higher branches of mathematics to denote the same quantities by dx, dy, dz. Hence we shall in future adopt this notation.

157. Equation 6 of Art. 154 may now be written

$$dz = \frac{\partial z}{\partial x} dx + \frac{\partial z}{\partial y} dy$$

when δx, δy, δz become infinitesimally small. This value of dz is termed the total differential of z with regard to x and y. The *total* differential of z is therefore equal to the *sum of the partial differentials* formed under the supposition that y and x are alternately constant.

Ex. Consider the surface

$$z = x^2 y^2,$$

then $\qquad \dfrac{\partial z}{\partial x} = 2xy^2 \text{ and } \dfrac{\partial z}{\partial y} = 2x^2 y,$

whence $\qquad dz = 2xy^2 dx + 2x^2 y dy.$

158. It is easy to pass from a form in which differentials are used to the equivalent form in terms of differential coefficients. For instance, the equation

$$dz = \frac{\partial z}{\partial x} dx + \frac{\partial z}{\partial y} dy$$

may be at once written

$$\frac{dz}{dt} = \frac{\partial z}{\partial x} \frac{dx}{dt} + \frac{\partial z}{\partial y} \frac{dy}{dt},$$

where t is some fourth variable in terms of which each of the variables x, y, z may be expressed; for

$$dz = \frac{dz}{dt} \cdot dt, \; dx = \frac{dx}{dt} \cdot dt, \; dy = \frac{dy}{dt} \cdot dt \text{ (Art. 156)}.$$

Similarly the equation $ds^2 = dx^2 + dy^2$
may, by the same article, be written in the language of differential coefficients as

$$\left(\frac{dx}{ds}\right)^2 + \left(\frac{dy}{ds}\right)^2 = 1,$$

or

$$\left(\frac{ds}{dt}\right)^2 = \left(\frac{dx}{dt}\right)^2 + \left(\frac{dy}{dt}\right)^2,$$

or

$$\left(\frac{ds}{dx}\right)^2 = 1 + \left(\frac{dy}{dx}\right)^2,$$

or

$$\left(\frac{ds}{dy}\right)^2 = 1 + \left(\frac{dx}{dy}\right)^2.$$

159. **Total Differential (Analytical).**

Two independent variables. We may investigate the total differential of the function $\phi(x, y)$ analytically as follows:

Let $u = \phi(x, y)$,
and when x becomes $x + h$ and y becomes $y + k$, let u become $u + \delta u$, then $u + \delta u = \phi(x + h, y + k)$
and $\delta u = \phi(x + h, y + k) - \phi(x, y)$

$$= \frac{\phi(x + h, y + k) - \phi(x, y + k)}{h} \cdot h + \frac{\phi(x, y + k) - \phi(x, y)}{k} \cdot k \dots \text{(A)}$$

And in proceeding to the limit when h becomes indefinitely small

$$\frac{\phi(x + h, y + k) - \phi(x, y + k)}{h}$$

becomes (by Art. 152) $\frac{\partial}{\partial x} \phi(x, y + k)$, and ultimately when k also diminishes indefinitely

$$\frac{\partial \phi(x, y)}{\partial x} \text{ or } \frac{\partial u}{\partial x} \text{ (Art. 153).}$$

Again $$\frac{\phi(x, y+k) - \phi(x, y)}{k}$$

at the same time becomes

$$\frac{\partial \phi(x, y)}{\partial y} \text{ or } \frac{\partial u}{\partial y}.$$

And lastly in the notation of differentials (Art. 156) the ultimate values of the ratios $\delta u : h : k$ may be expressed as $du : dx : dy$. Hence equation (A) becomes

$$du = \frac{\partial u}{\partial x} dx + \frac{\partial u}{\partial y} dy.$$

160. *Several independent variables.*

We may readily extend this result to a function of three or of any number of variables.

Let $$u = \phi(x_1, x_2, x_3),$$

and let the increments of x_1, x_2, x_3, be respectively h_1, h_2, h_3 and let the corresponding increment of u be δu; then

$$\delta u = \phi(x_1 + h_1, x_2 + h_2, x_3 + h_3) - \phi(x_1, x_2, x_3)$$

$$= \frac{\phi(x_1 + h_1, x_2 + h_2, x_3 + h_3) - \phi(x_1, x_2 + h_2, x_3 + h_3)}{h_1} h_1$$

$$+ \frac{\phi(x_1, x_2 + h_2, x_3 + h_3) - \phi(x_1, x_2, x_3 + h_3)}{h_2} h_2$$

$$+ \frac{\phi(x_1, x_2, x_3 + h_3) - \phi(x_1, x_2, x_3)}{h_3} h_3 ;$$

whence on taking the limit and substituting the ratios $du : dx_1 : dx_2 : dx_3$ instead of the ultimate ratios of $\delta u : h_1 : h_2 : h_3$,

we have $$du = \frac{\partial u}{\partial x_1} dx_1 + \frac{\partial u}{\partial x_2} dx_2 + \frac{\partial u}{\partial x_3} dx_3,$$

i.e., the total differential of u when x_1, x_2, x_3, all vary is the sum of the partial differentials obtained under the supposition that when each one in turn varies the others are constant.

161. And in exactly the same way if

$$u = \phi(x_1, x_2, \dots x_n),$$

we have $$du = \frac{\partial u}{\partial x_1} dx_1 + \frac{\partial u}{\partial x_2} dx_2 + \frac{\partial u}{\partial x_3} dx_3 + \dots + \frac{\partial u}{\partial x_n} dx_n.$$

162. Total Differential Coefficient.

If
$$u = \phi(x_1, x_2)$$
where x_1 and x_2 are known functions of a single variable x, we have
$$du = \frac{\partial u}{\partial x_1} dx_1 + \frac{\partial u}{\partial x_2} dx_2,$$
and remembering (Art. 156) that
$$du = \frac{du}{dx} dx, \; dx_1 = \frac{dx_1}{dx} dx, \; dx_2 = \frac{dx_2}{dx} dx,$$
we obtain
$$\frac{du}{dx} = \frac{\partial u}{\partial x_1} \cdot \frac{dx_1}{dx} + \frac{\partial u}{\partial x_2} \cdot \frac{dx_2}{dx}.$$

And similarly, if
$$u = \phi(x_1, x_2, \ldots, x_n),$$
where $x_1, x_2, \ldots, x_n$, are known functions of x, we obtain
$$\frac{du}{dx} = \frac{\partial u}{\partial x_1} \cdot \frac{dx_1}{dx} + \frac{\partial u}{\partial x_2} \cdot \frac{dx_2}{dx} + \ldots \frac{\partial u}{\partial x_n} \cdot \frac{dx_n}{dx}.$$

And further, if $x_1, x_2, x_3, \ldots, x_n$ be each known functions of several variables $x, y, z, \ldots$, we shall have in the same way the series of relations
$$\frac{\partial u}{\partial x} = \frac{\partial u}{\partial x_1} \cdot \frac{\partial x_1}{\partial x} + \frac{\partial u}{\partial x_2} \cdot \frac{\partial x_2}{\partial x} + \ldots \frac{\partial u}{\partial x_n} \cdot \frac{\partial x_n}{\partial x},$$
$$\frac{\partial u}{\partial y} = \frac{\partial u}{\partial x_1} \cdot \frac{\partial x_1}{\partial y} + \frac{\partial u}{\partial x_2} \cdot \frac{\partial x_2}{\partial y} + \ldots \frac{\partial u}{\partial x_n} \cdot \frac{\partial x_n}{\partial y},$$
$$\text{etc.}$$

163. An Important Case.

The case in which
$$u = \phi(x, y),$$
y being a function of x, is from its frequent occurrence worthy of special notice.

Here, by Art. 162,
$$\frac{du}{dx} = \frac{\partial \phi}{\partial x} + \frac{\partial \phi}{\partial y} \cdot \frac{dy}{dx}$$
since
$$\frac{dx}{dx} = 1.$$

164. Differentiation of an Implicit Function.

If we have
$$\phi(x, y) = 0,$$
then
$$\phi(x+h, y+k) = 0.$$
Hence
$$\frac{\phi(x+h, y+k) - \phi(x, y+k)}{h} + \frac{\phi(x, y+k) - \phi(x, y)}{k} \cdot \frac{k}{h} = 0;$$

which, when h and k are indefinitely diminished, becomes (as explained in Art. 159)

$$\frac{\partial\phi}{\partial x} + \frac{\partial\phi}{\partial y} \cdot \frac{dy}{dx} = 0,$$

or

$$\frac{dy}{dx} = -\frac{\dfrac{\partial\phi}{\partial x}}{\dfrac{\partial\phi}{\partial y}}.$$

This is a *very useful formula* for the determination of $\dfrac{dy}{dx}$ in cases in which the relation between x and y is *an implicit one*, of which the solution for y in terms of x is inconvenient or impossible.

Ex. $\phi(x, y) \equiv x^3 + y^3 - 3axy = 0$; find $\dfrac{dy}{dx}$.

Here

$$\left.\begin{aligned}\frac{\partial\phi}{\partial x} &= 3(x^2 - ay)\\[2mm]\frac{\partial\phi}{\partial y} &= 3(y^2 - ax)\end{aligned}\right\} \quad \therefore \ \frac{dy}{dx} = -\frac{x^2 - ay}{y^2 - ax}.$$

and

165. Order of Partial Differentiations Commutative.

Suppose we have any relation

$$y = \phi(x, a),$$

where a is a constant, and that by differentiation we obtain

$$\frac{dy}{dx} = F(x, a).$$

Then since the processes of differentiation take no cognizance of the particular values of any of the constants involved it is obvious that the result of differentiating $\phi(x, a')$ would be $F(x, a')$; that is, the operation of changing a to a' may be performed either before or after the differentiation, with the same result. We may put this statement into another form, thus: Let E_a be an operative symbol such that when applied to any function of a it will change a to a', *i.e.*, such that

$$E_a f(a) = f(a'),$$

then in operating upon the function $\phi(x, a)$ the operations E_a and $\dfrac{d}{dx}$ are commutative, that is,

$$E_a \frac{d}{dx}\phi(x, a) = \frac{d}{dx}E_a\phi(x, a) = F(x, a').$$

Next, suppose $\qquad z = \phi(x, y)$.

The partial differential operations $\dfrac{\partial}{\partial x}$ and $\dfrac{\partial}{\partial y}$ have been defined to be such that when the operation with regard to either variable is performed the other variable is to be considered constant. We propose to show that these operations are *commutative*,

i.e., that $\qquad \dfrac{\partial}{\partial x}\dfrac{\partial}{\partial y}z = \dfrac{\partial}{\partial y}\dfrac{\partial}{\partial x}z.$

Let E_y denote the operation of changing y to $y + \delta y$ in any function to which it is applied; then E_y and the partial operation $\dfrac{\partial}{\partial x}$ are *commutative symbols*. And

$$\frac{\partial}{\partial y}\frac{\partial}{\partial x}\phi(x, y) = Lt_{\delta y = 0}\frac{E_y\dfrac{\partial\phi(x, y)}{\partial x} - \dfrac{\partial\phi(x, y)}{\partial x}}{\delta y}, \text{ by Def.,}$$

$$= Lt_{\delta y = 0}\frac{\dfrac{\partial}{\partial x}E_y\phi(x, y) - \dfrac{\partial\phi(x, y)}{\partial x}}{\delta y}$$

$$= Lt_{\delta y = 0}\frac{\partial}{\partial x}\frac{E_y\phi(x, y) - \phi(x, y)}{\delta y}$$

$$= \frac{\partial}{\partial x}Lt_{\delta y = 0}\frac{E_y\phi(x, y) - \phi(x, y)}{\delta y}$$

$$= \frac{\partial}{\partial x}\frac{\partial}{\partial y}\phi(x, y).$$

166. Another Proof.

The ordinate $f(0, 0)$ of the point in which any surface $z = f(x, y)$ cuts the z-axis is clearly independent of the particular path traced by any point moving from the arbitrary position (x, y, z) to the ultimate position $\{0, 0, f(0, 0)\}$; notwithstanding that in some cases, in estimating the ultimate value $f(0, 0)$, it may be necessary to evaluate an undetermined form. In other words, whenever it is necessary to evaluate $f(h, k)$ for zero values of h and k, the order or manner of making h and k diminish to zero is indifferent, and it is allowable if we choose to suppose them to approach their ultimate values simultaneously.

Thus $\quad Lt_{h=0}\,Lt_{k=0}\,f(h, k) \equiv Lt_{k=0}\,Lt_{h=0}\,f(h, k) \equiv Lt_{h=k=0}\,f(h, k).$

Again, it was pointed out in the previous article that processes of differentiation take no cognizance of the *particular values* of any constants involved. It therefore follows that if

$$Lt_{h=0}\frac{\phi(x+h, a) - \phi(x, a)}{h} = F(x, a),$$

then will $\qquad Lt_{h=0}\dfrac{\phi(x+h, a') - \phi(x, a')}{h} = F(x, a');$

that is, a may be changed to a' either before or after the limit is taken, with the same final result.

Now, by definition,

$$\frac{\partial \phi(x, y)}{\partial x} = Lt_{h=0} \frac{\phi(x+h, y) - \phi(x, y)}{h},$$

and, since x and y are independent, we may regard y and its increment k as constants, while x is varying. Hence the value of $\frac{\partial \phi(x, y)}{\partial x}$, when $y+k$ is written for y, is

$$Lt_{h=0} \frac{\phi(x+h, y+k) - \phi(x, y+k)}{h}.$$

(This has also been established geometrically in Art. 153.)

Therefore,

$$\frac{\partial}{\partial y} \frac{\partial}{\partial x} \phi(x, y) = Lt_{k=0} \frac{Lt_{h=0} \frac{\phi(x+h, y+k) - \phi(x, y+k)}{h} - Lt_{h=0} \frac{\phi(x+h, y) - \phi(x, y)}{h}}{k}$$

$$= Lt_{k=0} \, Lt_{h=0} \frac{\phi(x+h, y+k) - \phi(x, y+k) - \phi(x+h, y) + \phi(x, y)}{hk},$$

and as it has been established that the order of proceeding to the limit is indifferent, $\frac{\partial}{\partial x} \frac{\partial}{\partial y} \phi(x, y)$ may be shewn equal to the same expression.

167. Extension of Rule.

This rule admits of easy extension by its repeated application. Thus

$$\left(\frac{\partial}{\partial x}\right)^2 \left(\frac{\partial}{\partial y}\right) \phi = \left(\frac{\partial}{\partial x}\right) \left(\frac{\partial}{\partial y}\right) \left(\frac{\partial}{\partial x}\right) \phi$$

$$= \frac{\partial}{\partial y} \left(\frac{\partial}{\partial x}\right)^2 \phi.$$

Similarly $\quad \left(\frac{\partial}{\partial x}\right)^m \left(\frac{\partial}{\partial y}\right)^n \phi = \left(\frac{\partial}{\partial y}\right)^n \left(\frac{\partial}{\partial x}\right)^m \phi.$

Also if we have more than two independent variables, for instance if $\quad u = \phi(x, y, z)$

$$\left(\frac{\partial}{\partial x}\right) \left(\frac{\partial}{\partial y}\right) \left(\frac{\partial}{\partial z}\right) u = \left(\frac{\partial}{\partial y}\right) \left(\frac{\partial}{\partial x}\right) \left(\frac{\partial}{\partial z}\right) u$$

$$= \left(\frac{\partial}{\partial y}\right) \left(\frac{\partial}{\partial z}\right) \left(\frac{\partial}{\partial x}\right) u = \text{etc.},$$

so that the order in which the differentiations are performed is immaterial in the final result.

168. Notation.

It is usual to adopt for

$$\left(\frac{\partial}{\partial x}\right)^2 u, \ \left(\frac{\partial}{\partial x}\right) \left(\frac{\partial}{\partial y}\right) u, \ \left(\frac{\partial}{\partial x}\right)^p \left(\frac{\partial}{\partial y}\right)^q \left(\frac{\partial}{\partial z}\right)^r u, \ \text{etc.},$$

the more convenient notation

$$\frac{\partial^2 u}{\partial x^2}, \quad \frac{\partial^2 u}{\partial x \partial y}, \quad \frac{\partial^{p+q+r} u}{\partial x^p \partial y^q \partial z^r}, \text{ etc.}$$

and the propositions above enunciated will then be written

$$\frac{\partial^2 u}{\partial x \partial y} = \frac{\partial^2 u}{\partial y \partial x},$$

$$\frac{\partial^3 u}{\partial x^2 \partial y} = \frac{\partial^3 u}{\partial y \partial x^2},$$

$$\frac{\partial^{m+n} u}{\partial x^m \partial y^n} = \frac{\partial^{m+n} u}{\partial y^n \partial x^m},$$

etc.

We shall also sometimes find it useful to further abbreviate the expressions $\frac{\partial^2 u}{\partial x^2}, \frac{\partial^2 u}{\partial x \partial y}, \frac{\partial^2 u}{\partial y^2}$, etc., into u_{xx}, u_{xy}, u_{yy}, etc.

169. The formulae here established may be easily verified in any particular example.

Ex. Let $u = \sin(xy)$,

then $u_x = y \cos(xy)$,

and $u_{yx} = \cos xy - xy \sin xy$ ....(1)

Again $u_y = x \cos xy$,

and $u_{xy} = \cos xy - xy \sin xy$, ...(2)

and the agreement of expressions (1) and (2) verifies for this example the result of Arts. 165, 166.

170. It is convenient to use the letters p, q, r, s, t, to denote the partial differential coefficients

$$\frac{\partial \phi}{\partial x}, \quad \frac{\partial \phi}{\partial y}, \quad \frac{\partial^2 \phi}{\partial x^2}, \quad \frac{\partial^2 \phi}{\partial x \partial y}, \quad \frac{\partial^2 \phi}{\partial y^2},$$

where ϕ is a given function of the two variables x and y.

Hence we have, if $z = \phi(x, y)$,

$$dz = p\,dx + q\,dy, \text{ Art. 159};$$

and to obtain $\frac{dy}{dx}$ from the implicit relation $\phi(x, y) = 0$, we have

$$\frac{dy}{dx} = -\frac{p}{q}.$$

171. **To obtain the Second Differential Coefficient of an Implicit Function.**

To obtain $\frac{d^2 y}{dx^2}$ we have only to differentiate the last result of the preceding article; thus,

$$\frac{d^2y}{dx^2} = -\frac{q\frac{dp}{dx} - p\frac{dq}{dx}}{q^2}.$$

Now

$$\frac{dp}{dx} = \frac{\partial p}{\partial x} + \frac{\partial p}{\partial y}\frac{dy}{dx} = r + s\left(-\frac{p}{q}\right) = \frac{qr - ps}{q},$$

and

$$\frac{dq}{dx} = \frac{\partial q}{\partial x} + \frac{\partial q}{\partial y}\frac{dy}{dx} = s + t\left(-\frac{p}{q}\right) = \frac{qs - pt}{q},$$

giving

$$\frac{d^2y}{dx^2} = -\frac{q\left(\dfrac{qr - ps}{q}\right) - p\left(\dfrac{qs - pt}{q}\right)}{q^2}$$

$$= -\frac{q^2r - 2pqs + p^2t}{q^3}.$$

Similarly $\dfrac{d^3y}{dx^3}$, etc., may be found, but the results are complicated.

EXAMPLES.

1. If

$$u = x^m y^n,$$

prove

$$\frac{du}{u} = m\frac{dx}{x} + n\frac{dy}{y},$$

and verify the formula

$$\frac{\partial^2 u}{\partial x \partial y} = \frac{\partial^2 u}{\partial y \partial x}.$$

2. Verify the formula $\dfrac{\partial^2 u}{\partial x \partial y} = \dfrac{\partial^2 u}{\partial y \partial x}$ in each of the following cases:

(1) $u = \sin^{-1}\dfrac{y}{x}$.

(2) $u = \dfrac{x^2 y^2}{a^2 - z^2}$.

(3) $u = \log\dfrac{x^2 + y^2}{xy}$.

(4) $u = x^y$.

3. If

$$u = \frac{xy}{2x + z},$$

show that

$$\frac{\partial^3 u}{\partial y \partial z^2} = \frac{\partial^3 u}{\partial z^2 \partial y}.$$

4. If

$$x = r\cos\theta \text{ and } y = r\sin\theta,$$

prove

$$dx = \cos\theta\, dr - r\sin\theta\, d\theta,$$

and

$$dy = \sin\theta\, dr + r\cos\theta\, d\theta;$$

and hence that

$$dx^2 + dy^2 = dr^2 + r^2 d\theta^2,$$

and that

$$x\, dy - y\, dx = r^2 d\theta.$$

5. If $\qquad u = \log(x^2 + y^2 + z^2)$,

prove $\qquad\qquad x\dfrac{\partial^2 u}{\partial y \partial z} = y\dfrac{\partial^2 u}{\partial z \partial x} = z\dfrac{\partial^2 u}{\partial x \partial y}$.

6. Prove that if $\qquad \dfrac{x^2}{a^2} + \dfrac{y^2}{b^2} = 1$,

$$\dfrac{dy}{dx} = -\dfrac{b^2 x}{a^2 y} \text{ and } \dfrac{d^2 y}{dx^2} = -\dfrac{b^4}{a^2 y^3}.$$

7. Show that if $\qquad x^m + y^m = a^m$,

$$\dfrac{d^2 y}{dx^2} = -(m-1)a^m \dfrac{x^{m-2}}{y^{2m-1}}.$$

8. Show that at the point of the surface

$$x^x y^y z^z = c \text{ where } x = y = z,$$

$$\dfrac{\partial^2 z}{\partial x \partial y} = -\{x \log ex\}^{-1}.$$

[Oxford, 1889.]

9. If there be an equation between three variables p, t, v, prove that

$$\left(\dfrac{dp}{dt}\right)_{v \text{ const.}} \times \left(\dfrac{dt}{dv}\right)_{p \text{ const.}} \times \left(\dfrac{dv}{dp}\right)_{t \text{ const.}} = -1.$$

172. *To find* $\dfrac{dy}{dx}$ *and* $\dfrac{dz}{dx}$ *from the equations*

$$F_1(x, y, z) = 0,$$
$$F_2(x, y, z) = 0.$$

Here, as in Art. 164,

$$\dfrac{\partial F_1}{\partial x} + \dfrac{\partial F_1}{\partial y} \cdot \dfrac{dy}{dx} + \dfrac{\partial F_1}{\partial z} \cdot \dfrac{dz}{dx} = 0,$$

$$\dfrac{\partial F_2}{\partial x} + \dfrac{\partial F_2}{\partial y} \cdot \dfrac{dy}{dx} + \dfrac{\partial F_2}{\partial z} \cdot \dfrac{dz}{dx} = 0.$$

Solving these equations we obtain

$$\dfrac{\dfrac{dy}{dx}}{\dfrac{\partial F_1}{\partial z} \cdot \dfrac{\partial F_2}{\partial x} - \dfrac{\partial F_2}{\partial z} \cdot \dfrac{\partial F_1}{\partial x}} = \dfrac{\dfrac{dz}{dx}}{\dfrac{\partial F_1}{\partial x} \cdot \dfrac{\partial F_2}{\partial y} - \dfrac{\partial F_2}{\partial x} \cdot \dfrac{\partial F_1}{\partial y}}$$

$$= \dfrac{1}{\dfrac{\partial F_1}{\partial y} \cdot \dfrac{\partial F_2}{\partial z} - \dfrac{\partial F_2}{\partial y} \cdot \dfrac{\partial F_1}{\partial z}},$$

which give the values of $\dfrac{dy}{dx}$ and $\dfrac{dz}{dx}$.

Ex. Given $\qquad\qquad y = F_1(x, z)$,

and $\qquad\qquad\qquad z = F_2(x, y)$,

prove $\qquad\qquad \dfrac{dy}{dx} = \dfrac{\dfrac{\partial F_1}{\partial x} + \dfrac{\partial F_1}{\partial z} \cdot \dfrac{\partial F_2}{\partial x}}{1 - \dfrac{\partial F_1}{\partial z} \cdot \dfrac{\partial F_2}{\partial y}}.$

173. *Given that*

$$V = \phi(x + \xi t, \; y + \eta t, \; z + \zeta t, \; \ldots)$$

where $\quad x, \, y, \, z \ldots, \; \xi, \, \eta, \, \zeta \ldots,$ *and* t

form a system of independent variables, to show that

$$\frac{\partial V}{\partial t} = \xi \frac{\partial V}{\partial x} + \eta \frac{\partial V}{\partial y} + \zeta \frac{\partial V}{\partial z} + \ldots$$

Let $\qquad x_1 = x + \xi t,$

$$y_1 = y + \eta t,$$

$$\text{etc.,}$$

so that $\qquad \dfrac{\partial x_1}{\partial x} = 1, \; \dfrac{\partial y_1}{\partial y} = 1, \text{ etc.,}$

$$\frac{\partial x_1}{\partial t} = \xi, \; \frac{\partial y_1}{\partial t} = \eta, \text{ etc.,}$$

$$\frac{\partial x_1}{\partial y} = 0, \; \frac{\partial y_1}{\partial x} = 0, \text{ etc.;}$$

then $\qquad V = \phi(x_1, \, y_1, \, z_1, \, \ldots),$

and $\qquad \dfrac{\partial V}{\partial x} = \dfrac{\partial V}{\partial x_1} \cdot \dfrac{\partial x_1}{\partial x} + \dfrac{\partial V}{\partial y_1} \cdot \dfrac{\partial y_1}{\partial x} + \ldots$ (Art. 162)

$$= \frac{\partial V}{\partial x_1}.$$

Similarly $\qquad \dfrac{\partial V}{\partial y} = \dfrac{\partial V}{\partial y_1}, \text{ etc.,}$

and $\qquad \dfrac{\partial V}{\partial t} = \dfrac{\partial V}{\partial x_1} \cdot \dfrac{\partial x_1}{\partial t} + \dfrac{\partial V}{\partial y_1} \cdot \dfrac{\partial y_1}{\partial t} + \ldots$

$$= \xi \frac{\partial V}{\partial x} + \eta \frac{\partial V}{\partial y} + \zeta \frac{\partial V}{\partial z} + \ldots$$

174. Hence we have the following identity of operators, viz. :—

$$\frac{\partial}{\partial t} \equiv \xi \frac{\partial}{\partial x} + \eta \frac{\partial}{\partial y} + \zeta \frac{\partial}{\partial z} + \ldots,$$

and as the *variables are all independent and the operators partial,* $\qquad \left(\dfrac{\partial}{\partial t} \right)^n \equiv \left(\xi \dfrac{\partial}{\partial x} + \eta \dfrac{\partial}{\partial y} + \zeta \dfrac{\partial}{\partial z} + \ldots \right)^n,$

the development being made in *formal analogy with the Multinomial Theorem.*

For example, in the case of

$$V = \phi(x + \xi t, \; y + \eta t),$$

we shall have
$$\frac{\partial V}{\partial t} = \xi \frac{\partial V}{\partial x} + \eta \frac{\partial V}{\partial y},$$

$$\frac{\partial^2 V}{\partial t^2} = \xi^2 \frac{\partial^2 V}{\partial x^2} + 2\xi\eta \frac{\partial^2 V}{\partial x \partial y} + \eta^2 \frac{\partial^2 V}{\partial y^2},$$
etc.

Taylor's Theorem. Extension.

175. To Expand $\phi(x+h, y+k)$ **in powers of** h **and** k.
By Taylor's Theorem we obtain

$$\phi(x+h, y+k) = \phi(x+h, y) + k\frac{\partial \phi(x+h, y)}{\partial y} + \frac{k^2}{2!}\frac{\partial^2 \phi(x+h, y)}{\partial y^2} + \cdots$$

and expanding each term we have

$$\phi(x+h, y+k) = \phi(x, y) + h\frac{\partial \phi}{\partial x} + \frac{h^2}{2!}\frac{\partial^2 \phi}{\partial x^2} + \cdots$$

$$+ k\frac{\partial \phi}{\partial y} + hk\frac{\partial^2 \phi}{\partial x \partial y} + \cdots$$

$$+ \frac{k^2}{2!}\frac{\partial^2 \phi}{\partial y^2} + \cdots$$

$$= \phi(x, y) + \left(h\frac{\partial \phi}{\partial x} + k\frac{\partial \phi}{\partial y}\right)$$

$$+ \frac{1}{2!}\left(h^2\frac{\partial^2 \phi}{\partial x^2} + 2hk\frac{\partial^2 \phi}{\partial x \partial y} + k^2\frac{\partial^2 \phi}{\partial y^2}\right) + \cdots$$

or, as it may be written symbolically,

$$\phi(x+h, y+k) = \phi(x, y) + \left(h\frac{\partial}{\partial x} + k\frac{\partial}{\partial y}\right)\phi + \frac{1}{2!}\left(h\frac{\partial}{\partial x} + k\frac{\partial}{\partial y}\right)^2\phi + \cdots$$

176. Since it is immaterial whether we first expand with regard to k and then with regard to h, or in the opposite order, we obtain by comparison of the coefficient of hk in the two results the important theorem

$$\frac{\partial^2 \phi}{\partial x \partial y} = \frac{\partial^2 \phi}{\partial y \partial x}$$

already established in Arts. 165, 166.

177. Agreeably with the notation of Art. 116, we may write the result of Art. 175 as

$$\phi(x+h, y+k) = e^{h\frac{\partial}{\partial x} + k\frac{\partial}{\partial y}}\phi(x, y)$$

178. Further Extension. Several Variables.

The form of the general term in the preceding case and the further extension of Taylor's Theorem to the expansion of a function of *several* variables is more readily investigated as follows:

Let $$\phi(x + \xi t,\ y + \eta t,\ \ldots)$$
be called $F(t)$. Then Maclaurin's Theorem gives

$$F(t) = F(0) + tF'(0) + \frac{t^2}{2!}F''(0) + \ldots + \frac{t^n}{n!}F^n(\theta t),$$

and by Art. 174

$$F^r(t) = \left(\xi\frac{\partial}{\partial x} + \eta\frac{\partial}{\partial y} + \ldots\right)^r \phi(x + \xi t,\ \ldots),$$

and since the variables $x,\ y,\ \ldots$, are independent of t, we may put $t = 0$ either before or after the operation has been performed.

Hence $$F^r(0) = \left(\xi\frac{\partial}{\partial x} + \eta\frac{\partial}{\partial y} + \ldots\right)^r \phi(x,\ y,\ \ldots).$$

We thus obtain

$$\phi(x + \xi t,\ y + \eta t,\ \ldots) = \phi(x,\ y,\ z,\ldots) + t\left(\xi\frac{\partial}{\partial x} + \eta\frac{\partial}{\partial y} + \ldots\right)\phi(x,\ y,\ \ldots)$$

$$+ \frac{t^2}{2!}\left(\xi\frac{\partial}{\partial x} + \ldots\right)^2\phi(x,\ \ldots) + \ldots$$

$$+ \frac{t^n}{n!}\left(\xi\frac{\partial}{\partial x} + \ldots\right)^n\phi(x + \xi\theta t,\ y + \eta\theta t,\ \ldots).$$

Now, putting $h = \xi t,\ k = \eta t,\ l = \zeta t,\ \ldots$, we obtain

$$\phi(x + h,\ y + k,\ z + l,\ \ldots) = \phi(x,\ y,\ z,\ \ldots)$$

$$+ \left(h\frac{\partial}{\partial x} + k\frac{\partial}{\partial y} + l\frac{\partial}{\partial z} + \ldots\right)\phi(x,\ \ldots)$$

$$+ \frac{1}{2!}\left(h\frac{\partial}{\partial x} + k\frac{\partial}{\partial y} + \ldots\right)^2\phi(x,\ \ldots) + \ldots$$

$$+ \frac{1}{n!}\left(h\frac{\partial}{\partial x} + k\frac{\partial}{\partial y} + \ldots\right)^n\phi(x + \theta h,\ y + \theta k,\ \ldots).$$

179. Extension of Maclaurin's Theorem.

Moreover, if we put $x = 0$ and $y = 0$, and then write x for h and y for k, we have an *extension of Maclaurin's Theorem* which, for two independent variables, may be written

$$\phi(x,\ y) = \phi(0,\ 0) + x\left(\frac{\partial\phi}{\partial x}\right)_0 + y\left(\frac{\partial\phi}{\partial y}\right)_0$$

$$+ \frac{1}{2!}\left\{x^2\left(\frac{\partial^2\phi}{\partial x^2}\right)_0 + 2xy\left(\frac{\partial^2\phi}{\partial x\partial y}\right)_0 + y^2\left(\frac{\partial^2\phi}{\partial y^2}\right)_0\right\}$$

$$+ \text{etc.}$$

180. If we now recur to Art. 154 we see that the true value of MR is $\qquad f(x+\delta x,\ y+\delta y)-f(x,\ y)$

$$=\frac{\partial f}{\partial x}\delta x+\frac{\partial f}{\partial y}\delta y+\frac{1}{2!}\Big(\frac{\partial^2 f}{\partial x^2}\delta x^2+2\frac{\partial^2 f}{\partial x\partial y}\delta x\delta y+\frac{\partial^2 f}{\partial y^2}\delta y^2\Big)+\text{etc.,}$$

showing what error was made in that article in taking MR' as an approximation to the correct value.

The student will find no difficulty in writing down the true values of the lengths of LQ or NS.

EULER'S THEOREMS ON HOMOGENEOUS FUNCTIONS.

181. *If* $u=Ax^{\alpha}y^{\beta}+Bx^{\alpha'}y^{\beta'}+\ldots=\Sigma Ax^{\alpha}y^{\beta}$, *say, where*

$$\alpha+\beta=\alpha'+\beta'=\ldots=n,$$

to show that $\qquad x\dfrac{\partial u}{\partial x}+y\dfrac{\partial u}{\partial y}=nu.$

By differentiation we obtain

$$\frac{\partial u}{\partial x}=\Sigma A\,\alpha x^{\alpha-1}y^{\beta},$$

$$\frac{\partial u}{\partial y}=\Sigma A\,\beta x^{\alpha}y^{\beta-1},$$

then
$$x\frac{\partial u}{\partial x}+y\frac{\partial u}{\partial y}=\Sigma A\,\alpha x^{\alpha}y^{\beta}+\Sigma A\,\beta x^{\alpha}y^{\beta}$$
$$=\Sigma A(\alpha+\beta)x^{\alpha}y^{\beta}$$
$$=n\Sigma Ax^{\alpha}y^{\beta}=nu.$$

It is clear that this theorem can be extended to the case of three or of any number of independent variables, and that if, for example, $\qquad u=Ax^{\alpha}y^{\beta}z^{\gamma}+Bx^{\alpha'}y^{\beta'}z^{\gamma'}+\ldots$

where $\qquad \alpha+\beta+\gamma=\alpha'+\beta'+\gamma'=\ldots=n,$

then will $\qquad x\dfrac{\partial u}{\partial x}+y\dfrac{\partial u}{\partial y}+z\dfrac{\partial u}{\partial z}=nu.$

The functions thus described are called *homogeneous functions of the* n^{th} *degree.*

182. We now put the same theorem in a more general form.

DEF. *A homogeneous function of the* n^{th} *degree is one which can be put in the form*

$$x^n F\Big(\frac{y}{x},\ \frac{z}{x},\ \ldots\Big).$$

· Let $$u = x^n F\left(\frac{y}{x}, \frac{z}{x}, \ldots\right).$$

Put $$\frac{y}{x} = Y, \quad \frac{z}{x} = Z, \text{ etc.,}$$

whence $$\frac{\partial Y}{\partial x} = -\frac{y}{x^2}, \quad \frac{\partial Z}{\partial x} = -\frac{z}{x^2}, \ldots$$

$$\frac{\partial Y}{\partial y} = \frac{1}{x}, \quad \frac{\partial Z}{\partial y} = 0, \text{ etc.}$$

Now, since $$u = x^n F(Y, Z, \ldots),$$

$$\frac{\partial u}{\partial x} = nx^{n-1} F(Y, Z, \ldots) + x^n \left\{ \frac{\partial F}{\partial Y} \cdot \frac{\partial Y}{\partial x} + \frac{\partial F}{\partial Z} \cdot \frac{\partial Z}{\partial x} + \ldots \right\}$$

$$= nx^{n-1} F(Y, Z, \ldots) - x^{n-2} \left\{ y\frac{\partial F}{\partial Y} + z\frac{\partial F}{\partial Z} + \ldots \right\},$$

$$\frac{\partial u}{\partial y} = x^n \frac{\partial F}{\partial Y} \cdot \frac{\partial Y}{\partial y} = x^{n-1} \frac{\partial F}{\partial Y},$$

$$\frac{\partial u}{\partial z} = x^n \frac{\partial F}{\partial Z} \cdot \frac{\partial Z}{\partial z} = x^{n-1} \frac{\partial F}{\partial Z},$$

$$\text{etc.} = \text{etc.}$$

Finally, multiplying by $x, y, z, \ldots$ respectively, and adding

$$x\frac{\partial u}{\partial x} + y\frac{\partial u}{\partial y} + z\frac{\partial u}{\partial z} + \ldots = nx^n F(Y, Z, \ldots) = nu.$$

183. If u be a homogeneous function of x and y of the nth degree, $\frac{\partial u}{\partial x}, \frac{\partial u}{\partial y}$ will be homogeneous functions of the $(n-1)$th degree, and applying the result of Art. 182 to these we have

$$\left(x\frac{\partial}{\partial x} + y\frac{\partial}{\partial y}\right)\frac{\partial u}{\partial x} = (n-1)\frac{\partial u}{\partial x},$$

$$\left(x\frac{\partial}{\partial x} + y\frac{\partial}{\partial y}\right)\frac{\partial u}{\partial y} = (n-1)\frac{\partial u}{\partial y}.$$

Multiplying by x and y we have on addition

$$x^2\frac{\partial^2 u}{\partial x^2} + 2xy\frac{\partial^2 u}{\partial x \partial y} + y^2\frac{\partial^2 u}{\partial y^2} = (n-1)\left(x\frac{\partial u}{\partial x} + y\frac{\partial u}{\partial y}\right)$$

$$= n(n-1)u.$$

Similarly we may proceed and finally by induction establish a general theorem of similar character, but of higher order; but it is better to adopt the method hereafter applied in Art. 186.

184. If $\quad V = u_n + u_{n-1} + u_{n-2} + \ldots + u_2 + u_1 + u_0,$
where u_n, u_{n-1}, ... are homogeneous functions of degrees n, $n-1$, ... respectively, then

$$x\frac{\partial V}{\partial x} + y\frac{\partial V}{\partial y} + \ldots$$

$$= \left(x\frac{\partial}{\partial x} + \ldots\right)u_n + \left(x\frac{\partial}{\partial x} + \ldots\right)u_{n-1} + \text{etc.}$$

$$= nu_n + (n-1)u_{n-1} + (n-2)u_{n-2} + \ldots + 2u_2 + u_1$$

$$= nV - \{u_{n-1} + 2u_{n-2} + 3u_{n-3} + \ldots + (n-1)u_1 + nu_0\}.$$

Hence if $V = 0$

$$x\frac{\partial V}{\partial x} + y\frac{\partial V}{\partial y} + \ldots + u_{n-1} + 2u_{n-2} + \ldots + nu_0 = 0.$$

185. Let $u = \phi(H_n)$, where H_n is a homogeneous function of the nth degree.

Suppose we obtain from this equation

$$H_n = F(u);$$

then $\qquad x\frac{\partial}{\partial x}F(u) + y\frac{\partial}{\partial y}F(u) + \ldots = nH_n,$

or $\qquad F'(u)\left\{x\frac{\partial u}{\partial x} + y\frac{\partial u}{\partial y} + \ldots\right\} = nF(u),$

or $\qquad x\frac{\partial u}{\partial x} + y\frac{\partial u}{\partial y} + \ldots = n\frac{F(u)}{F'(u)} \ldots\ldots\ldots\ldots\ldots(1)$

In the *particular case* in which $n = 0$ we therefore have

$$x\frac{\partial u}{\partial x} + y\frac{\partial u}{\partial y} + \ldots = 0 \ldots\ldots\ldots\ldots\ldots\ldots(2)$$

EXAMPLES.

Verify the following results by differentiation.

1. Let $\qquad u = x^3 + y^3 + 3xyz.$

This is clearly homogeneous and of the 3rd degree, whence

$$x\frac{\partial u}{\partial x} + y\frac{\partial u}{\partial y} + z\frac{\partial u}{\partial z} = 3u.$$

2. Let $\qquad u = \dfrac{x^{\frac{1}{4}} + y^{\frac{1}{4}}}{x^{\frac{1}{5}} + y^{\frac{1}{5}}} = x^{\frac{1}{20}}\dfrac{1 + \left(\frac{y}{x}\right)^{\frac{1}{4}}}{1 + \left(\frac{y}{x}\right)^{\frac{1}{5}}}.$

This is a homogeneous expression of degree $\frac{1}{20}$, whence

$$x\frac{\partial u}{\partial x} + y\frac{\partial u}{\partial y} = \frac{1}{20}u.$$

3. Let $\qquad u = \sin^{-1}\dfrac{\sqrt{x} - \sqrt{y}}{\sqrt{x} + \sqrt{y}}.$

Here Art. 182 gives $\qquad x\frac{\partial u}{\partial x} + y\frac{\partial u}{\partial y} = 0.$

4. Let
$$u = \tan^{-1} \frac{x^3 + y^3}{x - y}.$$

Here Art. 185 gives $\quad x\frac{\partial u}{\partial x} + y\frac{\partial u}{\partial y} = \sin 2u.$

5. Find which of the following functions are homogeneous, and in cases of homogeneity verify Euler's Theorem of the first degree :

$\quad\quad (a) \quad xe^{-y}.$

$\quad\quad (\beta) \quad ye^{-\frac{x}{y}}.$

$\quad\quad (\gamma) \quad (x-y)(\log x - \log y).$

$\quad\quad (\delta) \quad \sin^{-1}\frac{\sqrt{x^2+y^2}}{x+y}.$

6. Given $z = x^2 + y$ and $y = z^2 + x$, find the differential coefficients of the first order,

$\quad\quad (1) \quad$ when x is the independent variable,

$\quad\quad (2) \quad$ when y is the independent variable,

$\quad\quad (3) \quad$ when z is the independent variable.

7. Given $xyz = a^3$, find all the differential coefficients of the first and second orders, taking x and y for independent variables.

8. If
$$u = \sin^{-1}\frac{x+y}{\sqrt{x}+\sqrt{y}},$$
prove that $\quad x\frac{\partial u}{\partial x} + y\frac{\partial u}{\partial y} = \frac{1}{2}\tan u.$

9. If $\quad u = ax^2 + by^2 + cz^2 + 2fyz + 2gzx + 2hxy,$
show that, if it be possible to find values of x, y, z which will simultaneously satisfy
$$\frac{\partial u}{\partial x} = \frac{\partial u}{\partial y} = \frac{\partial u}{\partial z} = 0,$$
then will
$$\begin{vmatrix} a, & h, & g \\ h, & b, & f \\ g, & f, & c \end{vmatrix} = 0.$$

10. If u be a homogeneous function of the nth degree of any number of variables, prove that
$$\left(x\frac{\partial}{\partial x} + y\frac{\partial}{\partial y} + \dots\right)^m u = n^m u.$$

11. If $u = \phi(x, y)$ and $\psi(x, y) = 0$, prove that
$$\frac{du}{dx} = (\phi_x \psi_y - \phi_y \psi_x)/\psi_y.$$

12. If u be a homogeneous function of the nth degree in x, y, z, and if $u = f(X, Y, Z)$ where X, Y, Z are the first differential coefficients of u with regard to x, y, z respectively, prove that
$$X\frac{\partial f}{\partial X} + Y\frac{\partial f}{\partial Y} + Z\frac{\partial f}{\partial Z} = \frac{n}{n-1}u. \quad\quad\quad \text{[Oxford, 1886.]}$$

13. If ϖ denote the operator
$$x\frac{\partial}{\partial x} + y\frac{\partial}{\partial y} + \dots$$
and u be a homogeneous function of n dimensions in the variables x, y, z, $\dots$
show that $\quad \varpi(\varpi-1)(\varpi-2)\dots(\varpi-r)\log u = (-1)^r n \cdot r!$ $\quad$ [Oxford, 1888.]

186. General Proof of Euler's Theorems.

We now proceed to give a more complete investigation of Euler's results.

Let $u \equiv \phi(x, y, z \ldots)$ be any function expressible in the form

$$x^n F\left(\frac{y}{x}, \frac{z}{x}, \ldots\right).$$

It is observable that if $x+xt, y+yt, z+zt, \ldots$ be written instead of $x, y, z, \ldots$ in any such function we obtain the result

$$\phi(x+xt, y+yt, \ldots) = x^n(1+t)^n F\left(\frac{y+yt}{x+xt}, \ldots\right)$$

$$= x^n(1+t)^n F\left(\frac{y}{x}, \frac{z}{x}, \ldots\right)$$

$$= (1+t)^n u\,;$$

so that the effect is simply that of multiplying the original function by $(1+t)^n$.

Now, let V_m denote the symbol of operation obtained by expanding $(xX+yY+zZ+\ldots)^m$ by the Multinomial Theorem, and *after* expansion writing $\frac{\partial}{\partial x}, \frac{\partial}{\partial y}, \frac{\partial}{\partial z}, \ldots$ in place of X, Y, Z, etc.; then we have, upon expansion of each side of the above equality,

$$u + tV_1u + \frac{t^2}{2!}V_2u + \frac{t^3}{3!}V_3u + \ldots + \frac{t^r}{r!}V_ru + \ldots$$

$$= \left\{1 + nt + \frac{n(n-1)}{2!}t^2 + \frac{n(n-1)(n-2)}{3!}t^3 + \ldots\right.$$

$$\left. + \frac{n(n-1)\ldots(n-r+1)}{r!}t^r + \ldots\right\}u.$$

And on equating coefficients of like powers of t

$$V_1u = nu,$$
$$V_2u = n(n-1)u,$$
$$V_3u = n(n-1)(n-2)u,$$
$$\text{etc.}$$
$$V_ru = n(n-1)\ldots(n-r+1)u.$$

187. When there are two independent variables x and y, these become

$$x\frac{\partial u}{\partial x} + y\frac{\partial u}{\partial y} = nu,$$

$$x^2\frac{\partial^2 u}{\partial x^2} + 2xy\frac{\partial^2 u}{\partial x \partial y} + y^2\frac{\partial^2 u}{\partial y^2} = n(n-1)u,$$

$$\text{etc.}\,;$$

and for the case of three independent variables

$$x\frac{\partial u}{\partial x}+y\frac{\partial u}{\partial y}+z\frac{\partial u}{\partial z}=nu,$$

$$x^2\frac{\partial^2 u}{\partial x^2}+y^2\frac{\partial^2 u}{\partial y^2}+z^2\frac{\partial^2 u}{\partial z^2}+2yz\frac{\partial^2 u}{\partial y\partial z}+2zx\frac{\partial^2 u}{\partial z\partial x}+2xy\frac{\partial^2 u}{\partial x\partial y}$$
$$=n(n-1)u,$$

etc.

188. It may be observed that although the expressions

$$h^2\frac{\partial^2 u}{\partial x^2}+2hk\frac{\partial^2 u}{\partial x\partial y}+k^2\frac{\partial^2 u}{\partial y^2} \text{ and } \left(h\frac{\partial}{\partial x}+k\frac{\partial}{\partial y}\right)^2 u$$

are identical, care must be taken to distinguish between

$$x^2\frac{\partial^2 u}{\partial x^2}+2xy\frac{\partial^2 u}{\partial x\partial y}+y^2\frac{\partial^2 u}{\partial y^2}$$

and $\qquad \left(x\frac{\partial}{\partial x}+y\frac{\partial}{\partial y}\right)^2 u.$

It is apparent that the latter

$$=\left(x\frac{\partial}{\partial x}+y\frac{\partial}{\partial y}\right)\left(x\frac{\partial u}{\partial x}+y\frac{\partial u}{\partial y}\right)$$

$$=\left(x\frac{\partial}{\partial x}+y\frac{\partial}{\partial y}\right)\left(x\frac{\partial u}{\partial x}\right)+\left(x\frac{\partial}{\partial x}+y\frac{\partial}{\partial y}\right)\left(y\frac{\partial u}{\partial y}\right)$$

$$=\left(x^2\frac{\partial^2 u}{\partial x^2}+x\frac{\partial u}{\partial x}+xy\frac{\partial^2 u}{\partial y\partial x}\right)$$

$$+\left(xy\frac{\partial^2 u}{\partial x\partial y}+y\frac{\partial u}{\partial y}+y^2\frac{\partial^2 u}{\partial y^2}\right)$$

$$=x^2\frac{\partial^2 u}{\partial x^2}+2xy\frac{\partial^2 u}{\partial x\partial y}+y^2\frac{\partial^2 u}{\partial y^2}+x\frac{\partial u}{\partial x}+y\frac{\partial u}{\partial y},$$

and therefore differs from the former expression by the addition of the two terms

$$x\frac{\partial u}{\partial x}, \ y\frac{\partial u}{\partial y}.$$

189. Laplace's Equation.

The operator $\frac{\partial^2}{\partial x^2}+\frac{\partial^2}{\partial y^2}+\frac{\partial^2}{\partial z^2}$ ($\equiv \nabla^2$) plays a fundamental part in the Higher Physical Analysis.

The equation $\nabla^2 V=0$ is called Laplace's equation; and any homogeneous function of x, y, z which satisfies it is called a Spherical Harmonic.*

It is customary to denote $x^2+y^2+z^2$ by r^2.

* See Thomson and Tait, *Treatise on Natural Philosophy*, vol. I., p. 171.
Laplace, *Mécanique Celeste*, bk. II.

Ex. 1. Let $\qquad\qquad V = r^m.$

Then $\qquad\qquad\dfrac{\partial r}{\partial x} = \dfrac{x}{r},$

and we have $\qquad\dfrac{\partial V}{\partial x} = \dfrac{\partial V}{\partial r} \cdot \dfrac{\partial r}{\partial x} = m r^{m-2} x,$

and $\qquad\qquad\dfrac{\partial^2 V}{\partial x^2} = m(m-2) r^{m-4} x^2 + m r^{m-2}.$

Similarly, $\qquad\dfrac{\partial^2 V}{\partial y^2} = m(m-2) r^{m-4} y^2 + m r^{m-2},$

$$\dfrac{\partial^2 V}{\partial z^2} = m(m-2) r^{m-4} z^2 + m r^{m-2}.$$

$\therefore$ by addition, $\qquad \nabla^2 V = m(m-2) r^{m-2} + 3 m r^{m-2}$

or $\qquad\qquad\qquad \nabla^2 r^m = m(m+1) r^{m-2}.$

Since this expression vanishes when $m = -1$, it appears that $\dfrac{1}{r}$ is a spherical harmonic of degree -1.

Ex. 2. If V_n be a spherical harmonic of degree n, then will V_n / r^{2n+1} be a spherical harmonic of degree $-n-1$.

Let $\qquad\qquad u = V_n / r^{2n+1}.$

Then $\qquad\dfrac{\partial u}{\partial x} = \dfrac{\partial V_n}{\partial x} \cdot \dfrac{1}{r^{2n+1}} - (2n+1) V_n \cdot \dfrac{x}{r^{2n+3}},$

$$\dfrac{\partial^2 u}{\partial x^2} = \dfrac{\partial^2 V_n}{\partial x^2} \dfrac{1}{r^{2n+1}} - 2(2n+1) \dfrac{\partial V_n}{\partial x} \cdot \dfrac{x}{r^{2n+3}} + (2n+1)(2n+3) V_n \dfrac{x^2}{r^{2n+5}} - (2n+1) V_n \dfrac{1}{r^{2n+3}},$$

with similar expressions for $\dfrac{\partial^2 u}{\partial y^2}$ and $\dfrac{\partial^2 u}{\partial z^2}.$

Adding these together,

$$\nabla^2 u = \nabla^2 V_n \dfrac{1}{r^{2n+1}} - 2(2n+1) \dfrac{1}{r^{2n+3}} \left(x \dfrac{\partial V_n}{\partial x} + y \dfrac{\partial V_n}{\partial y} + z \dfrac{\partial V_n}{\partial z} \right) + 2n(2n+1) V_n \dfrac{1}{r^{2n+3}}.$$

Hence, remembering that $\qquad \nabla^2 V_n = 0,$

and $\qquad\qquad x \dfrac{\partial V_n}{\partial x} + y \dfrac{\partial V_n}{\partial y} + z \dfrac{\partial V_n}{\partial z} = n V_n,$

we have $\qquad\qquad\qquad \nabla^2 u = 0.$

Ex. 3. Show that each of the functions

$$\tan^{-1}\dfrac{y}{x}, \quad \dfrac{xz}{x^2+y^2}, \quad \dfrac{1}{r} \log \dfrac{r+z}{r-z}$$

satisfies Laplace's equation.

Ex. 4. If u and u' be functions of x, y, z, each satisfying $\nabla^2 V = 0$, prove that $\qquad\qquad \nabla^2(uu') = 2(u_x u'_x + u_y u'_y + u_z u'_z).$

190. Conjugate Functions.

When two real functions u and v of x and y are defined by the equation $u + \sqrt{-1}\, v = f(x + \sqrt{-1}\, y)$ they are said to be conjugate.

Differentiating, we have

$$\frac{\partial u}{\partial x} + \sqrt{-1}\,\frac{\partial v}{\partial x} = f'(x + \sqrt{-1}\,y),$$

$$\frac{\partial u}{\partial y} + \sqrt{-1}\,\frac{\partial v}{\partial y} = \sqrt{-1}\,f'(x + \sqrt{-1}\,y).$$

$\therefore \qquad \frac{\partial u}{\partial y} + \sqrt{-1}\,\frac{\partial v}{\partial y} = \sqrt{-1}\,\frac{\partial u}{\partial x} - \frac{\partial v}{\partial x}.$

Whence
$$\frac{\partial u}{\partial x} = \frac{\partial v}{\partial y}, \quad\dotfill(1)$$

and
$$\frac{\partial u}{\partial y} = -\frac{\partial v}{\partial x}. \quad\dotfill(2)$$

Again differentiating,
$$\frac{\partial^2 u}{\partial x^2} = \frac{\partial^2 v}{\partial x \partial y},$$

and
$$\frac{\partial^2 u}{\partial y^2} = -\frac{\partial^2 v}{\partial y \partial x},$$

whence
$$\left.\begin{array}{c} \dfrac{\partial^2 u}{\partial x^2} + \dfrac{\partial^2 u}{\partial y^2} = 0 \\[2mm] \dfrac{\partial^2 v}{\partial x^2} + \dfrac{\partial^2 v}{\partial y^2} = 0 \end{array}\right\} \dotfill(3)$$

and similarly

Ex. 1. If $u + \sqrt{-1}\,v$ be a homogeneous function of x, y, z, of degree $p + \sqrt{-1}\,q$, then

$$x\frac{\partial u}{\partial x} + y\frac{\partial u}{\partial y} + z\frac{\partial u}{\partial z} = pu - qv,$$

and
$$x\frac{\partial v}{\partial x} + y\frac{\partial v}{\partial y} + z\frac{\partial v}{\partial z} = pv + qu.$$

[THOMSON AND TAIT, Natural Philosophy.]

Ex. 2. If a and β be conjugate functions of a and b, whilst a and b are conjugate functions of x and y, prove that a and β are conjugate functions of x and y. [MAXWELL, Electricity.]

Ex. 3. If the equation $\dfrac{\partial^2 V}{\partial x^2} + \dfrac{\partial^2 V}{\partial y^2} = 0$ be satisfied when V is a given function of x, y, it will also be satisfied when V is the same function of a and b, where $a = \log \sqrt{x^2 + y^2}$ and $b = \tan^{-1}\dfrac{y}{x}$. [MATH. TRIPOS.]

EXAMPLES.

1. Verify the formula $\dfrac{\partial^2 u}{\partial x \partial y} = \dfrac{\partial^2 u}{\partial y \partial x}$ in the following cases:

(a) $u = \sin\dfrac{y}{x}.$

(β) $u = \log\{x \tan^{-1} \sqrt{x^2 + y^2}\}.$

2. Find $\dfrac{dy}{dx}$ (a) if $ax^2 + 2hxy + by^2 = 1$.

   (β) if $x^4 + y^4 = 5a^2xy$.

   (γ) if $(\cos x)^y = (\sin y)^x$.

   (δ) if $y^x + x^y = (x + y)^{x+y}$.

   (ϵ) if $x^y . y^x = x^{\cos y} + y^{\log x}$.

3. If $u = \sin^{-1}\dfrac{x}{y} + \tan^{-1}\dfrac{y}{x}$, show that $x\dfrac{\partial u}{\partial x} + y\dfrac{\partial u}{\partial y} = 0$.

4. If u, y, z be functions of x such that

$$y = \frac{d}{dx}\left(u\frac{dy}{dx}\right), \quad z = \frac{d}{dx}\left(u\frac{dz}{dx}\right),$$

prove that $\qquad\qquad \dfrac{d}{dx}u\left(y\dfrac{dz}{dx} - z\dfrac{dy}{dx}\right) = 0$.

5. If u and v be both functions of the same function of x and y, prove that $\dfrac{\partial u}{\partial x} \cdot \dfrac{\partial v}{\partial y} = \dfrac{\partial u}{\partial y} \cdot \dfrac{\partial v}{\partial x}$, and that $\dfrac{\partial}{\partial x}\left(u\dfrac{\partial v}{\partial y}\right) = \dfrac{\partial}{\partial y}\left(u\dfrac{\partial v}{\partial x}\right)$.

6. If $V = f(u, v)$, $u = f_1(x, y)$, $v = f_2(x, y)$, show how to find $\dfrac{\partial V}{\partial u}$ in terms of $\dfrac{\partial V}{\partial x}$ and $\dfrac{\partial V}{\partial y}$.

Ex. Given $u = x^2 + y^2$, $v = 2xy$, show that

$$x\frac{\partial V}{\partial x} - y\frac{\partial V}{\partial y} = 2(u^2 - v^2)^{\frac{1}{2}}\frac{\partial V}{\partial u}.$$

7. Verify Euler's Theorem

$$x\frac{\partial u}{\partial x} + y\frac{\partial u}{\partial y} = nu$$

for the functions   (a) $u = \sin\left(\dfrac{x - y}{x + y}\right)^{\frac{1}{2}}$.

(β) $u = x^3\log\dfrac{\sqrt[3]{y} - \sqrt[3]{x}}{\sqrt[3]{y} + \sqrt[3]{x}}$.

8. If $u = \phi(y + ax) + \psi(y - ax)$, prove $\dfrac{\partial^2 u}{\partial x^2} = a^2\dfrac{\partial^2 u}{\partial y^2}$.

9. If $u = x\phi\left(\dfrac{y}{x}\right) + \psi\left(\dfrac{y}{x}\right)$, prove $x^2\dfrac{\partial^2 u}{\partial x^2} + 2xy\dfrac{\partial^2 u}{\partial x\partial y} + y^2\dfrac{\partial^2 u}{\partial y^2} = 0$.

10. If $u = \dfrac{(x^2 + y^2)^m}{2m(2m - 1)} + x\phi\left(\dfrac{y}{x}\right) + \psi\left(\dfrac{y}{x}\right)$, prove that

$$x^2\frac{\partial^2 u}{\partial x^2} + 2xy\frac{\partial^2 u}{\partial x\partial y} + y^2\frac{\partial^2 u}{\partial y^2} = (x^2 + y^2)^m.$$

11. If $f(x, y) = 0$, $\phi(x, z) = 0$, show that

$$\frac{\partial\phi}{\partial x} \cdot \frac{\partial f}{\partial y} \cdot \frac{dy}{dz} = \frac{\partial f}{\partial x} \cdot \frac{\partial\phi}{\partial z}.$$

12. Find $\dfrac{dy}{dz}$ in terms of y and z from the equations :

$$a \sin x + b \sin y = c.$$
$$a \cos x + b \cos z = c. \qquad \text{[I. C. S. Exam.]}$$

13. If $x^4 + y^4 + 4a^2xy = 0$, shew that

$$(y^3 + a^2x)^3\dfrac{d^2y}{dx^2} = 2a^2xy(x^2y^2 + 3a^4).$$

14. If $\left(\dfrac{x}{a}\right)^n + \left(\dfrac{y}{b}\right)^n + \left(\dfrac{z}{c}\right)^n = 1$, find $\dfrac{\partial z}{\partial x}$ and $\dfrac{\partial^2 x}{\partial y \partial z}$. Also, find $\dfrac{dy}{dx}$

when the variables are connected by the two equations

$$\left(\dfrac{z}{c}\right)^n = \left(\dfrac{x}{a}\right)^n - \left(\dfrac{y}{b}\right)^n, \quad \dfrac{x}{a} + \dfrac{y}{b} + \dfrac{z}{c} = 1. \quad \text{[H. C. S. Exam.]}$$

15. If $u = F(x - y, \ y - z, \ z - x)$, prove $\dfrac{\partial u}{\partial x} + \dfrac{\partial u}{\partial y} + \dfrac{\partial u}{\partial z} = 0.$

16. If $u = \begin{vmatrix} x^2, & y^2, & z^2 \\ x, & y, & z \\ 1, & 1, & 1 \end{vmatrix}$, prove $\dfrac{\partial u}{\partial x} + \dfrac{\partial u}{\partial y} + \dfrac{\partial u}{\partial z} = 0.$

17. If $u = \operatorname{cosec}^{-1}\sqrt{\dfrac{x^{\frac{1}{2}} + y^{\frac{1}{2}}}{x^{\frac{1}{3}} + y^{\frac{1}{3}}}}$, show that

$$x^2\dfrac{\partial^2 u}{\partial x^2} + 2xy\dfrac{\partial^2 u}{\partial x \partial y} + y^2\dfrac{\partial^2 u}{\partial y^2} = \dfrac{\tan u}{12}\left(\dfrac{13}{12} + \dfrac{\tan^2 u}{12}\right).$$

18. Find the value of the expression $\dfrac{\partial^2 z}{\partial x^2} + \dfrac{\partial^2 z}{\partial y^2}$ when

$$a^2x^2 + b^2y^2 - c^2z^2 = 0. \qquad \text{[I. C. S. Exam.]}$$

19. If $V = Ax^2 + 2Bxy + Cy^2$, prove

$$\left(\dfrac{\partial V}{\partial x}\right)^2 \cdot \dfrac{\partial^2 V}{\partial y^2} - 2\dfrac{\partial V}{\partial x} \cdot \dfrac{\partial V}{\partial y} \cdot \dfrac{\partial^2 V}{\partial x \partial y} + \left(\dfrac{\partial V}{\partial y}\right)^2 \cdot \dfrac{\partial^2 V}{\partial x^2} = 8V(AC - B^2).$$

20. If $V = (1 - 2xy + y^2)^{-\frac{1}{2}}$, prove that

$$x\dfrac{\partial V}{\partial x} - y\dfrac{\partial V}{\partial y} = y^2 V^3.$$

Also that $\qquad \dfrac{\partial}{\partial x}\left\{(1 - x^2)\dfrac{\partial V}{\partial x}\right\} + \dfrac{\partial}{\partial y}\left\{y^2\dfrac{\partial V}{\partial y}\right\} = 0.$

21. If $\dfrac{x^2}{a^2} + \dfrac{y^2}{b^2} + \dfrac{z^2}{c^2} = 1$, and $lx + my + nz = 0$, prove that

$$\dfrac{dx}{\dfrac{ny}{b^2} - \dfrac{mz}{c^2}} = \dfrac{dy}{\dfrac{lz}{c^2} - \dfrac{nx}{a^2}} = \dfrac{dz}{\dfrac{mx}{a^2} - \dfrac{ly}{b^2}}.$$

22. If $\dfrac{x^2}{a^2} + \dfrac{y^2}{b^2} + \dfrac{z^2}{c^2} = 1$, and $\dfrac{x^2}{a^2+\lambda} + \dfrac{y^2}{b^2+\lambda} + \dfrac{z^2}{c^2+\lambda} = 1$, prove that

$$\frac{x(b^2-c^2)}{dx} + \frac{y(c^2-a^2)}{dy} + \frac{z(a^2-b^2)}{dz} = 0.$$

23. If $\dfrac{x^2}{a^2+u} + \dfrac{y^2}{b^2+u} + \dfrac{z^2}{c^2+u} = 1$, prove that

$$u_x{}^2 + u_y{}^2 + u_z{}^2 = 2(xu_x + yu_y + zu_z).\qquad [\text{Oxford, } 1888.]$$

24. If z and u be functions of x and y defined by

$$\{z - \phi(u)\}^2 = x^2(y^2 - u^2), \quad \{z - \phi(u)\}\phi'(u) = ux^2,$$

prove that
$$\frac{\partial z}{\partial x} \cdot \frac{\partial z}{\partial y} = xy.$$
$$[\text{Bertrand.}]$$

25. If $Pdx + Qdy$ be a perfect differential of some function of x, y,

prove that
$$\frac{\partial P}{\partial y} = \frac{\partial Q}{\partial x}.$$

26. If $Pdx + Qdy + Rdz$ can be made a perfect differential of some function of x, y, z by multiplying each term by a common factor,

show that $P\left(\dfrac{\partial Q}{\partial z} - \dfrac{\partial R}{\partial y}\right) + Q\left(\dfrac{\partial R}{\partial x} - \dfrac{\partial P}{\partial z}\right) + R\left(\dfrac{\partial P}{\partial y} - \dfrac{\partial Q}{\partial x}\right) = 0.$

27. If $z = \left(x\dfrac{\partial}{\partial x} - 1\right)\{f(y+x) - \phi(y-x)\}$, prove that

$$x\left(\frac{\partial^2 z}{\partial x^2} - \frac{\partial^2 z}{\partial y^2}\right) = 2\frac{\partial z}{\partial x}.\qquad [\text{Oxford, } 1889.]$$

28. If f be any function of X and Y where X and Y are defined by the equations $X = \phi(x, y)$, $Y = \psi(x, y)$, prove that

$$\frac{1}{m!n!}\frac{\partial^{m+n}f}{\partial x^m \partial y^n} = \Sigma\Sigma\frac{C_{r,s}}{r!s!}\frac{\partial^{r+s}f}{\partial X^r \partial Y^s}$$

where $C_{r,s}$ is the coefficient of $h^m k^n$ in

$$\{\phi(x+h,\, y+k) - \phi(x, y)\}^r \{\psi(x+h,\, y+k) - \psi(x, y)\}^s.$$
$$[\text{Math. Tripos, } 1888.]$$

29. If u be a homogeneous and symmetrical function of x and y of n dimensions, and if its expanded form is $\Sigma Q_r x^r y^{n-r}$, prove that

$$\Sigma\{(2r - n)Q_r\} = 0.\qquad [\text{Gregory's Examples.}]$$

30. If $f(x_1, x_2, x_3 \ldots x_n)$ be any homogeneous function which becomes $F(X_1, X_2 \ldots X_n)$ by any linear substitution for the variables $x_1, x_2 \ldots$ in terms of $X_1, X_2 \ldots$ and if $x_1', x_2', x_3' \ldots$; $X_1', X_2', X_3' \ldots$ be simultaneous values of the two systems, prove that

$$x_1'f_{x_1} + x_2'f_{x_2} + x_3'f_{x_3} + \ldots = X_1'F_{X_1} + X_2'F_{X_2} + X_3'F_{X_3} + \ldots$$

APPLICATIONS TO PLANE CURVES.

CHAPTER VII.

TANGENTS AND NORMALS.

191. Equation of TANGENT.

It was shown in Art. 36 that the equation of the tangent at the point (x, y) on the curve $y = f(x)$ is

$$Y - y = \frac{dy}{dx}(X - x), \dots\dots\dots\dots\dots\dots(1)$$

X and Y being the current co-ordinates of any point on the tangent.

Suppose the equation of the curve to be given in the form $f(x, y) = 0$.

It is shown in Art. 164 that

$$\frac{dy}{dx} = -\frac{\frac{\partial f}{\partial x}}{\frac{\partial f}{\partial y}}.$$

Substituting this expression for $\frac{dy}{dx}$ in (1) we obtain

$$Y - y = -\frac{\frac{\partial f}{\partial x}}{\frac{\partial f}{\partial y}}(X - x),$$

or

$$(X - x)\frac{\partial f}{\partial x} + (Y - y)\frac{\partial f}{\partial y} = 0 \dots\dots\dots\dots\dots(2)$$

for the equation of the tangent.

192. Simplification for Algebraic Curves.

If $f(x, y)$ be an algebraic function of x and y of degree n, suppose it made *homogeneous in $x, y,$ and z by the introduction of a proper power of the linear unit z* wherever necessary.

143

Call the function thus altered $f(x, y, z)$. Then $f(x, y, z)$ is a homogeneous algebraic function of the nth degree; hence we have by Euler's Theorem (Art. 181)

$$x\frac{\partial f}{\partial x} + y\frac{\partial f}{\partial y} + z\frac{\partial f}{\partial z} = nf(x, y, z) = 0,$$

by virtue of the equation to the curve.

Adding this to equation (2), the equation of the tangent takes the form

$$X\frac{\partial f}{\partial x} + Y\frac{\partial f}{\partial y} + z\frac{\partial f}{\partial z} = 0 \dots\dots\dots\dots\dots(3)$$

where the z is to be put $= 1$ after the differentiations have been performed.

Ex. $\qquad f(x, y) \equiv x^4 + a^2xy + b^3y + c^4 = 0.$

The equation, when made *homogeneous in x, y, z by the introduction of a proper power of z, is*

$$f(x, y, z) \equiv x^4 + a^2xyz^2 + b^3yz^3 + c^4z^4 = 0,$$

and
$$\frac{\partial f}{\partial x} = 4x^3 + a^2yz^2,$$

$$\frac{\partial f}{\partial y} = a^2xz^2 + b^3z^3,$$

$$\frac{\partial f}{\partial z} = 2a^2xyz + 3b^3yz^2 + 4c^4z^3.$$

Substituting these in Equation 3, and putting $z = 1$, we have for the equation of the tangent to the curve at the point (x, y)

$$X(4x^3 + a^2y) + Y(a^2x + b^3) + 2a^2xy + 3b^3y + 4c^4 = 0.$$

With very little practice the introduction of the z can be performed *mentally*. It is generally *more advantageous* to use equation (3) than equation (2), because (3) gives the result *in its simplest form*, whereas if (2) be used it is often necessary to reduce by substitutions from the equation of the curve.

193. Application to General Rational Algebraic Curve.

If the equation of the curve be written in the form

$$f(x, y) \equiv u_n + u_{n-1} + u_{n-2} + \dots + u_2 + u_1 + u_0 = 0$$

(where u_r represents the sum of all the terms of the rth degree), then when made homogeneous by the introduction where necessary of a proper power of z we shall have

$$f(x, y, z) \equiv u_n + u_{n-1}z + u_{n-2}z^2 + \dots$$
$$+ u_2z^{n-2} + u_1z^{n-1} + u_0z^n,$$

and
$$\frac{\partial f}{\partial z} = u_{n-1} + 2u_{n-2}z + 3u_{n-3}z^2 + \dots$$
$$+ (n-2)u_2z^{n-3} + (n-1)u_1z^{n-2} + nu_0z^{n-1},$$

and therefore substituting in (3) and putting $z=1$, the equation of the tangent is

$$X\frac{\partial f}{\partial x}+Y\frac{\partial f}{\partial y}+u_{n-1}+2u_{n-2}+3u_{n-3}+\cdots$$
$$+(n-2)u_2+(n-1)u_1+nu_0=0\ldots\ldots\ldots\ldots(4)$$

194. NORMAL.

DEF. *The normal at any point of a curve is a straight line through that point and perpendicular to the tangent to the curve at that point.*

Let the axes be assumed rectangular. The equation of the normal may then be at once written down. For if the equation of the curve be $y=f(x)$,

the tangent at (x, y) is $Y-y=\dfrac{dy}{dx}(X-x)$,

and the normal is therefore

$$(X-x)+(Y-y)\frac{dy}{dx}=0.$$

If the equation of the curve be given in the form

$$f(x, y)=0,$$

the equation of the tangent is

$$(X-x)\frac{\partial f}{\partial x}+(Y-y)\frac{\partial f}{\partial y}=0,$$

and therefore that of the normal is

$$\frac{X-x}{\dfrac{\partial f}{\partial x}}=\frac{Y-y}{\dfrac{\partial f}{\partial y}}.$$

Ex. 1. Consider the ellipse $\dfrac{x^2}{a^2}+\dfrac{y^2}{b^2}=1$.

This requires z^2 in the last term to make a homogeneous equation in x, y, and z. We have then

$$\frac{x^2}{a^2}+\frac{y^2}{b^2}-z^2=0.$$

Hence the equation of the tangent is

$$X\cdot\frac{2x}{a^2}+Y\cdot\frac{2y}{b^2}-z\cdot2z=0,$$

where z is to be put $=1$. Hence we get

$$\frac{Xx}{a^2}+\frac{Yy}{b^2}=1 \text{ for the tangent,}$$

and therefore

$$\frac{X-x}{\dfrac{x}{a^2}}=\frac{Y-y}{\dfrac{y}{b^2}} \text{ for the normal.}$$

K

Ex. 2. Take the general equation of a conic

$$ax^2 + 2hxy + by^2 + 2gx + 2fy + c = 0.$$

When made homogeneous this becomes

$$ax^2 + 2hxy + by^2 + 2gxz + 2fyz + cz^2 = 0.$$

The equation of the tangent is therefore

$$X(ax + hy + g) + Y(hx + by + f) + gx + fy + c = 0,$$

and that of the normal is

$$\frac{X - x}{ax + hy + g} = \frac{Y - y}{hx + by + f}.$$

Ex. 3. Consider the curve $\qquad \dfrac{y}{a} = \log \sec \dfrac{x}{a}.$

Then $\qquad\qquad\qquad\qquad\qquad \dfrac{dy}{dx} = \tan \dfrac{x}{a},$

and the equations of the tangent and normal are respectively

$$Y - y = \tan \frac{x}{a}(X - x),$$

and $\qquad (Y - y)\tan \dfrac{x}{a} + (X - x) = 0.$

195. If $f(x, y) = 0$ and $F(x, y) = 0$ be two curves intersecting at the point x, y, their respective tangents at that point are

$$Xf_x + Yf_y + Zf_z = 0$$

and $\qquad\qquad\qquad X F_x + Y F_y + Z F_z = 0.$

(Z is often written for z for the sake of symmetry.)

The angle at which these lines cut is

$$\tan^{-1}\frac{f_x F_y - f_y F_x}{f_x F_x + f_y F_y}.$$

Hence if the curves touch $\qquad f_x/F_x = f_y/F_y$;

and if they cut orthogonally, $\qquad f_x F_x + f_y F_y = 0.$

Ex. If $\xi + \iota\eta = f(x + \iota y)$, the curves given by $\xi = $ constant, and by $\eta = $ constant, form two families such that each member of the first set cuts orthogonally each member of the second.

For by Art. 190, $\qquad \dfrac{\partial \xi}{\partial x} = \dfrac{\partial \eta}{\partial y}$ and $\dfrac{\partial \xi}{\partial y} = -\dfrac{\partial \eta}{\partial x}.$

whence $\qquad\qquad \dfrac{\partial \xi}{\partial x} \cdot \dfrac{\partial \eta}{\partial x} + \dfrac{\partial \xi}{\partial y} \cdot \dfrac{\partial \eta}{\partial y} = 0,$

which is the condition that the tangents at the points of intersection should include a right angle.

196. If the form of a curve be given by the equations

$$x = \phi(t), \ y = \psi(t),$$

the tangent at the point determined by the third variable t is by Equation 1, Art. 191,

$$Y - \psi(t) = \frac{\psi'(t)}{\phi'(t)}\{X - \phi(t)\},$$

or $\qquad X\psi'(t) - Y\phi'(t) = \phi(t)\psi'(t) - \psi(t)\phi'(t).$

Similarly by Art. 194 the corresponding normal is

$$X\phi'(t) + Y\psi'(t) = \phi(t)\phi'(t) + \psi(t)\psi'(t).$$

EXAMPLES.

1. Find the equations of the tangents and normals at the point (x, y) on each of the following curves :—

(1) $x^2 + y^2 = c^2.$ $\qquad\qquad$ (5) $\qquad x^2 y + xy^2 = a^3.$

(2) $\qquad y^2 = 4ax.$ $\qquad\qquad$ (6) $\qquad\qquad e^y = \sin x.$

(3) $\qquad xy = k^2.$ $\qquad\qquad$ (7) $x^3 - 3axy + y^3 = 0.$

(4) $\qquad y = c \cosh\dfrac{x}{c}.$ $\qquad$ (8) $\qquad (x^2 + y^2)^2 = a^2(x^2 - y^2).$

2. Write down the equations of the tangents and normals to the curve $y(x^2 + a^2) = ax^2$ at the points where $y = \dfrac{a}{4}.$

3. Prove that $\dfrac{x}{a} + \dfrac{y}{b} = 1$ touches the curve $y = be^{-\frac{x}{a}}$ at the point where the curve crosses the axis of y.

4. Find where the tangent is parallel to the axis of x and where it is perpendicular to that axis for the following curves :—

$\qquad$ (a) $ax^2 + 2hxy + by^2 = 1.$

$\qquad$ (β) $y = \dfrac{x^3 - a^3}{ax}.$

$\qquad$ (γ) $y^3 = x^2(2a - x).$

5. Find the tangent and normal at the point determined by θ on

$\qquad$ (a) The ellipse $\qquad \begin{aligned} x &= a \cos\theta \\ y &= b \sin\theta \end{aligned} \Big\}.$

$\qquad$ (β) The cycloid $\qquad \begin{aligned} x &= a(\theta + \sin\theta) \\ y &= a(1 - \cos\theta) \end{aligned} \Big\}.$

$\qquad$ (γ) The epicycloid $\begin{aligned} x &= A \cos\theta - B \cos\dfrac{A}{B}\theta \\ y &= A \sin\theta - B \sin\dfrac{A}{B}\theta \end{aligned} \Bigg\}.$

6. If $p = x \cos a + y \sin a$ touch the curve

$$\frac{x^m}{a^m} + \frac{y^m}{b^m} = 1,$$

prove that $\qquad p^{\frac{m}{m-1}} = (a \cos a)^{\frac{m}{m-1}} + (b \sin a)^{\frac{m}{m-1}}.$

Hence write down the polar equation of the locus of the foot of the perpendicular from the origin on the tangent to this curve.

Examine the cases of an ellipse and of a rectangular hyperbola.

7. Find the condition that the conics $ax^2 + by^2 = 1$, $a'x^2 + b'y^2 = 1$ shall cut orthogonally.

8. Prove that, if the axes be oblique and inclined at an angle ω, the equation of the normal to $y = f(x)$ at (x, y) is

$$(Y - y)\left(\cos \omega + \frac{dy}{dx}\right) + (X - x)\left(1 + \cos \omega \frac{dy}{dx}\right) = 0.$$

9. Show that the parabolas $x^2 = ay$ and $y^2 = 2ax$ intersect upon the Folium of Descartes $x^3 + y^3 = 3axy$; and find the angles between each pair at the points of intersection.

197. Tangents at the Origin.

It will be shown by a general method in a subsequent article (291) that in the case in which a curve, whose equation is given in the rational algebraic form, passes through the origin, the equation of the tangent or tangents at that point can be at once written down by inspection; the rule being to *equate to zero the terms of lowest degree* in the equation of the curve.

Ex. In the curve $x^2 + y^2 + ax + by = 0$, $ax + by = 0$ is the equation of the tangent at the origin; and in the curve $(x^2 + y^2)^2 = a^2(x^2 - y^2)$, $x^2 - y^2 = 0$ is the equation of a pair of tangents at the origin.

It is easy to deduce this result from the equation of the tangent established in Chapter II. That equation is

$$Y - y = m(X - x) \text{ where } m = \frac{dy}{dx}.$$

At the origin this becomes $\qquad Y = mX,$

where the limiting value or values of m are to be found.

Let the equation of the curve be arranged in homogeneous sets of terms, and suppose the lowest set to be of the rth degree. The equation may be written $\quad x^r f_r\left(\frac{y}{x}\right) + x^{r+1} f_{r+1}\left(\frac{y}{x}\right) + \dots x^n f_n\left(\frac{y}{x}\right) = 0.$

Dividing by x^r, and putting $y = mx$, and then $x = 0$ and $y = 0$, the above reduces to the form $\qquad f_r(m) = 0,$

an equation which has r roots giving the directions in which the several branches of the curve pass through the origin. If $m_1, m_2, m_3, \dots m_r$ be the roots, the equations of the several tangents are

$$y = m_1 x, \ y = m_2 x, \ \dots y = m_r x.$$

These are all contained in the one equation

$$f_r\left(\frac{y}{x}\right)=0;$$

and this is the result obtained by "*equating to zero the terms of lowest degree*" in the equation of the curve, thus proving the rule.

Ex. Find the equations of the tangents at the origin in the following curves :—

(a) $(x^2+y^2)^2=a^2x^2-b^2y^2$.

(β) $x^5+y^5=5ax^2y^2$.

(γ) $(y-a)^2\dfrac{x^2+y^2}{y^2}=b^2$.

GEOMETRICAL RESULTS.

198. Cartesians. Intercepts.

From the equation $Y-y=\dfrac{dy}{dx}(X-x)$

it is clear that the *intercepts* which the tangent cuts off from the axes of x and y are respectively

$$x-\frac{y}{\dfrac{dy}{dx}} \text{ and } y-x\frac{dy}{dx},$$

for these are respectively the values of X when $Y=0$ and of Y when $X=0$.

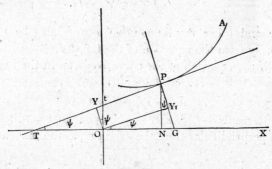

Fig. 22.

Let PN, PT, PG be the ordinate, tangent, and normal to the curve, and let PT make an angle ψ with the axis of x; then $\tan\psi=\dfrac{dy}{dx}$. Let the tangent cut the axis of y in t, and let OY, OY_1 be perpendiculars from O, the origin, on the tangent and normal. Then the above values of the intercepts are also obvious from the figure.

199. Subtangent, etc.

Def. The line TN is called the *subtangent* and the line NG is called the *subnormal*.

From the figure

$$Subtangent = TN = y \cot \psi = \frac{y}{\dfrac{dy}{dx}}.$$

$$Subnormal = NG = y \tan \psi = y\frac{dy}{dx}.$$

$$Normal = PG = y \sec \psi = y\sqrt{1+\tan^2\psi} = y\sqrt{1+\left(\frac{dy}{dx}\right)^2}.$$

$$Tangent = TP = y \operatorname{cosec} \psi = y\frac{\sqrt{1+\tan^2\psi}}{\tan \psi} = y\frac{\sqrt{1+\left(\dfrac{dy}{dx}\right)^2}}{\dfrac{dy}{dx}}.$$

$$OY = Ot \cos \psi = \frac{y-x\dfrac{dy}{dx}}{\sqrt{1+\tan^2\psi}} = \frac{y-x\dfrac{dy}{dx}}{\sqrt{1+\left(\dfrac{dy}{dx}\right)^2}}.$$

$$OY_1 = OG \cos \psi = \frac{ON+NG}{\sqrt{1+\tan^2\psi}} = \frac{x+y\dfrac{dy}{dx}}{\sqrt{1+\left(\dfrac{dy}{dx}\right)^2}}.$$

These and other results may of course also be obtained analytically from the equation of the tangent.

Thus if the equation of the curve be given in the form

$$f(x, y) = 0$$

the tangent $\qquad Xf_x + Yf_y + Zf_z = 0$

makes intercepts $-f_z/f_x$ and $-f_z/f_y$ upon the co-ordinate axes, and the perpendicular from the origin upon the tangent is

$$f_z/\sqrt{f_x^2+f_y^2};$$

and indeed, any lengths or angles desired may be written down by the ordinary methods and formulae of analytical geometry.

Ex. 1. For the chainette $y = c \cosh\dfrac{x}{c}$, we have $y_1 = \sinh\dfrac{x}{c}$,

Hence $\qquad$ subtangent $= \dfrac{y}{y_1} = c \coth\dfrac{x}{c}$,

$\qquad\qquad$ subnormal $= yy_1 = c \sinh\dfrac{x}{c} \cosh\dfrac{x}{c}$,

$\qquad\qquad$ normal $\quad = y\sqrt{1+y_1^2} = \dfrac{y^2}{c}$, etc.

Ex. 2. In the general equation

$$y^n + (a_0 + a_1 x)y^{n-1} + (b_0 + b_1 x + b_2 x^2)y^{n-2} + \ldots = 0,$$

show that if for a given abscissa each ordinate be divided by the corresponding subtangent the algebraic sum of the resulting quotients is constant.

If $y_1, y_2, y_3, \ldots$ be the several ordinates and $s_1, s_2 \ldots$ the several subtangents,

$$\Sigma y_r = -(a_0 + a_1 x),$$

hence, differentiating,

$$\Sigma \frac{dy_r}{dx} = -a_1,$$

and

$$s_r = y_r \bigg/ \frac{dy_r}{dx}.$$

$\therefore$

$$\Sigma \frac{y_r}{s_r} = -a_1.$$

200. Values of $\dfrac{ds}{dx}$, $\dfrac{dx}{ds}$, etc.

Let P, Q be contiguous points on a curve. Let the co-ordinates of P be (x, y) and of Q $(x+\delta x, y+\delta y)$. Then the

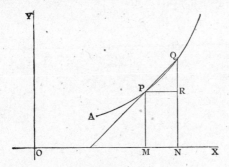

Fig. 23.

perpendicular $PR = \delta x$, and $RQ = \delta y$. Let the arc AP measured from some fixed point A on the curve be called s and the arc $AQ = s + \delta s$. Then arc $PQ = \delta s$. When Q travels along the curve so as to come indefinitely near to P, the arc PQ and the chord PQ ultimately differ by a small quantity of higher order than the arc PQ itself (Art. 34).

Hence, rejecting infinitesimals of order higher than the second, we have

$$\delta s^2 = (\text{chord } PQ)^2 = (\delta x^2 + \delta y^2),$$

or

$$1 = Lt\left(\frac{\delta x^2}{\delta s^2} + \frac{\delta y^2}{\delta s^2}\right) = \left(\frac{dx}{ds}\right)^2 + \left(\frac{dy}{ds}\right)^2.$$

Similarly
$$Lt\frac{\delta s^2}{\delta x^2} = Lt\left(1 + \frac{\delta y^2}{\delta x^2}\right),$$

or
$$\left(\frac{ds}{dx}\right)^2 = 1 + \left(\frac{dy}{dx}\right)^2;$$

and in the same manner
$$\left(\frac{ds}{dy}\right)^2 = 1 + \left(\frac{dx}{dy}\right)^2.$$

If ψ be the angle which the tangent makes with the axis of x we have as in Art. 37,
$$\tan \psi = Lt\frac{RQ}{PR} = Lt\frac{\delta y}{\delta x} = \frac{dy}{dx},$$

and also
$$\cos \psi = Lt\frac{PR}{\text{chord } PQ} = Lt\frac{PR}{\text{arc } PQ} = Lt\frac{\delta x}{\delta s} = \frac{dx}{ds},$$

and
$$\sin \psi = Lt\frac{RQ}{\text{chord } PQ} = Lt\frac{RQ}{\text{arc } PQ} = Lt\frac{\delta y}{\delta s} = \frac{dy}{ds}.$$

EXAMPLES.

1. Find the length of the perpendicular from the origin on the tangent at the point x, y of the curve $x^4 + y^4 = c^4$.

2. Show that in the curve $y = be^{\frac{x}{a}}$ the subtangent is of constant length.

3. Show that in the curve $by^2 = (x+a)^3$ the square of the subtangent varies as the subnormal.

4. For the parabola $y^2 = 4ax$, prove
$$\frac{ds}{dx} = \sqrt{\frac{a+x}{x}}.$$

5. Prove that for the ellipse $\frac{x^2}{a^2} + \frac{y^2}{b^2} = 1$, if $x = a \sin \phi$,
$$\frac{ds}{d\phi} = a\sqrt{1 - e^2\sin^2\phi}.$$

6. For the cycloid
$$\left.\begin{array}{l} x = a \text{ vers } \theta \\ y = a(\theta + \sin \theta) \end{array}\right\},$$
prove
$$\frac{ds}{dx} = \sqrt{\frac{2a}{x}}.$$

7. In the curve
$$y = a \log \sec\frac{x}{a},$$
prove
$$\frac{ds}{dx} = \sec\frac{x}{a}, \quad \frac{ds}{dy} = \operatorname{cosec}\frac{x}{a}, \quad \text{and} \quad x = a\psi.$$

8. Show that the portion of the tangent to the curve
$$x^{\frac{2}{3}} + y^{\frac{2}{3}} = a^{\frac{2}{3}},$$
which is intercepted between the axes, is of constant length.

Find the area of the triangle formed by the axes and the tangent.

9. Find for what value of n the length of the subnormal of the curve $xy^n = a^{n+1}$ is constant. Also for what value of n the area of the triangle included between the axes and any tangent is constant.

10. Prove that for the catenary or chainette $y = c \cosh \dfrac{x}{c}$, the length of the perpendicular from the foot of the ordinate on the tangent is of constant length.

11. In the tractory

$$x = \sqrt{c^2 - y^2} + \frac{c}{2} \log \frac{c - \sqrt{c^2 - y^2}}{c + \sqrt{c^2 - y^2}},$$

prove that the portion of the tangent intercepted between the point of contact and the axis of x is of constant length.

201. Polar Co-ordinates.

If the equation of the curve be referred to polar co-ordinates, suppose O to be the pole and P, Q two contiguous points on the curve. Let the co-ordinates of P and Q be (r, θ) and $(r + \delta r, \theta + \delta \theta)$ respectively. Let PN be the perpendicular on OQ, then NQ differs from δr and NP from $r \delta \theta$ *by small quantities of a higher order than* $\delta \theta$ (Art. 31).

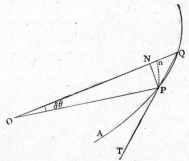

Fig. 24.

Let the arc measured from some fixed point A to P be called s, and from A to Q, $s + \delta s$. Then arc $PQ = \delta s$. Hence, rejecting infinitesimals of order higher than the second, we have

$$\delta s^2 = (\text{chord } PQ)^2 = (NQ^2 + PN^2) = (\delta r^2 + r^2 \delta \theta^2),$$

and therefore

$$\left(\frac{dr}{ds}\right)^2 + r^2\left(\frac{d\theta}{ds}\right)^2 = 1, \text{ or } \left(\frac{ds}{dr}\right)^2 = 1 + r^2\left(\frac{d\theta}{dr}\right)^2,$$

or

$$\left(\frac{ds}{d\theta}\right)^2 = r^2 + \left(\frac{dr}{d\theta}\right)^2,$$

according as we divide by δs^2, δr^2, or $\delta \theta^2$ before proceeding to the limit.

202. **Inclination of the Radius Vector to the Tangent.**

Next, let ϕ be the angle which the tangent at any point P makes with the radius vector, then

$$\tan \phi = r\frac{d\theta}{dr}, \quad \cos \phi = \frac{dr}{ds}, \quad \sin \phi = \frac{rd\theta}{ds}.$$

For, with the figure of the preceding article, since, when Q has moved along the curve so near to P that Q and P may be considered as ultimately coincident, QP becomes the tangent at P and the angles OQT and OPT are each of them ultimately equal to ϕ, and

$$\tan \phi = Lt \tan NQP = Lt\frac{NP}{QN} = Lt\frac{r\delta\theta}{\delta r} = r\frac{d\theta}{dr};$$

$$\cos \phi = Lt \cos NQP = Lt\frac{NQ}{\text{chord } QP} = Lt\frac{NQ}{\text{arc } QP} = Lt\frac{\delta r}{\delta s} = \frac{dr}{ds};$$

$$\sin \phi = Lt \sin NQP = Lt\frac{NP}{\text{chord } QP} = Lt\frac{NP}{\text{arc } QP} = Lt\frac{r\delta\theta}{\delta s} = \frac{rd\theta}{ds}.$$

Ex. Find the angle ϕ in the case of the curve $r^n = a^n\sec(n\theta + a)$, and prove that this curve is intersected by the curve $r^n = b^n\sec(n\theta + \beta)$ at an angle which is independent of a and b.   [I. C. S., 1886.]

Taking the logarithmic differential,

$$\frac{1}{r}\frac{dr}{d\theta} = \tan(n\theta + a),$$

whence $$\frac{\pi}{2} - \phi = n\theta + a.$$

In a similar manner for the second curve

$$\frac{\pi}{2} - \phi' = n\theta + \beta,$$

ϕ' being the angle which the radius vector makes with the tangent to the second curve. Hence the angle between the tangents at the point of intersection is $a \sim \beta$.

203. **Polar Subtangent, Subnormal, etc.**

Let OY be the perpendicular from the origin on the tangent at P. Let TOt be drawn through O perpendicular to OP and cutting the tangent in T and the normal in t. Then OT is called the "*Polar Subtangent*" and Ot is called the "*Polar Subnormal.*"

It is clear that $OT = OP \tan\phi = r^2\frac{d\theta}{dr}$,....................(1)

and that $Ot = OP \cot \phi = \frac{dr}{d\theta}$.........................(2)

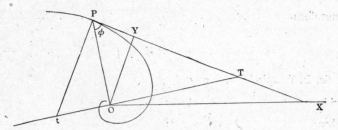

Fig. 25.

204. It is often found convenient when using polar co-ordinates to write $\dfrac{1}{u}$ for r, and therefore $-\dfrac{1}{u^2}\dfrac{du}{d\theta}$ for $\dfrac{dr}{d\theta}$. With this notation, Polar Subtangent $= r^2\dfrac{d\theta}{dr} = -\dfrac{d\theta}{du}$.

Ex. In the conic $\qquad lu = 1 + e\cos\theta$

we have $\qquad\qquad l = -e\sin\theta\dfrac{d\theta}{du}$.

Thus the length of the polar subtangent is $l/e\sin\theta$.

Also, from the figure, the angular co-ordinate of its extremity is $\theta - \dfrac{\pi}{2}$.

Hence the co-ordinates of $T(r_1,\ \theta_1)$ satisfy the equation

$$r_1 = l/e\sin\left(\frac{\pi}{2} + \theta_1\right).$$

The locus of the extremity is therefore

$$lu = e\cos\theta\ ;$$

that is, the directrix corresponding to that focus which is taken as origin.

205. **Perpendicular from Pole on Tangent, etc.**

Let $\qquad OY = p$ and $PY = t$.

Then $\qquad\quad p = r\sin\phi$,

and therefore

$$\frac{1}{p^2} = \frac{1}{r^2}\operatorname{cosec}^2\phi = \frac{1}{r^2}(1 + \cot^2\phi) = \frac{1}{r^2}\left\{1 + \frac{1}{r^2}\left(\frac{dr}{d\theta}\right)^2\right\}\ ;$$

therefore $\qquad \dfrac{1}{p^2} = \dfrac{1}{r^2} + \dfrac{1}{r^4}\left(\dfrac{dr}{d\theta}\right)^2$ ....(1)

$$= u^2 + \left(\frac{du}{d\theta}\right)^2 \ \dots\dots\dots\dots\dots\dots\dots\dots\dots\dots\dots\dots(2)$$

Similarly $\qquad\qquad t = r\cos\phi\ ;$

therefore $\qquad \dfrac{1}{t^2} = \dfrac{1}{r^2}\sec^2\phi = \dfrac{1}{r^2}(1 + \tan^2\phi)$

$$= \frac{1}{r^2}\left\{1 + r^2\left(\frac{d\theta}{dr}\right)^2\right\}\ ;$$

therefore
$$\frac{1}{t^2} = \frac{1}{r^2} + \left(\frac{d\theta}{dr}\right)^2 \dots\dots\dots\dots\dots\dots\dots(3)$$

$$= u^2 + u^4\left(\frac{d\theta}{du}\right)^2 \dots\dots\dots\dots\dots\dots(4)$$

Ex. In the spiral $\quad r = a\dfrac{\theta^2}{\theta^2 - 1}$

we have $\quad\quad\quad au = 1 - \theta^{-2}$,

whence $\quad\quad\quad a\dfrac{du}{d\theta} = 2\theta^{-3}$;

and therefore, squaring and adding,

$$\frac{a^2}{p^2} = 1 - 2\theta^{-2} + \theta^{-4} + 4\theta^{-6}.$$

Thus, corresponding to $\theta = \pm 1$, we have

$$\frac{a^2}{p^2} = 4 \quad \text{and} \quad p = \pm\frac{a}{2}.$$

EXAMPLES.

1. In the equiangular spiral $r = ae^{\theta \cot a}$, prove
$$\frac{dr}{ds} = \cos a \quad \text{and} \quad p = r\sin a.$$

2. For the involute of a circle, viz.,
$$\theta = \frac{\sqrt{r^2 - a^2}}{a} - \cos^{-1}\frac{a}{r},$$

prove $\quad\quad\quad \cos\phi = \dfrac{a}{r}.$

3. In the parabola $\dfrac{2a}{r} = 1 - \cos\theta$, prove the following results:—

    (a) $\phi = \pi - \dfrac{\theta}{2}.$

    (β) $p = \dfrac{a}{\sin\dfrac{\theta}{2}}.$

    (γ) $p^2 = ar.$

    (δ) Polar subtangent $= 2a\operatorname{cosec}\theta.$

4. For the cardioide $r = a(1 - \cos\theta)$, prove

    (a) $\phi = \dfrac{\theta}{2}.$

    (β) $p = 2a\sin^3\dfrac{\theta}{2}.$

    (γ) $p^2 = \dfrac{r^3}{2a}.$

    (δ) Polar subtangent $= 2a\dfrac{\sin^3\dfrac{\theta}{2}}{\cos\dfrac{\theta}{2}}.$

206. Polar Equation of the Tangent.

Let the polar co-ordinates of the point of contact be $\left(\dfrac{1}{U}, a\right)$;
and let U' be the value of $\dfrac{du}{d\theta}$ for the curve at that point.

The equation of any straight line may be written in the
form $\qquad u = A\cos(\theta - a) + B\sin(\theta - a),$ ....(1)

A and B being the arbitrary constants.   Let this straight line
represent the required tangent.

By differentiation

$$\frac{du}{d\theta} = -A\sin(\theta - a) + B\cos(\theta - a).$$ ....(2)

Now, since the tangent touches the curve, the value of $\dfrac{du}{d\theta}$
at the point of contact is the same for the curve and for the
tangent.   Hence, putting $\theta = a$ in equations (1) and (2), we
have $\qquad U = A$ and $U' = B,$

whence the required equation will be

$$u = U\cos(\theta - a) + U'\sin(\theta - a)$$ ....(3)

207. Polar Equation of the Normal.

The equation of *any* straight line at right angles to the
tangent given by equation (3) of the preceding article may be
written in the form

$$Cu = U'\cos(\theta - a) - U\sin(\theta - a),$$

C being an arbitrary constant.

This equation is to be satisfied by $u = U$, $\theta = a$ for the point
of contact of the tangent; therefore substituting we have

$$CU = U',$$

whence the required equation of the normal is

$$\frac{U'}{U}u = U'\cos(\theta - a) - U\sin(\theta - a).$$

Ex. Find the polar equation of the normal at the point $\theta = 2a$ on the
cardioide $r = a(1 + \cos\theta)$, and show that three normals can be drawn from a
given point to a cardioide.

Here $\qquad\qquad\qquad \dfrac{dr}{d\theta} = -a\sin\theta.$

Hence
$$\frac{U'}{U^2} = a \sin 2a,$$

and
$$\frac{U'}{U} = \frac{\sin 2a}{1 + \cos 2a} = \tan a.$$

Hence the equation becomes

$$a \sin 2a \,.\, u = \tan a \cos(\theta - 2a) - \sin(\theta - 2a),$$

or
$$r \sin(3a - \theta) = \frac{a}{2}(\sin 3a + \sin a)\dots\dots\dots\dots\dots\dots\dots(1)$$

If we write x and y for $r \cos \theta$ and $r \sin \theta$ and t for $\tan a$, this may be

written
$$(3t - t^3)x - (1 - 3t^2)y = \frac{a}{2}\{(3t - t^3) + t(1 + t^2)\},$$

or
$$t^3 x - 3t^2 y + t(2a - 3x) + y = 0, \dots\dots\dots\dots\dots\dots\dots\dots\dots(2)$$

giving a *cubic* to determine the values of tan a corresponding to the three normals which pass through a given point (x, y).

208. Class of a Curve of the nth degree.

DEF. *The number of tangents which can be drawn from a given point to a rational algebraic curve is called its class.*

Let the equation of the curve be $f(x, y) = 0$. The equation of the tangent at the point (x, y) is

$$X\frac{\partial f}{\partial x} + Y\frac{\partial f}{\partial y} + z\frac{\partial f}{\partial z} = 0,$$

where z is to be put equal to unity after the differentiation is performed. If this pass through the point h, k we have

$$h\frac{\partial f}{\partial x} + k\frac{\partial f}{\partial y} + z\frac{\partial f}{\partial z} = 0.$$

This is an equation of the $(n-1)^{\text{th}}$ degree in x and y and represents a curve of the $(n-1)^{\text{th}}$ degree *passing through the points of contact* of the tangents drawn from the point (h, k) to the curve $f(x, y) = 0$. These two curves have $n(n-1)$ points of intersection, and therefore there are in general $n(n-1)$ *points of contact* corresponding to $n(n-1)$ *tangents, real or imaginary*, which can be drawn from a given point to a curve of the nth degree.[*]

It appears then that if the degree of a curve be n, *its class is $n(n-1)$*; for example, the classes of a conic, a cubic, a quartic are the second, sixth, twelfth respectively.

[*] Poncelet, *Annales de Gergonne*, vol. VIII. ; Bobillier, ibid. vol. XIX.

209. Number of Normals which can be drawn to a Curve to pass through a given point.

Let h, k be the point through which the normals are to pass.

The equation of the normal to the curve $f(x, y) = 0$ at the point (x, y) is

$$\frac{X-x}{\dfrac{\partial f}{\partial x}} = \frac{Y-y}{\dfrac{\partial f}{\partial y}}.$$

If this pass through h, k,

$$(h-x)\frac{\partial f}{\partial y} = (k-y)\frac{\partial f}{\partial x}.$$

This equation is of the nth degree in x and y and represents a curve which goes *through the feet of all normals* which can be drawn from the point h, k to the curve. Combining this with $f(x, y) = 0$, which is also of the nth degree, it appears that there are n^2 points of intersection, and that therefore there can be n^2 *normals, real or imaginary*, drawn to a given curve to pass through a given point.

For example, if the curve be an ellipse, $n = 2$, and the number of normals is 4. Let $\dfrac{x^2}{a^2} + \dfrac{y^2}{b^2} = 1$ be the equation of the curve, then

$$(h-x)\frac{y}{b^2} = (k-y)\frac{x}{a^2}$$

is the curve which, with the ellipse, determines the feet of the normals drawn from the point (h, k). This is a rectangular hyperbola which passes through the origin and through the point (h, k).

The student should consider how it is that an *infinite* number of normals can be drawn from the centre of a circle to the circumference.

210. The curves

$$(h-x)\frac{\partial f}{\partial x} + (k-y)\frac{\partial f}{\partial y} = 0 \dots\dots\dots\dots\dots\dots(1)$$

and

$$(h-x)\frac{\partial f}{\partial y} - (k-y)\frac{\partial f}{\partial x} = 0, \dots\dots\dots\dots\dots\dots(2)$$

on which lie the points of contact of tangents and the feet of the normals respectively, which can be drawn to the curve $f(x, y) = 0$ so as to pass through the point (h, k), are the same for the curve $f(x, y) = a$. And, as equations (1) and (2) do not depend on a, they represent *the loci of the points of contact and of the feet of the normals* respectively for all values of a, that is, for all members of the family of curves obtained by varying a in $f(x, y) = a$ in any manner.

211. Polar Curves.

The curve $\qquad h\dfrac{\partial f}{\partial x} + k\dfrac{\partial f}{\partial y} + z\dfrac{\partial f}{\partial z} = 0$

is called the "*First Polar Curve*" of the point h, k with regard to the curve $f(x, y) = 0$; z being a linear unit introduced as explained previously to make $f(x, y)$ homogeneous in x, y, z, and put equal to unity after the differentiation is performed.

As this is a curve of the $(n-1)^{\text{th}}$ degree it is clear that the first polar of a point with regard to a conic is a *straight line*, the first polar with regard to a cubic is a *conic*, and so on.

The first polar *of the origin* is given by

$$\frac{\partial f}{\partial z} = 0.$$

If the curve be put in the form
$$u_n + u_{n-1} + u_{n-2} + \ldots + u_2 + u_1 + u_0 = 0,$$
the first polar of the origin is
$$u_{n-1} + 2u_{n-2} + 3u_{n-3} + \ldots + (n-1)u_1 + nu_0 = 0.$$
In the particular case of the conic
$$u_2 + u_1 + u_0 = 0$$
the polar line of the origin has for its equation
$$u_1 + 2u_0 = 0.$$
For the cubic $\qquad u_3 + u_2 + u_1 + u_0 = 0$
the polar conic of the origin is
$$u_2 + 2u_1 + 3u_0 = 0.$$

EXAMPLES.

1. Through the point h, k tangents are drawn to the curve
$$Ax^3 + By^3 = 1;$$
show that the points of contact lie on a conic.

2. If from any point P normals be drawn to the curve whose equation is $y^m = max^n$, show that the feet of the normals lie on a conic, of which the straight line joining P to the origin is a diameter. Find the position of the axes of this conic.

3. The points of contact of tangents from the point h, k to the curve $x^3 + y^3 = 3axy$ lie on a conic which passes through the origin.

4. Through a given point h, k tangents are drawn to curves where the ordinate varies as the cube of the abscissa. Show that the locus of the points of contact is the rectangular hyperbola
$$2xy + kx - 3hy = 0,$$
and the locus of the remaining point in which each tangent cuts the curve is the rectangular hyperbola
$$xy - 4kx + 3hy = 0.$$

212. The p, r or Pedal Equation of a Curve.

In many curves the relation between the perpendicular on the tangent and the radius vector of the point of contact from some given point is very simple, and when known it frequently forms a very useful equation to the curve; especially indeed in investigating certain Statical and Dynamical properties.

213. Pedal Equation deduced from Cartesian.

Suppose the curve to be given by its Cartesian Equation and the origin to be taken at the point with regard to which it is required to find the Pedal Equation of the curve. Let x, y be the co-ordinates of any point on the curve; then, if $F(x, y) = 0$ be the equation of the curve, that of the tangent is

$$XF_x + YF_y + zF_z = 0,$$

where z is as usual to be put equal unity after the differentiation is performed.

If p be the perpendicular from the origin on the tangent at (x, y) we have

$$p^2 = \frac{F_z^2}{F_x^2 + F_y^2} \quad\quad\quad\quad\quad (1)$$

Also

$$r^2 = x^2 + y^2, \quad\quad\quad\quad\quad (2)$$

and

$$F(x, y) = 0 \quad\quad\quad\quad\quad (3)$$

If x and y be eliminated between these three equations the required relation between p and r is obtained.

Ex. If $F(x, y) = 0$ be

$$\frac{x^2}{a^2} + \frac{y^2}{b^2} = 1,$$

we have

$$\frac{x^2}{a^4} + \frac{y^2}{b^4} = \frac{1}{p^2}$$

and

$$x^2 + y^2 = r^2 ;$$

therefore

$$\begin{vmatrix} \dfrac{1}{a^2}, & \dfrac{1}{b^2}, & 1 \\[2mm] \dfrac{1}{a^4}, & \dfrac{1}{b^4}, & \dfrac{1}{p^2} \\[2mm] 1, & 1, & r^2 \end{vmatrix} = 0,$$

or

$$\frac{a^2 b^2}{p^2} + r^2 = a^2 + b^2.$$

This result may be at once obtained by eliminating CD from the equations

$$CP^2 + CD^2 = a^2 + b^2$$

and

$$CD \cdot p = ab,$$

CP and CD being conjugate semi-diameters.

214. Pedal Equation deduced from Polar.

Let the curve be given in Polar co-ordinates and the pole be taken at the point with regard to which it is required to find the pedal equation of the curve. Let r, θ be the co-ordinates of any point on the curve, and p the length of the perpendicular from the pole on the tangent at r, θ. If

$$F(r, \theta) = 0 \dots\dots\dots\dots\dots\dots\dots\dots\dots\dots\dots(1)$$

be the equation of the curve, then we have (see Fig. 25)

$$p = r \sin \phi, \dots\dots\dots\dots\dots\dots\dots\dots\dots(2)$$

and

$$\tan \phi = \frac{r d\theta}{dr} \dots\dots\dots\dots\dots\dots\dots\dots\dots\dots(3)$$

Eliminate θ and ϕ between the equations (1), (2), (3), and the required equation between p and r will be obtained.

Ex. Given $r^m = a^m \sin m\theta$, required its pedal equation.

Taking logarithms and differentiating,

$$\frac{m}{r} \frac{dr}{d\theta} = m \frac{\cos m\theta}{\sin m\theta};$$

therefore　　　　　　　$\cot \phi = \cot m\theta$, or $\phi = m\theta$.

Again,　　　　　　　$p = r \sin \phi = r \sin m\theta$

$$= r \cdot \frac{r^m}{a^m};$$

therefore　　　　　　　$p = \frac{r^{m+1}}{a^m}.$

The following special cases of this example are worthy of notice, and will furnish exercises for the student.

Value of m.	Equation.	Name.	Pedal Equation.
-2	$r^2 \sin 2\theta + a^2 = 0$	Rectangular Hyperbola	$rp = a^2$
-1	$r \sin \theta + a = 0$	Straight line	$p = a$
$-\frac{1}{2}$	$\frac{2a}{r} = 1 - \cos \theta$	Parabola	$p^2 = ar$
$\frac{1}{2}$	$r = \frac{a}{2}(1 - \cos \theta)$	Cardioide	$p^2 a = r^3$
1	$r = a \sin \theta$	Circle	$pa = r^2$
2	$r^2 = a^2 \sin 2\theta$	Lemniscate of Bernoulli	$pa^2 = r^3$

EXAMPLES.

1. Show geometrically that the pedal equation of a circle with regard to a point on the circumference is $pd = r^2$, d being the diameter of the circle.

2. Show that the pedal equation of the ellipse

$$\frac{x^2}{a^2} + \frac{y^2}{b^2} = 1$$

with regard to a focus is $\quad \dfrac{b^2}{p^2} = \dfrac{2a}{r} - 1.$

3. Show that the pedal equation of the parabola $y^2 = 4ax$ with regard to its vertex is $\quad a^2(r^2 - p^2)^2 = p^2(r^2 + 4a^2)(p^2 + 4a^2).$

4. Show that the pedal equation of the curve $r = a^\theta$ is of the form $p = mr$ where m is a constant.

5. Show that the pedal equation of the tetracuspidal hypocycloid $x^{\frac{2}{3}} + y^{\frac{2}{3}} = a^{\frac{2}{3}}$ is $r^2 + 3p^2 = a^2$.

6. Show that for the epicycloid given by

$$\left. \begin{array}{l} x = (a+b)\cos\theta - b\cos\dfrac{a+b}{b}\theta \\[2mm] y = (a+b)\sin\theta - b\sin\dfrac{a+b}{b}\theta \end{array} \right\},$$

$$p = (a+2b)\sin\frac{a}{2b}\theta ; \quad \psi = \frac{a+2b}{2b}\theta ; \quad p = (a+2b)\sin\frac{a\psi}{a+2b} ;$$

and that the pedal equation is

$$r^2 = a^2 + 4\frac{(a+b)b}{(a+2b)^2}p^2.$$

215. It is found useful to remember the following pedal equations.

(1) Circle (point on circumference), $\qquad pd = r^2.$

(2) Parabola (focus), $\qquad p^2 = ar.$

(3) $\left. \begin{array}{l} \text{Ellipse} \\ \text{Hyperbola} \end{array} \right\}$ (focus), $\qquad \dfrac{b^2}{p^2} = \dfrac{2a}{r} \mp 1.$

(4) $\left. \begin{array}{l} \text{Ellipse} \\ \text{Hyperbola} \end{array} \right\}$ (centre), $\qquad \dfrac{a^2 b^2}{p^2} \pm r^2 = a^2 \pm b^2.$

(5) Equiangular Spiral $r = ae^{\theta\cot a}$ (pole), $\quad p = r\sin a.$

(6) General class $r^m = a^m\sin m\theta, \qquad pa^m = r^{m+1}.$

(7) General class of epi- and hypo-cycloids, $p^2 = Ar^2 + B.$

PEDAL CURVES.

216. DEF. *If a perpendicular be drawn from a fixed point on a variable tangent to a curve, the locus of the foot of the perpendicular is called the "FIRST POSITIVE PEDAL" of the original curve with regard to the given point.*

To find the first positive pedal with regard to the origin of any curve whose **Cartesian Equation** *is given.*

Let $$F(x, y) = 0 \dots\dots\dots\dots\dots\dots\dots\dots(1)$$

be the equation of the curve.

Suppose $X \cos a + Y \sin a = p$ touches this curve.

By comparison of this equation with

$$X \frac{\partial F}{\partial x} + Y \frac{\partial F}{\partial y} + z \frac{\partial F}{\partial z} = 0$$

we have $$\frac{\dfrac{\partial F}{\partial x}}{\cos a} = \frac{\dfrac{\partial F}{\partial y}}{\sin a} = \frac{\dfrac{\partial F}{\partial z}}{-p} = \lambda, \text{ say} \dots\dots\dots\dots\dots(2)$$

If x, y, λ be eliminated between the four equations (1) and (2) a result will remain which depends on p and a only. And since p, a are the polar co-ordinates of the foot of the perpendicular, if r be written for p and θ for a, the polar equation of the locus required will be obtained.

Ex. Find the first positive pedal of the curve
$$Ax^m + By^m = 1.$$

The tangent is $$AXx^{m-1} + BYy^{m-1} = 1.$$

Compare this with $$X \cos a + Y \sin q = p,$$

$$Ax^{m-1} = \frac{\cos a}{p}, \text{ and } By^{m-1} = \frac{\sin a}{p}.$$

Hence $$A\left(\frac{\cos a}{Ap}\right)^{\frac{m}{m-1}} + B\left(\frac{\sin a}{Bp}\right)^{\frac{m}{m-1}} = 1.$$

Therefore the polar equation of the locus required is

$$r^{\frac{m}{m-1}} = \frac{\cos^{\frac{m}{m-1}}\theta}{A^{\frac{1}{m-1}}} + \frac{\sin^{\frac{m}{m-1}}\theta}{B^{\frac{1}{m-1}}}.$$

217. *To find the Pedal with regard to the Pole of any curve whose* **Polar Equation** *is given.*

Let $$F(r, \theta) = 0 \dots\dots\dots\dots\dots\dots\dots\dots(1)$$

be the equation of the curve.

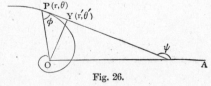

Fig. 26.

Let r', θ' be the polar co-ordinates of the point Y, which is the foot of the perpendicular OY drawn from the pole on a tangent. Let OA be the initial line. Then

$$\theta = A\hat{O}P = A\hat{O}Y + \hat{YOP}$$

$$= \theta' + \frac{\pi}{2} - \phi; \dots\dots\dots\dots\dots\dots\dots\dots\dots\dots(2)$$

also $$\tan\phi = r\frac{d\theta}{dr}, \dots\dots\dots\dots\dots\dots\dots\dots\dots\dots\dots(3)$$

and $$r' = r\sin\phi,$$

or $$\left. \frac{1}{r'^2} = \frac{1}{r^2} + \frac{1}{r^4}\left(\frac{dr}{d\theta}\right)^2 \right\} \text{ (Art. 205). } \dots\dots\dots\dots(4)$$

If r, θ, ϕ be eliminated from equations 1, 2, 3, and 4, there will remain an equation in r', θ'. The dashes may then be dropped and the required equation will be obtained.

Ex. To find the equation of the first positive pedal of the curve

$$r^m = a^m \cos m\theta.$$

Taking the logarithmic differential

$$\frac{m}{r}\frac{dr}{d\theta} = -m\tan m\theta;$$

therefore $$\cot\phi = -\tan m\theta;$$

therefore $$\phi = \frac{\pi}{2} + m\theta.$$

But $$\theta = \theta' + \frac{\pi}{2} - \phi,$$

therefore $$\theta = \theta' - m\theta, \text{ or } \theta = \frac{\theta'}{m+1}.$$

Again $$r' = r\sin\phi = r\cos m\theta$$

$$= a\cos^{\frac{1}{m}} m\theta . \cos m\theta$$

$$= a\cos^{\frac{m+1}{m}} \frac{m\theta'}{m+1}.$$

Hence the equation of the pedal curve is

$$r'^{\frac{m}{m+1}} = a^{\frac{m}{m+1}}\cos\frac{m}{m+1}\theta.$$

218. DEF. If there be a series of curves which we may designate as

$$A, A_1, A_2, A_3, \dots A_n, \dots$$

such that each is the *first positive pedal* curve of the one which immediately precedes it; then A_2, A_3, etc., are respectively called the *second, third, etc., positive pedals* of A. Also, any one of this series of curves may be regarded as the original curve, *e.g.*, A_3; then A_2 is called the *first negative pedal of A_3*, A_1 *the second negative pedal,* and so on.

Ex. 1. Find the kth positive pedal of
$$r^m = a^m \cos m\theta.$$
It has been shown that the first positive pedal is
$$r^{m_1} = a^{m_1} \cos m_1\theta,$$
where
$$m_1 = \frac{m}{1+m}.$$

Similarly the second positive pedal is
$$r^{m_2} = a^{m_2} \cos m_2\theta,$$
where
$$m_2 = \frac{m_1}{1+m_1} = \frac{m}{1+2m};$$
and generally the kth positive pedal is
$$r^{m_k} = a^{m_k} \cos m_k\theta,$$
where
$$m_k = \frac{m}{1+km}.$$

Ex. 2. Find the kth negative pedal of the curve
$$r^m = a^m \cos m\theta.$$

We have shown above that $r^m = a^m \cos m\theta$ is the kth positive pedal of the curve $r^n = a^n \cos n\theta$, provided $m = \dfrac{n}{1+kn}.$

This gives
$$n = \frac{m}{1-km}.$$
Hence the kth negative pedal of $r^m = a^m \cos m\theta$ is
$$r^n = a^n \cos n\theta,$$
where
$$n = \frac{m}{1-km}.$$

EXAMPLES.

1. Show that the first positive pedal of a circle with regard to any point is a Limaçon $(r = a + b \cos \theta)$, which becomes a Cardioide $\{r = a(1+\cos \theta)\}$ when the point is on the circumference.

2. Show that the first positive pedal of a central conic with regard to the centre is of the form $r^2 = A + B \cos 2\theta$, which becomes a Bernoulli's Lemniscate $(r^2 = a^2 \cos 2\theta)$ when the conic is a rectangular hyperbola.

3. Show that the first positive pedal of the parabola $y^2 = 4ax$ with regard to the vertex is the cissoid
$$x(x^2 + y^2) + ay^2 = 0.$$

4. Show that the first positive pedal of the curve
$$x^3 + y^3 = a^3$$
is
$$(x^2 + y^2)^{\frac{3}{2}} = a^{\frac{3}{2}}(x^{\frac{3}{2}} + y^{\frac{3}{2}}).$$

5. Show that the first positive pedal of the curve
$$x^{\frac{2}{3}} + y^{\frac{2}{3}} = a^{\frac{2}{3}}$$
is
$$r = \pm a \sin \theta \cos \theta.$$
Also that the tangential polar equation of the curve is
$$p = \mp \frac{a}{2} \sin 2\psi.$$

6. Show that the first positive pedal of the curve

$$x^m y^n = a^{m+n}$$

is $\qquad r^{m+n} = a^{m+n} \dfrac{(m+n)^{m+n}}{m^m \cdot n^n} \cos^m\theta \sin^n\theta.$

7. Show that the fourth negative pedal of the cardioide $r = a(1 + \cos\theta)$ is a parabola.

8. Show that the fourth and fifth positive pedals of the curve

$$r^{\frac{2}{9}}\cos\frac{2}{9}\theta = a^{\frac{2}{9}}$$

are respectively a rectangular hyperbola and a Lemniscate.

9. Show that the nth positive pedal of the spiral $r = ae^{\theta\cot a}$ is

$$r = a\,\sin^n a\, e^{n\left(\frac{\pi}{2} - a\right)\cot a}\, e^{\theta\cot a}.$$

219. It is useful to remember the following pedals.

Original Curve.	The Given Point.	Name of Pedal.
(1.) Circle,	point on circumference,	Cardioide.
(2.) Circle,	any point,	Limaçon.
(3.) Parabola,	focus,	Tangent at vertex.
(4.) Parabola,	vertex,	Cissoid.
(5.) Central conic,	focus,	Auxiliary circle.
(6.) Central conic,	centre,	$r^2 = a^2\cos^2\theta \pm b^2\sin^2\theta.$
(7.) Rectangular hyperbola,	centre,	$\left\{\begin{array}{l}\text{Lemniscate of}\\ \quad\text{Bernoulli.}\end{array}\right.$
(8.) Equiangular spiral,	pole,	Equiangular spiral.
(9.) $r^m = a^m\cos m\theta$,	pole,	$r^{\frac{m}{m+1}} = a^{\frac{m}{m+1}}\cos\dfrac{m}{m+1}\theta.$

220. Tangential-Polar, or p, ψ Equation of a Curve.

If ψ be the angle which the tangent to a curve makes with any fixed straight line, the relation between p and ψ often forms a very simple and elegant equation of the curve. This relation has been called by Dr. Ferrers the Tangential-Polar Equation.

The p, ψ equation may be deduced at once from the equation of the first positive pedal.

If $r = f(\theta)$ be the pedal curve, then, since $\psi = \dfrac{\pi}{2} + \theta$ (see Fig. 26, Art. 217), the equation between p and ψ is clearly

$$p = f\left(\psi - \frac{\pi}{2}\right).$$

Ex. 1. The p, ψ equation of $Ax^2 + By^2 = 1$ is

$$p^2 = \frac{\sin^2\psi}{A} + \frac{\cos^2\psi}{B} \text{ (Art. 216).}$$

Ex. 2. The pedal of $\dfrac{2a}{r} = 1 + \cos\theta$ with regard to the origin is $r\cos\theta = a$, and therefore its p, ψ equation is $p\sin\psi = a$.

221. Relations between p, t, ρ, etc.

Let PY, QY' be tangents at the contiguous points P, Q on the curve, and let OY, OY' be perpendiculars from O upon these tangents. Let OZ be drawn at right angles to $Y'Y$ produced. Let the tangents at P and Q intersect at T, and let them cut the initial line OX in R and S. Let the normals at P and Q intersect in C.

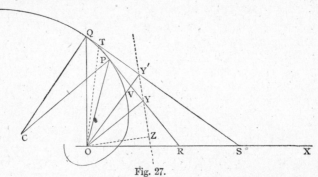

Fig. 27.

Let the co-ordinates of P be (r, θ), and let those of Q be $(r + \delta r, \ \theta + \delta\theta)$. Let $OY = p$, $OY' = p + \delta p$, $P\hat{R}X = \psi$, $Q\hat{S}X = \psi + \delta\psi$. Then $S\hat{T}R$, $P\hat{C}Q$, $Y\hat{O}Y'$ each $= \delta\psi$. Let $PY = t$, and arc $PQ = \delta s$. Let OY' cut TY in V; then, since $O\hat{Y}V$ is a right angle and $Y\hat{O}V = \delta\psi$ a small angle of the first order, OV differs from OY by a quantity of higher order than the first (Art. 32).

Hence VY' differs from δp by a quantity of higher order than δp, and $\qquad TY' \tan \delta\psi = VY'$,

therefore $\qquad TY' \dfrac{\tan \delta\psi}{\delta\psi} = \dfrac{VY'}{\delta\psi}$,

and proceeding to the limit $\qquad t = \dfrac{dp}{d\psi}$ ....(1)

Similarly, if PC be called ρ we have
$$\text{arc } PQ = PC \cdot \delta\psi,$$
neglecting infinitesimals of higher order than $\delta\psi$, therefore
$$PC = \frac{\text{arc } PQ}{\delta\psi},$$
and proceeding to the limit,
$$\rho = \frac{ds}{d\psi} \quad ....(2)$$

Again
$$\delta t = Y'Q - YP$$
$$= (Y'T + TQ) - (YV + VT - PT)$$
$$= (PT + TQ) + (Y'T - VT) - YV.$$

Now $YV = p \tan \delta\psi$,

and remembering that when $\delta\psi$ is an infinitesimal of the first order, VT and $Y'T$, $PT + TQ$ and δs, $\tan \delta\psi$ and $\delta\psi$, each differ by quantities of order higher than the first, we have, upon dividing by $\delta\psi$ and proceeding to the limit,

$$\frac{dt}{d\psi} = \frac{ds}{d\psi} - p,$$

or
$$\rho = p + \frac{d^2p}{d\psi^2}, \text{ by (1) and (2)}\ldots\ldots\ldots\ldots\ldots(3)$$

222. Perpendicular on Tangent to Pedal.

From the same figure it is clear that since $Y\widehat{O}Y' = Y\widehat{T}Y'$, the points O, Y, Y', T are concyclic, and therefore $O\widehat{Y}Z = \pi - O\widehat{Y}Y' = O\widehat{T}Y'$; and the triangles OYZ and OTY' are similar. Therefore $\dfrac{OZ}{OY} = \dfrac{OY'}{OT}.$

And in the limit when Q comes into coincidence with P, Y comes into coincidence with Y, and the limiting position of $Y'Y$ is the tangent to the pedal curve. Let the perpendicular on the tangent at Y to the pedal curve be called p_1, then the above ratio becomes
$$\frac{p_1}{p} = \frac{p}{r},$$

or
$$p_1 r = p^2.$$

223. Circle on Radius Vector for Diameter touches Pedal.

It is clear also from the figure of Art. 221 that the circle on the radius vector as diameter touches the first positive pedal of the curve. For OT is in the limit a radius vector; and the circle on OT as diameter passing through Y and Y', two contiguous points on the pedal, must in the limit have the same tangent at Y as the pedal curve, and must therefore touch it.

224. Pedal Equation of Pedal Curve.

Let $r = f(p)$ be the pedal equation of a given curve. Then, since $p_1 r = p^2$, we have $p_1 = \dfrac{p^2}{f(p)}$, and therefore, writing r for p and p for p_1, the pedal equation of the first positive pedal curve is $p = \dfrac{r^2}{f(r)}.$

Ex. The first positive pedal of the rectangular hyperbola $r = \dfrac{a^2}{p}$ is

$$p = \dfrac{r^2}{\dfrac{a^2}{r}} = \dfrac{r^3}{a^2},$$

which is the p, r equation of Bernoulli's Lemniscate, as is also obvious from Art. 218.

EXAMPLES.

1. Write down the pedal equations of the first positive pedals of the curves given in the table of Art. 214.

2. From the origin O is drawn a perpendicular OP_1 to the tangent at P, similarly OP_2 is drawn perpendicular to the tangent at P_1 to the locus of P_1, and so on.   Show that the figure $PP_1P_2 \dots$ is equiangular, but cannot be equilateral.   [OXFORD, 1888.]

3. Show that the kth pedal, positive or negative, of $\dfrac{p}{r} = f(r)$ is

$$\dfrac{p}{r} = f\left(\dfrac{r^{k+1}}{p^k}\right).$$

225. We may also prove the results of Art. 221 as follows:—
Let the tangent P_1T make an angle ψ with the initial line.
Then the perpendicular makes an angle $\alpha = \psi - \dfrac{\pi}{2}$ with the same line.   Let $OY = p$.   Let P_1P_2 be the normal, and P_2 its

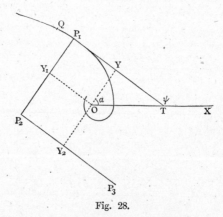

Fig. 28.

point of intersection with the normal at the contiguous point Q.   Let OY_1 be the perpendicular from O upon the normal. Call this p_1.   Let P_2P_3 be drawn at right angles to P_1P_2, and let the length of OY_2, the perpendicular upon it from O, be p_2.

The equation of P_1T is clearly

$$p = x \cos a + y \sin a \quad ....(1)$$

The contiguous tangent at Q has for its equation

$$p + \delta p = x \cos(a + \delta a) + y \sin(a + \delta a) ....(2)$$

Hence subtracting and proceeding to the limit it appears that

$$\frac{dp}{da} = -x \sin a + y \cos a ....(3)$$

is a straight line passing through the point of intersection of (1) and (2); also being perpendicular to (1) it is the equation of the normal P_1P_2.

Similarly $\qquad \dfrac{d^2p}{da^2} = -x \cos a - y \sin a ....(4)$

represents a straight line through the point of intersection of two contiguous positions of the line P_1P_2 and perpendicular to P_1P_2, viz., the line P_2P_3, and so on for further differentiations.

From this it is obvious that

$$OY_1 = \frac{dp}{da} = \frac{dp}{d\psi}, \text{ since } \frac{d\psi}{da} = 1 ;$$

$$OY_2 = \frac{d^2p}{da^2} = \frac{d^2p}{d\psi^2},$$

$$\text{etc.}$$

Hence $\qquad t = P_1Y = \dfrac{dp}{d\psi},$

and $\qquad \rho = P_1P_2 = OY + OY_2 = p + \dfrac{d^2p}{d\psi^2}.$

226. **Tangential Equation of a Curve.**

DEF. The tangential equation of a curve is the *condition that the line* $lx + my + n = 0$ *may touch* the curve.

Method 1. Let $F(x, y) = 0$ be the curve, then the tangent at x, y is $\qquad XF_x + YF_y + ZF_z = 0.$

Comparing this with $\quad lX + mY + n = 0.$

$$\frac{F_x}{l} = \frac{F_y}{m} = \frac{F_z}{n} = \lambda, \text{ say.}$$

If x, y, λ be eliminated between these equations, and $F(x, y) = 0$, or $lx + my + n = 0$, a relation between l, m, n will result. This is the equation required.

Method 2.   We may also proceed thus.   Eliminate y between $F(x, y) = 0$ and $lx + my + n = 0$; we obtain an equation in x, say $\phi(x) = 0$.   For tangency this equation must have a pair of equal roots.   The condition for this will be found by eliminating x between $\phi(x) = 0$ and $\phi'(x) = 0$.

In following this method, instead of eliminating y it is often better to make a homogeneous equation between $F(x, y) = 0$ and $lx + my + n = 0$, and then express that the resulting equation for the ratio $y : x$ has a pair of equal roots.

Ex.   Find the tangential equation of the conic

$$ax^2 + 2hxy + by^2 + 2gx + 2fy + c = 0.$$

The first process gives us $ax + hy + g = \dfrac{\lambda}{2}l,$

$$hx + by + f = \dfrac{\lambda}{2}m,$$

$$gx + fy + c = \dfrac{\lambda}{2}n.$$

Also $lx + my + n = 0.$

The eliminant from these four equations is

$$\begin{vmatrix} a, & h, & g, & l \\ h, & b, & f, & m \\ g, & f, & c, & n \\ l, & m, & n, & 0 \end{vmatrix} = 0,$$

which may be written

$$Al^2 + Bm^2 + Cn^2 + 2Fmn + 2Gnl + 2Hlm = 0,$$

where $A, B, C, \ldots$ are the co-factors of the determinant

$$\begin{vmatrix} a, & h, & g \\ h, & b, & f \\ g, & f, & c \end{vmatrix}.$$

INVERSION.

227.   Def.   Let O be the pole, and suppose any point P be given; then if a second point Q be taken on OP, or OP produced, such that $OP . OQ = \text{constant}$, k^2 say, then Q is said to be the *inverse of the point P with respect to a circle of radius k and centre O*, (or shortly, with respect to O).

If the point P move in any given manner, the *path of Q is said to be inverse to the path of P.*   If (r, θ) be the polar co-ordinates of the point P, and (r', θ) those of the inverse point Q, then $rr'=k^2$. Hence, if the locus of P be $f(r,\theta)=0$, that of Q will be $f\left(\dfrac{k^2}{r},\theta\right)=0$.

For example, the curves $r^m=a^m\cos m\theta$ and $r^m\cos m\theta=a^m$ are inverse to each other with regard to a circle of radius a.

228. Again, if (x,y) be the Cartesian co-ordinates of P, and (x',y') those of Q, then

$$x=r\cos\theta=\frac{k^2}{r'}\cos\theta=k^2\frac{r'\cos\theta}{r'^2}=k^2\frac{x'}{x'^2+y'^2},$$

and similarly

$$y=\frac{k^2y'}{x'^2+y'^2}.$$

Hence, if the locus of P be given in Cartesians as

$$F(x,y)=0,$$

the locus of Q will be

$$F\left(\frac{k^2x}{x^2+y^2},\frac{k^2y}{x^2+y^2}\right)=0.$$

Ex. The inverse of the straight line $x=a$ with regard to a circle of radius k and centre at the origin is

$$\frac{k^2x}{x^2+y^2}=a,$$

or

$$x^2+y^2=\frac{k^2}{a}x,$$

a circle which touches the axis of y at the origin.

EXAMPLES.

1. Show that the inverse of the parabola $y^2=4ax$ with regard to a circle whose centre is at the origin and radius the semi-latus rectum is the pedal of the parabola $y^2+4ax=0$ with regard to the vertex.

2. Show that the inverse of the conic $u_2+u_1+u_0=0$ with regard to the origin is the quartic curve

$$k^4u_2+k^2u_1(x^2+y^2)+u_0(x^2+y^2)^2=0.$$

3. Show that the inverse of the general curve of the nth degree, viz.,

$$u_n+u_{n-1}+u_{n-2}+\ldots+u_1+u_0=0,$$

with regard to the origin is

$$k^{2n}u_n+k^{2n-2}u_{n-1}r^2+k^{2n-4}u_{n-2}r^4+\ldots+k^2u_1r^{2n-2}+u_0r^{2n}=0,$$

where $r^2=x^2+y^2$.

4. Show that the inverse of a conic with regard to the focus is a Limaçon (Equation $r=a+b\cos\theta$), which becomes a cardioide if the conic be a parabola.

5. Show that the Equation of the inverse of a conic with regard to the centre is of the form $r^2=A+B\cos 2\theta$, which becomes a Lemniscate of Bernoulli if the conic be a rectangular hyperbola.

229. Tangents to Curve and Inverse inclined to Radius Vector at Supplementary Angles

If P, P' be two contiguous points on a curve, and Q, Q' the inverse points, then, since $OP \cdot OQ = OP' \cdot OQ'$, the points P, P', Q', Q are concyclic; and since the angles OPT and $OQ'T$ are therefore supplementary, it follows that in the limit when P'

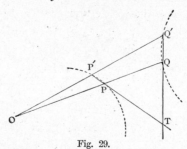

Fig. 29.

ultimately coincides with P and Q' with Q, the tangents at P and Q make supplementary angles with OPQ.

The ultimate ratio of corresponding elementary arcs, viz.,

$$\frac{ds}{ds'} = Lt\frac{PP'}{QQ'} = Lt\frac{OP}{OQ'} = \frac{OP}{OQ} = \frac{OP \cdot OQ}{OQ^2} = \frac{k^2}{r'^2} = \frac{r^2}{k^2}.$$

230. It follows from the preceding article that when two curves intersect, their inverses intersect at the same angle; and as particular cases, if two curves touch, their inverses touch, and if the original curves cut orthogonally their inverses cut orthogonally.

Ex. 1. It is an obvious property of two confocal and co-axial parabolas whose concavities are turned in opposite directions that they cut at right angles. By inverting this proposition, the focus being the pole of inversion, it is clear that the curves which cut orthogonally each member of the family of cardioides $r = a(1 + \cos \theta)$ found by giving different values to a, are also cardioides.

Ex. 2. Show by inverting a conic with regard to its focus that the circle
$$x^2 + y^2 = l(e + \cos a)x + l\sin a \cdot y$$
touches the Limaçon $r = l + le \cos \theta$ at the point given by $\theta = a$.

231. If P, P' be *any* two points, and Q, Q' their inverse points, then as before (Art. 229) the triangles OPP', $OQ'Q$ are similar and

$$\frac{PP'}{QQ'} = \frac{OP}{OQ'} = \frac{k^2}{OQ \cdot OQ'}.$$

Thus

$$PP' = k^2 \cdot \frac{QQ'}{OQ \cdot OQ'}.$$

Ex. 1. If a, b, c be points in a straight line in the order indicated, then

$$ab + bc = ac.$$

Suppose A, B, C to be the inverse points of a, b, c with regard to any point O. Then O, A, B, C are concyclic and

$$k^2\frac{AB}{OA \cdot OB} + k^2\frac{BC}{OB \cdot OC} = k^2\frac{AC}{OA \cdot OC},$$

whence $$OC \cdot AB + OA \cdot BC = OB \cdot AC,$$

the result known as Ptolemy's Theorem.

Ex. 2. If O, A, B, C ... J, K be points on a circle, prove

$$\frac{AB}{OA \cdot OB} + \frac{BC}{OB \cdot OC} + \cdots + \frac{JK}{OJ \cdot OK} = \frac{AK}{OA \cdot OK}.$$

[MATH. TRIPOS, 1890.]

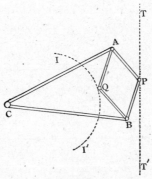

Fig. 30.

232. Mechanical Construction of the Inverse of a Curve.

In the accompanying figure AC, CB, BQ, QA, PA, PB is a system of freely jointed rods, of which $AC = BC$, and

$$AQ = QB = BP = PA.$$

At P and Q sockets are placed to carry tracing pencils. A pin fixes C to the drawing board. The system is then movable about C. It is clear from elementary geometry that C, Q, P are in a straight line, and that

$$CP \cdot CQ = CA^2 - AQ^2,$$

and is therefore constant. Hence whatever curve P is made to trace out, Q *will trace out its inverse*, the point C being the pole of inversion.

In the figure P is represented as tracing a *straight line*, in which case Q will trace an *arc of a circle*, as shown in Art. 228.

Peaucellier has utilized this construction for the conversion of circular into rectilinear motion.

POLAR RECIPROCALS.

233. Polar Reciprocal of a Curve with regard to a given Circle.

DEF. If OY be the perpendicular from the pole upon the tangent to a given curve, and if a point Z be taken on OY or OY produced *such that* $OY.OZ$ *is constant* ($=k^2$ say), the locus of Z is called the *polar reciprocal* of the given curve with regard to a circle of radius k and centre at O.

From the definition it is obvious that this curve is the *inverse of the first positive pedal* curve, and therefore its equation can at once be found.

Ex. *Polar reciprocal of an ellipse with regard to its centre.*

For the ellipse
$$\frac{x^2}{a^2}+\frac{y^2}{b^2}=1,$$

the condition that $p=x\cos a+y\sin a$ touches the curve is
$$p^2=a^2\cos^2a+b^2\sin^2a.$$

Hence the polar equation of the pedal with regard to the origin is
$$r^2=a^2\cos^2\theta+b^2\sin^2\theta.$$

Again, the inverse of this curve is
$$\frac{k^4}{r^2}=a^2\cos^2\theta+b^2\sin^2\theta,$$

or
$$a^2x^2+b^2y^2=k^4,$$

which is therefore the equation of the polar reciprocal of the ellipse with regard to a circle with centre at the origin and radius k.

234. The method may therefore be stated thus :—

First *find the condition that* $p=x\cos a+y\sin a$ *will touch the given curve.* Then *write* $\dfrac{k^2}{r}$ *for* p *and* θ *for* a *in that condition.* The result is the required polar reciprocal with regard to a circle of radius k and centre at the origin.

235. Polar Reciprocal with regard to a given Conic.

DEF. If $S=0$ be any curve and $U=0$ a given conic, the *locus of the poles with regard to* U *of tangents to* S is called the *Polar Reciprocal of the curve* S *with regard to the conic* U.

Let the equation of a tangent to S be
$$p=X\cos a+Y\sin a,$$

and the condition of tangency
$$p=f(a).$$

If x, y be the pole of this tangent with regard to $U=0$, the tangent must be coincident with the polar

$$XU_x + YU_y + ZU_z = 0 \; ;$$

therefore $\qquad \dfrac{\cos \alpha}{p} = -\dfrac{U_x}{U_z}, \quad \dfrac{\sin \alpha}{p} = -\dfrac{U_y}{U_z}.$

Hence $\qquad \dfrac{1}{p^2} = \dfrac{U_x^2 + U_y^2}{U_z^2}$ and $\tan \alpha = \dfrac{U_y}{U_x}.$

Hence the equation of the Polar Reciprocal is

$$U_x^2 + U_y^2 = U_z^2 \bigg/ \left\{ f\left(\tan^{-1}\dfrac{U_y}{U_x} \right) \right\}^2.$$

For further information on the subject of reciprocal polars and the methods of reciprocation the student is referred to Dr. Salmon's *Treatise on Conic Sections*, chap. XV.

EXAMPLES.

1. If the tangent at x_1, y_1 to the curve $x^3 + y^3 = a^3$ meet the curve again in (X, Y), show that

$$X/x_1 + Y/y_1 = -1.$$

Illustrate the result by means of a figure. [OXFORD, 1889.]

2. In the four-cusped hypocycloid

$$x^{\frac{2}{3}} + y^{\frac{2}{3}} = a^{\frac{2}{3}},$$

show that if $\qquad x = a \cos^3 \alpha$ then $y = a \sin^3 \alpha,$

and that the equation of the tangent at the point determined by α is

$$x \sin \alpha + y \cos \alpha = a \sin \alpha \cos \alpha.$$

Hence show that the locus of intersection of tangents at right angles to one another is $\qquad r^2 = \dfrac{a^2}{2} \cos^2 2\theta.$

3. In the semicubical parabola $ay^2 = x^3$ the tangent at any point P cuts the axis of y in M and the curve in Q. , O is the origin and N the foot of the ordinate of P. Prove that MN and OQ are equally inclined to the axis of x.

4. At any point of a curve where the ordinate varies as the cube of the abscissa, a tangent is drawn; where it cuts the curve another tangent is drawn; where this cuts the curve a third is drawn, and so on. Prove that the abscissae of the points of contact form a geometrical progression, and also the ordinates.

E.D.C. $\qquad\qquad\qquad\qquad$ M

5. If p_1 and p_2 be the perpendiculars from the origin cn the tangent and normal respectively at the point (x, y), and if $\tan \psi = \dfrac{dy}{dx}$, prove that
$$p_1 = x \sin \psi - y \cos \psi,$$
and
$$p_2 = x \cos \psi + y \sin \psi.$$

Hence prove that
$$p_2 = \frac{dp_1}{d\psi}.$$

6. The tangent at a point P of the cissoid $y^2(a - x) = x^3$ meets the curve again in Q and the tangent at Q meets the curve again in R. If O be the origin, prove that
$$\cot ROQ - \cot POQ = \tfrac{1}{2} \cot POR. \qquad \text{[Oxford, 1885.]}$$

7. The curve $x^3 + y^3 = 3axy$ is cut in the points P, Q, other than the origin by two lines drawn through the origin which are harmonic conjugates of the axes. Prove that the tangents at P, Q will intersect on the curve. $\qquad$ [Oxford, 1890.]

8. Show that, if the curves $r = f(\theta)$, $r = F(\theta)$ intersect at (r, θ), the angle between their tangents at the point of intersection is
$$\tan^{-1}\frac{F(\theta)f'(\theta) - F'(\theta)f(\theta)}{F'(\theta)f'(\theta) + F(\theta)f(\theta)}.$$

9. Prove that the locus of the extremity of the polar subtangent of the curve $u + f(\theta) = 0$ is $u = f'\!\left(\dfrac{\pi}{2} + \theta\right)$.

10. Prove that the locus of the extremity of the polar subnormal of the curve $r = f(\theta)$ is $\qquad r = f'\!\left(\theta - \dfrac{\pi}{2}\right)$.

Hence show that the locus of the extremity of the polar subnormal in the equiangular spiral $r = ae^{m\theta}$ is another equiangular spiral.

11. In the curve $\qquad r = \dfrac{1 + \tan\dfrac{\theta}{2}}{m + n \tan\dfrac{\theta}{2}}$

the locus of the extremity of the polar subtangent is a cardioide.
$$\text{[Professor Wolstenholme.]}$$

12. If the normals at the points (r_1, θ_1), (r_2, θ_2), (r_3, θ_3) on the cardioide $r = a(1 + \cos \theta)$ be concurrent, show that
$$\tan \frac{\theta_1}{2} + \tan \frac{\theta_2}{2} + \tan \frac{\theta_3}{2} + 3 \tan \frac{\theta_1}{2} \tan \frac{\theta_2}{2} \tan \frac{\theta_3}{2} = 0.$$
$$\text{[Oxford, 1890.]}$$

13. If in the last question $r_1 + r_2 + r_3 = 2a$, show that the locus of the point of concourse of the normals is a circle passing through the pole. $\qquad$ [Oxford, 1886.]

14. Show that the locus of intersection of the normals at the ends of a focal chord of a cardioide is a circle.

15. Show that tangents at the ends of a focal chord of the cardioide $r = a(1 + \cos \theta)$ intersect at right angles on a circle of radius $\dfrac{3a}{2}$ and centre $\left(\dfrac{a}{2}, 0\right)$.

16. If n_1, n_2, n_3, n_4 be the lengths of the four normals and t_1, t_2, t_3 the lengths of the three tangents drawn from any point to the semicubical parabola $ay^2 = x^3$, then will

$$27 n_1 n_2 n_3 n_4 = a t_1 t_2 t_3. \qquad \text{[MATH. TRIPOS, 1890.]}$$

17. The polar equation of the pedal of the curve

$$(x^2 + y^2 - a^2)^3 + 27 a^2 x^2 y^2 = 0$$

with respect to the point h, k may be written in the form

$$r = a \sin \theta \cos \theta - (h \cos \theta + k \sin \theta). \qquad \text{[OXFORD, 1888.]}$$

18. Determine the relation between p and r for the curve

$$y^2(3a - x) = (x - a)^3. \qquad \text{[OXFORD, 1889.]}$$

19. Show that the polar reciprocal of the curve $r^m = a^m \cos m\theta$ with regard to a circle whose centre is at the pole is of the form

$$r^{\frac{m}{m+1}} \cos \frac{m}{m+1} \theta = b^{\frac{m}{m+1}}.$$

20. Show that the polar reciprocal of the curve $x^m y^n = a^{m+n}$ with regard to a circle whose centre is at the origin is another curve of the same kind.

21. Show that the first positive pedal of the curve $p = \dfrac{r^{m+1}}{a^m}$ is

$$p^{m+1} a^m = r^{2m+1},$$

and that its polar reciprocal with regard to a circle of radius a whose centre is at the origin is $\qquad p^{m+1} = a^m r.$

22. Show that the inverse of the curve $p = f(r)$ with regard to a circle whose radius is k and centre at the pole is

$$p = \frac{r^2}{k^2} f\left(\frac{k^2}{r}\right),$$

and that the polar reciprocal is

$$\frac{k^2}{r} = f\left(\frac{k^2}{p}\right).$$

23. Show that the pedal of the inverse of $p = f(r)$ with regard to a circle whose radius is k and centre at the origin is

$$\frac{k^2 p^2}{r^3} = f\left(\frac{k^2 p}{r^2}\right).$$

24. Show that the pedal of the inverse of $p = \dfrac{r^{m+1}}{a^m}$ with regard to a circle whose radius is k and centre at the origin is

$$p = \left(\frac{a}{k^2}\right)^{\frac{m}{m-1}} r^{\frac{2m-1}{m-1}}.$$

25. Show that the polar reciprocal of the curve $r^m = a^m \cos m\theta$ with regard to the hyperbola $r^2 \cos 2\theta = a^2$ is

$$r^{\frac{m}{m+1}} \cos \frac{m}{m+1} \theta = a^{\frac{m}{m+1}}.$$

26. The locus of a point X is defined by the equation

$$F(\rho_1,\ \rho_2,\ \rho_3,\ \dots\ \rho_n) = a,$$

where $\rho_1, \rho_2, \dots$ are the distances of X from n fixed points $P_1, P_2, \dots P_n$. Show that the equation of its inverse with regard to any origin O is

$$F\left(\frac{r_1\rho_1'}{R},\ \frac{r_2\rho_2'}{R},\ \dots\ \frac{r_n\rho_n'}{R}\right) = a,$$

where $\rho_1', \rho_2', \dots$ are the distances of X', the inverse of X from the n fixed points $Q_1, Q_2, \dots$ which are the respective inverses of $P_1, P_2, \dots$; $r_1, r_2, r_3, \dots$ are the lengths of $OP_1, OP_2, \dots$; and $R = OX'$.

27. Show that the inverse with regard to any pole O of the Cartesian oval whose equation is $lr + mr' = n$, where r, r' are the distances of any point on the curve from two fixed points F_1, F_2, is

$$l \cdot OF_1 \cdot \rho_1 + m \cdot OF_2 \cdot \rho_2 = n\rho_3,$$

where ρ_1, ρ_2 are the distances of any point on the inverse curve from the points which are the inverses of F_1, F_2, and ρ_3 is the distance of the same point from the pole of inversion.

28. Show that the inverse of a Cassini's oval defined by the equation $\qquad\qquad rr' = \text{constant}$
is of the form $\qquad\qquad \rho_1\rho_2 = A\rho_3^2,$
the letters ρ_1, ρ_2, ρ_3 denoting the distances of any point on the inverse curve from certain fixed points.

29. If all the normals be drawn from a given point P to any number of given curves, and if P move so that the sum of the squares of the normals $\qquad PQ_1^2 + PQ_2^2 + \dots + PQ_n^2 = \text{constant},$
the normal to the locus of P will always pass through the centre of mean position of the points $Q_1, Q_2, Q_3, \dots Q_n$. [Frenet.]

30. A straight line AOP of given length always passes through a fixed point O, while A describes a given straight line AT; show that if PT be the tangent at P to the locus of P, the projection of PT on $AOP = AO$.

31. The point P moves so that $OP \cdot O'P = $ constant, O, O' being fixed points. If OY, $O'Y'$ be the perpendiculars from O and O' on the tangent at P to the locus of P, prove that

$$PY : PY' :: OP^2 : O'P^2.$$

32. Prove that the normal to the curve $f(r_1, r_2) = 0$, where r_1, r_2 are the distances of any point on the curve from two fixed points, divides the line joining the fixed points in the ratio

$$r_1 \frac{\partial f}{\partial r_2} : r_2 \frac{\partial f}{\partial r_1}.$$

[MATH. TRIPOS, 1888.]

33. A and B are fixed points and P a variable one lying on a curve given by the relation $f(\theta_1, \theta_2) = 0$ between the angles $PAB(= \theta_1)$ and $PBA(= \theta_2)$. Prove that the tangent at P to the curve divides AB in the ratio

$$\sin^2\theta_1 \frac{\partial f}{\partial \theta_1} : \sin^2\theta_2 \frac{\partial f}{\partial \theta_2}.$$

[OXFORD.]

34. O and O' are two fixed points, P any point in a curve defined by the equation

$$\frac{1}{r} - \frac{1}{r'} = \frac{1}{c},$$

where $r = OP$, $r' = O'P$, and c is constant. Prove that the distance between P and the consecutive curve obtained by changing c to $c + \delta c$ is ultimately

$$\frac{\delta c}{\sqrt{1 + \dfrac{3c^2}{rr'} + \dfrac{a^2c^4}{r^3r'^3}}},$$

where $a = OO'$.

[SMITH'S PRIZE.]

35. In a system of curves defined by an equation containing a variable parameter investigate at any point the normal distance between two consecutive curves, and determine the form of the equation for a system of parallel curves.

[PROFESSOR CAYLEY, *Messenger of Mathematics*, vol. V.]

CHAPTER VIII.

ASYMPTOTES.

236. DEF. *If a straight line cut a curve in two points at an infinite distance from the origin and yet is not itself wholly at infinity, it is called an asymptote to the curve.*

237. Equations of the Asymptotes.

Let the equation of any curve of the nth degree be arranged in homogeneous sets of terms and expressed as

$$x^n\phi_n\left(\frac{y}{x}\right)+x^{n-1}\phi_{n-1}\left(\frac{y}{x}\right)+x^{n-2}\phi_{n-2}\left(\frac{y}{x}\right)+\ldots=0. \ldots\ldots(\text{A})$$

To find where this curve is cut by any straight line whose equation is
$$y=\mu x+\beta \ldots\ldots\ldots\ldots\ldots\ldots\ldots\ldots(\text{B})$$

substitute $\mu+\dfrac{\beta}{x}$ for $\dfrac{y}{x}$ in equation (A), and the resulting equation

$$x^n\phi_n\left(\mu+\frac{\beta}{x}\right)+x^{n-1}\phi_{n-1}\left(\mu+\frac{\beta}{x}\right)+x^{n-2}\phi_{n-2}\left(\mu+\frac{\beta}{x}\right)\ldots=0\ldots(\text{C})$$

gives the abscissae of the points of intersection.

Applying Taylor's Theorem to expand each of these functional forms, equation (C) may be written

$$x^n\phi_n(\mu)+x^{n-1}\left|\begin{array}{l}\beta\phi_n{}'(\mu)+x^{n-2}\\ +\phi_{n-1}(\mu)\end{array}\right|\begin{array}{l}\dfrac{\beta^2}{2!}\phi''_n(\mu)+\ldots\\ +\beta\phi'_{n-1}(\mu)\\ +\phi_{n-2}(\mu)\end{array}=0.\ldots(\text{D})$$

This is an equation of the nth degree, *proving that a straight line will in general intersect a curve of the nth degree in n points real or imaginary.*

The straight line $y=\mu x+\beta$ is at *our choice*, and therefore the two constants μ and β may be chosen, so as to satisfy any pair of consistent equations. Suppose we choose μ and β, so that

$$\phi_n(\mu) = 0 \dots \dots \dots \dots \dots \dots \dots \dots \text{(E)}$$

and

$$\beta\phi'_n(\mu) + \phi_{n-1}(\mu) = 0 \dots \dots \dots \dots \dots \dots \text{(F)}$$

The two highest powers of x now disappear from equation (D), and that equation has therefore *two infinite roots*.

If, then, $\mu_1, \mu_2, \dots, \mu_n$ be the n values of μ deduced from equation (E) (which is of the nth degree in μ), the corresponding values of β will in general be given by

$$\beta_1 = -\frac{\phi_{n-1}(\mu_1)}{\phi'_n(\mu_1)}, \ \beta_2 = -\frac{\phi_{n-1}(\mu_2)}{\phi'_n(\mu_2)}, \dots$$

and the n straight lines

$$\left.\begin{array}{c} y = \mu_1 x + \beta_1 \\ y = \mu_2 x + \beta_2 \\ \cdot \ \ \cdot \ \ \cdot \ \ \cdot \ \ \cdot \\ y = \mu_n x + \beta_n \end{array}\right\} \begin{array}{l} \text{are the } \textit{asymptotes} \\ \textit{of the curve.} \end{array}$$

238. Rule.

Hence, in order to find the asymptotes of any given curve, we may either *substitute* $\mu x + \beta$ *for* y in the equation of the curve, and then *by equating the coefficients of the two highest powers of x to zero find μ and β*. Or we may assume the result of the preceding article, which may be enunciated in the following practical way:—*In the highest degree terms put $x = 1$ and $y = \mu$ [the result of this is to form $\phi_n(\mu)$] and equate to zero. Hence find μ. Form $\phi_{n-1}(\mu)$ in a similar way from the terms of degree $n-1$, and differentiate $\phi_n(\mu)$, then the values of β are found by substituting the several values of μ in the formula* $\beta = -\dfrac{\phi_{n-1}(\mu)}{\phi'_n(\mu)}.$

Ex. *Find the asymptotes of the cubic*

$$2x^3 - x^2y - 2xy^2 + y^3 + 2x^2 + xy - y^2 + x + y + 1 = 0.$$

Here

$$\phi_3(\mu) = \mu^3 - 2\mu^2 - \mu + 2 = 0 ;$$

therefore

$$(\mu - 1)(\mu + 1)(\mu - 2) = 0 ;$$

giving

$$\mu = 1, \ -1, \text{ or } 2.$$

Again,

$$\phi_2(\mu) = 2 + \mu - \mu^2,$$

and

$$\phi'_3(\mu) = 3\mu^2 - 4\mu - 1 ;$$

therefore

$$\beta = \frac{\mu^2 - \mu - 2}{3\mu^2 - 4\mu - 1}.$$

Hence if $\qquad\qquad \mu=1, \quad \beta=1,$

if $\qquad\qquad\qquad \mu=-1, \quad \beta=0,$

and if $\qquad\qquad \mu=2, \quad \beta=0.$

Hence the asymptotes of the curve are

$$y=x+1,$$
$$y=-x,$$
$$y=2x.$$

EXAMPLES.

1. The asymptotes of

$$y^3-6xy^2+11x^2y-6x^3+x+y=0$$

are $\qquad\qquad y=x, \ y=2x, \ y=3x.$

2. The asymptotes of $\ y^3-x^2y+2y^2+4y+x=0$

are $\qquad\qquad y=0, \ y-x+1=0, \ y+x+1=0.$

239. Number of Asymptotes to a Curve of the nth Degree.

It is clear that since $\phi_n(\mu)=0$ is in general of the nth degree in μ, and $\beta\phi'_n(\mu)+\phi_{n-1}(\mu)=0$ is of the first degree in β, that *n values of* μ, and no more, can be found from the first equation, while the *n corresponding values of* β can be found from the second. Hence *n asymptotes, real or imaginary, can be found for a curve of the nth degree.*

240. If the degree of an equation be odd it is proved in Theory of Equations that there must be one real root at least. Hence any curve of an odd degree must have at least one real asymptote, and therefore must extend to infinity. *No curve therefore of an odd degree can be closed.* Neither can a curve of odd degree have an even number of real asymptotes, or a curve of even degree an odd number.

241. If, however, the term y^n be missing from the terms of the nth degree in the equation of the curve, the term μ^n will also be missing from the equation $\phi_n(\mu)=0$, and there will therefore be an *apparent loss of degree* in this equation. It is clear, however, that in this case, since the coefficient of μ^n is zero, one root of the equation $\phi_n(\mu)=0$ is infinite, and therefore the corresponding asymptote is at right angles to the axis of x; *i.e., parallel to that of y.* This leads us to the special consideration of such asymptotes as may be parallel to either of the axes of co-ordinates.

242. Asymptotes Parallel to the Axes.

Let the curve arranged as in equation (A), Art. 237, be

$$a_0x^n + a_1x^{n-1}y + a_2x^{n-2}y^2 + \ldots + a_{n-1}xy^{n-1} + a_ny^n$$
$$+ b_1x^{n-1} + b_2x^{n-2}y + \ldots\ldots\ldots\ldots + b_ny^{n-1}$$
$$+ c_2x^{n-2} + \ldots$$
$$+ \ldots = 0 \ldots\ldots\ldots\ldots\ldots\ldots\ldots(A')$$

If arranged in descending powers of x this is

$$a_0x^n + (a_1y + b_1)x^{n-1} + \ldots = 0 \ldots\ldots\ldots\ldots(B')$$

Hence, if a_0 vanish, and y be so chosen that

$$a_1y + b_1 = 0,$$

the coefficients of the two highest powers of x in equation (B') vanish, and therefore *two of its roots are infinite.* Hence the straight line $a_1y + b_1 = 0$ is an asymptote.

In the same way, if $a_n = 0$, $a_{n-1}x + b_n = 0$ is an asymptote.

Again, if $a_0 = 0$, $a_1 = 0$, $b_1 = 0$, and if y be so chosen that

$$a_2y^2 + b_2y + c_2 = 0,$$

three roots of equation (B') become infinite, and the lines represented by $\qquad a_2y^2 + b_2y + c_2 = 0$

represent a pair of asymptotes, real or imaginary, parallel to the axis of x.

Hence the rule to find those asymptotes which are parallel to the axes is, "*equate to zero the coefficients of the highest powers of x and y.*"

Ex. *Find the asymptotes of the curve*

$$x^2y^2 - x^2y - xy^2 + x + y + 1 = 0.$$

Here the coefficient of x^2 is $y^2 - y$ and the coefficient of y^2 is $x^2 - x$. Hence $x = 0$, $x = 1$, $y = 0$, and $y = 1$ are asymptotes. Also, since the curve is one of the fourth degree, we have thus obtained all the asymptotes.

EXAMPLES.

1. The asymptotes of $y^2(x^2 - a^2) = x$ are

$$\left.\begin{array}{l} y = 0 \\ x = \pm a \end{array}\right\}.$$

2. The co-ordinate axes are the asymptotes of

$$xy^3 + x^3y = a^4.$$

3. The asymptotes of the curve $x^2y^2 = c^2(x^2 + y^2)$ are the sides of a square.

243. Partial Fractions Method.

The values of β, viz.,

$$-\frac{\phi_{n-1}(\mu_1)}{\phi'_n(\mu_1)}, \quad -\frac{\phi_{n-1}(\mu_2)}{\phi'_n(\mu_2)}, \text{ etc.}$$

are *exactly the constants required in putting*

$$-\frac{\phi_{n-1}(t)}{\phi_n(t)}$$

into partial fractions.*

This gives a very easy way of obtaining the asymptotes. For if

$$-\frac{\phi_{n-1}(t)}{\phi_n(t)} = \frac{\beta_1}{t-\mu_1} + \frac{\beta_2}{t-\mu_2} + \frac{\beta_3}{t-\mu_3} + \cdots$$

the asymptotes will be

$$y = \mu_1 x + \beta_1,$$
$$y = \mu_2 x + \beta_2,$$
$$\text{etc.}$$

Ex. *Find the asymptotes of the curve*
$$(x^2 - y^2)(x + 2y) + 5(x^2 + y^2) + x + y = 0.$$

Here
$$\frac{\phi_{n-1}(t)}{\phi_n(t)} = 5\frac{t^2 + 1}{(2t+1)(t-1)(t+1)} = \frac{-\dfrac{25}{3}}{2t+1} + \frac{\dfrac{5}{3}}{t-1} + \frac{5}{t+1}.$$

Hence the asymptotes are
$$2y + x = -\frac{25}{3},$$
$$y - x = \frac{5}{3},$$
$$y + x = 5.$$

244. Particular Cases of the General Theorem.

We return to a closer consideration of the equations

$$\phi_n(\mu) = 0, \dots\dots\dots\dots\dots\dots\dots\dots\dots\text{(E)}$$
$$\beta\phi'_n(\mu) + \phi_{n-1}(\mu) = 0, \dots\dots\dots\dots\dots\dots\text{(F)}$$

of Art. 237.

It is proved in Theory of Equations that if an equation such as $\phi_n(\mu) = 0$ have a pair of roots equal, say μ_1, then $\phi'_n(\mu_1) = 0$.

---

* Suppose the single factor $t - \mu_1$ to occur in $\phi_n(t)$. Let
$$\phi_n(t) = (t - \mu_1)\chi(t).$$
Hence, differentiating $\phi'_n(t) = \chi(t) + (t - \mu_1)\chi'(t),$
and putting $t = \mu_1$, $\phi'_n(\mu_1) = \chi(\mu_1).$

But if $\dfrac{A}{t - \mu_1}$ be the partial fraction corresponding to the factor $t - \mu_1$,

$$A = -\frac{\phi_{n-1}(\mu_1)}{\chi(\mu_1)} \text{ (Art. 109)}$$
$$= -\frac{\phi_{n-1}(\mu_1)}{\phi'_n(\mu_1)}.$$

I. Let the roots of $\phi_n(\mu)=0$ be μ_1, μ_2, ..., μ_n, supposed *all different*, so that $\phi'_n(\mu)$ does not vanish for any of these roots. Also, suppose $\phi_n(\mu)$ *and* $\phi_{n-1}(\mu)$ *to contain a common factor* $\mu-\mu_1$ say, then $\phi_{n-1}(\mu_1)=0$, and therefore $\beta_1=0$.

Hence the corresponding asymptote is $y=\mu_1 x$ and *passes through the origin*.

II. Next, suppose *two of the roots* of the equation $\phi_n(\mu)=0$ to be equal, e.g., $\mu_2=\mu_1$, then $\phi'_n(\mu_1)=0$. In this case, if $\phi_{n-1}(\mu)$ do not contain $\mu-\mu_1$ as one of its factors, the value β determined from equation (F) is infinite. The line $y=\mu_1 x+\beta_1$ then does indeed cut the curve in two points at an infinite distance from the origin, but it *makes an infinite intercept* on the axis of y and therefore this line *lies wholly at infinity*. Such a straight line is not in general called an asymptote, but it *will however count as one of the n theoretical asymptotes discussed in Art. 239*.

III. But if $\phi_n(\mu)=0$ have *a pair of equal roots each* $=\mu_1$, we have $\phi'_n(\mu_1)=0$, and *if* μ_1 *be also a root of* $\phi_{n-1}(\mu)=0$ the value of β cannot be determined from equation (F). We may however choose β so that the coefficient of x^{n-2} in equation (D) of Art. 237 vanishes, that is so that

$$\frac{\beta^2}{2}\phi''_n(\mu)+\beta\phi'_{n-1}(\mu)+\phi_{n-2}(\mu)=0,$$

from which two values of β, real or imaginary, may be deduced. Let the roots of this equation be β_1 and β_1'. We thus obtain the equations of *two parallel straight lines*

$$y=\mu_1 x+\beta_1, \quad y=\mu_1 x+\beta_1',$$

which each cut the curve in three points at an infinite distance from the origin. In this case there is a double point on the curve at infinity (see Art. 286).

It is clear that in this case *any* straight line parallel to $y=\mu_1 x$ will cut the curve in *two* points at infinity. But of all this system of parallel straight lines the two whose equations we have just found are *the only ones which cut the curve in three points at infinity*, and therefore the *name asymptote is confined to them*. The one equation which includes both straight lines is obtained at once by substituting $y-\mu_1 x$ for β in the equation to obtain β and is

$$(y-\mu_1 x)^2\phi''_n(\mu_1)+2(y-\mu_1 x)\phi'_{n-1}(\mu_1)+2\phi_{n-2}(\mu_1)=0.$$

Ex. *Find the asymptotes of the cubic curve*
$$x^3 + 2x^2y + xy^2 - x^2 - xy + 2 = 0.$$

Equating to zero the coefficient of y^2 we obtain $x = 0$, the only asymptote parallel to either axis.

Putting $\mu x + \beta$ for y,
$$x^3 + 2x^2(\mu x + \beta) + x(\mu x + \beta)^2 - x^2 - x(\mu x + \beta) + 2 = 0,$$

or rearranging,
$$x^3(1 + 2\mu + \mu^2) + x^2(2\beta + 2\mu\beta - 1 - \mu) + x(\beta^2 - \beta) + 2 = 0.$$

$1 + 2\mu + \mu^2 = 0$ gives two roots $\mu = -1$. $2\beta + 2\mu\beta - 1 - \mu = 0$ is an identity if $\mu = -1$, and this fails to find β.

Proceeding to the next coefficient, $\beta^2 - \beta = 0$ gives $\beta = 0$ or 1.

Hence the three asymptotes are $x = 0$, and the pair of parallel lines
$$y + x = 0,$$
$$y + x = 1.$$

245. Form of the Curve at Infinity. Another Method for Oblique Asymptotes.

Let P_r, F_r be used to denote rational algebraical expressions which contain terms of the rth and lower, but of no higher degrees.

Suppose the equation of a curve of the nth degree to be thrown into the form
$$(ax + by + c)P_{n-1} + F_{n-1} = 0. \quad\ldots\ldots\ldots\ldots\ldots(1)$$

Then *any* straight line parallel to $ax + by = 0$ obviously cuts the curve in *one* point at infinity; and to find the particular member of this family of parallel straight lines which cuts the curve in a second point at infinity, let us examine what is the ultimate linear form to which the curve gradually approximates as we travel to infinity in the above direction, thus obtaining the ultimate direction of the curve and forming the equation of the tangent at infinity. To do this we make the x and y of the curve become *large in the ratio given by* $x : y = -b : a$, and we obtain the equation
$$ax + by + c + \operatorname{Lt}_{y = -\frac{a}{b}x = \infty}\left(\frac{F_{n-1}}{P_{n-1}}\right) = 0.$$

If this limit be finite we have arrived at the equation of a straight line which at infinity represents the limiting form of the curve, and which satisfies the definition of an asymptote.

To obtain the value of the limit it is advantageous to put $x = -\dfrac{b}{t}$ and $y = \dfrac{a}{t}$, and then after simplification make $t = 0$.

Ex. *Find the asymptote of*
$$x^3 + 3x^2y + 3xy^2 + 2y^3 = x^2 + y^2 + x.$$
We may write this curve as
$$(x+2y)(x^2 + xy + y^2) = x^2 + y^2 + x,$$
whence the equation of the asymptote is given by
$$x + 2y = Lt_{x=-2y=\infty} \frac{x^2 + y^2 + x}{x^2 + xy + y^2},$$
and putting $x = \dfrac{-2}{t}$, $y = \dfrac{1}{t}$ we have

$$x + 2y = Lt_{t=0} \frac{\dfrac{4}{t^2} + \dfrac{1}{t^2} - \dfrac{2}{t}}{\dfrac{4}{t^2} - \dfrac{2}{t^2} + \dfrac{1}{t^2}} = Lt_{t=0} \frac{5 - 2t}{3} = \frac{5}{3},$$

i.e.,
$$x + 2y = \frac{5}{3}.$$

EXAMPLE. Show that $x + y = \dfrac{a}{2}$ is the only real asymptote of the curve
$$(x+y)(x^4 + y^4) = a(x^4 + a^4).$$

246. Next, suppose the equation of a curve put into the form
$$(ax + by + c)F_{n-1} + F_{n-2} = 0,$$
then the line $ax + by + c = 0$ cuts the curve in two points at infinity, for no terms of the nth or $(n-1)^{\text{th}}$ degrees remain in the equation determining the points of intersection. Hence in general the line $ax + by + c = 0$ is an asymptote. We say, *in general*, because if F_{n-1} be of the form $(ax + by + c)P_{n-2}$, itself containing a factor $ax + by + c$, there will, as in Art. 244, III., be a *pair of asymptotes* parallel to $ax + by + c = 0$, each cutting the curve in *three* points at infinity. The equation of the curve then becomes
$$(ax + by + c)^2 P_{n-2} + F_{n-2} = 0,$$
and the equations of the parallel asymptotes are
$$ax + by + c = \pm \sqrt{-Lt \frac{F_{n-2}}{P_{n-2}}},$$
where x and y in the limit on the right-hand side become infinite in the ratio $\dfrac{x}{y} = -\dfrac{b}{a}$.

Or, if the curve be written in the form
$$(ax + by)^2 P_{n-2} + (ax + by)F_{n-2} + f_{n-2} = 0,$$
in proceeding to infinity in the direction $ax + by = 0$, we have
$$(ax + by)^2 + (ax + by) \cdot Lt \frac{F_{n-2}}{P_{n-2}} + Lt \frac{f_{n-2}}{P_{n-2}} = 0$$

when the limits are to be obtained by putting $x=-\dfrac{b}{t}$, $y=\dfrac{a}{t}$, and then diminishing t indefinitely.   We thus obtain a pair of parallel asymptotes

$$ax+by=\alpha \text{ and } ax+by=\beta$$

where α and β are the roots of

$$\rho^2+\rho \, Lt\frac{F_{n-2}}{P_{n-2}}+Lt\frac{f_{n-2}}{P_{n-2}}=0.$$

And other particular forms which the equation of the curve may assume can be treated similarly.

Ex. 1. *To find the pair of parallel asymptotes of the curve*

$$(2x-3y+1)^2(x+y)-8x+2y-9=0.$$

Here $$2x-3y+1=\pm\sqrt{Lt\frac{8x-2y+9}{x+y}},$$

where x and y become infinite in the direction of the line $2x=3y$.

Putting $x=\dfrac{3}{t}$, $y=\dfrac{2}{t}$, the right side becomes ±2.   Hence the asymptotes required are $$2x-3y=1 \text{ and } 2x-3y+3=0.$$

Ex. 2. *Find the asymptotes of*

$$(x-y)^2(x^2+y^2)-10(x-y)x^2+12y^2+2x+y=0.$$

Here $$(x-y)^2-10(x-y)Lt_{x=y=\infty}\frac{x^2}{x^2+y^2}+12Lt_{x=y=\infty}\frac{y^2}{x^2+y^2}=0.$$

or $$(x-y)^2-5(x-y)+6=0,$$

giving the parallel asymptotes $x-y=2$ and $x-y=3$.

247. Asymptotes by Inspection.

It is now clear that if the equation $F_n=0$ break up into linear factors so as to represent a system of n straight lines no two of which are parallel, they will be the asymptotes of any curve of the form $$F_n+F_{n-2}=0.$$

Ex. 1. $$(x-y)(x+y)(x+2y-1)=3x+4y+5$$

is a cubic curve whose asymptotes are obviously

$$x-y=0,$$
$$x+y=0,$$
$$x+2y-1=0.$$

Ex. 2. $$(x-y)^2(x+2y-1)=3x+4y+5.$$

Here $x+2y-1=0$ is one asymptote.   The other two asymptotes are parallel to $y=x$.   Their equations are

$$x-y=\pm\sqrt{Lt_{t=0}\frac{3+4+5t}{1+2-t}}=\pm\sqrt{\frac{7}{3}}.$$

248. Case in which all the Asymptotes pass through the Origin.
If then, when the equation of a curve is arranged in homogeneous set of terms, as

$$u_n + u_{n-2} + u_{n-3} + \ldots = 0,$$

it be found that there are no terms of degree $n-1$, and if also u_n contain no repeated factor, the n straight lines passing through the origin, and whose equation is $u_n = 0$, are the n asymptotes.

EXAMPLES.

Find the asymptotes of the following curves :—

1. $y^3 = x^2(2a - x)$.
2. $y^3 = x(a^2 - x^2)$.
3. $x^3 + y^3 = a^3$.
4. $y(a^2 + x^2) = a^2x$.
5. $axy = x^3 - a^3$.
6. $y^2(2a - x) = x^3$.
7. $x^3 + y^3 = 3axy$.
8. $x^2y + y^2x = a^3$.
9. $x^2y^2 = (a + y)^2(b^2 - y^2)$.
10. $x^2y^2 = a^2y^2 - b^2x^2$.
11. $xy(x - y) - a(x^2 - y^2) = b^3$.
12. $(a^2 - x^2)y^2 = x^2(a^2 + x^2)$.
13. $xy^2 = 4a^2(2a - x)$.
14. $y^2(a - x) = x(b - x)^2$.
15. $x^2y = x^3 + x + y$.
16. $xy^2 + a^2y = x^3 + mx^2 + nx + p$.
17. $x^3 + 2x^2y - xy^2 - 2y^3 + 4y^2 + 2xy + y - 1 = 0$.
18. $x^3 - 2x^2y + xy^2 + x^2 - xy + 2 = 0$.
19. $y(x - y)^3 = y(x - y) + 2$.
20. $x^3 + 2x^2y - 4xy^2 - 8y^3 - 4x + 8y = 1$.
21. $(x + y)^2(x + 2y + 2) = x + 9y - 2$.
22. $3x^3 + 17x^2y + 21xy^2 - 9y^3 - 2ax^2 - 12axy - 18ay^2 - 3a^2x + a^2y = 0$.

249. Intersections of a Curve with its Asymptotes.
If a curve of the nth degree have n asymptotes, no two of which are parallel, we have seen in Art. 247 that the equations of the asymptotes and of the curve may be respectively written

$$F_n = 0,$$

and $\qquad\qquad F_n + F_{n-2} = 0.$

The n asymptotes therefore intersect the curve again at points lying upon the curve $F_{n-2} = 0$. Now each asymptote cuts its curve in two points at infinity, and therefore in $n - 2$ other points. Hence these $n(n-2)$ points lie on a certain curve of degree $n-2$. For example,

1. The asymptotes of a *cubic* will cut the curve again in *three points lying in a straight line;*

2. The asymptotes of a *quartic* curve will cut the curve again in *eight points lying on a conic section;*

and so on with curves of higher degree.

EXAMPLES.

1. Find the equation of a cubic which has the same asymptotes as the curve $x^3 - 6x^2y + 11xy^2 - 6y^3 + x + y + 1 = 0$, and which touches the axis of y at the origin, and goes through the point $(3, 2)$.

2. Show that the asymptotes of the cubic $x^2y - xy^2 + xy + y^2 + x - y = 0$ cut the curve again in three points which lie on the line $x + y = 0$.

3. Find the equation of the conic on which lie the eight points of intersection of the quartic curve $xy(x^2 - y^2) + a^2y^2 + b^2x^2 = a^2b^2$ with its asymptotes.

4. Show that the four asymptotes of the curve

$$(x^2 - y^2)(y^2 - 4x^2) - 6x^3 + 5x^2y + 3xy^2 - 2y^3 - x^2 + 3xy - 1 = 0$$

cut the curve again in eight points which lie on a circle.

5. Form the equation of the cubic curve which has $x = 0$, $y = 0$, $\dfrac{x}{a} + \dfrac{y}{b} = 1$ for asymptotes, and cuts its asymptotes in the three points where they intersect the line $\dfrac{x}{a'} + \dfrac{y}{b'} = 1$, and also passes through the point a, b.

6. Form the equation of a quartic curve which has $x = 0$, $y = 0$, $y = x$, $y = -x$ for asymptotes, which passes through the point a, b, and cuts its asymptotes again in eight points lying upon the circle $x^2 + y^2 = a^2$.

250. Common Transversal of a Curve and its Asymptotes.
The equation of the asymptotes and that of the curve coincide in the terms of the nth and $(n-1)^{\text{th}}$ degrees. Hence, if we put both equations into polars, the sums of the roots of the two equations for r are equal; also, the origin is arbitrary. Hence, if through any point O a line $OP_1P_2P_3\ldots$ be drawn to cut the curve in the points $P_1, P_2, P_3, \ldots$ and the asymptotes in $p_1, p_2, p_3, \ldots$ then $\Sigma OP = \Sigma Op$, whence, if $\Sigma OP = 0$, it follows that $\Sigma Op = 0$, so that both systems of points have the same centre of mean position. Hence also the algebraical sum of the intercepts between the curve and its asymptotes is zero.

[NEWTON.]

A well known case of this is that of the hyperbola, where, if O be the middle point of P_1P_2, $OP_1 + OP_2 = 0$, and therefore $Op_1 + Op_2 = 0$, and therefore O is also the middle point of p_1p_2, whence it follows that in that case $P_1p_1 = p_2P_2$.

251. Other Definitions of "Asymptotes."

Other definitions have been given of an asymptote, *e.g.*, (a) That an asymptote is the *limiting position of the tangent* to a curve when the point of contact moves away along the curve to an infinite distance from the origin, while the tangent itself does not ultimately lie wholly at infinity; again, (β) That an asymptote is a straight line whose *distance from a point on the curve diminishes indefinitely* as the point moves away along the curve to an infinite distance from the origin.

252. To prove the Consistency of the Several Definitions.

We propose to show that the results derived from these definitions are the same as those derived from our definition in Art. 236.

Consider definition (a).

Let the curve be
$$U \equiv u_n + u_{n-1} + u_{n-2} + \ldots + u_0 = 0.$$
The equation of the tangent is
$$X\frac{\partial U}{\partial x} + Y\frac{\partial U}{\partial y} + u_{n-1} + 2u_{n-2} + \ldots + nu_0 = 0.$$

We shall now suppose the point of contact x, y to move to ∞ along some branch of the curve. We shall therefore only retain the highest powers of x and y which occur, viz., those of the $(n-1)^{\text{th}}$ degree. Thus we must retain only $\dfrac{\partial u_n}{\partial x}$ for $\dfrac{\partial U}{\partial x}$, $\dfrac{\partial u_n}{\partial y}$ for $\dfrac{\partial U}{\partial y}$, and u_{n-1} for $u_{n-1} + 2u_{n-2} + \ldots + nu_0$.

Hence in the limit we shall have
$$Lt\left\{ X\frac{\partial u_n}{\partial x} + Y\frac{\partial u_n}{\partial y} + u_{n-1} \right\} = 0,$$

or
$$Y = X\left\{ -Lt\frac{\dfrac{\partial u_n}{\partial x}}{\dfrac{\partial u_n}{\partial y}} \right\} - Lt\left\{ \frac{u_{n-1}}{\dfrac{\partial u_n}{\partial y}} \right\},$$

and it is easy to see that this agrees with the equation of an asymptote found in Art. 237.

253. We next consider definition (β); we have already shown that $ax + by + c = 0$ is, according to our definition, in general an asymptote of the curve
$$(ax + by + c)F_{n-1} + F_{n-2} = 0.$$
The perpendicular from any point x, y of this curve upon the line
$$ax + by + c = 0$$
is
$$\frac{ax + by + c}{\sqrt{a^2 + b^2}} = -\frac{1}{\sqrt{a^2 + b^2}}\frac{F_{n-2}}{F_{n-1}},$$

and the limit of this expression is clearly zero when x and y become infinite in the ratio $-b : a$, provided that the terms of degree $n-1$ in F_{n-1} do not contain $ax+by$ as a factor, for the degree of the denominator is higher than that of the numerator. Hence the *distance between the curve and the asymptote is ultimately a vanishing quantity*, and the line

$$ax+by+c=0$$

is such as to satisfy definition (β).

254. The Curve in General lies on Opposite Sides of the Asymptote at Opposite Extremities.

Let the straight line $ax+by+c=0$ be an asymptote of the curve, and suppose there is no other asymptote of the curve parallel to this. The equation of the curve is of the form $(ax+by+c)F_{n-1}+F_{n-2}=0$; and, as in the last article, the perpendicular from any point x, y of the curve on this asymptote is given by

$$P=-\frac{1}{\sqrt{a^2+b^2}}\frac{F_{n-2}}{F_{n-1}}.$$

When x and y become very large in the ratio given by

$$\frac{y}{x}=-\frac{a}{b},$$

this may ultimately be written as

$$P=\frac{k}{x}f\left(\frac{y}{x}\right),$$

where k is a constant, and it is therefore obvious that P changes sign with x.

Hence in general the curve at the opposite extremities of this asymptote lies on opposite sides of it.

255. Exceptions.

If, however, $ax+by$ be a factor of the terms of highest degree in F_{n-2}, we may write the equation of the curve

$$(ax+by+c)F_{n-1}+F_{n-3}=0,$$

so that the perpendicular on the asymptote is now given by

$$P=\frac{ax+by+c}{\sqrt{a^2+b^2}}=-\frac{1}{\sqrt{a^2+b^2}}\frac{F_{n-3}}{F_{n-1}};$$

and when x and y become very large in the ratio given by

$$\frac{y}{x}=-\frac{a}{b},$$

this can be ultimately written

$$\frac{k}{x^2}f\left(\frac{y}{x}\right).$$

This, however, though ultimately vanishing, does not change

sign with x, so that in this case the curve at *opposite extremities* of the asymptote *lies on the same side* of it.

256. Again, if the equation of the curve be expressible in the form
$$(ax+by+c)^2 P_{n-2} + F_{n-2} = 0,$$
the expression for the length of the perpendicular is in the limit of the form $f\left(\dfrac{y}{x}\right)$. This does not in general ultimately vanish, and therefore in general $ax+by+c=0$ is not an asymptote, but is parallel to a pair of asymptotes. This case has been discussed in Art. 246.

257. If, however, the curve assumes the form
$$(ax+by+c)^2 F_{n-2} + F_{n-3} = 0,$$
the length of the perpendicular is given by
$$(\text{Perpendicular})^2 = -\frac{1}{a^2+b^2}\frac{F_{n-3}}{F_{n-2}}.$$
Hence, if the ratio of $\dfrac{y}{x}$ be that of $-\dfrac{a}{b}$ when x and y become infinite, this may ultimately be written
$$\frac{k}{x}f\left(\frac{y}{x}\right),$$
and therefore $\quad$ Perpendicular $= \pm\sqrt{\dfrac{k}{x}\cdot f\left(\dfrac{y}{x}\right)},$

which ultimately vanishes, but x cannot change sign or the perpendicular will become imaginary at one extremity of the asymptote. Hence the line is *only asymptotic at one end* and the curve approaches the asymptote *on opposite sides*.

And in the same way other particular forms may be discussed.

258. **Curvilinear Asymptotes.**

If there be two curves which continually approach each other so that for a common abscissa the limit of the difference of the ordinates is zero, or for a common ordinate the limit of the difference of the abscissae is zero when that common abscissa or common ordinate is infinite, these curves are said to be asymptotic to each other. For example, the curves
$$y = Ax^2 + Bx + C + \frac{D}{x},$$
$$y = Ax^2 + Bx + C$$
are asymptotic; for the difference of their ordinates for any common abscissa x is $\dfrac{D}{x}$, a quantity whose limit is zero when x is infinite.

259. Linear Asymptote obtained by Expansion. Stirling's Method. *

If it be possible to express the equation of a given curve in the form $y = Ax + B + \dfrac{C}{x} + \dfrac{D}{x^2} + \cdots,$

then the line $y = Ax + B$ is clearly asymptotic to the curve. This method of obtaining rectilinear asymptotes is frequently useful.

260. To find on which side of the Asymptote the Curve lies.

The sign of C (Art. 259) is useful in determining on which side of the asymptote the curve lies.

Let y be the ordinate of the curve, y' that of the asymptote,

then $\qquad\qquad y - y' = \dfrac{C}{x} + \dfrac{D}{x^2} + \cdots.$

If x be taken sufficiently large, the sign of $\dfrac{C}{x}$ governs the sign of the whole of the right-hand side.

Suppose x and y to be positive, *i.e.*, in the *first quadrant*, then $y - y'$ will have in the limit the same sign as C. If C be *positive*, $y - y'$ will be positive, and the ordinate of the curve will be greater than that of the asymptote, and the curve will therefore approach the asymptote *from above*. Similarly, if C be *negative*, $y - y'$ will be negative, and the curve will approach the asymptote from *below*. And in the same way for portions in the other quadrants.

Ex. 1. *Find the asymptotes of the curve*
$$y^2(x^2 - a^2) = x^2(x^2 - 4a^2).$$

Here $x^2 - a^2 = 0$ gives $x = a$ and $x = -a$, two asymptotes parallel to the axis of y.

Again, $\qquad\qquad y = \pm x \left(\dfrac{1 - \dfrac{4a^2}{x^2}}{1 - \dfrac{a^2}{x^2}} \right)^{\frac{1}{2}}$

$$= \pm x \left(1 - \frac{4a^2}{x^2}\right)^{\frac{1}{2}} \left(1 - \frac{a^2}{x^2}\right)^{-\frac{1}{2}}$$

$$= \pm x \left\{1 - \frac{2a^2}{x^2} \cdots\right\} \left\{1 + \frac{1}{2}\frac{a^2}{x^2} + \cdots\right\}$$

$$= \pm x \left\{1 - \frac{3a^2}{2x^2} + \cdots\right\}$$

$$= \pm x \mp \frac{3a^2}{2x} + \cdots.$$

* *Lin. Tert. Ord. Newtonianæ*, p. 48.

Hence the asymptotes are $\quad y = \pm x$ }.
and $\qquad\qquad\qquad\qquad\; x = \pm a$ }

Again, considering $\qquad y = x - \dfrac{3a^2}{2x} + \ldots$

it appears that if x be positive the ordinate of the curve is less than the ordinate of the asymptote, and therefore the curve approaches the line $y = x$ in the positive quadrant from below. Similarly the curve approaches the asymptote $y = -x$ in the fourth quadrant from above.

The student should observe that the curve cuts the axes where $x = \pm 2a$, and also at the origin where the tangents are $y = \pm 2x$. Also that y is imaginary when x^2 lies between a^2 and $4a^2$. There should now be no difficulty in drawing a graph of the curve.

Ex. 2. *Find the asymptotes of*
$$(y - x)^2 x - 3y(y - x) + 2x = 0,$$
and examine how the curve is placed with reference to them.

Here the coefficient of y^2 is $x - 3$; therefore $x = 3$ is an asymptote.

Also the curve may be written
$$(y - x)^2 - 3(y - x)\frac{y}{x} + 2 = 0,$$
and therefore, in the direction $y = x$ at infinity, this ultimately takes the form $\qquad (y - x)^2 - 3(y - x) + 2 = 0.$

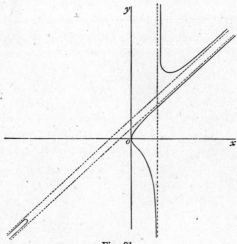

Fig. 31.

Hence $y - x = 1$ and $y - x = 2$ are asymptotes.

Put $\qquad\qquad\qquad y - x = A + \dfrac{B}{x} + \ldots,$

therefore the equation of the curve becomes
$$\left(A + \frac{B}{x} + \ldots\right)^2 x - 3\left(x + A + \frac{B}{x} + \ldots\right)\left(A + \frac{B}{x} + \ldots\right) + 2x = 0,$$
or $\qquad x(A^2 - 3A + 2) + \{2AB - 3(A^2 + B)\} + \ldots = 0.$

Equating to zero the several coefficients

$$A^2 - 3A + 2 = 0,$$
$$2AB - 3(A^2 + B) = 0,$$

etc.,

whence $A = 1$ or 2,
$$B = -3 \text{ or } 12,$$

etc.

Hence the equation of the curve may be expressed in either of the ways

$$y = x + 1 - \frac{3}{x} \ldots , \quad y = x + 2 + \frac{12}{x} \ldots .$$

Hence to the right of the y-axis the curve lies below the asymptote

$$y = x + 1,$$

and above the asymptote $y = x + 2$.

On the left side of the y-axis the curve is above

$$y = x + 1,$$

and below $y = x + 2$.

The student will easily verify

(a) that neither of the cross asymptotes cuts the curve again in a point whose co-ordinates are finite ;

(β) that the asymptote $x = 3$ cuts the curve where $y = 3\frac{2}{3}$;

(γ) that the product of the roots for y is $\dfrac{x(x^2 + 2)}{x - 3}$, and is positive unless x lies between 0 and 3, but is then negative ;

(δ) that y is imaginary if x lies between 0 and -24 ;

(ϵ) that the tangent at the origin is $x = 0$.

Figure 31 is a tracing of the curve.

EXAMPLES.

1. Find the asymptotes of the curve $y = x\dfrac{x^2 + a^2}{x^2 - a^2}$.   Find on which side of the oblique asymptote the curve lies in the positive quadrant.   Show also that the hyperbola $x(y - x) = 2a^2$ is asymptotic to this cubic curve.

2. Find the asymptotes of the curve $y^2 = x^2\dfrac{x + a}{x - a}$, and find on which side the curve approaches these asymptotes.

3. Show that the curve $x = \dfrac{y^3 - a^3}{ay}$ has a rectilinear asymptote $y = 0$, and a parabolic asymptote $y^2 = ax$.

4. Show that the curve $x^2 y = x^4 + x^3 + x^2 + x + 1$ has a parabolic asymptote whose vertex is at the point $(-\frac{1}{2}, \frac{3}{4})$, and whose latus rectum $= 1$.

5. Show that the curve $x^2 y = x^3 + x^2 + x + 1$ has a hyperbolic asymptote whose eccentricity $= \dfrac{2}{\sqrt{2 + \sqrt{2}}}$.

261. General Investigation.

In order to express the general equation

$$x^n \phi_n\left(\frac{y}{x}\right) + x^{n-1} \phi_{n-1}\left(\frac{y}{x}\right) + x^{n-2} \phi_{n-2}\left(\frac{y}{x}\right) + \ldots = 0 \ldots\ldots\ldots (1)$$

in the form $$y = \mu x + \beta + \frac{\gamma}{x} + \frac{\delta}{x^2} + \ldots, \quad \ldots\ldots\ldots\ldots\ldots\ldots(2)$$

substitute for y from (2) in (1); then, since the result must be an identity, the coefficient of each power of x will be zero. This will give sufficient equations to determine $\mu, \beta, \gamma, \ldots$.

The result of this substitution is

$$x^n \phi_n(\mu) + x^{n-1} \left| \begin{array}{l} \beta\phi'_n(\mu) \\ + \phi_{n-1}(\mu) \end{array} \right. + x^{n-2} \left| \begin{array}{l} \gamma\phi'_n(\mu) + \ldots = 0 \\ + \dfrac{\beta^2}{2!}\phi''_n(\mu) \\ + \beta\phi'_{n-1}(\mu) \\ + \phi_{n-2}(\mu) \end{array} \right.$$

which gives us the series of equations

$$\phi_n(\mu) = 0, \quad\ldots\ldots\ldots\ldots(\text{i.})$$

$$\beta\phi'_n(\mu) + \phi_{n-1}(\mu) = 0, \quad\ldots\ldots\ldots\ldots(\text{ii.})$$

$$\gamma\phi'_n(\mu) + \frac{\beta^2}{2!}\phi''_n(\mu) + \beta\phi'_{n-1}(\mu) + \phi_{n-2}(\mu) = 0, \quad\ldots\ldots\ldots(\text{iii.})$$

$$\cdot\quad\cdot\quad\cdot\quad\cdot\quad\cdot\quad\cdot\quad\cdot\quad\cdot\quad\cdot\quad\cdot\quad\cdot\quad\cdot$$

Hence $\mu, \beta, \gamma \ldots$ are determined.

262. Parabolic Branches.

In the case when $\phi_n(\mu) = 0$ has equal roots μ_1, it follows as in Art. 244 that $\phi_n'(\mu_1) = 0$. If then $\phi_{n-1}(\mu_1)$ does not also vanish it appears that the second of the above equations (ii.) cannot be satisfied by any finite value of β. Hence the assumption that the equation of the curve can be thrown into the form (2) with μ_1 for the coefficient of x is no longer tenable.

The equation of the curve is now of the form

$$(y - \mu_1 x)^2 v_{n-2} + u_{n-1} + u_{n-2} + \ldots + u_0 = 0 \quad\ldots\ldots\ldots\ldots(3)$$

where u_{n-1} does not contain the factor $y - \mu_1 x$.

We may write this

$$(y - \mu_1 x)^2 + x \cdot \frac{u_{n-1}}{x v_{n-2}} + \frac{u_{n-2}}{v_{n-2}} + \ldots = 0,$$

and if we put α for $Lt \dfrac{u_{n-1}}{x v_{n-2}}$ and β for $Lt \dfrac{u_{n-2}}{v_{n-2}}$ when x and y become infinite in the ratio $1 : \mu_1$ the curve ultimately approximates to the parabolic form

$$(y - \mu_1 x)^2 + \alpha x + \beta = 0 \quad\ldots\ldots\ldots\ldots\ldots(4)$$

This parabola, although a first approximation to the shape of the curve, is not in general asymptotic to it, but serves to suggest that in closely examining the parabolic branches we should endeavour to expand y in the form

$$\frac{y}{x} = \mu + \frac{A}{x^{\frac{1}{2}}} + \frac{B}{x} + \frac{C}{x^{\frac{3}{2}}} + \frac{D}{x^2} + \ldots \quad \ldots \ldots \ldots \ldots \ldots (5)$$

and discard for this case the expansion (2) assumed in the last article.

If we substitute this in

$$x^n \phi_n\left(\frac{y}{x}\right) + x^{n-1}\phi_{n-1}\left(\frac{y}{x}\right) + x^{n-2}\phi_{n-2}\left(\frac{y}{x}\right) + x^{n-3}\phi_{n-3}\left(\frac{y}{x}\right) + \ldots = 0 \quad (1)$$

and expand as before, the result (after collecting the coefficients of the powers of x) is

$$x^n \phi_n(\mu)$$
$$+ x^{n-\frac{1}{2}}[A\,\phi_n'(\mu)]$$
$$+ x^{n-1}\left[B\phi_n'(\mu) + \frac{A^2}{2}\phi_n''(\mu) + \phi_{n-1}(\mu)\right]$$
$$+ x^{n-\frac{3}{2}}\left[C\phi'_n(\mu) + AB\phi''_n(\mu) + \frac{A^3}{6}\phi'''_n(\mu) + A\phi'_{n-1}(\mu)\right]$$
$$+ x^{n-2}\left[D\phi_n'(\mu) + \frac{B^2}{2}\phi_n''(\mu) + AC\phi_n''(\mu) + \frac{A^2B}{2}\phi'''_n(\mu)\right.$$
$$\left. + \frac{A^4}{24}\phi''''_n(\mu) + B\phi'_{n-1}(\mu) + \frac{A^2}{2}\phi''_{n-1}(\mu) + \phi_{n-2}(\mu)\right]$$
$$+ \text{etc.} \qquad = 0,$$

and equating to zero the several coefficients

$$\phi_n(\mu) = 0 \text{ (and by supposition } \phi'_n(\mu) = 0,$$

$$\frac{A^2}{2}\phi''_n(\mu) + \phi_{n-1}(\mu) = 0,$$

$$B\phi''_n(\mu) + \frac{A^2}{6}\phi'''_n(\mu) + \phi'_{n-1}(\mu) = 0,$$

$$AC\phi''_n(\mu) + \frac{B^2}{2}\phi''_n(\mu) + \frac{A^2B}{2}\phi'''_n(\mu) + \frac{A^4}{24}\phi''''_n(\mu)$$
$$+ B\phi'_{n-1}(\mu) + \frac{A^2}{2}\phi''_{n-1}(\mu) + \phi_{n-2}(\mu) = 0,$$

etc.,

which determine the hitherto unknown constants

$$A, B, C \ldots.$$

The parabola $\quad (y - \mu x - B)^2 = A^2 x + 2AC$

is then asymptotic to the curve, and the side of the parabola on which the curve lies is indicated by the sign of D.

It should be noticed that the first approximation
$$(y - \mu x)^2 = A^2 x$$
is not in general asymptotic to the curve.

263. In practice it is found more convenient to adopt a method of successive approximation to obtain the ultimate form of a parabolic branch at an infinite distance from the origin. This method will be indicated best by an example.

Ex. Obtain the rectilinear asymptote of the curve $(y - x)^2(y + x) = 2ax^2$, and examine the parabolic branch.

The rectilinear asymptote is parallel to $y + x = 0$. We may write the equation

$$y + x = 2a\frac{x^2}{(y - x)^2}$$

$$= 2a\frac{x^2}{4x^2} \text{ to a first approximation}$$

$$= \frac{a}{2}, \dots\dots\dots\dots\dots\dots\dots\dots\dots\dots\dots(1)$$

giving the equation of the asymptote.

Proceeding to a second approximation,

$$y + x = 2a\frac{x^2}{\left(\frac{a}{2} - 2x\right)^2}$$

$$= \frac{a}{2}\left(1 - \frac{a}{4x}\right)^{-2}$$

$$= \frac{a}{2} + \frac{a^2}{4x} \dots\dots\dots\dots\dots\dots\dots\dots\dots(2)$$

This indicates that the curve lies above the asymptote on the right-hand side of the y-axis, but below on the left.

To examine the parabolic branch.

The axis of the asymptotic parabola is clearly in the direction $y = x$.

For a first approximation to the shape at infinity,

$$y - x = \sqrt{\frac{2ax^2}{x + x}} = \sqrt{ax} \dots\dots\dots\dots\dots\dots(3)$$

For a second approximation, substitute *this* value of y and we obtain

$$y - x = \sqrt{\frac{2ax^2}{x + x + \sqrt{ax}}}$$

$$= \sqrt{\frac{2ax}{2 + \sqrt{\frac{a}{x}}}}$$

$$= \sqrt{ax}\left(1 + \frac{1}{2}\sqrt{\frac{a}{x}}\right)^{-\frac{1}{2}}$$

$$= \sqrt{ax}\left(1 - \frac{1}{4}\sqrt{\frac{a}{x}}\dots\right),$$

or $\qquad y - x = \sqrt{ax} - \frac{a}{4} \dots\dots\dots\dots\dots\dots\dots(4)$

To obtain a third approximation, use the value of y given by Equation (4).

Thus $\quad y - x = \sqrt{\dfrac{2ax^2}{x+x+\sqrt{ax}-\dfrac{a}{4}}} = \sqrt{ax}\left(1+\tfrac{1}{2}\sqrt{\dfrac{a}{x}}-\dfrac{a}{8x}\right)^{-\frac{1}{2}},$

or $\qquad\qquad\qquad y - x = \sqrt{ax} - \tfrac{1}{4}a + \dfrac{5}{32}\dfrac{a^{\frac{3}{2}}}{x^{\frac{1}{2}}}.$ ....(5)

It appears, therefore, that though the first approximation (3) indicates the ultimate shape of the curve at infinity, it is not asymptotic to the curve.

The second approximation (4) gives a parabola which, as is seen from (5), is such that the limit of the difference of its ordinate from that of the curve is zero, and though not itself being that parabola which *most closely* approximates to the shape of the curve at ∞, is nevertheless useful in the tracing of the curve. This is the dotted parabola of the tracing shown below.

The third approximation (5) shows that the ordinate of the upper branch of this parabola is less than that of the curve, and that the ordinate of the lower branch of this parabola is greater than that of the curve, so that both branches of the curve approach this parabola from the outside.

Equation (5) shows that the true asymptotic parabola is

$$\left(y-x+\frac{a}{4}\right)^2 = ax + \frac{5}{16}a^2,$$

which is coaxial with the parabola (4) shown in the figure.

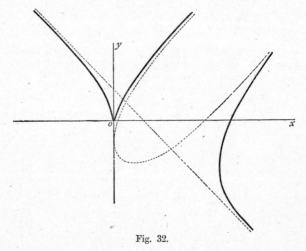

Fig. 32.

264. For further information on the subject of curvilinear asymptotes the student is referred to Frost's *Curve Tracing*, chapters VII. and VIII.

265. Polar Co-ordinates.

Let the equation of the curve be

$$r^n f_n(\theta) + r^{m-1} f_{n-1}(\theta) + \ldots + f_0(\theta) = 0, \ldots\ldots\ldots\ldots\ldots(1)$$

or

$$u^n f_0(\theta) + u^{n-1} f_1(\theta) + \ldots + f_n(\theta) = 0. \ldots\ldots\ldots\ldots(2)$$

To find the directions in which $r = \infty$ or $u = 0$ we have

$$f_n(\theta) = 0 \ldots\ldots\ldots\ldots\ldots\ldots\ldots\ldots\ldots(3)$$

Let the roots of this equation be

$$\theta = a, \ \beta, \ \gamma, \ \ldots.$$

Let $X\widehat{O}P = a$. Then the radius OP, the curve, and the asymptote meet at infinity towards P. Let $OY(=p)$ be the

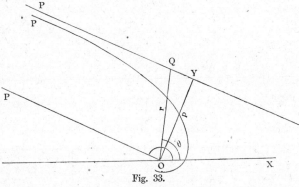

Fig. 33.

perpendicular upon the asymptote. Since OY is at right angles to OP it is the polar subtangent, and $p = -\dfrac{d\theta}{du}$. Let $X\widehat{O}Y = a'$, and let Q be any point whose co-ordinates are r, θ upon the asymptote. Then the equation of the asymptote is

$$p = r \cos (\theta - a') \ldots\ldots\ldots\ldots\ldots\ldots\ldots\ldots(4)$$

It is clear from the figure that $a' = a - \dfrac{\pi}{2}$.

To find the value of $-\dfrac{d\theta}{du}$ when $u = 0$ differentiate equation (2), and put $u = 0$ and $\theta = a$, and we obtain

$$\left(\frac{du}{d\theta}\right)_{u=0} f_{n-1}(a) + f'_n(a) = 0 \ldots\ldots\ldots\ldots\ldots(5)$$

Substituting the value of $\left(-\dfrac{d\theta}{du}\right)_{u=0}$ hence deduced for p in equation (4) we have

$$\frac{f_{n-1}(a)}{f'_n(a)} = r \cos \left(\theta - a + \frac{\pi}{2}\right)$$

$$= r \sin (a - \theta).$$

Hence the equations of the asymptotes are

$$r \sin (a - \theta) = \frac{f_{n-1}(a)}{f'_n(a)},$$

$$r \sin (\beta - \theta) = \frac{f_{n-1}(\beta)}{f'_n(\beta)},$$

etc.

COR. The case most often met with is that in which $n = 1$, when the equation of the curve is $r f_1(\theta) + f_0(\theta) = 0$. Then $f_1(\theta) = 0$ gives a, β, γ, etc., and the asymptotes are

$$r \sin (a - \theta) = \frac{f_0(a)}{f'_1(a)}, \ \text{ etc.}$$

266. The equivalent Cartesian form

$$y = x \tan a + \sec a \left(\frac{d\theta}{du} \right)_{\theta = a}$$

will be found convenient to remember and somewhat easier to *draw* the asymptote from than the polar equation.

267. Rule for Drawing the Asymptote.

After having found the value of $\left(\dfrac{d\theta}{du} \right)_{u=0}$ suppose we stand at the origin and look in the direction of that value of θ which makes $u = 0$. Draw a line at right angles to that direction through the origin and of length equal to the value of $\left(-\dfrac{d\theta}{du} \right)_{u=0}$ to the right hand or the left according as that value is positive or negative. Through the end of this line draw a perpendicular to it of indefinite length. This straight line will be the asymptote.

268. To deduce the Polar Asymptote from the Polar Tangent.

The same results may be deduced from the equation of a tangent (Art. 206).

The result $u = U \cos (\theta - a) + U' \sin (\theta - a)$ at once reduces to $\dfrac{1}{U'} = r \sin (\theta - a)$, when $U = 0$. Putting

$$-\frac{1}{U'} = \frac{f_{n-1}(a)}{f'_n(a)},$$

as found in the last article, we again obtain the equation

$$r \sin (a - \theta) = \frac{f_{n-1}(a)}{f'_n(a)}.$$

Ex. *Find the asymptotes of the curve*
$$r = a \tan \theta \text{ or } r \cos \theta - a \sin \theta = 0.$$

Here $\qquad\qquad f_1(\theta) = \cos \theta$ and $f_0(\theta) = -a \sin \theta.$

$\cos \theta = 0$ gives $\qquad\qquad a = \dfrac{\pi}{2}, \quad \beta = \dfrac{3\pi}{2}, \text{ etc.},$

and $\qquad\qquad\qquad \dfrac{f_0(a)}{f'_1(a)} = \dfrac{-a \sin a}{-\sin a} = a.$

Hence $\qquad\qquad \left. \begin{aligned} r \sin\left(\dfrac{\pi}{2} - \theta\right) &= a \text{ or } r \cos \theta = a \\ r \sin\left(\dfrac{3\pi}{2} - \theta\right) &= a \text{ or } r \cos \theta = -a \end{aligned} \right\}$

are the asymptotes.

Or, using the Cartesian formula of Art. 266,
$$u = \frac{1}{a} \cot \theta.$$

$\therefore \qquad\qquad u = 0$ if $\theta = n\pi + \dfrac{\pi}{2}$, and $-\dfrac{d\theta}{du} = a \sin^2 \theta = a$

for this angle.

Hence the formula $\quad y \cos a = x \sin a + \left(\dfrac{d\theta}{du}\right)_{u=0}$

becomes $\qquad\qquad\qquad x = \pm a.$

269. An Exceptional Case.

In forming Equation 5, Article 265, it has been assumed that the value of $\left(\dfrac{du}{d\theta}\right)_{u=0}$ there obtained is not indeterminate; and, further, that none of the coefficients of the several powers of u become infinite in the limit when θ is put equal to a. If on differentiating Equation 2 and putting $u = 0$ and $\theta = a$ any term should occur which is indeterminate, it must be retained and the true value of $\left(\dfrac{d\theta}{du}\right)_{u=0}$ evaluated, either in an elementary manner or by the methods laid down for undetermined forms in Chap. XIV.

EXAMPLES.

1. $r\theta^{\frac{1}{2}} = a.$ 5. $r = 2a \sin \theta \tan \theta.$
2. $r\theta = a.$ 6. $r \sin 2\theta = a \cos 3\theta.$
3. $r \sin n\theta = a.$ 7. $r = a + b \cot n\theta.$
4. $r = a \operatorname{cosec} \theta + b.$ 8. $r^n \sin n\theta = a^n.$

9. Show that all the asymptotes of the curve $r \tan n\theta = a$ touch the circle $r = \dfrac{a}{n}.$

270. Circular Asymptotes.

In many polar equations when θ is increased indefinitely it happens that the equation takes the form of an equation in r, which represents one or more concentric circles.

For example, in the curve $\quad r = a\dfrac{\theta}{\theta - 1}$,

which may be written $\quad r = a\dfrac{1}{1 - \dfrac{1}{\theta}}$,

it is clear that if θ becomes very large the curve approaches indefinitely near the limiting circle $r = a$.

Such a circle is called an *asymptotic circle* of the curve.

EXAMPLES.

1. Find the asymptotes of the curves

    (i.) $x^5 + a^3xy - y^5 = 0$.

    (ii.) $y^4 - x^4 = a^2xy$.

2. Show that there is an infinite number of asymptotes of the curve $y = (a - x)\tan\dfrac{\pi x}{2a}$, viz.,

$$x = -a, \quad x = \pm 3a, \quad x = \pm 5a, \quad \text{etc.}$$

3. Prove that any tangent to the curve $3xy^2 = c^3$ is divided by the asymptotes and the curve into segments which bear a constant ratio to each other.   [Oxford, 1889.]

4. Find the asymptotes of the curve

$$x^2(x + y)(x - y)^2 + ax^3(x - y) - a^2y^3 = 0. \quad \text{[Oxford, 1889.]}$$

5. Find the asymptotes of the curve

$$(x - y)^2(x - 2y)(x - 3y) - 2a(x^3 - y^3) - 2a^2(x + y)(x - 2y) = 0.$$
$$\text{[Oxford, 1888.]}$$

6. Determine the asymptotes of the sextic

$$(x^2 - 2y^2)^2\{2(x^2 + 2y^2) - 3\} = \{3(x^2 + 2y^2) - 4\}^2.$$
$$\text{[Oxford, 1886.]}$$

7. If $r = \dfrac{a\theta^2}{\theta^2 - 1}$, the curve has two rectilinear asymptotes at a distance $\dfrac{a}{2}$ from the pole, making angles ± 1 with the prime radius. Also, there is a circular asymptote.

8. Find the asymptotes of the curve

$$r\theta \cos\theta = a\cos 2\theta. \quad \text{[Oxford, 1889.]}$$

9. Find the asymptotes of the curve

$$r\theta \cos\theta = ae^\theta. \quad \text{[Oxford, 1888.]}$$

10. Show that there is an infinite series of parallel asymptotes to the curve $\quad r = \dfrac{a}{\theta \sin\theta} + b$,

and show that their distances from the pole are in Harmonical Progression. Find the circular asymptote.

11. Show that the curve $\theta^2(ar - r^2) = b^2$ has a circular asymptote.

12. If $u = f(\theta)$ be the equation of a curve and $f(\theta) = 0$ gives a root $\theta = a$, the corresponding asymptote is
$$y = x \tan a + \frac{\sec a}{f'(a)}.$$

Ex. For $r\theta = a(\theta^2 - \pi^2)$ the asymptote is $y + a\pi^2 = 0$.

13. Show that if $y = xf(x)$ be the equation of a curve which admits of a rectilinear asymptote, then
$$Y = X\left[f\left(\frac{1}{x}\right)\right]_{x=0} + \left[\frac{d}{dx}f\left(\frac{1}{x}\right)\right]_{x=0}$$
is its equation.

Apply this method to find the asymptote of $x^3 + y^3 = 3axy$.

[BAILY AND LUND.]

14. Show that one of the asymptotes of the curve
$$x^3(x - 2y)^2 - 8ay^3(x - 2y + 2a) - 2a^3xy = 0$$
touches it at a point whose co-ordinates are finite.   [OXFORD, 1890.]

15. Determine the asymptotes of the curve
$$4(x^4 + y^4) - 17x^2y^2 - 4x(4y^2 - x^2) + 2(x^2 - 2) = 0,$$
and show that they pass through the points of intersection of the curve with the ellipse $x^2 + 4y^2 = 4$.   [OXFORD, 1890.]

16. Prove that the mn intersections of two curves of the mth and n^{th} degrees, and the mn intersections of the asymptotes of each with those of the other lie on a curve of the $(m + n - 2)^{\text{th}}$ degree.

Examine the case of a number of the asymptotes being the same for both curves.   [MATH. TRIPOS, 1876.]

17. Determine completely the relation of the line $ax + by = 0$ to the curve $(ax + by)^2 v_{n-2} + (ax + by)w_{n-2} + u_{n-3} + \ldots + u_0 = 0$ where u_r, v_r, w_r are homogeneous functions of x and y of degree r.

Trace the curve $\dfrac{a^2}{x^2} + \dfrac{b^2}{y^2} = 1$, and determine the form it assumes when a is diminished indefinitely.   [MATH. TRIPOS, 1884.]

18. Obtain the rectilinear asymptotes of the curve
$$y^2(x^2 - y^2) - 2ay^3 + 2a^3x = 0,$$
and the parabolic asymptotes of
$$y^4 - 2xy^2(x + a) + (x + a)x^3 = 0.$$ [OXFORD, 1887.]

19. Form the equation of a quartic curve which has asymptotes $x - y = 0$ and $x + y = 0$, the curve being supposed to approach each asymptote at one extremity only, but from both sides of that asymptote, and also to touch the axis of y at the origin.

20. Form the equation of a quartic curve with asymptotes $y = 0$, $x + y = 0$, $x - y = 0$, the curve being supposed to approach $y = 0$ from opposite sides at the same extremity, but the other two asymptotes from the same side and at opposite extremities in each case. The curve is also to touch the axis of y at the origin and to pass through the point $(2a, a)$.

21. Find the equation of a curve of the fourth degree which has two coincident asymptotes $x + y = 1$, an asymptote $x - y = 1$ and a fourth parallel to this, and of which the origin is a double point, the branches touching the axes of co-ordinates.   [MATH. TRIPOS, 1887.]

22. Find the equation of a quartic which has $y = \pm x \pm 1$ for asymptotes, which cuts the x-axis in four contiguous points at the origin, and the y axis in three points (other than the origin), for which the product of the ordinates is -1.

23. Obtain the asymptotes of the curve $(y - b)(y - c)x^2 = a^2 y^2$, and find upon which sides of the asymptotes the curve lies.

24. Show that the curve $y + x + a - \dfrac{a^3}{3x^2} = 0$ is asymptotic to the folium of Descartes $x^3 + y^3 = 3axy$.   Hence find on which side of the linear asymptote the curve lies.

25. For the quartic $ax^4 - by^4 + c^3 xy = 0$ show that

$$y = \frac{x a^{\frac{1}{4}}}{b^{\frac{1}{4}}} + \frac{c^3}{4 a^{\frac{1}{2}} b^{\frac{1}{2}} x} - \frac{c^6}{4^2 . 1 . 2 a^{\frac{5}{4}} b^{\frac{3}{4}} x^3} \cdots .$$

Draw the asymptotes, and determine on which sides the curve lies.
                              [VINCE, FLUXIONS; PEACOCK.]

26. Find the asymptotes of the quartic

$$(y^2 \mp x^2)\{(\tfrac{1}{2}y - 1)^2 \mp x^2\} + \mu(y + a) = 0,$$

examining in the several cases on which side of the asymptotes the curve lies.   [A. BEER.]

27. In the curve $y^3 = 6x^3 y + x^6$ there are no rectilinear asymptotes, but the curve is asymptotic to the parabola $y = x^2 + 2x$.

28. Find the asymptotes of the curve $y(y - x)^2(y + 2x) = 9cx^3$, showing that the parabola $(y - x + 2c)^2 = 3cx + 17c^2$ is asymptotic to the curve.   [FROST, Curve Tracing.]

29. Show that the curve

$$(y - 2x)^2(y + x) + (y + 3x)(y - x) + x = 0$$

has a parabolic branch to which $3y^2 - 12xy + 12x^2 + 5x = 0$ is a first approximation, and to which the parabola $3(y - 2x + \tfrac{13}{18})^2 + 5x + \tfrac{19}{108} = 0$ is asymptotic.

30. Find the rectilineal asymptotes and the parabolic branches at infinity of the curve

$$(y-x)^4 + (y-x)^2 2y + (y-x)(3x-y) - 2x - 2y + 1 = 0,$$

and find the position of its points of intersection with

$$(y-x)^2 + x + y = 0. \qquad \text{[OXFORD, 1888.]}$$

31. Find the asymptotes of the curve

$$r(\sin \alpha - \sin \theta) = a \sin \alpha \cos \theta.$$

Examine the case when α becomes a right angle.

[WOLSTENHOLME, *Educational Times.*]

32. Show that a cubic curve with a double point cannot have parallel asymptotes. A cubic has three given asymptotes which form an equilateral triangle. Show that if the curve possess a cusp it must lie on the inscribed circle of the triangle.

[MATH. TRIPOS, 1890.]

33. If the equation of a curve be written

$$x^n\phi_n\left(\frac{y}{x}\right) + x^{n-1}\phi_{n-1}\left(\frac{y}{x}\right) + x^{n-2}\phi_{n-2}\left(\frac{y}{x}\right) + \ldots = 0$$

and if $\phi_n(\mu_1) = 0$, $\phi_n{}'(\mu_1) = 0$, $\phi_{n-1}(\mu_1) = 0$, and $\phi'_{n-1}(\mu_1) = 0$, show that there are two parallel asymptotes equidistant from the origin, whose equations are

$$y = \mu_1 x \pm \sqrt{-\frac{2\phi_{n-2}(\mu_1)}{\phi''_n(\mu_1)}}.$$

34. Show that the first approximation to the difference of the ordinates of the curve

$$x^n\phi_n\left(\frac{y}{x}\right) + x^{n-1}\phi_{n-1}\left(\frac{y}{x}\right) + x^{n-2}\phi_{n-2}\left(\frac{y}{x}\right) + \ldots = 0$$

and its rectilinear asymptote $y = \mu x + \beta$ for a point whose abscissa is x is

$$-\frac{\phi''_n(\mu)[\phi_{n-1}(\mu)]^2 - 2\phi'_n(\mu)\phi'_{n-1}(\mu)\phi_{n-1}(\mu) + 2\phi_{n-2}(\mu)[\phi'_n(\mu)]^2}{2x[\phi'_n(\mu)]^3},$$

assuming that no other asymptote is parallel to this one. Show from this result that the curve at opposite extremities is in general also on opposite sides of the asymptote.

35. Prove that an algebraic curve of the nth degree represented by the equation

$$x^n f_0\left(\frac{y}{x}\right) + x^{n-1}f_1\left(\frac{y}{x}\right) + x^{n-2}f_2\left(\frac{y}{x}\right) + \ldots = 0$$

has two parallel asymptotes, provided $f_0(\mu)$, $f_0''(\mu)$, $f_1(\mu)$ vanish for the same value of μ; and that the approximations to the corresponding infinite branches of the curve are given by

$$y = \mu x + \nu - \{\tfrac{1}{6}\nu^3 f_0'''(\mu) + \tfrac{1}{2}\nu^2 f_1''(\mu) + \nu f_2'(\mu) + f_3(\mu)\}/x\{\nu f_0''(\mu) + f_1'(\mu)\},$$

where ν is a root of the equation

$$\tfrac{1}{2}\nu^2 f_0''(\mu) + \nu f_1'(\mu) + f_2(\mu) = 0.$$

Find also an approximation for the case of equal roots.

[MATH. TRIPOS, 1888.]

36. Show that the asymptotes of the general curve of the nth degree

$$(a_0, a_1, \ldots, a_n \! \! \nmid x, y)^n + n(b_0, b_1, \ldots, b_{n-1} \! \! \nmid x, y)^{n-1} + \ldots = 0$$

will all pass through one point if

$$\begin{Vmatrix} a_0, & a_1, & a_2, & \ldots, & a_{n-1} \\ a_1, & a_2, & a_3, & \ldots, & a_n \\ b_0, & b_1, & b_2, & \ldots, & b_{n-1} \end{Vmatrix} = 0,$$

and that the co-ordinates of that point are

$$\frac{a_1 b_1 - a_2 b_0}{a_0 a_2 - a_1^2}, \quad \frac{a_1 b_0 - a_0 b_1}{a_0 a_2 - a_1^2}.$$

[The notation $(a_0, a_1, \ldots, a_n \! \! \nmid x, y)^n$ is used for the general binary quantic of the nth degree, viz.

$$a_0 x^n + n a_1 x^{n-1} y + \frac{n(n-1)}{2!} a_2 x^{n-2} y^2 + \ldots + a_n y^n.]$$

CHAPTER IX.

SINGULAR POINTS.

271. Concavity. Convexity.

In the treatment of plane curves the terms concavity and convexity with regard to a point are applied with their ordinary signification. Thus, for example, any arc of a circle is said to be concave to all points within the circle ; whilst to a point without the circle the portion lying between that point and the chord of contact of tangents drawn from the point is said to be convex and the remainder of the circumference concave.

272. In general the portion of a curve in the immediate neighbourhood of any specified point lies entirely on one side of the tangent at that point. This is clear from the definition of a tangent, which is considered as the limiting position of a

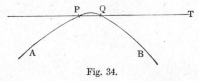

Fig. 34.

chord. There is an ultimately coincident cross and recross at the point of contact, as shown at the ultimately coincident points P, Q in fig. 34 ; so that the immediately neighbouring portions AP, QB must in general lie on the same side of the tangent PT.

273. We may thus give the following definition of concavity and convexity. Let P be any point of a curve in the midst of continuous curvature. Let A and B be two points near together on the same branch of the curve passing through P, but on opposite sides of P. Then in the limit when the arc

211

AB is indefinitely diminished the curve is concave in the immediate neighbourhood of P to all points on the same side of the tangent as the arc APB and convex to all points on the opposite side.

274. Point of Inflexion.   Stationary Tangent.

The kind of point discussed in Art. 272 is an ordinary point on a curve.   It may however happen that for some point on the curve the tangent, after its cross and recross, *crosses the curve again at a third* ultimately coincident point.   Such a point can be seen magnified in Fig. 35.

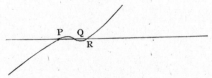

Fig. 35.

In this case it is clear that two successive tangents coincide in position: viz., the limiting positions of the chords PQ, QR. The tangent at such a point is therefore said to be "*stationary*," and the point is called a "*point of contrary flexure*" or a "*point of inflexion*" on the curve.   The tangent on the whole crosses its curve at such a point, and the curve changes from being concave to points on one side of the tangent to being convex to the same set of points.

275. Point of Undulation.

Again, there may be a point on the curve for which the

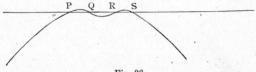

Fig. 36.

tangent crosses its curve in four ultimately coincident points, P, Q, R, S, as seen magnified in Fig. 36, and the point is then called a "*point of undulation*" on the curve.   There are now three contiguous tangents coincident, and the tangent on the whole does not cross its curve.   And it is clear that singularities of similar character but of a higher order may arise.

276. Analytical Tests.   Concavity and Convexity.

It is easy to apply analysis to the investigation of the form of a curve at any particular point.

Let us examine the point x, y on the curve $y = \phi(x)$.

Let P be the point to be considered, P_1 an adjacent point on

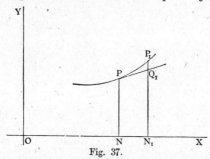

Fig. 37.

the curve.   Let PN, $P_1 N_1$ be the ordinates of P and P_1, and suppose $P_1 N_1$ to cut the tangent at P in Q_1.   Then $ON = x$, $NP = y = \phi(x)$.

Let $\qquad ON_1 = x + h,$

then $\qquad N_1 P_1 = \phi(x + h)$

$$= \phi(x) + h\phi'(x) + \frac{h^2}{2!}\phi''(x) + \dots, \quad \dots\dots(1)$$

by Taylor's Theorem.   Again, the equation of the tangent at P is $\qquad Y - y = \phi'(x)(X - x).$

Putting $\qquad X = x + h$

we obtain $\qquad Y = y + h\phi'(x) = \phi(x) + h\phi'(x), \dots\dots\dots(2)$

which gives the value of $N_1 Q_1$.

Hence the ordinate of the curve exceeds the ordinate of the tangent by

$$N_1 P_1 - N_1 Q_1 = \frac{h^2}{2!}\phi''(x) + \frac{h^3}{3!}\phi'''(x) + \dots \quad \dots\dots\dots(3)$$

Now, if h be taken sufficiently small, the sign of the right-hand side will be governed by that of its first term; and this term does not change sign with h because it contains an even power of h, viz., the square.   Hence, *in general*, on whichever side of P the point P_1 be taken, $N_1 P_1 - N_1 Q_1$ will have the same sign—positive if $\phi''(x)$ be positive, and negative if $\phi''(x)$ be negative; and therefore the element of the curve at P is *convex* or *concave* to the foot of the ordinate at P according as $\phi''(x)$ *is positive or negative*.

We have drawn our figure with the portion of the curve considered above the axis of x. If, however, it had been below, the signs of N_1P_1 and N_1Q_1 would both have been negative and we should have had the contrary result. But observing that $\phi(x)$ is positive for points above the axis of x, and negative for points below, we may obviously state the unrestricted rule that the elementary portion of the curve $y=\phi(x)$ in the neighbourhood of the point (x, y) is *convex or concave to the foot of the ordinate according as $\phi(x)\phi''(x)$ or $y\dfrac{d^2y}{dx^2}$ is positive or negative*.

277. Points of Inflexion.

If $\phi''(x)=0$ at the point under consideration, we have

$$N_1P_1-N_1Q_1=\frac{h^3}{3!}\phi'''(x)+\frac{h^4}{4!}\phi''''(x)+...,$$

and, as before, the sign of the right-hand side, when h is taken sufficiently small, is governed by the sign of its first term. But this now depends on h^3, and therefore changes sign with h; that is, the ordinate of the curve is greater than the ordinate

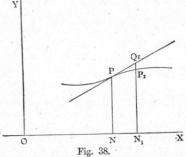

Fig. 38.

of the tangent on one side of P, but less on the other. The tangent now crosses the curve at its point of contact, and the point is of the kind described in Art. 274, and called a *point of inflexion*. A *necessary* condition then for a point of inflexion is that $\phi''(x)$ if not infinite should vanish, and the sign of $\phi'''(x)$ determines the character of the inflexion; for (assuming the element above the axis of x) if $\phi'''(x)$ be positive, $N_1P_1-N_1Q_1$ changes from negative to positive in passing from negative to positive values of h : *i.e.*, in passing through P the change is from concavity to convexity with regard to the foot of the ordinate. But if $\phi'''(x)$ be negative, the change is from convexity to concavity, and this latter is the case represented in the figure.

278. **Point of Undulation.**

Again, if $\phi'''(x) = 0$ at the same point, and $\phi''''(x)$ do not vanish, the first term in the expansion of $N_1P_1 - N_1Q_1$ depends on h^4, and therefore this expression does not change sign in passing through P. The tangent therefore on the whole does not cross its curve at P. The point is of the kind described in Art. 275 and called a *point of undulation.*

279. **Higher Degrees of Singularity.**

It will now appear that, if by two successive differentiations a result of the form

$$\frac{d^2y}{dx^2} = A(x-a)^{2n}(x-b)^{2m+1}$$

be deduced from the equation to the curve, although $\dfrac{d^2y}{dx^2}$ vanishes both at the points given by $x = a$ and by $x = b$, yet it only undergoes a change of sign when it passes through $x = b$, the index of the factor $x - b$ being odd. Hence at the points given by $x = a$ there is no ultimate change in the direction of flexure, while at those given by $x = b$ there is a change. The points given by $x = a$ look to the eye like ordinary points on a curve, while those given by $x = b$ resemble points of inflexion, and indeed have been for distinction called by Cramer points of *visible inflexion,*[*] although the singularity is of a higher order than that described in Art. 274, which is the case of $m = 0$. If $n = 1$, the points given by $x = a$ are points of undulation, such as described in Art. 275. *So that for an Inflexional Point the condition* $\dfrac{d^2y}{dx^2} = 0$, *though necessary, is not sufficient. The complete criterion is that* $\dfrac{d^2y}{dx^2}$ *should change sign. If* $\dfrac{d^2y}{dx^2}$ *vanish, but do not change sign, the curve at the point under consideration is undulatory.*

280. **Case when the Tangent is parallel to the y-axis.**

The test of concavity or convexity has been shown to depend upon the sign of $\dfrac{d^2y}{dx^2}$. In the case, however, of an arc, the tangent to which is parallel to the axis of y, the value of $\dfrac{dy}{dx}$ and

* Dr. Salmon, *Higher Plane Curves*, p. 35. Cramer, *Analyse des Lignes Courbes*, Geneva.

of all subsequent differential coefficients is infinite.   But in
this case it is obvious that it would be convenient to consider
y instead of x for the independent variable, and then the sign
of $\dfrac{d^2x}{dy^2}$ will test the concavity or convexity to the foot of the
ordinate drawn from the point under consideration to the axis
of y.

Similarly, at a point of inflexion at which the tangent is
parallel to the axis of y, $\dfrac{d^2x}{dy^2}$ must change sign.

And in other cases whenever it is more convenient to use y
instead of x for our independent variable, we are of course at
liberty to do so with an interchange of the letters x and y in
the formula quoted.

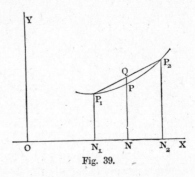

Fig. 39.

281. *The test for concavity or convexity may also be investigated as follows :—*

Let P be any point of the curve, co-ordinates x and y.   Let
the adjacent points on the curve P_1 and P_2 have co-ordinates,
$(x-h,\ y_1)$ and $(x+h,\ y_2)$ respectively.   Let the ordinate of P
cut the chord P_1P_2 in Q.   Then if h be made infinitesimally
small, the portion of the curve in the immediate neighbourhood
of P will be convex or concave to N, according as NP is $<$ or
$> NQ$, *i.e.*, as $\qquad\qquad$ y is $<$ or $> \dfrac{y_1+y_2}{2}$.

Now $\qquad\qquad$ $y_2 = y + h\dfrac{dy}{dx} + \dfrac{h^2}{2!}\dfrac{d^2y}{dx^2} + \ldots,$

$\qquad\qquad\qquad$ $y_1 = y - h\dfrac{dy}{dx} + \dfrac{h^2}{2!}\dfrac{d^2y}{dx^2} - \ldots,$

so that the criterion depends upon whether

$$y \text{ be} < \text{or} > y + \frac{h^2}{2!}\frac{d^2y}{dx^2} + \cdots,$$

and proceeding to the limit the curve is convex or concave to N according as $\dfrac{d^2y}{dx^2}$ is positive or negative.

Ex. 1. Consider the curve $y = 2\sqrt{ax}$. Is it convex or concave to the foot of the ordinate?

Here
$$\frac{d^2y}{dx^2} = -\tfrac{1}{2}\frac{\sqrt{a}}{x^{\frac{3}{2}}},$$

and
$$y\frac{d^2y}{dx^2} = -\frac{a}{x}.$$

Hence $y\dfrac{d^2y}{dx^2}$ is negative for all positive values of x (and negative values of x are not admissible), so that the curve in the neighbourhood of any specified point is concave to the foot of the ordinate of that point.

Ex. 2. Consider the curve $x = y^3 + 3y^2$. Has it a point of inflexion?

Here
$$\frac{d^2x}{dy^2} = 6(y + 1),$$

so that $\dfrac{d^2x}{dy^2}$ changes sign as y passes through the value $y = -1$. Therefore the point $(2, -1)$ is a point of inflexion on the curve.

282. Convexity and Concavity of a Polar Curve.

Suppose the equation of a curve to be given in polar co-ordinates as $u = f(\theta)$, and that it is required to find a test of convexity or concavity towards the pole.

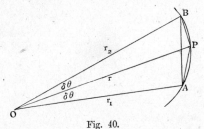

Fig. 40.

Let O be the pole, P the point of the curve to be examined.

Let the co-ordinates of P be denoted by r, θ, and let A, B be two points on the curve adjacent to P, and one on each side of it whose co-ordinates are respectively $(r_1, \theta - \delta\theta)$ and $(r_2, \theta + \delta\theta)$. Then the curve in the immediate neighbourhood of P will be concave or convex to O, according as

$$\triangle AOP + \triangle BOP \text{ is} > \text{or} < \triangle AOB$$

when we proceed to the limit.   That is, according as

$$r_1 r \sin \delta\theta + rr_2 \sin \delta\theta > \text{or} < r_1 r_2 \sin 2\delta\theta,$$

or $$r_1 r + rr_2 > \text{or} < 2r_1 r_2 \cos \delta\theta ;$$

i.e., as $$u_2 + u_1 > \text{or} < 2u \cos \delta\theta,$$

where we have written $r_1 = \dfrac{1}{u_1}$, etc.

Now, by Taylor's Theorem,

$$u_2 = u + \frac{du}{d\theta}\delta\theta + \frac{d^2u}{d\theta^2}\frac{\delta\theta^2}{2!} + \dots,$$

$$u_1 = u - \frac{du}{d\theta}\delta\theta + \frac{d^2u}{d\theta^2}\frac{\delta\theta^2}{2!} - \dots,$$

and therefore

$$u_1 + u_2 = 2\left(u + \frac{d^2u}{d\theta^2}\frac{\delta\theta^2}{2!} + \dots\right),$$

whence we have concavity or convexity to the pole according

as $$2u + 2\frac{d^2u}{d\theta^2}\frac{\delta\theta^2}{2!} + \dots \text{ is } > \text{or} < 2u\left(1 - \frac{\delta\theta^2}{2!} + \dots\right),$$

and proceeding to the limit according as

$$u + \frac{d^2u}{d\theta^2} \text{ is } > \text{or} < 0.$$

283. Polar Condition for a Point of Inflexion.

At a point of inflexion the curve changes from concavity to convexity, and therefore the necessary condition is that $u + \dfrac{d^2u}{d\theta^2}$ should change sign.

Ex. *Find the point of inflexion on the curve* $r = a\theta^{-\frac{1}{2}}$.
Here $$au = \theta^{\frac{1}{2}},$$

therefore $$a\frac{d^2u}{d\theta^2} = -\frac{1}{4}\theta^{-\frac{3}{2}}.$$

Hence, putting $$u + \frac{d^2u}{d\theta^2} = 0$$

to find for what value of θ a change of sign can occur, we have
$$\theta^{\frac{1}{2}} - \tfrac{1}{4}\theta^{-\frac{3}{2}} = 0,$$
$$\theta^2 = \tfrac{1}{4},$$
$$\theta = \pm\tfrac{1}{2}.$$

And the positive value only is admissible, giving
$$\left.\begin{array}{l} r = a\sqrt{2} \\ \theta = \tfrac{1}{2} \end{array}\right\}$$

as the polar co-ordinates of the point of inflexion.

284. Condition for Pedal Equations.

It will be obvious from a figure that for an element of a curve which is concave towards the pole p and r increase or decrease together. But for convexity p increases as r decreases and *vice versa*. Thus for concavity $\dfrac{dp}{dr}$ is positive; for convexity negative.

At a point of inflexion $\dfrac{dp}{dr}$ changes sign.

285. This condition is deducible at once from the polar condition, for

since
$$p^{-2} = u^2 + \left(\frac{du}{d\theta}\right)^2$$

$$-\frac{1}{p^3}\frac{dp}{du} = u + \frac{d^2u}{d\theta^2}$$

or
$$u + \frac{d^2u}{d\theta^2} = \frac{r^2}{p^3}\frac{dp}{dr},$$

whence the result follows immediately.

EXAMPLES.

1. Show that the curve $y = e^x$ is at every point convex to the foot of the ordinate of that point.

2. Show that for the cubical parabola
$$a^2y = (x-b)^3$$
there is a point of inflexion whose abscissa is b.

3. Show that there are points of inflexion at the origin on each of the curves

(a) $y = x\cos\dfrac{x}{a}$.

(β) $y = a\tan\dfrac{x}{b}$.

(γ) $y = x^2\log(1-x)$.

4. Show that there is a point of inflexion on the curve
$$y = e^{x^{\frac{1}{3}}}$$
at the point $(8, e^2)$.

5. Show that every point in which the curve of sines
$$\frac{y}{a} = \sin\frac{x}{b}$$
cuts the axis of x is a point of inflexion on the curve.

6. Determine the nature of the point where $x = b$ on the curve
$$(y - a - x)^4 = a(x-b)^3.$$

7. Show that the curve
$$(y-a)^3 = a^3 - 2a^2x + ax^2$$
is always concave towards the foot of the ordinate. How is it situated with regard to points on the y-axis?

8. Ascertain whether the spiral
$$r\cosh\theta = a$$
is convex or concave towards the pole.

9. Show that if the origin be a point of inflexion on the curve
$$u_1 + u_2 + u_3 + \ldots = 0$$
u_2 will contain u_1 for a factor.

10. Show that there is a point of inflexion at the origin on the cubic
$$y = axy + by^2 + cx^3.$$

11. Show that there is a point of undulation at the origin on the curve
$$y = ax^4 + bx^2y^2 + cy^4.$$

12. Find the positions of the points of inflexion on the curve
$$12y = x^4 - 16x^3 + 42x^2 + 12x + 1.$$

13. Prove that the curve
$$y = be^{-\left(\frac{x}{a}\right)^n}$$
has a point of inflexion given by
$$x = a\sqrt[n]{\frac{n-1}{n}}.$$

14. Prove that the point $\left(-2, \dfrac{-2}{e^2}\right)$ is a point of inflexion on the curve
$$y = xe^x.$$

MULTIPLE POINTS AND TANGENTS.

286. Nature of a Multiple Point.

A singularity of different nature from those above described occurs on a curve at a point where two branches intersect, as at the point A in the accompanying figure. It will appear from an inspection of the figure that at such a point as the one drawn there are *two* tangents to the curve, one for each branch.

Fig. 41.

Each tangent cuts the curve in two ultimately coincident points, such as P, Q on one branch, and it incidentally intersects the other branch through A in a third point R, ultimately also coinciding with A. Each tangent therefore at such a point intersects the curve in *three* ultimately coincident points at the point of contact; and if the curve be of the nth degree, each tangent will cut the curve again in $n-3$ points real or imaginary. In this respect the tangent at such a point resembles the tangent at a point of inflexion, for (Art. 274) the point of contact of a tangent at a point of inflexion counts for three of the n intersections of the line with the curve.

287. Points through which more than one branch of a curve passes are called "*multiple points*" on the curve. If two branches pass through the point A, as in the above figure, A is called a "*double point.*" If three branches pass through any point, that point is called a "*triple point*" on the curve ; and generally, if through any point r branches of the curve pass, that point is referred to as a "*multiple point of the rth order*" on the curve. From what has been said with regard to the tangents at a double point it will be obvious that there are r tangents (real or imaginary) at a multiple point of the rth order, one for each branch. At such a point each of these r tangents cuts its own branch in general in two points, and each of the other branches in one point : *i.e.*, in $r+1$ points altogether, all ultimately coincident with the multiple point. Such a tangent therefore cuts the curve in $n-r-1$ other points real or imaginary. But if at the multiple point there happen to be a point of inflexion on the branch considered, the tangent will cut that branch in three points instead of two at the point of contact, making $r+2$ points of intersection with the curve at the multiple point, and therefore reducing the remaining number of points of intersection to $n-r-2$.

288. **Species of Double Points.**

Consider the case of a double point. The tangents there may be real, coincident or imaginary.

CASE 1. If the tangents be real and not coincident, there are two real branches of the curve passing through the point, and the point is called a *node* or *crunode*.

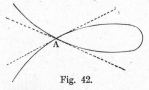

Fig. 42.

CASE 2. If the tangents be imaginary, there are no real points on the curve in the immediate neighbourhood of the point considered, and we are unable to travel *along the curve* from such a point in any real direction. Such a point is therefore simply an isolated point, whose co-ordinates satisfy the equation to the curve, and is called a "*conjugate point*" or "*acnode.*"

CASE 3. If the tangents at the double point be coincident, the two branches of the curve will touch at the point considered. The point is then in general of the character called a *stationary point, cusp* or *spinode*.

289. Two Species of Cusps.

There are two kinds of cusps, as shown in the accompanying figures.

Fig. 43.   Fig. 44.

(*a*) In fig. 43 the branches *PA*, *QA* lie on opposite sides of the tangent at *A*. This is referred to as a cusp of *the first species* or a *keratoid* cusp (*i.e.*, cusp like *horns*).

(*β*) In Fig. 44 the branches *PA*, *QA* lie on the same side of the tangent at *A*. This is called a cusp of *the second species* or a *ramphoid* cusp (*i.e.*, cusp like a *beak*).

290. A Multiple Point can be considered as a Combination of Double Points.

A *triple* point may obviously be considered as a combination of three double points, for of the three branches intersecting at the point each pair form a double point at their point of intersection. And in general a *multiple* point of the rth order may be considered as the result of the combination of $\dfrac{r(r-1)}{2}$ double points, since this is the number of ways of combining the r branches two at a time.

291. To examine the Nature of the Origin.

If the equation of a curve be rational and algebraic, it may be written in the form

$$\begin{aligned}
&a\\
&+b_1x+b_2y\\
&+c_1x^2+c_2xy+c_3y^2\\
&+\ldots\\
&+k_1x^n+k_2x^{n-1}y+\ldots+k_{n+1}y^n=0\ldots\ldots\ldots\ldots(\text{A})
\end{aligned}$$

If this be put into polar co-ordinates it becomes

$$a$$
$$+r(b_1\cos\theta + b_2\sin\theta)$$
$$+r^2(c_1\cos^2\theta + c_2\cos\theta\sin\theta + c_3\sin^2\theta)$$
$$+\dots$$
$$+r^n(k_1\cos^n\theta + k_2\cos^{n-1}\theta\sin\theta + \dots + k_{n+1}\sin^n\theta) = 0.\dots\dots(\text{B})$$

Let O be the pole and OA the initial line. Then equation (B) gives the points P_1, P_2, P_3 ..., in which a radius vector

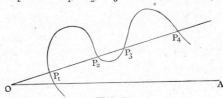

Fig. 45.

$OP_1P_2\dots$, making a given angle θ with OA, cuts the curve. The roots of this equation are OP_1, OP_2, OP_3, ...

It is clearly of the nth degree, and therefore has n roots. These may, however, become imaginary in pairs.

I. If $a=0$ it will be obvious from either the Cartesian equation (A) or the Polar equation (B) that the curve *passes through the origin* O. In this case one root of the equation (B) is zero, and in the figure $OP_1 = 0$.

II. In this case, if θ be so chosen as to make

$$b_1\cos\theta + b_2\sin\theta = 0,$$

a second root of the equation (B) vanishes, and therefore we infer that a straight line making an angle $\tan^{-1}\left(-\dfrac{b_1}{b_2}\right)$ with the initial line cuts the curve in two contiguous points at the origin, and *therefore is the tangent there*. The Cartesian equation of this line is obvious upon multiplying by r, viz.,

$$b_1 x + b_2 y = 0.$$

Hence if a curve pass through the origin, the *terms of first degree* (if any such exist) *on being equated to zero form the equation of the tangent* at the origin. (See Art. 197.)

III. If $a=0$, $b_1=0$, and $b_2=0$, then in general it is possible to choose θ so that

$$c_1\cos^2\theta + c_2\cos\theta\sin\theta + c_3\sin^2\theta = 0,$$

and then three roots of equation (B) will vanish; that is to say, of the pair of lines whose equation is $c_1 x^2 + c_2 xy + c_3 y^2 = 0$ each cuts the curve at the origin in three contiguous points. There are therefore two branches of the curve intersecting at the origin, to each of which a tangent can be drawn, and of the three contiguous points in which it has been seen that each of these tangents cuts the curve two lie on one branch and the other on the remaining branch. The origin is in this case *a double point on the curve*, and the terms of lowest degree in the equation of the curve, viz.,

$$c_1 x^2 + c_2 xy + c_3 y^2,$$

when equated to zero form the equation of the tangents at the origin. The *tangent of the angle between these straight lines* is given by

$$\tan \phi = \frac{\sqrt{c_2{}^2 - 4c_1 c_3}}{c_1 + c_3}.$$

If $c_2{}^2 > 4c_1 c_3$, the tangents are real and not coincident, and there is *a node* at the origin.

If $c_2{}^2 = 4c_1 c_3$, the tangents are coincident, and the two branches of the curve touch, and there is *in general a cusp* at the origin.

If $c_2{}^2 < 4c_1 c_3$, there are no real tangents at the origin, although the co-ordinates of the origin satisfy the equation of the curve; there is then a *conjugate point* at the origin.

If $c_1 + c_3 = 0$, the tangents at the origin *intersect at right angles*.

IV. If $a = 0$, $b_1 = 0$, $b_2 = 0$, $c_1 = 0$, $c_2 = 0$, $c_3 = 0$, the origin is a *triple point* on the curve, and (as shown in III. for the tangents at a double point) the tangents at the origin are

$$d_1 x^3 + d_2 x^2 y + d_3 xy^2 + d_4 y^3 = 0.$$

V. And generally, if the lowest terms of an equation are of the rth degree, the origin is a "*multiple point of the rth order*" on the curve, and the terms of the rth degree equated to zero give the r tangents there.

292. **To examine the Character of any Specified Point on a Curve.**

Results similar to those of the preceding article may be deduced for *any* point on the curve.

Let the straight line $\dfrac{x-h}{l} = \dfrac{y-k}{m} = \rho$ be drawn through a given point (h, k) to cut the curve $f(x, y) = 0$. Then

$$x = h + l\rho,$$
$$y = k + m\rho.$$

The use of these equations is obviously equivalent to a double transformation of co-ordinates, the first to parallel axes through h, k, the second to polars.

Substituting for x and y in the equation of the curve we obtain
$$f(h+l\rho, \ k+m\rho)=0$$
to find the points P_1, P_2, .. in which a radius vector through the point h, k cuts the curve.

If this be expanded by the extended form of Taylor's Theorem, the equation becomes

$$f(h,\ k)+\rho\left(l\frac{\partial}{\partial h}+m\frac{\partial}{\partial k}\right)f+\frac{\rho^2}{2!}\left(l\frac{\partial}{\partial h}+m\frac{\partial}{\partial k}\right)^2 f+\ldots$$
$$+\frac{\rho^n}{n!}\left(l\frac{\partial}{\partial h}+m\frac{\partial}{\partial k}\right)^n f+\ldots=0.$$

which is exactly analogous to equation (B) of Art. 291, and corresponding results follow.

I. If $f(h,\ k)=0$, one root of the equation for ρ vanishes and the point h, k *lies on the curve* (which is otherwise obvious).

II. In this case, if the ratio $l:m$ be now so chosen that

$$l\frac{\partial f}{\partial h}+m\frac{\partial f}{\partial k}=0,$$

then another root vanishes, and this relation gives the *direction of the tangent*, whose equation is therefore

$$(x-h)\frac{\partial f}{\partial h}+(y-k)\frac{\partial f}{\partial k}=0,$$

as found in Art. 191.

III. But if $\frac{\partial f}{\partial h}=0$ and $\frac{\partial f}{\partial k}=0$, as well as $f(h,\ k)=0$, then all lines through h, k cut the curve in two contiguous points. But if the ratio $l:m$ be so chosen that

$$l^2\frac{\partial^2 f}{\partial h^2}+2lm\frac{\partial^2 f}{\partial h\partial k}+m^2\frac{\partial^2 f}{\partial k^2}=0,$$

we have in general, as in Art. 291, III., two directions in which a radius vector drawn through $(h,\ k)$ cuts the curve in three contiguous points. The point $(h,\ k)$ is a *double point on the curve*, since two branches of the curve pass through this point; and of the three contiguous points in which each of the above-mentioned radii vectores meets the curve, two lie on one branch and one on the other. The equation of the two tangents is

$$(x-h)^2\frac{\partial^2 f}{\partial h^2}+2(x-h)(y-k)\frac{\partial^2 f}{\partial h\partial k}+(y-k)^2\frac{\partial^2 f}{\partial k^2}=0.$$

IV. Further, if $\frac{\partial^2 f}{\partial h^2}=0$, $\frac{\partial^2 f}{\partial h\partial k}=0$, and $\frac{\partial^2 f}{\partial k^2}=0$, in addition to $\frac{\partial f}{\partial h}=0$, $\frac{\partial f}{\partial k}=0$, and $f(h, k)=0$, identically for the same values of h, k, and if on going to terms of the third order we find that all these do *not* identically vanish, the point (h, k) is a *triple point* on the curve.

V. And generally the conditions for the existence of a *multiple point of the* r^{th} *order* at a given point h, k of the curve are that $f(x, y)$ and all its differential coefficients up to those of the $(r-1)^{\text{th}}$ order inclusive should vanish when $x=h$ and $y=k$; and then the equation of the r tangents at that point will be

$$(x-h)^r\frac{\partial^r f}{\partial h^r}+r(x-h)^{r-1}(y-k)\frac{\partial^r f}{\partial h^{r-1}\partial k}+\ldots+(y-k)^r\frac{\partial^r f}{\partial k^r}=0.$$

293. Special Case of Double Point.

Recurring to the case of a double point at a point (h, k), since the equation of the tangents is

$$(x-h)^2\frac{\partial^2 f}{\partial h^2}+2(x-h)(y-k)\frac{\partial^2 f}{\partial h\partial k}+(y-k)^2\frac{\partial^2 f}{\partial k^2}=0,$$

the angle between these tangents is given by

$$\tan\phi=\frac{2\sqrt{\left(\frac{\partial^2 f}{\partial h\partial k}\right)^2-\frac{\partial^2 f}{\partial h^2}\cdot\frac{\partial^2 f}{\partial k^2}}}{\frac{\partial^2 f}{\partial h^2}+\frac{\partial^2 f}{\partial k^2}},$$

and the point h, k is a *node* or *conjugate* point according as

$$\left(\frac{\partial^2 f}{\partial h\partial k}\right)^2 \text{ is } \genfrac{}{}{0pt}{}{>}{<} \frac{\partial^2 f}{\partial h^2}\cdot\frac{\partial^2 f}{\partial k^2},$$

and is *in general a cusp* if

$$\left(\frac{d^2 f}{\partial h\partial k}\right)^2=\frac{\partial^2 f}{\partial h^2}\cdot\frac{\partial^2 f}{\partial k^2},$$

with the preliminary conditions in each case that

$$f(h, k)=0, \quad \frac{\partial f}{\partial h}=0, \quad \text{and} \quad \frac{\partial f}{\partial k}=0.$$

We say *in general a cusp;* for it will be seen that in some cases when the above conditions hold the curve *becomes imaginary in the neighbourhood of the point* considered, which must therefore be classed as a conjugate point. In the case of the coincidence of tangents, further investigation is therefore necessary. The mode of procedure is indicated below in the method for the investigation of the character of a cusp. It appears that

$$\left(\frac{\partial^2 f}{\partial x \partial y}\right)^2 = \frac{\partial^2 f}{\partial x^2} \cdot \frac{\partial^2 f}{\partial y^2}$$

represents a curve which cuts $f(x, y) = 0$ in all its cusps; and that

$$\frac{\partial^2 f}{\partial x^2} + \frac{\partial^2 f}{\partial y^2} = 0$$

is a curve which cuts $f(x, y) = 0$ in all the double points at which the tangents are at right angles.

294. To search for Double Points.

The rule therefore to search for double points on a curve $f(x, y) = 0$ is as follows. Find $\frac{\partial f}{\partial x}$ and $\frac{\partial f}{\partial y}$; equate each to zero and solve. Test whether any of the solutions satisfy the equation of the curve. If so, apply the tests for the character of each of the points denoted, *i.e.*, try whether

$$\left(\frac{\partial^2 f}{\partial x \partial y}\right)^2 \text{ be } \begin{array}{c} \geq \\ = \\ < \end{array} \frac{\partial^2 f}{\partial x^2} \cdot \frac{\partial^2 f}{\partial y^2}. \qquad \begin{array}{l} \text{node} \\ \text{cusp} \\ \text{conjugate point.} \end{array} \Big\}$$

295. To discriminate the Species of a Cusp.

METHOD I. Suppose the position of a cusp to have been found by the foregoing rules. Transfer the origin to the cusp. The transformed equation will be of the form

$$(ax + by)^2 + u_3 + u_4 + \ldots = 0, \ldots\ldots\ldots\ldots\ldots\ldots(1)$$

where $ax + by = 0$ is the tangent at the origin, and $u_3, u_4, \ldots$ are homogeneous rational algebraical functions of x and y of the degrees indicated by their respective suffixes.

Let P be the length of the perpendicular drawn from a point x, y of the curve, very near the cusp, upon the tangent

$$ax + by = 0.$$

Then

$$P = \frac{ax + by}{\sqrt{a^2 + b^2}}. \qquad \ldots\ldots\ldots\ldots\ldots\ldots(2)$$

If y be eliminated between equations (1) and (2), an equation is obtained giving P in terms of x. It is our object to consider only the two small perpendiculars from points on the curve near the origin, and having a given small abscissa x; hence in comparison with P^2 we reject cubes and all higher powers of P and also all such terms as P^2x, P^2x^2, ... which may arise on substitution.

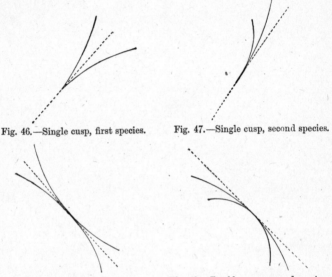

Fig. 46.—Single cusp, first species.   Fig. 47.—Single cusp, second species.

Fig. 48.—Double cusp, first species.   Fig. 49.—Double cusp, second species.

Fig. 50.—Double cusp, change of species.   Osculinflexion.

We shall then have a quadratic to determine P. If, when x is made very small, the roots be imaginary, the branches of the curve through the origin are unreal, and therefore there is a conjugate point at the origin. If the roots be real, but *of opposite signs,* the two small perpendiculars lie on opposite sides of the tangent, and there is a *cusp of the first species* at the origin. If the roots be real and *of like sign* the perpendiculars lie on the same side and the cusp *is of the second species,* and the sign of the roots determines on which side of the tangent the cusp lies.

Complete information is also afforded by this method as to whether the cusp is *single or double, i.e.,* as to whether the branches of the curve extend from the cusp towards one extremity only of the tangent, or towards both extremities as shown in the annexed figures.

The reality of the roots of the quadratic for P will in some cases *depend upon,* and in others be *independent of* the sign of x. In the former cases the cusp is *single ;* in the latter, *double.* Moreover, if double, we can detect whether the cusp is of the same or of different species towards opposite extremities of the tangent. When the cusp is of different species towards opposite extremities the point is called by Cramer a *point of Osculinflexion.*

In adopting the above process it will clearly be sufficient to put $P = ax + by$, thus dropping the $\sqrt{a^2 + b^2}$ for the sake of brevity; the effect of this being to consider a line whose length is proportional to that of the perpendicular instead of the perpendicular itself.

Ex. 1. *Examine the character of the origin on the curve*

$$x^4 - 4x^2y - 2xy^2 + 4y^2 = 0.$$

Here the tangent at the origin is $y = 0$. According to the rule put $y = P$. The quadratic for P is

$$P^2(4 - 2x) - 4Px^2 + x^4 = 0.$$

The roots of this equation are real or imaginary according as

$$4x^4 \text{ is } > \text{ or } < x^4(4 - 2x),$$

i.e., according as x is positive or negative. Hence the cusp is "*single*" and lies to the right of the axis of y. Moreover the product of the roots is $\dfrac{x^4}{4 - 2x}$ and is positive when x is very small, and the roots are therefore of the same sign. The origin is therefore a *single cusp of the second species.* Moreover the sum of the roots is positive, so that the two branches near the origin *lie in the first quadrant.*

Ex. 2. *Examine the character of the curve*

$$x^4 - 3x^2y - 3xy^2 + 9y^2 = 0$$

at the origin. Here $y = 0$ is a tangent at the origin. Put $y = P$. The quadratic for P is

$$P^2(9 - 3x) - 3x^2P + x^4 = 0.$$

The roots are real or imaginary according as $9x^4 - 4(9 - 3x)x^4$ is positive or negative, *i.e.*, as $-27x^4 + 12x^5$ is positive or negative.

Now, when x is very small, x^5 is *negligible in comparison with* x^4, and therefore the above expression is negative for very small positive or negative values of x. The roots of the equation for P are therefore imaginary, and the origin is a *conjugate point* on the curve.

Ex. 3. *Examine the character of the curve*

$$y = F(x) \pm (x - h)^{\frac{2m+1}{2n}} f(x) \dots\dots\dots\dots\dots\dots\dots(1)$$

in the neighbourhood of the point $x = h$, $y = F(h)$, m *and* n *being positive integers.*

By Taylor's Theorem we may write

$$F(x + h) = F(h) + ax + bx^2 + \dots$$

and

$$[f(x + h)]^2 = a_1 + b_1x + \dots,$$

where a_1 being $[f(h)]^2$ is necessarily positive.

Hence on transforming our origin to the point $\{h, F(h)\}$ we obtain for the transformed equation

$$(y - ax - bx^2 - \dots)^2 = x^{\frac{2m+1}{n}}(a_1 + b_1x + \dots). \dots\dots\dots\dots\dots(2)$$

Examining the form of the curve at the origin, there are obviously coincident tangents if $\dfrac{2m+1}{n}$ be > 2.

Put $y - ax = P$, then

$$P^2 - 2P(bx^2 + \dots) + b^2x^4 - a_1 x^{\frac{2m+1}{n}} - \dots = 0.$$

That the roots of this quadratic are real, if x be positive and small, is obvious from equation (2); also, that the roots are imaginary for small negative values of x. There is therefore a *single cusp extending to the right of the new axis of y.*

Again, the product of the roots $= b^2x^4 - a_1 x^{\frac{2m+1}{n}} - \dots$.

If $\dfrac{2m+1}{n} > 4$, this product has the same sign as x^4 when x is taken sufficiently small, and therefore is positive, giving a cusp of the *second species.*

If $\dfrac{2m+1}{n} < 4$, the term $-a_1 x^{\frac{2m+1}{n}}$ is the important term in the product and is negative, x being positive. There is therefore in this case a cusp of the *first species.*

We have assumed that the *coefficient* b or $\dfrac{1}{2!}F''(h)$ *is not zero.* If however this coefficient vanish, it is easy to make the corresponding change in the subsequent investigation.

Ex. 4. *Examine the nature of the double point on the curve*

$$(x+y)^3 - \sqrt{2}(y-x+2)^2 = 0.$$

Here
$$\frac{\partial\phi}{\partial x} = 3(x+y)^2 + 2\sqrt{2}(y-x+2) = 0,$$
$$\frac{\partial\phi}{\partial y} = 3(x+y)^2 - 2\sqrt{2}(y-x+2) = 0.$$

These give
and
$$x+y=0,$$
$$y-x+2=0,$$

or
$$x=1,$$
$$y=-1.$$

Now this point obviously lies upon the curve, and there is therefore a multiple point of some description there.

Again,
$$\frac{\partial^2\phi}{\partial x^2} = 6(x+y) - 2\sqrt{2} = -2\sqrt{2} \text{ at the point } (1, -1),$$

$$\frac{\partial^2\phi}{\partial y^2} = 6(x+y) - 2\sqrt{2} = -2\sqrt{2},$$

$$\frac{\partial^2\phi}{\partial x\partial y} = 6(x+y) + 2\sqrt{2} = 2\sqrt{2}.$$

Hence at this point
$$\frac{\partial^2\phi}{\partial x^2}\frac{\partial^2\phi}{\partial y^2} = \left(\frac{\partial^2\phi}{\partial x\partial y}\right)^2,$$

and we have a double point at which the tangents are coincident.

Next, transforming to the point $(1, -1)$ for origin, the equation becomes

$$(x+y)^3 - \sqrt{2}(y-x)^2 = 0.$$

According to the rule we put $y-x=P$. Then rejecting terms in P^3 and P^2x we have
$$P^2 - 6x^2\sqrt{2}P - 4x^3\sqrt{2} = 0.$$

The roots are real if
$$18x^4 + 4\sqrt{2}x^3 > 0,$$

which is the case if x be very small and positive. There is therefore a *single cusp* at the point $(1, -1)$.

Again, the product of the roots $= -4x^3\sqrt{2}$, and is negative when x is small. This indicates that the cusp is one of the *first species*.

[This curve is obviously only a transformation of the semi-cubical parabola $y^2 = x^3$.]

Ex. 5. *Search for a multiple point upon the curve*

$$x^7 + 2x^4 + 2x^3y + 2x^3 + x^2 + 2xy + y^2 + 2x + 2y + 1 = 0.$$

Here
$$\frac{\partial\phi}{\partial x} = 7x^6 + 8x^3 + 6x^2y + 6x^2 + 2x + 2y + 2 = 0. \quad\ldots\ldots\ldots\ldots(\text{i.})$$

$$\frac{\partial\phi}{\partial y} = 2x^3 + 2x + 2y + 2 = 0. \quad\ldots\ldots\ldots\ldots\ldots\ldots\ldots(\text{ii.})$$

From the second equation $y = -x^3 - x - 1$.

Substituting in (i.)
$$7x^6 - 6x^5 = 0,$$

whence
$$x=0 \text{ or } \tfrac{6}{7},$$

and therefore
$$y=-1 \text{ or } -\tfrac{853}{343}.$$

It is obvious that the latter solution cannot satisfy the equation to the curve.

Transforming to the point $(0, -1)$, the equation becomes

$$x^7 + 2x^4 + 2x^3 y + (x+y)^2 = 0,$$

indicating that there is either a cusp at the new origin to which $x+y=0$ is a tangent, or a conjugate point.

Put $x+y=P$, then $P^2 + 2Px^3 + x^7 = 0.$

The roots will be real if $x^6 - x^7$ is positive, which is true when x is positive and less than 1, and also when x is negative. Hence there is a *double* cusp. The product of the roots is x^7, which is positive or negative according as x is positive or negative. It is therefore ramphoid on the right-hand side of the new y-axis and keratoid on the left-hand side, and therefore there is an osculinflexion. Also the sum of the roots is $-2x^3$, and is therefore positive when x is negative; hence on the left side of the new y-axis the upper portion of the curve deviates from the tangent more rapidly than the lower portion.

296. METHOD II. Another method of discrimination of the species of a cusp depends upon the test for concavity or convexity. Find the two values of $\dfrac{d^2 y}{dx^2}$ (or $\dfrac{d^2 x}{dy^2}$, see Art. 280). If these have *opposite signs* very near to the cusp, the two branches starting from the cusp are in general *one concave and the other convex* to the foot of the ordinate, and the cusp is of the *first species*. But if the *signs be the same*, the two branches are either *both concave or both convex* to the foot of the ordinate, and the cusp is of the *second species*. In the case however when the x-axis is a tangent at the cusp, the cusp will be keratoid when *both branches are convex* to points on the axis near the cusp. But in this case the values of $\dfrac{d^2 y}{dx^2}$ are of opposite sign. Hence the above test still holds.

Ex. *Discuss the form of the curve* $y = x \pm x^{\frac{3}{2}}$ *at the origin.*

Here $y_2 = \pm 3/4 \sqrt{x}.$

Hence only positive values of x are admissible and the two values of y_2 have opposite signs. The origin is therefore a *single cusp of the first species.*

297. Singularities on the Reciprocal Curve.

Since to a tangent to a curve corresponds a point on its polar reciprocal, it will be evident that to the points in which a straight line cuts the one correspond the tangents which can be drawn from a given point to the other. If the one has a multiple point of the pth order the other has a multiple tangent touching its curve at p distinct points; to a double point on the one corresponds a double tangent or bi-tangent to the other; to a stationary point on the one corresponds a stationary tangent on the other.

These considerations tend to show that the multiple-tangent should be classed as a distinct singularity.

EXAMPLES.

1. Show that for the semi-cubical parabola
$$ay^2 = x^3$$
the origin is a cusp of the first species.

2. Show that the origin is a cusp of the first species on the curve
$$a(y - x)^2 = x^3.$$

3. Show that the curves
$$y^2 = x^2 \sin \frac{x}{a}, \quad y^2 = x^2 \tan \frac{x}{a}$$
have cusps of the first kind at the origin.

4. Show that at the origin on the curve
$$y^2 = bx \sin \frac{x}{a}$$
there is a node or a conjugate point according as a and b have like or unlike signs.

5. Show that for the Cissoid $y^2 = \dfrac{x^3}{2a - x}$
the origin is a cusp of the first species.

6. Examine the nature of the point on the curve
$$y - 2 = x(1 + x + x^{\frac{3}{2}})$$
where it cuts the y-axis.

7. In the curve $\qquad a^3 y^2 - 2abx^2 y = x^5$
show that there is an osculinflexion at the origin. [CRAMER.]

8. Search for the double point on
$$(y - 2)^2 = x(x - 1)^2,$$
and find the directions of the tangents there.

9. Determine the position and species of the cusps of the following curves:—

$$(a.)\ (2y + x + 1)^2 = 4(1 - x)^5,$$
$$(b.)\ (y + x)^{\frac{2}{3}} - (y - x)^{\frac{2}{3}} = 1,$$
$$(c.)\ xy^2 + 2a^2 y - ax^2 - 3a^2 x - 3a^3 = 0.$$

10. Examine the nature of the point $(-a, a)$ on the curve
$$x^4 - ay^3 + 2ax^2 y + 4ax^3 + 3a^2 y^2 + 4a^2 xy + 4a^2 x^2 - a^3 y = 0.$$

11. Show that at the point $(-1, -2)$ there is a cusp of the first species on the curve $\qquad x^3 + 2x^2 + 2xy - y^2 + 5x - 2y = 0.$

12. Show that at each of the four points of intersection of the curve
$$(ax)^{\frac{2}{3}} + (by)^{\frac{2}{3}} = (a^2 - b^2)^{\frac{2}{3}}$$
with the axes there is a cusp of the first species.

13. Show that the origin is a conjugate point on the curve
$$x^4 - ax^2y + axy^2 + a^2y^2 = 0.$$

14. Show that at the origin there is a single cusp of the second species on the curve $x^4 - 2ax^2y - axy^2 + a^2y^2 = 0.$

15. Show that the curve $y^2 = 2x^2y + x^3y + x^3$
has a single cusp of the first species at the origin.

16. Show that the curve $y^2 = 2x^2y + x^4y + x^4$
has a double keratoid cusp at the origin.

17. Show that the curve $y^2 = 2x^2y + x^4y - 2x^4$
has a conjugate point at the origin.

298. Singularities of Transcendental Curves.

In addition to the singularities above discussed others occur occasionally in transcendental curves, due to discontinuities in the values of y, $\dfrac{dy}{dx}$, etc.   For instance, if the value of y be discontinuous at a certain point the curve suddenly stops there and the point is called a "*point d'arrêt*" or "*stop point.*"

Consider the curve $y = a^{\frac{1}{x}}$; $(a > 1)$.
When $x = -\infty$, $y = 1$, and as x increases from $-\infty$ to zero y is always positive and decreases down to zero.   As soon, however, as x becomes positive, being still indefinitely small, y suddenly becomes infinitely great, and as x increases to $+\infty$ y gradually diminishes down to unity.   The origin is a *point d'arrêt* on this curve, and the shape is that shown in the annexed figure.

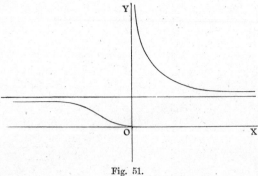

Fig. 51.

Next suppose that the value of y is continuous, but that at a certain point $\dfrac{dy}{dx}$ becomes discontinuous, so that two branches of the curve meet at a certain angle at the same point and stop there.   Such a point is called a "*point saillant.*"

299. Branch of Conjugate Points.

It sometimes happens that a curve possesses an infinite series of conjugate points, satisfying the equation to the curve and forming a branch of isolated points. M. Vincent, in a memoir published in vol. xv. of Gergonne's "Annales des Math.," has discussed several such cases, and calls such discontinuous branches by the name *branches pointillées*.

Ex. In tracing the curve $y = x^x$, it is clear that, when $x = \infty$, $y = \infty$; and when $x = 1$, $y = 1$. Also that as x decreases from ∞ to 1, y also decreases from ∞ to 1. Between $x = 1$ and $x = 0$ y is less than 1; and when $x = 0$, $y = 1$ (see Chap. XIV.). There is therefore a continuous branch of the curve, viz., ∞PB, above the axis of x.

Again, whenever x is a fraction with an even denominator there are

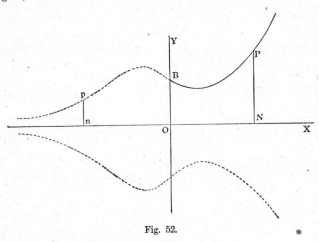

Fig. 52.

two real values of y, differing only in sign; *e.g.*,

$$(\tfrac{1}{4})^{\frac{1}{2}} = \pm \sqrt{\tfrac{1}{2}},$$

whilst, whenever the denominator of x is odd, there is but one real value for y. There is therefore a set of conjugate points below the axis forming a discontinuous branch, of the same shape as the continuous branch above the axis.

Next consider what happens when x is negative. Let the co-ordinates of any point P on the branch in the first quadrant be (x, y), then $ON = x$. Take $On = -x$ along the negative portion of the axis of x, then, if p be the corresponding point on the curve, we have

$$pn = (-x)^{-x}, \quad PN = x^x,$$

and therefore $\qquad pn \cdot PN = (-1)^x,$

which may be $= 1$, -1, or imaginary, according to the particular value of *x*. Hence, when the ordinate *pn* is real, its magnitude is inverse to that of the corresponding ordinate *PN*. Hence on this curve we have two infinite series of conjugate points, as shown in the figure.

For an account of M. Vincent's memoir and criticisms upon it see Dr. Salmon's "Higher Plane Curves," 2nd ed., p. 275, or a paper by Mr. D. F. Gregory, "Camb. Math. Journal," vol. i., pp. 231, 264.

300. Maclaurin's Theorem with regard to Cubics.

If a radius vector OPQ be drawn through a point of inflexion (O) of a cubic, cutting the curve again in P and Q, to show that the locus of the extremities of the harmonic means between OP and OQ, is a straight line.

If the origin be taken at the point of inflexion and the tangent at the point of inflexion as the axis of y, the equation of the cubic must assume the form

$$y^3 + xu = 0 \dots\dots\dots\dots\dots(1)$$

where u is the most general expression of the second and lower degrees, viz., $ax^2 + 2hxy + by^2 + 2gx + 2fy + c,$

for it is clear that the axis of y cuts this curve in three points ultimately coincident with the origin.

The equation (1) when put into polars takes the form

$$Lr^2 + Mr + N = 0,$$

where $L = \sin^3\theta + (a\cos^2\theta + 2h\sin\theta\cos\theta + b\sin^2\theta)\cos\theta,$

$M = (2g\cos\theta + 2f\sin\theta)\cos\theta,$

$N = c\cos\theta.$

If r_1, r_2 be the roots of this quadratic, and ρ the harmonic mean between them, we have

$$\frac{2}{\rho} = \frac{1}{r_1} + \frac{1}{r_2} = -\frac{M}{N} = -\frac{2g\cos\theta + 2f\sin\theta}{c},$$

which shows that the Cartesian Equation of the locus of the extremity of the harmonic mean is the straight line

$$gx + fy + c = 0.$$

301. It is obvious from Art. 211 that the equation of the polar conic of the cubic (1) with regard to the origin is

$$x(2gx + 2fy) + 2cx = 0,$$

or $$x(gx + fy + c) = 0.$$

Hence the polar conic of a point of inflexion on a cubic breaks up into two straight lines, one of which is the tangent at the point of inflexion, and the other the locus of the extremities of the harmonic means of the radii vectores through the point of inflexion. It appears from this that only three tangents can be drawn from a point of inflexion on a cubic to the curve, viz., one to each of the points in which the line $gx + fy + c = 0$ meets the curve, and consequently also that their three points of contact lie in a straight line.

302. If a Cubic have three real points of Inflexion they are Collinear.

It follows immediately from Maclaurin's Theorem above proved that if A and B be two points of inflexion on a cubic, the line AB produced will cut the curve in a third point C, which is also a point of inflexion on the cubic. For if B, B_1, B_2 be the three ultimately coincident points on the cubic, which lie in a straight line (B being a point of inflexion), let AB, AB_1, AB_2 cut the curve in C, C_1, C_2, and let AH, AH_1, AH_2 be the harmonic means between AB, AC; AB_1, AC_1; AB_2, AC_2 respectively, then H, H_1, H_2 lie in a straight line by Maclaurin's Theorem, and B, B_1, B_2 lie in a straight line; therefore by a theorem in conic sections C, C_1, C_2 also lie in a straight line, and they are ultimately coincident points. C is therefore a point of inflexion.

303. Number of points necessary to define a Curve of the nth Degree.

The number of terms in the general equation of the nth degree

is
$$1 + 2 + 3 + \ldots + (n+1) = \frac{(n+1)(n+2)}{2}.$$

It therefore contains $\dfrac{(n+1)(n+2)}{2} - 1$ or $\dfrac{n(n+3)}{2}$ independent constants.

Hence in general a curve of the nth degree may be drawn to pass through $\dfrac{n(n+3)}{2}$ arbitrarily chosen points.

304. Maximum Number of Double Points on a Curve of the nth Degree.

There cannot be more than $\frac{1}{2}(n-1)(n-2)$ double points on an n-tic curve.

For if there could be $\dfrac{(n-1)(n-2)}{2}+1$ double points, a curve of degree $n-2$ could be drawn to pass through them and through any $n-3$ other arbitrary points on the curve, for

$$\frac{(n-1)(n-2)}{2}+1+n-3=\frac{(n-2)(n+1)}{2}$$

and therefore these would make just sufficient points to completely define the new curve. But the number of intersections would be

$$2\left\{\frac{(n-1)(n-2)}{2}+1\right\}+(n-3),$$

or $n(n-2)+1,$

which is one more than possible for curves of degrees n and $n-2$.

[margin note: factor 2 ∴ double points]

EXAMPLES.

1. Show that a cubic curve cannot have more than one double point, and cannot have a triple point.

Examine the case of the curve

$$2(x^3+y^3)-3(3x^2+y^2)+12x=4,$$

and show that there are apparently two nodes at $(1, 1)$ and at $(2, 0)$ respectively. Explain this result.

2. Show that a quartic cannot have more than three double points, and cannot have a double point and a triple point.

3. The curve whose equation is

$$x^4+y^4=2a^2(x^2+y^2)-a^4$$

has four double points. Find them; account for this, and trace the curve.

[CRAMER.]

4. All curves of the third degree which pass through eight given points also pass through a ninth common point.

5. All the double points of a family of cubics determined by seven given points lie on a sextic.

305. Use of Homogeneous Co-ordinates.

Let $f(x, y, z)=0$ be the equation of any curve of the nth degree, which may be considered expressed either in trilinears, areals or Cartesians made homogeneous by the introduction of a proper power of $z(=1)$ where requisite.

Let (x_1, y_1, z_1) be the coordinates of any fixed point A, and let (X, Y, Z) be the current co-ordinates of any point P on the secant AP. Let AP cut the curve in the points $Q_1, Q_2, \dots$ Let any of the points $Q(x, y, z)$ divide AP in the ratio $\lambda : \mu$ where $\lambda + \mu = 1$.

Then
$$x = \lambda X + \mu x_1,$$
$$y = \lambda Y + \mu y_1,$$
$$z = \lambda Z + \mu z_1,$$

Hence $\quad f(\lambda X + \mu x_1, \ \lambda Y + \mu y_1, \ \lambda Z + \mu z_1) = 0.$

This may be expanded in two ways by Taylor's Theorem; and to abbreviate the algebra let $f(X, Y, Z)$ be written f and $f(x_1, y_1, z_1)$ be written f_1, also denote the operations

$$\left(x_1 \frac{\partial}{\partial X} + y_1 \frac{\partial}{\partial Y} + z_1 \frac{\partial}{\partial Z} \right)^r$$

and
$$\left(X \frac{\partial}{\partial x_1} + Y \frac{\partial}{\partial y_1} + Z \frac{\partial}{\partial z_1} \right)^r$$

by V^r and V_1^r respectively.

Then we have

$$\lambda^n f + \frac{\lambda^{n-1}\mu}{1!} Vf + \frac{\lambda^{n-2}\mu^2}{2!} V^2 f + \dots + \frac{\lambda^{n-r}\mu^r}{r!} V^r f + \dots + \frac{\mu^n}{n!} V^n f$$
$$= 0 \dots\dots(1)$$

or

$$\mu^n f_1 + \frac{\mu^{n-1}\lambda}{1!} V_1 f_1 + \frac{\mu^{n-2}\lambda^2}{2!} V_1^2 f_1 + \dots + \frac{\mu^r \lambda^{n-r}}{(n-r)!} V_1^{n-r} f_1 + \dots + \frac{\lambda^n}{n!} V_1^n f_1$$
$$= 0 \dots\dots(2)$$

Either of these equations gives the n values of the ratio $\frac{\mu}{\lambda}$, viz. $\frac{PQ_1}{Q_1 A}, \frac{PQ_2}{Q_2 A}, \dots$

Comparing the coefficients we have the series of identities

$$\frac{1}{n!} V_1^n f_1 = f,$$

$$\frac{1}{(n-1)!} V_1^{n-1} f_1 = Vf,$$

$$\text{etc.,}$$

$$\frac{1}{2!} V_1^2 f_1 = \frac{1}{(n-2)!} V^{n-2} f,$$

$$V_1 f_1 = \frac{1}{(n-1)!} V^{n-1} f,$$

$$f_1 = \frac{1}{n!} V^n f.$$

306. Polar Curves.

The several loci defined by the equations
$$V_1 f_1 = 0,$$
$$V_1^2 f_1 = 0,$$
$$V_1^3 f_1 = 0,$$
$$\text{etc.,}$$
are respectively called the polar line, the polar conic, the polar cubic; and so on.

The curve $V_1^{n-1} f_1 = 0$, or, which is the same thing, $Vf = 0$, has been called (Art. 211) the first polar of the point x_1, y_1, z_1. Similarly the curves $V^2 f = 0$, $V^3 f = 0$, etc., are called the second, third, etc., polar curves. It is clear then that

> the $n-1^{\text{th}}$ polar curve is the polar line,
> the $n-2^{\text{th}}$ polar curve is the polar conic;
> and so on.

307. Geometrical Interpretations.

The geometrical meanings of these equations will be obvious :—

If $V_1 f_1 = 0$, the sum of the roots of Equation (2) vanishes, *i.e.*
$$\Sigma \frac{\mu}{\lambda} = 0,$$

or
$$\Sigma \frac{PQ}{AQ} = 0,$$

or putting $AQ_1 = r_1$, etc., and $AP = R$,
$$\Sigma \frac{R - r}{r} = 0,$$

giving
$$\Sigma \left(\frac{1}{r} - \frac{1}{R} \right) = 0,$$

or
$$\frac{n}{R} = \frac{1}{r_1} + \frac{1}{r_2} + \frac{1}{r_3} + \dots + \frac{1}{r_n}.$$

This property is due to Cotes, and the special case of it when the curve is a conic gives rise to the name polar line.

If $V_1^2 f_1 = 0$, we have $\Sigma \frac{PQ_1}{AQ_1} \cdot \frac{PQ_2}{AQ_2} = 0$,

which may be interpreted as before, and similarly for the higher polar curves.

It appears that since each of these curves is completely defined by its geometrical property it is totally independent of any system of co-ordinates used in its description.

308. Polar Curves of the Origin.

Taking Cartesians, if the origin be chosen at the point A, $x_1 = y_1 = 0$, and it appears that the polar line, polar conic, polar cubic, etc., of the origin respectively reduce to

$$\frac{\partial^{n-1}f}{\partial z^{n-1}} = 0, \quad \frac{\partial^{n-2}f}{\partial z^{n-2}} = 0, \quad \frac{\partial^{n-3}f}{\partial z^{n-3}} = 0, \quad \text{etc.}$$

If the Cartesian equation be written

$$u_0 + u_1 + u_2 + u_3 + \ldots + u_n = 0$$

this becomes when the z is introduced

$$u_0 z^n + u_1 z^{n-1} + u_2 z^{n-2} + u_3 z^{n-3} + \ldots + u_n = 0,$$

and the equations of the several polars of the origin are

$$\frac{n!}{1} u_0 z + (n-1)! \, u_1 = 0,$$

$$\frac{n!}{2!} u_0 z^2 + (n-1)! \, u_1 z + (n-2)! \, u_2 = 0,$$

$$\frac{n!}{3!} u_0 z^3 + \frac{(n-1)!}{2!} u_1 z^2 + \frac{(n-2)!}{1!} u_2 z + (n-3)! \, u_3 = 0,$$

$$\text{etc.,}$$

i.e. $\quad n u_0 + u_1 = 0,$

$$\frac{n(n-1)}{1 \cdot 2} u_0 + (n-1)u_1 + u_2 = 0,$$

$$\frac{n(n-1)(n-2)}{1 \cdot 2 \cdot 3} u_0 + \frac{(n-1)(n-2)}{1 \cdot 2} u_1 + (n-2)u_2 + u_3 = 0,$$

$$\text{etc.}$$

309. General Conclusions.

If the point A which has been taken for origin lie on the curve, then $u_0 = 0$, and the polar curves all have $u_1 = 0$ for tangent at the origin.

If also the first degree terms are absent from the equation of the curve, they are absent too from all the polars, and the terms of lowest degree throughout the whole system are u_2. We therefore draw the following conclusions:—

(a.) The polar curves at any point on the original curve all touch it at the point in question.

(b.) The polar curves at any multiple point all have a multiple point of the same order, with the same tangents as the multiple point on the original curve.

(c.) The polar conic at a double point on a curve breaks up into two straight lines, viz., the tangents at the multiple point.

(d.) The polar conic at a cusp breaks up into two straight lines coincident with the tangent at the cusp.

(e.) The polar conic at a point of inflexion breaks up into two straight lines, one of which is the tangent at the inflexional point and the other does not in general pass through that point.

[For in this case u_2 must contain u_1 for a factor, $= u_1 v_1$ say, so the polar conic becomes

$$u_1(v_1 + n - 1) = 0 ;$$

the line $v_1 + n - 1 = 0$ is called the Harmonic Polar of the point of Inflexion (see Art. 301).]

310. First Polar. Cases of Node or Cusp.

If a curve have a node at any point let the origin be taken there and the tangents at the node for axes.

The curve then takes the form

$$u \equiv xyz^{n-2} + u_3 z^{n-3} + u_4 z^{n-4} + \ldots = 0.$$

The first polar of x_1, y_1, z_1, viz.

$$x_1 \frac{\partial u}{\partial x} + y_1 \frac{\partial u}{\partial y} + z_1 \frac{\partial u}{\partial z} = 0$$

becomes $x_1(yz^{n-2} + \ldots) + y_1(xz^{n-2} + \ldots) + \ldots = 0,$

the lowest degree terms only being retained.   And since these terms are linear it appears that the first polar of any point x_1, y_1, z_1 goes through the origin and therefore through all the other double points on the curve.

If the curve have a cusp and the origin be taken there with the tangent at the cusp as x-axis the equation of the curve takes the form

$$u \equiv y^2 z^{n-2} + u_3 z^{n-3} + u_4 z^{n-4} + \ldots = 0,$$

and the first polar of any point x_1, y_1, z_1 is

$$y_1(2yz^{n-2} + \ldots) + \ldots = 0$$

the term of lowest degree only being retained.

Hence this curve also touches the x-axis at the origin.

Thus the first polar of any point goes through all the cusps and *touches* the curve at each.

311. The Hessian.

We have seen that at all double points and points of inflexion the polar conic degenerates into two straight lines. Hence its discriminant vanishes. Also, conversely. Now the equation of the polar conic of the curve $u = f(x, y, z) = 0$ corresponding to the point x_1, y_1, z_1 is $\qquad V_1^2 f_1 = 0,$

or $\qquad\qquad X^2 \dfrac{\partial^2 f}{\partial x_1^2} + \ldots + 2 YZ \dfrac{\partial^2 f}{\partial y_1 \partial z_1} + \ldots = 0.$

Hence if x_1, y_1, z_1 be a double point or a point of inflexion,

we have $\qquad \begin{vmatrix} \dfrac{\partial^2 f}{\partial x_1^2}, & \dfrac{\partial^2 f}{\partial x_1 \partial y_1}, & \dfrac{\partial^2 f}{\partial z_1 \partial x_1} \\[2ex] \dfrac{\partial^2 f}{\partial y_1 \partial x_1}, & \dfrac{\partial^2 f}{\partial y_1^2}, & \dfrac{\partial^2 f}{\partial y_1 \partial z_1} \\[2ex] \dfrac{\partial^2 f}{\partial z_1 \partial x_1}, & \dfrac{\partial^2 f}{\partial y_1 \partial z_1}, & \dfrac{\partial^2 f}{\partial z_1^2} \end{vmatrix} = 0\,;$

that is, the curve

$$H(u) \equiv \begin{vmatrix} u_{xx}, & u_{xy}, & u_{xz} \\ u_{yx}, & u_{yy}, & u_{yz} \\ u_{zx}, & u_{zy}, & u_{zz} \end{vmatrix} = 0$$

cuts the original curve $u = 0$ in all its multiple points and points of inflexion.

The determinant $H(u)$ is called the Hessian of u from M. Otto Hesse, the discoverer of the relation between the curves $\qquad\qquad u = 0, \quad H(u) = 0.$

312. Number of the Points of Inflexion.

The degree of this curve is clearly $3(n-2)$. Hence it cannot have more than $3n(n-2)$ intersections with the original curve.

Thus in a curve with no multiple points upon it there will be $3n(n-2)$ points of inflexion real or imaginary.

313. Cases of Node and Cusp.

If the curve has a node let the origin be taken there, and the tangents to the node for axes.

The equation to the curve now becomes

$$u \equiv xyz^{n-2} + u_3 z^{n-3} + u_4 z^{n-4} + \ldots \quad = 0.$$

Hence

$$u_{xx} = \frac{\partial^2 u_3}{\partial x^2} z^{n-3} + \ldots \qquad\qquad ; \quad u_{yz} = (n-2)xz^{n-3} + \ldots ;$$

$$u_{yy} = \frac{\partial^2 u_3}{\partial y^2} z^{n-3} + \ldots \qquad\qquad ; \quad u_{zx} = (n-2)yz^{n-3} + \ldots ;$$

$$u_{zz} = (n-2)(n-3)xyz^{n-4} + \ldots ; \quad u_{xy} = z^{n-2} + \ldots \qquad ;$$

the lowest degree terms only in x and y being retained in each case.

Hence in

$$H(u) \equiv u_{xx} \cdot u_{yy} \cdot u_{zz} + 2u_{yz} \cdot u_{zx} \cdot u_{xy} - u_{xx} \cdot u_{yz}^2 - u_{yy} \cdot u_{zx}^2 - u_{zz} \cdot u_{xy}^2$$
$$= 0,$$

the lowest degree terms are of the form Axy. Hence the Hessian has a node also at the origin and the tangents to the node of the Hessian coincide with the tangents to the node on the original curve.

It is easy to prove further that when the curve has a multiple point of order k the Hessian has a multiple point of order $3k - 4$ at the same point and that each of the tangents at the multiple point is a tangent to one or other of the $3k - 4$ branches of the Hessian. (See Dr. Salmon's *Higher Plane Curves*, 2nd ed., page 58.)

We next consider the case of a cusp. Let the origin be taken at the cusp and the tangent for the x-axis. Then the equation to the curve becomes

$$u \equiv y^2 z^{n-2} + u_3 z^{n-3} + u_4 z^{n-4} + \ldots = 0.$$

Here

$$u_{xx} = \frac{\partial^2 u_3}{\partial x^2} z^{n-3} + \ldots \qquad\qquad ; \quad u_{yz} = 2(n-2)yz^{n-3} + \ldots ;$$

$$u_{yy} = 2z^{n-2} + \ldots \qquad\qquad ; \quad u_{zx} = (n-3)\frac{\partial u_3}{\partial x} \cdot z^{n-4} + \ldots ;$$

$$u_{zz} = (n-2)(n-3)y^2 z^{n-4} + \ldots ; \quad u_{xy} = \frac{\partial^2 u_3}{\partial x \partial y} z^{n-3} + \ldots ;$$

the lowest degree terms only in x and y being retained.

Hence in $H(u) = 0$ the lowest degree terms in x and y are of the form $A \cdot \dfrac{\partial^2 u_3}{\partial x^2} \cdot y^2$.

So the Hessian has a triple point with two coincident tangents $y = 0$ and a third tangent $\dfrac{\partial^2 u_3}{\partial x^2} = 0$.

314. Plücker's Equations.

We are now in a position to establish Plücker's Equations for the number of tangents which can be drawn from a given point to a curve of the nth degree and for the number of points of inflexion upon it.

It was established in Art. 208 that the first polar cuts the curve in $n(n-1)$ points. The first polar however goes through all the double points and in the case of a cusp touches the curve there. Hence a node counts as *two* and a cusp as *three* points of intersection. Thus if there be δ nodes and κ cusps the class of the curve, viz. $n(n-1)$, is diminished by $2\delta + 3\kappa$. Hence if m be the class

$$m = n(n-1) - 2\delta - 3\kappa \dots\dots\dots\dots\dots\dots(1)$$

Again, let ι be the number of inflexions on the curve. Then it has been established that if there are no multiple points

$$\iota = 3n(n-2).$$

But it has been shown that the Hessian passes also through all the double points and has tangents coincident with those of the curve. Hence each node counts for *six* intersections of the Hessian with the curve. And since at each cusp on the curve the Hessian has a triple point, two tangents being the coincident tangents to the curve at the cusp, each cusp counts for 8 intersections $(3+3+2)$. Thus the number of inflexions is diminished by $6\delta + 8\kappa$ and stands as

$$\iota = 3n(n-2) - 6\delta - 8\kappa \dots\dots\dots\dots\dots\dots(2)$$

By considering the reciprocal curve for which

a stationary point gives rise to a stationary tangent,
a double point gives rise to a double tangent,
a stationary tangent gives rise to a stationary point,

it follows that if τ be the number of double or bi-tangents, *i.e.* tangents having contact at more than one point of their length, and m the degree of the reciprocal curve, *i.e.* the class of the original curve

$$n = m(m-1) - 2\tau - 3\iota, \dots\dots\dots\dots\dots\dots(3)$$
$$\kappa = 3m(m-2) - 6\tau - 8\iota \dots\dots\dots\dots\dots\dots(4)$$

These four equations are due to Plücker.

315. Deficiency.

The number $\frac{1}{2}(n-1)(n-2)-\delta-\kappa$, by which the number of double points falls short of the maximum possible is called the deficiency of the curve.

1. Prove that the four equations established in Art. 314 are not independent.

2. Show that the geometrical property of the polar conic may be expressed as
$$\frac{n(n-1)}{2}\frac{1}{\rho^2}-\frac{n-1}{\rho}\Sigma\frac{1}{r_1}+\Sigma\frac{1}{r_1 r_2}=0.$$

3. If A be a point of inflexion on a curve and $A, P_1, P_2, ..., P_{n-1}$ be a secant cutting the Harmonic polar of the point of inflexion in Q, prove that
$$\frac{n-1}{AQ}=\frac{1}{AP_1}+\frac{1}{AP_2}+...+\frac{1}{AP_{n-1}}.$$

4. Form the Hessian of $x^3+y^3=3axy$, and find the number of points of inflexion.   [OXFORD, 1885.]

5. Establish the equations
$$2\tau=n(n-2)(n^2-9)-2(n^2-n-6)(2\delta+3\kappa)+4\delta(\delta-1)+12\delta\kappa+9\kappa(\kappa-1),$$
$$2\delta=m(m-2)(m^2-9)-2(m^2-m-6)(2\tau+3\iota)+4\tau(\tau-1)+12\tau\iota+9\iota(\iota-1).$$
[PLÜCKER.]

6. Prove that the deficiency of a curve is the same as that of its reciprocal.

316. Unicursal Curves.

When a curve has its full number of double points, so that its deficiency is zero, the current co-ordinates can each be expressed as rational algebraic functions of some single parameter.

For supposing that there are $\frac{(n-1)(n-2)}{2}$ double points, a curve of the $(n-2)^{th}$ degree may be made to pass through them and through $n-3$ other points on the curve. Then since
$$\frac{(n-1)(n-2)}{2}+n-3=\frac{(n-2)(n+1)}{2}-1,$$

the points now chosen are insufficient by one to completely determine the new curve. Its equation will therefore contain one arbitrary constant and may therefore be written
$$u+\lambda v=0,$$

with an undetermined parameter λ.

Eliminating y between this equation and that of the given curve, we have remaining an equation between x and λ of degree $n(n-2)$ determining the abscissae of the points of intersection. Of the $n(n-2)$ roots all but one are known, being the abscissae of the $\frac{1}{2}(n-1)(n-2)$ double points each counted twice and the abscissae of the chosen $n-3$ points

for $$n(n-2) - \left\{ 2\frac{(n-1)(n-2)}{2} + n - 3 \right\} = 1.$$

If then the corresponding factors be divided out we are left with x, the abscissa of any other point on the original curve, expressed as a rational integral function of λ. In the same way y may be similarly expressed.

317. Though it is impossible to compress into the limits of the present volume a complete account of the singularities of curves, it is hoped that the later articles of this chapter will form a fair introduction to a study of their general properties in Dr. Salmon's Treatise, to which the student is referred for more detailed information and to which also the Author desires to acknowledge his indebtedness.

EXAMPLES.

1. Write down the equations of the tangents at the origin for each of the following curves :—

(a) $\quad y + c = c \cosh \dfrac{x}{c}.$

(β) $\quad y = a \tan \dfrac{x}{b}.$

(γ) $\quad y^2 = x \log(1+x).$

(δ) $\quad x^3 + y^3 = 3axy.$

2. Show that on the curve
$$(ay - x^2)^2 = bx^3$$
there is a cusp of the first species at the origin, and a point of inflexion whose abscissa is $\frac{9}{64}b$.

3. Show that the Trident curve
$$axy + a^3 = x^3$$
has a point of inflexion at the point in which it cuts the axis of x, and show that the tangent at the point of inflexion makes with the axis of x an angle $\tan^{-1}3$.

4. Show that the curve $b(ay - x^2)^2 = x^5$
has a cusp of the second species at the origin.

5. Show that, if n be greater than 2, the curve
$$b^{n-4}(ay - x^2)^2 = x^n$$
has a cusp at the origin of the first or second species according as n is less or greater than 4.

6. Find the two points of inflexion of the curve
$$\frac{y}{c} = \frac{x^2}{9a^2} + \left(\frac{x-a}{a}\right)^{\frac{1}{3}}$$
and draw figures showing the characters of the inflexions.

7. Show that the points of inflexion on the cubic
$$y = \frac{a^2 x}{x^2 + a^2}$$
are given by $x = 0$ and $x = \pm a\sqrt{3}$.

Show that these three points of inflexion lie on the straight line
$$x = 4y.$$

8. Show that the curve $au = \theta^n$ has a point of inflexion where
$$au = \{n(1-n)\}^{\frac{n}{2}}.$$

9. Find by polars the points of inflexion on the curve
$$2x(x^2 + y^2) = a(2x^2 + y^2).$$

10. Show that the origin is a triple point on the curve
$$x^4 + y^4 = axy^2,$$
and that there is a cusp of the first species there.

11. Show that the abscissae of the points of inflexion on the curve
$$y^n = f(x)$$
are roots of the equation
$$\frac{n-1}{n}\{f'(x)\}^2 = f(x)f''(x).$$

12. Show that the abscissae of the points of inflexion on the curve
$$y = e^{-\lambda x} \tan \mu x$$
are given by $2\mu \sec^2 \mu x(\mu \tan \mu x - \lambda) + \lambda^2 \tan \mu x = 0.$

13. Show that the curve $y = \dfrac{x^3 + ax^2 + a^3}{x^2 - a^2}$
has a point of inflexion at the point whose abscissa is
$$-a\frac{\sqrt[3]{3} + 1}{\sqrt[3]{3} - 1}.$$

14. Show that there are two points of inflexion on the cubic
$$x^3 + y^3 = a^3$$
at the points $(a, 0)$, $(0, a)$ respectively. .

15. In the curve $x^3 + y^3 = ax^2$ show that there is a cusp of the first kind at the origin, and a point of inflexion where $x = a$.

16. In the curve $y^2 = (x - a)(x - b)(x - c)$ show that if $a = b$ there is a node, cusp, or conjugate point at $x = a$ according as a is $>$, $=$, or $<c$. Also show that the points of inflexion have for their abscissae $x = \dfrac{4c - a}{3}$. Hence show that the points of inflexion on this curve are real or imaginary according as the curve has a conjugate point or a node.

17. Show that for the curve
$$r = a(1 - \cos \theta)$$
there is a cusp of the first kind at the origin.

18. Show that the curve
$$r^2\cos^2\theta = a^2\cos 2\theta$$
has a double point at the origin.

19. Show that the curve $r = a \sin n\theta$ has a multiple point at the origin of order n or $2n$ according as n is odd or even.

20. Show that the curve $r = \dfrac{a\theta^2}{1 + \theta^2}$ has a cusp of the first kind at the pole.

21. Show that if the cubic
$$xy^2 + ey = ax^3 + bx^2 + cx + d$$
have a centre, then will $b = 0$ and $d = 0$ and the centre is at the origin.

In this case show also that the origin is a point of inflexion on the curve.

22. Show that there is a conjugate point on the locus
$$x^3 + y^3 + 3cxy = c^3$$
at the point $(-c, -c)$. Trace the curve.

23. Show that the curve $x^5 + y^5 = 5ax^2y^2$ has two cusps of the first species at the origin, and that $x + y = a$ is an asymptote.

24. Show that the curve $by^2 = x^3\sin^2\dfrac{x}{a}$ has a cusp of the first species at the origin and is symmetrical with regard to the axis of x. Show also that it has an infinite series of conjugate points lying at equal distances from each other along the negative portion of the axis of x.

25. Show that the curve $y - x = \log_e \dfrac{ey^2}{4x}$

has a node at the point (1, 2).

26. Show that the curve

$$(x^2 + y^2)^2 = a(3x^2y - y^3)$$

has a triple point at the origin, and that the angles between the branches through the origin are equal.

27. Show that the curve

$$(x^2 + y^2)^{\frac{5}{2}} = 4axy(x^2 - y^2)$$

has a multiple point of the eighth order at the origin, and that the curve consists of eight equal loops.

28. Show that for the Conchoid

$$x^2y^2 = (a + y)^2(b^2 - y^2),$$

if b be $>a$ there is a node at $x = 0$, $y = -a$, and if $b = a$ there is a cusp at the same point.

29. The curve whose tangent is of an invariable magnitude is always convex towards the foot of the ordinate.

30. Examine the nature of the origin on the curve

$$y^5 + ax^4 - b^2xy^2 = 0. \qquad \text{[CRAMER.]}$$

31. Examine the nature of the origin on the curve

$$x^4 - ayx^2 + by^3 = 0. \qquad \text{[ROLLE.]}$$

32. Examine for multiple points the curve

$$x^4 - 2ay^3 - 3a^2y^2 - 2a^2x^2 + a^4 = 0. \qquad \text{[PEACOCK.]}$$

33. Examine the singularities of the curve

$$x^4 - 4ax^3 - 2ay^3 + 4a^2x^2 + 3a^2y^2 - a^4 = 0.$$

There are nodes at the points (0, a), (a, 0), (2a, a). Find the directions of the tangents at these points.

34. Show that the curve

$$x^4 - 2x^2y - xy^2 - 2x^2 - 2xy + y^2 - x + 2y + 1 = 0$$

has a single cusp of the second kind at the point (0, -1).

35. Search for double points on the curve

$$y^4 - 8y^3 - 12xy^2 + 16y^2 + 48xy + 4x^2 - 64x = 0. \qquad \text{[ROLLE.]}$$

36. Show that there are two double points in all respects similar

on the curve $\quad x^4 - 2ax^3\sqrt{2} + 2a^2x^2 - ay^3 - a^2y^2 = 0,$

and that there is an inflexion at each double point.

[CRAMER, Lignes Courbes.]

37. Determine the double points, distinguishing their species, on the sextic $(x^2 - 2y^2)^2\{2(x^2 + 2y^2) - 3\} = \{3(x^2 + 2y^2) - 4\}^2$.

[OXFORD, 1886.]

38. Determine the double points on

$$(x^2 - y^2)(x - 1)(2x - 3) + 4(x^2 + y^2 - 2x)^2 = 0. \quad [\text{PLÜCKER.}]$$

39. The points of contact of parallel tangents to a curve of the nth degree lie on a curve of the $(n-1)^{\text{th}}$ degree. [SERRET.]

40. If A be any point on a curve, and $AP_1P_2 \ldots P_{n-1}$ be a secant cutting the curve in $P_1, P_2, \ldots P_{n-1}$ and the polar conic of A in Q,

prove $\qquad \dfrac{n-1}{AQ} = \dfrac{1}{AP_1} + \dfrac{1}{AP_2} + \ldots + \dfrac{1}{AP_{n-1}}.$

41. A nodal cubic intersects in the points P and P' two lines which are harmonically conjugate with respect to the tangents at the node. Prove that the tangents at P, P' meet on the curve.

42. Prove that the locus of the cusp of a cubic with three given asymptotes is the maximum ellipse inscribed in the triangle formed by the asymptotes. [PLÜCKER.]

43. If (x, y, z) be a double point on a curve $u = 0$, and if

$$lX + mY + nZ = 0$$

be a tangent at the double point, then will

$$\frac{x}{l}u_{xx} + \frac{y}{m}u_{yy} + \frac{z}{n}u_{zz} = 0$$

and $\qquad l^2 x u_{yz} + m^2 y u_{zx} + n^2 z u_{xy} = 0.$ [OXFORD, 1886.]

44. If the equation to a plane curve be $\phi = 0$, where ϕ is a function of x and y which fulfils the condition $\dfrac{\partial^2 \phi}{\partial x^2} + \dfrac{\partial^2 \phi}{\partial y^2} = 0$, prove that if n branches of the curve meet in a multiple point their tangents will form $2n$ angles with each other, each equal to $\dfrac{\pi}{n}$. [SMITH'S PRIZE, 1877.]

45. Prove that the Hessian of the cubic

$$x^3 + y^3 + z^3 + 6mxyz = 0$$

is $\qquad x^3 + y^3 + z^3 - \dfrac{1 + 2m^3}{m^2}xyz = 0,$

and show that the curve and its Hessian have the same points of inflexion. [SALMON, *H. P. C.*]

CHAPTER X.

CURVATURE.

318. Angle of Contingence.

Let PQ be an arc of a curve. Suppose that between P and Q there is no point of inflexion or other singularity, but that the bending is continuously in one direction. Let LPR and MQ be the tangents at P and Q, intersecting at T and cutting

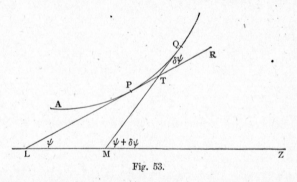

Fig. 53.

a given fixed straight line LZ in L and M. Then the angle RTQ is called the *angle of contingence* of the arc PQ.

The angle of contingence of any arc is therefore the difference of the angles which the tangents at its extremities make with any given fixed straight line. It is also obviously the angle *turned through* by a line which rolls along the curve from one extremity of the arc to the other.

319. Measure of Curvature.

It is clear that the *whole bending* or *curvature* which the curve undergoes between P and Q is greater or less according as the angle of contingence RTQ is greater or less. The fraction $\dfrac{\text{angle of contingence}}{\text{length of arc}}$ is called the *average bending* or *average curvature* of the arc. We shall define the *curvature* of a curve in the immediate neighbourhood of a given point to be *the rate of deflection* from the tangent at that point. And we shall take as a measure of this rate of deflection at the given point the limit of the expression $\dfrac{\text{angle of contingence}}{\text{length of arc}}$ when the length of the arc measured from the given point and therefore also the angle of contingence are indefinitely diminished.

320. Curvature of a Circle.

In the case of the circle the curvature is the same at every point and is measured by the RECIPROCAL OF THE RADIUS.

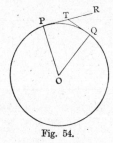

Fig. 54.

For let r be the radius, O the centre. Then

$$R\widehat{T}Q = P\widehat{O}Q = \frac{\text{arc }PQ}{r},$$

the angle being supposed measured in circular measure. Hence

$$\frac{\text{angle of contingence}}{\text{length of arc}} = \frac{1}{r},$$

and this is true whether the limit be taken or not. Hence the "curvature" of a circle at any point is measured by the reciprocal of the radius.

321. Circle of Curvature.

If three contiguous points P, Q, R be taken on a curve, a circle may be drawn to pass through them. When the points are indefinitely close together, PQ and QR are ultimately tangents both to the curve and to the circle. Hence at the point of ultimate coincidence the curve and the circle have the *same angle of contingence*, viz., the angle *RQZ* (see Fig. 55). Moreover, the *arcs PR* of the circle and the curve differ by a small quantity of order higher than their own, and therefore *may be considered equal in the limit* (see Art. 34). Hence the curvatures of this circle and of the curve at the point of contact are equal. It is therefore convenient to describe the curvature of a curve at a given point by reference to a circle thus drawn, the reciprocal of the radius being a correct measure

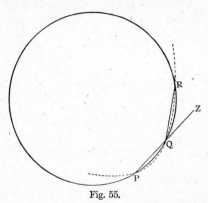

Fig. 55.

of the *rate of bend*. We shall therefore consider such a circle to exist for each point of a curve and shall speak of it as the **circle of curvature** of that point. Its radius and centre will be called the **radius** and **centre of curvature** respectively, and a chord of this circle drawn through the point of contact in any direction will be referred to as the **chord of curvature** in that direction.

322. Formula for Radius of Curvature.

Referring to the figure of Art. 318, let the arc *AP* measured from some fixed point *A* on the curve up to *P* be called *s*, and *AQ*, $s + \delta s$; let the angle $PLZ = \psi$, and $QMZ = \psi + \delta\psi$. Then the angle of contingence $RTQ = \delta\psi$ and the measure of the curvature $= Lt\dfrac{\delta\psi}{\delta s} = \dfrac{d\psi}{ds}$. If therefore the radius of curvature be called ρ, we have $\dfrac{1}{\rho} = \dfrac{d\psi}{ds}$, or $\rho = \dfrac{ds}{d\psi}$ ....(A)

323. This formula may also be arrived at thus. Let *PQ* and *QR* (Fig. 55) be considered equal chords, and therefore when

we proceed to the limit the elementary arcs PQ and QR may be considered equal. Call each δs, and the angle $RQZ = \delta\psi$.

Now the radius of the circum-circle of the triangle PQR is

$$\frac{PR}{2\sin PQR}.$$

Hence $\rho = Lt\dfrac{PR}{2\sin PQR} = Lt\dfrac{2\delta s}{2\sin\delta\psi} = Lt\dfrac{\delta s}{\delta\psi}\cdot\dfrac{\delta\psi}{\sin\delta\psi} = \dfrac{ds}{d\psi}.$

Also, it is clear that the lines which bisect at right angles the chords PQ, QR intersect at the circum-centre of PQR, i.e., in the limit the centre of curvature of any point on a curve may be considered as the *point of intersection of the normal at that point with the normal at a contiguous and ultimately coincident point.*

324. The formula (A) is useful in the case in which the equation of the curve is given in its intrinsic form, i.e. when the equation is given as a relation between s and ψ (Art. 346). For example, that relation for a catenary is $s = c\tan\psi$, whence

$$\rho = \frac{ds}{d\psi} = c\sec^2\psi,$$

and the rate of its deflection at any point is measured by

$$\frac{1}{\rho} = \frac{\cos^2\psi}{c} = \frac{c}{s^2 + c^2}.$$

325. Transformations.

This formula however must be transformed so as to suit each of the systems of co-ordinates in which it is usual to express the equation of a curve. These transformations we proceed to perform.

We have the equations

$$\cos\psi = \frac{dx}{ds}, \quad \sin\psi = \frac{dy}{ds}.$$

Hence, differentiating each of these with respect to s,

$$-\sin\psi\frac{d\psi}{ds} = \frac{d^2x}{ds^2}, \quad \cos\psi\frac{d\psi}{ds} = \frac{d^2y}{ds^2},$$

whence

$$\frac{1}{\rho} = \frac{-\dfrac{d^2x}{ds^2}}{\dfrac{dy}{ds}} = \frac{\dfrac{d^2y}{ds^2}}{\dfrac{dx}{ds}}\dots\dots\dots\dots\dots\dots(\text{B})$$

and by squaring and adding

$$\frac{1}{\rho^2} = \left(\frac{d^2x}{ds^2}\right)^2 + \left(\frac{d^2y}{ds^2}\right)^2 \dots\dots\dots\dots\dots(\text{C})$$

These formulae (B) and (C) are only suitable for the case in which both x and y are known functions of s.

326. Cartesian Formula.　Explicit Functions.

Again, since $\qquad \tan \psi = \dfrac{dy}{dx},$

we have $\qquad \sec^2 \psi \dfrac{d\psi}{dx} = \dfrac{d^2y}{dx^2}$

by differentiating with regard to x.

Now $\qquad\qquad \dfrac{d\psi}{dx} = \dfrac{d\psi}{ds} \cdot \dfrac{ds}{dx} = \dfrac{1}{\rho \cos \psi};$

therefore $\qquad \sec^3 \psi \cdot \dfrac{1}{\rho} = \dfrac{d^2y}{dx^2},$

and $\qquad\qquad \sec^2 \psi = 1 + \tan^2 \psi = 1 + \left(\dfrac{dy}{dx}\right)^2;$

therefore $\qquad\qquad \rho = \dfrac{\left\{ 1 + \left(\dfrac{dy}{dx}\right)^2 \right\}^{\frac{3}{2}}}{\dfrac{d^2y}{dx^2}} \dotfill (\mathrm{D})$

This important form of the result is adapted to the evaluation of the radius of curvature when the equation of the curve is given in Cartesian co-ordinates, y being an explicit function of x.

327. Cartesians.　Implicit Functions.

We may throw this into another shape specially adapted to Cartesian curves, in which neither variable can be expressed explicitly as a function of the other.

Thus if $\phi(x, y) = 0$ be the equation to the curve, we have

$$\phi_x + \phi_y \frac{dy}{dx} = 0,$$

and differentiating again

$$\frac{\partial \phi_x}{\partial x} + \frac{\partial \phi_x}{\partial y} \cdot \frac{dy}{dx} + \left(\frac{\partial \phi_y}{\partial x} + \frac{\partial \phi_y}{\partial y} \cdot \frac{dy}{dx}\right)\frac{dy}{dx} + \phi_y \frac{d^2y}{dx^2} = 0,$$

or $\qquad \phi_{xx} + 2\phi_{xy}\dfrac{dy}{dx} + \phi_{yy}\left(\dfrac{dy}{dx}\right)^2 + \phi_y\dfrac{d^2y}{dx^2} = 0.$

Hence substituting for $\dfrac{dy}{dx}$ and $\dfrac{d^2y}{dx^2}$ in the formula

$$\rho = \pm \frac{\left\{ 1 + \left(\dfrac{dy}{dx}\right)^2 \right\}^{\frac{3}{2}}}{\dfrac{d^2y}{dx^2}},$$

we have
$$\rho = \frac{\left(1+\dfrac{\phi_x^2}{\phi_y^2}\right)^{\frac{3}{2}}\phi_y}{\phi_{xx}+2\phi_{xy}\left(-\dfrac{\phi_x}{\phi_y}\right)+\phi_{yy}\left(-\dfrac{\phi_x}{\phi_y}\right)^2},$$

or
$$\rho = \frac{(\phi_x^2+\phi_y^2)^{\frac{3}{2}}}{\phi_{xx}\phi_y^2-2\phi_{xy}\phi_x\phi_y+\phi_{yy}\phi_x^2}\dots\dots\dots\dots\dots(E)$$

328. A curve is frequently defined by giving the two Cartesian co-ordinates x, y in terms of a third variable, e.g., the equation of a cycloid is most conveniently expressed as

$$x=a(\theta+\sin\theta), \quad y=a(1-\cos\theta).$$

Formula (D) is very easily modified to meet the requirements of this case.

Let
$$\left.\begin{array}{l}x=F(t)\\y=f(t)\end{array}\right\} \text{ be the equations of the curve.}$$

Then
$$\frac{dy}{dx}=\frac{\dfrac{dy}{dt}}{\dfrac{dx}{dt}}=\frac{f'(t)}{F'(t)},$$

and
$$\frac{d^2y}{dx^2}=\frac{d}{dt}\cdot\left(\frac{dy}{dx}\right)\cdot\frac{dt}{dx}$$

$$=\frac{\dfrac{d^2y}{dt^2}\cdot\dfrac{dx}{dt}-\dfrac{d^2x}{dt^2}\cdot\dfrac{dy}{dt}}{\left(\dfrac{dx}{dt}\right)^3}$$

$$=\frac{f''(t)\cdot F'(t)-f'(t)\cdot F''(t)}{\{F'(t)\}^3},$$

and formula (D) becomes

$$\rho = \frac{\left\{\left(\dfrac{dx}{dt}\right)^2+\left(\dfrac{dy}{dt}\right)^2\right\}^{\frac{3}{2}}}{\dfrac{d^2y}{dt^2}\cdot\dfrac{dx}{dt}-\dfrac{d^2x}{dt^2}\cdot\dfrac{dy}{dt}}=\frac{\{[F'(t)]^2+[f'(t)]^2\}^{\frac{3}{2}}}{f''(t)\cdot F'(t)-f'(t)\cdot F''(t)}\dots\dots\dots\dots(F)$$

Ex. In the above-mentioned case of *the cycloid*

$$\frac{dx}{d\theta}=a(1+\cos\theta), \qquad \frac{d^2x}{d\theta^2}=-a\sin\theta,$$

$$\frac{dy}{d\theta}=a\sin\theta, \qquad \frac{d^2y}{d\theta^2}=a\cos\theta.$$

and by formula (F)

$$\rho=\frac{a\{(1+\cos\theta)^2+\sin^2\theta\}^{\frac{3}{2}}}{\cos\theta(1+\cos\theta)+\sin^2\theta}=\frac{8a\cos^3\dfrac{\theta}{2}}{2\cos^2\dfrac{\theta}{2}}=4a\cos\frac{\theta}{2}.$$

329. Curvature at the Origin.

When the curve passes through the origin the values of $\frac{dy}{dx}(=p)$ and $\frac{d^2y}{dx^2}(=q)$ at the origin may be deduced by substituting for y the expression $px+\frac{qx^2}{2!}+\dots$ (the expansion of y by Maclaurin's Theorem) and equating coefficients of like powers of x in the identity obtained. The radius of curvature at the origin may then be at once deduced from the formula

$$\rho=\pm\frac{(1+p^2)^{\frac{3}{2}}}{q}\ [\text{Formula (D)}].$$

Ex. Let the curve be

$$ax+by$$
$$+a'x^2+2h'xy+b'y^2$$
$$+\dots\dots \qquad =0.$$

Putting

$$y=px+\frac{q}{2!}x^2+\dots$$

we have

$$\begin{vmatrix} a \\ +bp \end{vmatrix} x+ \begin{vmatrix} a' \\ +2h'p \\ +b'p^2 \\ +\dfrac{bq}{2} \end{vmatrix} x^2+\dots \equiv 0,$$

therefore

$$a+bp=0,$$

and

$$a'+2h'p+b'p^2+\frac{bq}{2}=0,$$

etc.

giving

$$p=-\frac{a}{b}\ \text{and}\ q=-2\frac{a'+2h'p+b'p^2}{b},$$

whence

$$\rho=\pm\frac{(1+p^2)^{\frac{3}{2}}}{q}=\frac{1}{2}\frac{(a^2+b^2)^{\frac{3}{2}}}{a'b^2-2h'ab+b'a^2}.$$

This result of course might be deduced at once from formula (E).

330. It will be noticed that, if the lowest terms of the equation be of the second degree, we should get a quadratic equation giving two values for p, and consequently also two values for q. These indicate the two values of ρ corresponding to the two branches of the curve passing through the origin.

Ex. *Find the radii of curvature at the origin for the curve*

$$y^2-3xy+2x^2-x^3+y^4=0.$$

Substituting $px+\frac{q}{2!}x^2+\dots$ for y we have

$$\begin{vmatrix} p^2 \\ -3p \\ +2 \end{vmatrix} x^2+ \begin{vmatrix} pq \\ -\frac{3}{2}q \\ -1 \end{vmatrix} x^3+\dots \equiv 0,$$

whence
$$p^2 - 3p + 2 = 0,$$
$$pq - \tfrac{3}{2}q - 1 = 0,$$
etc.,

whence $\qquad\qquad p = 1$ or 2,

and $\qquad\qquad q = -2$ or 2,

and therefore $\qquad \rho = \dfrac{(1+p^2)^{\frac{3}{2}}}{q} = \dfrac{2^{\frac{3}{2}}}{-2} = -\sqrt{2} = -1\text{·}414...,$

or $\qquad\qquad\qquad = \dfrac{5^{\frac{3}{2}}}{2} = \dfrac{5}{2}\sqrt{5} = 5\text{·}590....$

The difference of sign introduced by the q indicates that the two branches passing through the origin bend in opposite directions.

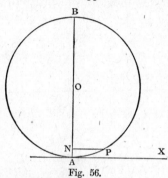

Fig. 56.

331. Newtonian Method.

The Newtonian Method of finding the curvature of the curve at the origin is instructive and interesting. Suppose the axes taken so that the axis of x is a tangent to the curve at the point A, and the axis of y, viz., AB, is therefore the normal. Let APB be the circle of curvature, P the point adjacent to and ultimately coincident with A in which the curve and the circle intersect. Then

$$PN^2 = AN \cdot NB,$$

or $\qquad\qquad NB = \dfrac{PN^2}{AN}.$

Now in the limit

$$NB = AB = \text{twice the radius of curvature.}$$

Hence $\qquad \rho = Lt\,\dfrac{1}{2}\dfrac{PN^2}{AN} = Lt\,\dfrac{x^2}{2y}.$ ....(G)

Similarly, if the axis of y be the tangent at the origin, we have $\qquad\qquad \rho = Lt\,\dfrac{y^2}{2x}.$

Ex. *Find the radius of curvature at the origin for the curve*
$$2x^4 + 3y^4 + 4x^2y + xy - y^2 + 2x = 0.$$

In this case the *axis* of y is a tangent at the origin, and therefore we shall endeavour to find $Lt\dfrac{y^2}{2x}$.

Dividing by x $\quad 2x^3 + 3y^2 . \dfrac{y^2}{x} + 4xy + y - \dfrac{y^2}{x} + 2 = 0.$

Now, at the origin $Lt\dfrac{y^2}{x} = 2\rho$, $x = 0$, $y = 0$, and the equation becomes
$$-2\rho + 2 = 0, \quad \text{or} \quad \rho = 1.$$

332. The same method may be applied when the tangent to the curve at the origin does not coincide with one of the axes; but as the method of Art. 329 is very simple we leave the investigation as an exercise to the student.

Ex. Establish in the above manner the result of the Example in Art. 329.

EXAMPLES.

1. Apply formula (A) to the curves
$$s = a\psi, \quad s = a\sin\psi, \quad s = a\sec^3\psi, \quad \psi = \text{gd}\,\frac{s}{a}.$$

2. Apply formula (D) to the curves
$$y^2 = 4ax, \quad y = c\cosh\frac{x}{c}.$$

3. Apply formula (E) to the curve
$$ax + by + a'x^2 + 2h'xy + b'y^2 + \ldots = 0$$
to find the radius of curvature at the origin.

4. Apply formula (F) to the ellipse
$$\left.\begin{aligned} x &= a\cos\theta \\ y &= b\sin\theta \end{aligned}\right\}.$$

5. Prove that in the case of the equiangular spiral whose intrinsic equation is $\qquad s = a(e^{m\psi} - 1),$
$$\rho = mae^{m\psi}.$$

6. For the tractrix $s = c\log\sec\psi$ prove that $\rho = c\tan\psi$.

7. Show that in the curve $\quad y = x + 3x^2 - x^3$
the radius of curvature at the origin $= \cdot 4714\ldots$, and that at the point $(1, 3)$ it is infinite.

8. Show that in the curve
$$y^2 - 3xy - 4x^2 + x^3 + x^4y + y^5 = 0$$
the radii of curvature at the origin are
$$\frac{85}{2}\sqrt{17} \quad \text{and} \quad 5\sqrt{2}.$$

9. Show that the radii of curvature of the curve
$$y^2 = x^2\frac{a + x}{a - x}$$
for the origin $\qquad = \pm a\sqrt{2},$
and for the point $(-a, 0)$ $\qquad = \dfrac{a}{4}.$

10. Show that the radii of curvature at the origin for the curve
$$x^3 + y^3 = 3axy$$
are each
$$= \frac{3a}{2}.$$

11. Prove that the chord of curvature parallel to the axis of y for the curve
$$y = a \log \sec \frac{x}{a}$$
is of constant length.

12. Prove that for the curve $\quad s = m(\sec^3\psi - 1),$
$$\rho = 3m \tan \psi \sec^3\psi,$$
and hence that
$$3m \frac{dy}{dx} \frac{d^2y}{dx^2} = 1.$$
Also, that this differential equation is satisfied by the semicubical parabola
$$27my^2 = 8x^3.$$

13. Prove that for the curve
$$s = a \log \cot \left(\frac{\pi}{4} - \frac{\psi}{2}\right) + a\frac{\sin \psi}{\cos^2\psi},$$
$$\rho = 2a \sec^3\psi ;$$
and hence that
$$\frac{d^2y}{dx^2} = \frac{1}{2a},$$
and that this differential equation is satisfied by the parabola
$$x^2 = 4ay.$$

14. Show that for the curve in which $s = ae^{\frac{x}{c}}$
$$c\rho = s(s^2 - c^2)^{\frac{1}{2}}.$$

15. Show that the curve for which $s = \sqrt{8ay}$ (the cycloid) has for its intrinsic equation $\quad s = 4a \sin \psi.$

Hence prove
$$\rho = 4a\sqrt{1 - \frac{y}{2a}}.$$

16. Prove that the curve for which $y^2 = c^2 + s^2$ (the catenary) has for its intrinsic equation $\quad s = c \tan \psi.$

Hence prove $\rho = \frac{y^2}{c} =$ the part of the normal intercepted between the curve and the x-axis.

17. Show that for the curve $x^m + y^m = k^m$
we may write ρ in the form
$$\frac{k}{m-1} \frac{\left(\cos^{4\frac{1-m}{m}} \phi + \sin^{4\frac{1-m}{m}} \phi\right)^{\frac{3}{2}}}{\cos^{2\frac{1-2m}{m}} \phi \sin^{2\frac{1-2m}{m}} \phi}, \text{ where } x = k \cos^{\frac{2}{m}}\phi.$$
Examine the cases $m = 2, \frac{2}{3}, 1.$

18. For the rectangular hyperbola
$$xy = k^2,$$
prove that
$$\rho = \frac{r^3}{2k^2},$$
r being the central radius vector of the point considered.

333. Formula for Pedal Equations.

Since a curve and its circle of curvature at any point P intersect in three contiguous and ultimately coincident points they may be regarded as having two contiguous tangents common. Therefore the values of $r+\delta r$ and $p+\delta p$ are common in addition to those of r and p; *i.e.* the value of $\dfrac{dr}{dp}$ is common. Now let O be the pole and C the centre of curva-

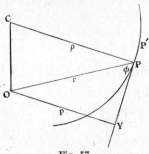

Fig. 57.

ture corresponding to the point P on the curve.

Then
$$OC^2 = r^2 + \rho^2 - 2r\rho \cos OPC$$
$$= r^2 + \rho^2 - 2r\rho \sin \phi$$
$$= r^2 + \rho^2 - 2\rho p.$$

Considering this as referring to the circle (for which OC and ρ are constant) we obtain by differentiating

$$0 = 2r\frac{dr}{dp} - 2\rho,$$

and it has been pointed out that the values of r and $\dfrac{dr}{dp}$ are the same at the point P for the curve and for the circle. Hence for the curve itself we also have

$$\rho = r\frac{dr}{dp} \quad \dots\dots\dots\dots\dots\dots\dots\dots\dots\dots\dots\text{(H)}$$

Ex. In the equation $p^2 = Ar^2 + B$, which represents any epi- or hypo-cycloid [p. 163, Ex. 6], we have
$$p = Ar\frac{dr}{dp},$$
and therefore $\qquad\qquad \rho \propto p.$

The equiangular spiral, in which $p \propto r$, is included as the case in which
$$B = 0.$$

334. Polar Curves.

We shall next reduce the formula to a shape suited for application to curves given by their polar equations.

We proved in Art. 205

$$\frac{1}{p^2} = u^2 + \left(\frac{du}{d\theta}\right)^2.$$

Hence

$$-\frac{1}{p^3}\frac{dp}{d\theta} = \left(u + \frac{d^2u}{d\theta^2}\right)\frac{du}{d\theta},$$

or

$$\frac{dp}{du} = -p^3\left(u + \frac{d^2u}{d\theta^2}\right).$$

Now

$$\rho = \frac{rdr}{dp} \text{ and } r = \frac{1}{u};$$

therefore

$$\rho = -\frac{1}{u^3}\frac{du}{dp} = \frac{1}{p^3u^3\left(u + \frac{d^2u}{d\theta^2}\right)},$$

or

$$\rho = \frac{\left\{u^2 + \left(\frac{du}{d\theta}\right)^2\right\}^{\frac{3}{2}}}{u^3\left(u + \frac{d^2u}{d\theta^2}\right)}. \ldots\ldots \ldots\ldots\ldots\ldots(I)$$

335. This may easily be put in the r, θ form thus:—

Since

$$u = \frac{1}{r},$$

we have

$$\frac{du}{d\theta} = -\frac{1}{r^2}\frac{dr}{d\theta},$$

and therefore

$$\frac{d^2u}{d\theta^2} = \frac{2}{r^3}\left(\frac{dr}{d\theta}\right)^2 - \frac{1}{r^2}\frac{d^2r}{d\theta^2};$$

therefore

$$\rho = \frac{\left\{\frac{1}{r^2} + \frac{1}{r^4}\left(\frac{dr}{d\theta}\right)^2\right\}^{\frac{3}{2}}}{\frac{1}{r^3}\left\{\frac{1}{r} + \frac{2}{r^3}\left(\frac{dr}{d\theta}\right)^2 - \frac{1}{r^2}\frac{d^2r}{d\theta^2}\right\}}$$

$$= \frac{\left\{r^2 + \left(\frac{dr}{d\theta}\right)^2\right\}^{\frac{3}{2}}}{r^2 + 2\left(\frac{dr}{d\theta}\right)^2 - r\frac{d^2r}{d\theta^2}}. \ldots\ldots\ldots\ldots\ldots(J)$$

336. Tangential-Polar Form.

In Art. 221 it was proved that

$$\rho = p + \frac{d^2 p}{d\psi^2}. \quad \dots\dots\dots\dots\dots\dots(\kappa)$$

giving us a formula for the radius of curvature suitable for p, ψ equations.

Ex. It is known that the general p, ψ equation of all epi- and hypo-cycloids can be written in the form

$$p = A \sin B\psi \text{ (p. 163, Ex. 6)}.$$

Hence $\qquad\qquad \rho = A \sin B\psi - AB^2 \sin B\psi,$

and therefore $\qquad\qquad \rho \propto p,$

thus again proving the result of the Example in Art. 333.

337. Point of Inflexion.

At a point of inflexion the radius of curvature is infinite. This is geometrically obvious from the fact that it is the radius of a circle which passes through three collinear points. We may hence deduce various forms of the condition for a point of inflexion ; thus if $\qquad\qquad \rho = \infty,$

we get $\qquad\qquad \dfrac{d\psi}{ds} = 0$ from (A),

$$\frac{d^2 y}{dx^2} = 0 \text{ from (D)},$$

$$\frac{\partial^2 \phi}{\partial x^2} \cdot \left(\frac{\partial \phi}{\partial y}\right)^2 - 2\frac{\partial^2 \phi}{\partial x \partial y} \cdot \frac{\partial \phi}{\partial x} \cdot \frac{\partial \phi}{\partial y} + \frac{\partial^2 \phi}{\partial y^2} \cdot \left(\frac{\partial \phi}{\partial x}\right)^2 = 0 \text{ from (E)},$$

$$u + \frac{d^2 u}{d\theta^2} = 0 \text{ from (I)},$$

$$r^2 + 2\left(\frac{dr}{d\theta}\right)^2 - r\frac{d^2 r}{d\theta^2} = 0 \text{ from (J)},$$

some of which have already been established otherwise.

338. List of Formulae.

The formulae proved above are now collected for convenience.

$$\rho = \frac{ds}{d\psi} \dots\dots\dots\dots\dots\dots\dots\dots\dots(\text{A})$$

$$\frac{1}{\rho} = -\frac{\dfrac{d^2 x}{ds^2}}{\dfrac{dy}{ds}} = \frac{\dfrac{d^2 y}{ds^2}}{\dfrac{dx}{ds}} \dots\dots\dots\dots\dots\dots(\text{B})$$

$$\frac{1}{\rho^2} = \left(\frac{d^2x}{ds^2}\right)^2 + \left(\frac{d^2y}{ds^2}\right)^2 \dots\dots\dots\dots\dots\dots\dots(C)$$

$$\rho = \frac{\left\{1 + \left(\frac{dy}{dx}\right)^2\right\}^{\frac{3}{2}}}{\frac{d^2y}{dx^2}} \dots\dots\dots\dots\dots\dots\dots\dots(D)$$

$$\rho = \frac{(p^2 + q^2)^{\frac{3}{2}}}{rq^2 - 2spq + tp^2} \dots\dots\dots\dots\dots\dots(E)$$

$$\rho = \frac{(F'^2 + f'^2)^{\frac{3}{2}}}{F'f'' - f'F''} \dots\dots\dots\dots\dots\dots\dots(F)$$

$$\rho = Lt\frac{x^2}{2y} \dots\dots\dots\dots\dots\dots\dots\dots\dots(G)$$

$$\rho = r\frac{dr}{dp} \dots\dots\dots\dots\dots\dots\dots\dots\dots\dots(H)$$

$$\rho = \frac{(u^2 + u_1^2)^{\frac{3}{2}}}{u^3(u + u_2)} \dots\dots\dots\dots\dots\dots\dots\dots(I)$$

$$\rho = \frac{(r^2 + r_1^2)^{\frac{3}{2}}}{r^2 + 2r_1^2 - rr_2} \dots\dots\dots\dots\dots\dots(J)$$

$$\rho = p + \frac{d^2p}{d\psi^2} \dots\dots\dots\dots\dots\dots\dots\dots\dots(K)$$

EXAMPLES.

1. Apply formula (H) to the curves
$$p^2 = ar, \quad ap = r^2, \quad p = \frac{r^{m+1}}{a^m}.$$

2. Apply formula (I) to the reciprocal spiral
$$au = \theta.$$

3. Apply the polar formula for radius of curvature to show that the radius of the circle $r = a\cos\theta$ is $\frac{a}{2}$.

4. Show that for the cardioide $r = a(1 + \cos\theta)$
$$\rho = \frac{4a}{3}\cos\frac{\theta}{2}; \ i.e., \propto \sqrt{r}.$$

Also deduce the same result from the pedal equation of the curve, viz.,
$$p\sqrt{2a} = r^{\frac{3}{2}}.$$

5. Show that at the points in which the Archimedean spiral $r = a\theta$ intersects the reciprocal spiral $r\theta = a$ their curvatures are in the ratio $3:1$

6. For the equiangular spiral $r = ae^{m\theta}$ prove that the centre of curvature is at the point where the perpendicular to the radius vector through the pole intersects the normal.

7. Prove that for the curve $\quad r = a\sec 2\theta,$

$$\rho = -\frac{r^4}{3p^3}.$$

8. For any curve prove the formula

$$\rho = \frac{r}{\sin\phi\left(1 + \dfrac{d\phi}{d\theta}\right)}$$

where $\qquad\qquad \tan\phi = \dfrac{rd\theta}{dr}.$

Deduce the ordinary formula in terms of r and θ.

9. Show that the chord of curvature through the pole for the curve

$$p = f(r)$$

is given by $\qquad\quad \text{chord} = 2p\dfrac{dr}{dp} = 2\dfrac{f(r)}{f'(r)}.$

10. Show that the chord of curvature through the pole of the cardioide

$$r = a(1 + \cos\theta) \text{ is } \frac{4}{3}r.$$

11. Show that the chord of curvature through the pole of the equiangular spiral $\qquad\qquad r = ae^{m\theta}$ is $2r.$

12. Show that the chord of curvature through the pole of the curve

$$r^m = a^m\cos m\theta \text{ is } \frac{2r}{m+1}.$$

Examine the cases when $m = -2, -1, -\frac{1}{2}, \frac{1}{2}, 1, 2.$

13. Show that the radius of curvature of the curve

$$r = a\sin n\theta$$

at the origin is $\qquad\qquad \dfrac{na}{2}.$

14. For the curve $\qquad r^m = a^m\cos m\theta,$

prove that $\qquad\qquad \rho = \dfrac{a^m}{(m+1)r^{m-1}}.$

Examine the particular cases of a rectangular hyperbola, lemniscate, parabola, cardioide, straight line, circle.

339. Centre of Curvature.

The Cartesian co-ordinates of the centre of curvature may be found thus :—

Let Q be the centre of curvature corresponding to the point P of the curve. Let OX be the axis of x; O the origin; x, y

the co-ordinates of P; $\bar{x}, \bar{y}$ those of Q; ψ the angle the tangent makes with the axis of x. Draw PN, QM perpendiculars

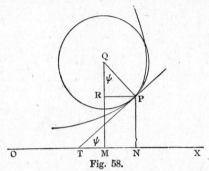

Fig. 58.

upon the x-axis and PR a perpendicular upon QM. Then

$$\bar{x} = OM = ON - RP$$
$$= ON - QP \sin \psi,$$
$$= x - \rho \sin \psi,$$

and

$$\bar{y} = MQ = NP + RQ$$
$$= y + \rho \cos \psi.$$

Now

$$\tan \psi = \frac{dy}{dx};$$

therefore

$$\sin \psi = \frac{\dfrac{dy}{dx}}{\sqrt{1 + \left(\dfrac{dy}{dx}\right)^2}},$$

and

$$\cos \psi = \frac{1}{\sqrt{1 + \left(\dfrac{dy}{dx}\right)^2}}.$$

Also

$$\rho = \frac{\left\{1 + \left(\dfrac{dy}{dx}\right)^2\right\}^{\frac{3}{2}}}{\dfrac{d^2y}{dx^2}}.$$

Hence

$$\bar{x} = x - \frac{\dfrac{dy}{dx}\left\{1 + \left(\dfrac{dy}{dx}\right)^2\right\}}{\dfrac{d^2y}{dx^2}} \qquad \qquad \text{......................(}\alpha\text{)}$$

$$\bar{y} = y + \frac{1 + \left(\dfrac{dy}{dx}\right)^2}{\dfrac{d^2y}{dx^2}} \qquad \qquad \text{......................(}\beta\text{)}$$

INVOLUTES AND EVOLUTES.

340. DEF. The locus of the centres of curvature of all points of a given plane curve is called the *evolute* of that curve. If the evolute itself be regarded as the original curve, a curve of which it is the evolute is called an *involute*.

The equation of the evolute of a given curve may be found by eliminating x and y between equations (α), (β) of the last article and the equation of the curve.

Ex. *To find the locus of the centres of curvature of the parabola*

$$y = \frac{x^2}{4a}.$$

Here
$$\frac{dy}{dx} = \frac{x}{2a}, \quad \frac{d^2y}{dx^2} = \frac{1}{2a}.$$

Hence
$$\bar{x} = x - \frac{\frac{dy}{dx}\left\{1 + \left(\frac{dy}{dx}\right)^2\right\}}{\frac{d^2y}{dx^2}} = -\frac{x^3}{4a^2};$$

$$\bar{y} = y + \frac{1 + \left(\frac{dy}{dx}\right)^2}{\frac{d^2y}{dx^2}} = 2a + \frac{3x^2}{4a};$$

whence
$$(\bar{y} - 2a)^3 = \frac{27x^6}{64a^3} = \frac{27a\bar{x}^2}{4}.$$

Hence the equation of the evolute is

$$4(y - 2a)^3 = 27ax^2.$$

341. Evolute touched by the Normals.

Let P_1, P_2, P_3 be contiguous points on a given curve, and let the normals at P_1, P_2 and at P_2, P_3 intersect at Q_1, Q_2 respectively. Then in the limit when P_2, P_3 move along the

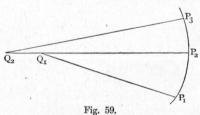

Fig. 59.

curve to ultimate coincidence with P_1 the limiting positions of Q_1, Q_2 are the centres of curvature corresponding to the points P_1, P_2 of the curve. Now Q_1 and Q_2 both lie on the normal at P_2, and therefore it is clear that the normal is a tangent to the locus of such points as Q_1, Q_2, *i.e.*, each of the normals of the original curve is *a tangent to the evolute;* and it will be seen in the chapter on Envelopes that in general the best method of investigating the equation of the evolute of any proposed curve is to consider it as the *envelope of the normals* of that curve.

342. **There is but one Evolute, but an infinite number of Involutes.**

Let $ABCD$ ... be the original curve on which the successive points A, B, C, D, ... are indefinitely close to each other. Let $a, b, c, ...$ be the successive points of intersection of normals at A, B, C, ... and therefore the centres of curvature of those points. Then looking at $ABC...$ as the original curve, $abcd...$ is its *evolute*. And regarding $abcd...$ as the original curve, $ABCD...$ is *an involute*.

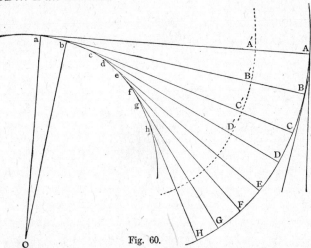

Fig. 60.

If we suppose any equal lengths AA', BB', CC', ... to be taken along each normal, as shown in the figure, then a new curve is formed, viz., $A'B'C'...$, which may be called a *parallel* to the original curve, having the same normals as the original curve and therefore having the same evolute. It is therefore clear that if any curve be given it can have but *one evolute*, but an infinite number of curves may have the same evolute, and therefore any curve may have an *infinite number of involutes*. The involutes of a given curve thus form a system of *parallel curves*.

343. Involutes traced out by the several points of a string unwound from a curve.

Since a is the centre of the circle of curvature for the point A (Fig. 60), $aA = aB$

$\qquad\qquad\qquad\qquad\qquad = bB + \text{elementary arc } ab \text{ (Art. 34)}.$

Hence $aA - bB = \text{arc } ab.$

Similarly $bB - cC = \text{arc } bc,$

$\qquad\qquad\qquad cC - dD = \text{arc } cd,$

$\qquad\qquad\qquad\qquad\qquad \text{etc.,}$

$\qquad\qquad\qquad fF - gG = \text{arc } fg.$

Hence by addition

$\qquad\qquad aA - gG = \text{arc } ab + \text{arc } bc + \ldots + \text{arc } fg$

$\qquad\qquad\qquad\qquad = \text{arc } ag.$

Hence the *difference between the radii of curvature at two points of a curve is equal to the length of the corresponding arc of the evolute.* Also, if the evolute $abc\ldots$ be regarded as a rigid curve and a string be unwound from it, being kept tight, then the *points of the unwinding string describe a system of parallel curves, each of which is an involute of the curve* $abcd\ldots$, one of them coinciding with the original curve $ABC\ldots$. It is from this property that the names involute and evolute are derived.

344. Radius of Curvature of the Evolute.

It is easy to find an expression for the radius of curvature at that point of the evolute which corresponds to any given point of the original curve.

Let O (Fig. 60) be the centre of curvature for the point a of the evolute. The angle $\delta\psi'$ between the normals at a, b

$\qquad = $ the angle between the tangents at a, b

$\qquad = $ the angle between the tangents at A, B to the original

$\qquad\qquad$ curve

$\qquad = \delta\psi$.

And if s' be the arc of the evolute measured from some fixed point up to a, and ρ' the radius of curvature of the evolute at a, and ρ that of the original curve at A, we have, rejecting infinitesimals of order higher than the first,

$$\delta s' = \text{arc } ab = \delta\rho,$$

and therefore $\rho' = Lt \dfrac{\delta s'}{\delta\psi'} = Lt \dfrac{\delta\rho}{\delta\psi} = \dfrac{d\rho}{d\psi} = \dfrac{d^2s}{d\psi^2},$

s being the arc of the original curve measured from some fixed point up to A, and ψ the angle which the tangent at A makes with some fixed straight line.

345. From Articles 337, 340, it will follow that to an inflexional or undulatory point on a curve will correspond an asymptote on the evolute. For an inflexional point the evolute will be asymptotic at opposite ends of the normal and on opposite sides. For an undulatory point it will be asymptotic on opposite sides at the same extremity.

EXAMPLES.

1. For the parabola $\quad\quad y^2 = 4ax,$

prove $\quad\quad\quad\quad\quad\quad \bar{x} = 2a + 3x,$

$$\bar{y} = -2\frac{x^{\frac{3}{2}}}{a^{\frac{1}{2}}},$$

$$\rho = 2\frac{SP^{\frac{3}{2}}}{a^{\frac{1}{2}}},$$

SP being the focal distance of the point of the parabola whose co-ordinates are (x, y).

2. Show that the circles of curvature of the parabola $y^2 = 4ax$ for the ends of the latus rectum have for their equations

$$x^2 + y^2 - 10ax \pm 4ay - 3a^2 = 0,$$

and that they cut the curve again in the points $(9a, \mp 6a)$.

3. Show that the evolute of the parabola $y^2 = 4ax$ is the semicubical

parabola $\quad\quad\quad\quad 27ay^2 = 4(x - 2a)^3,$

and that the length of the evolute from the cusp to the point where it

meets the parabola $\quad\quad\quad = 2a(3\sqrt{3} - 1).$

4. Show that in a parabola the radius of curvature is twice the part of the normal intercepted between the curve and the directrix.

5. Prove that in an ellipse, centre C, the radius of curvature at any

point P is given by $\quad\quad \rho = \dfrac{CD^3}{ab} = \dfrac{a^2b^2}{p^3} = \dfrac{(rr')^{\frac{3}{2}}}{ab},$

where a, b are the semi-axes, r, r' are the focal distances of P, p the perpendicular from the centre on the tangent at P, and CD the semi-diameter conjugate to CP.

6. Show that in any conic

$$\rho = \frac{(\text{normal})^3}{(\text{semi-latus-rectum})^2}.$$

7. For the ellipse $\dfrac{x^2}{a^2} + \dfrac{y^2}{b^2} = 1,$

prove
$$\left.\begin{aligned} \bar{x} &= \frac{a^2 - b^2}{a^4} x^3 \\ \bar{y} &= \frac{b^2 - a^2}{b^4} y^3 \end{aligned}\right\}.$$

Hence show that the equation of the evolute is

$$(ax)^{\frac{2}{3}} + (by)^{\frac{2}{3}} = (a^2 - b^2)^{\frac{2}{3}},$$

and prove that the whole length of the evolute

$$= 4\left(\frac{a^2}{b} - \frac{b^2}{a}\right).$$

8. Show that the co-ordinates of the centre of curvature of any curve may be written

$$\left\{ \tfrac{1}{2}\frac{\dfrac{d^2 r^2}{dy^2}}{\dfrac{d^2 x}{dy^2}},\quad \tfrac{1}{2}\frac{\dfrac{d^2 r^2}{dx^2}}{\dfrac{d^2 y}{dx^2}} \right\}.$$

INTRINSIC EQUATION.

346. The relation between the length of the arc (s) of a given curve, measured from a given fixed point on the curve, and the angle between the tangents at its extremities (ψ) has been aptly styled by Dr. Whewell the *Intrinsic Equation* of the curve. For many curves this relation takes a very elegant form. The name seems specially suitable to a relation between such quantities as these, depending as it does upon no external system of co-ordinates. The method of obtaining the intrinsic equation from the Cartesian or polar relation is dependent in general upon processes of integration. If the equation of the curve be given as $y = f(x)$, the axis of x being supposed a tangent at the origin, and the length of the arc being measured from the origin, we have

$$\tan \psi = f'(x),\dots\dots\dots\dots\dots\dots\dots (1)$$

and
$$\frac{ds}{dx} = \sqrt{1 + [f'(x)]^2}.\dots\dots\dots\dots\dots (2)$$

If s be determined by integration from (2) and x eliminated between the result and equation (1), the required relation between s and ψ will be obtained.

Ex. 1. *Intrinsic equation of a circle.*

If ψ be the angle between the initial tangent at A and the tangent at the point P, and a the radius of the circle, we have

$$P\widehat{O}A = P\widehat{T}X = \psi,$$

and therefore

$$s = a\psi.$$

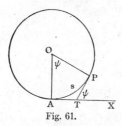

Fig. 61.

Ex. 2. *In the case of the catenary whose equation is*

$$y = c \cosh \frac{x}{c}$$

the intrinsic equation is

$$s = c \tan \psi.$$

For

$$\tan \psi = \frac{dy}{dx} = \sinh \frac{x}{c},$$

and

$$\frac{ds}{dx} = \sqrt{1 + \sinh^2 \frac{x}{c}} = \cosh \frac{x}{c},$$

and therefore

$$s = c \sinh \frac{x}{c},$$

the constant of integration being chosen so that x and s vanish together. whence

$$s = c \tan \psi.$$

EXAMPLES.

1. Show that the cycloid

$$\begin{aligned} x &= a(\theta + \sin \theta) \\ y &= a(1 - \cos \theta) \end{aligned}$$

has for its intrinsic equation $s = 4a \sin \psi$.

2. Show that the epi- or hypo-cycloid given by

$$\begin{aligned} x &= (a+b)\cos \theta - b \cos \frac{a+b}{b}\theta \\ y &= (a+b)\sin \theta - b \sin \frac{a+b}{b}\theta \end{aligned}$$

has an intrinsic equation of the form

$$s = A \sin B\psi.$$

347. Intrinsic Equation of the Evolute.

Let $s = f(\psi)$ be the equation of the given curve. Let s' be the length of the arc of the evolute measured from some fixed point A to any other point Q. Let O and P be the points on

the original curve corresponding to the points A, Q on the
evolute; ρ_0, ρ the radii of curvature at O and P; ψ' the angle
the tangent QP makes with OA produced, and ψ the angle the
tangent PT makes with the tangent at O.

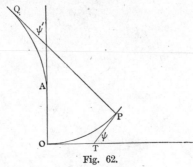

Fig. 62.

Then $\psi' = \psi$, and $s' = \rho - \rho_0 = \dfrac{ds}{d\psi} - \rho_0,$

or $s' = f'(\psi') - \rho_0,$

the intrinsic equation of the evolute.

348. Intrinsic Equation of an Involute.

With the same figure, if the curve AQ be given by the
equation $s' = f(\psi'),$

we have $\rho = s' + \rho_0,$ $\rho = \dfrac{ds}{d\psi},$ and $\psi = \psi',$

whence $s = \int \{f(\psi') + \rho_0\} d\psi'.$

349. Evolutes of Cycloids or Epi- and Hypo-Cycloids.

If we apply the result of Art. 347 to the intrinsic equation
$s = A \sin B\psi$, we get for the equation of the evolute
$$s' = AB \cos B\psi' - \rho_0,$$
or, dropping the dashes,
$$s = AB \cos B\psi,$$
if s be supposed measured from the point where $\psi = \dfrac{\pi}{2B}.$

This proves that the *evolute of an epi- or hypo-cycloid is
a similar epi- or hypo-cycloid.* Also, the case in which $B = 1$
shows that the *evolute of a cycloid is an equal cycloid.*

[For further information on Intrinsic Equations the student is referred
to Boole, *Differential Equations*, p. 263, and to *Camb. Phil. Trans.*, vol.
VIII., p. 689, and vol. IX., p. 150.]

EXAMPLES.

1. If A be the area of the portion of a curve included between the curve, two radii of curvature, and the evolute, prove

$$\rho = 2\frac{dA}{ds}.$$

2. Show that the evolute of an equiangular spiral is an equal equiangular spiral.

3. Show that the intrinsic equation of the evolute of a parabola is

$$s = 2a(\sec^3\psi - 1).$$

4. Given the pedal equation of a curve, viz., $p = f(r)$; show that the pedal equation of its evolute may be found by eliminating p and r between this equation and the equations

$$r'^2 = \rho^2 + r^2 - 2\rho p, \dots\dots\dots\dots\dots\dots\dots\dots\dots(a)$$
$$p'^2 = r^2 - p^2.\dots\dots\dots\dots\dots\dots\dots\dots(\beta)$$

Again, that if the equation $p' = f(r')$ of a curve be given, the general differential equation of its involutes may be obtained by eliminating p', r' between this equation and the equations (a), (β).

5. Show that the curve whose equation is

$$p^2 = r^2 - a^2$$

is an involute of a circle, and that its intrinsic equation is

$$s = a\frac{\psi^2}{2}.$$

6. Show that the evolute of the epi- or hypo-cycloid denoted by

$$p^2 = Ar^2 + B$$

is another epi- or hypo-cycloid denoted by

$$p^2 = Ar^2 + B\left(1 - \frac{1}{A}\right).$$

7. Show that the pedal equation of the evolute of the curve

$$r^m = a^m \sin m\theta$$

is obtained by eliminating r between

$$r'^2 = \frac{a^{2m} + (m^2 - 1)r^{2m}}{(m+1)^2 r^{2m-2}}$$

and

$$p'^2 = r^2\frac{a^{2m} - r^{2m}}{a^{2m}}.$$

CONTACT.

350. First, consider the point P at which two curves cut.

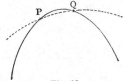

Fig. 63.

It is clear that in general each has its own tangent at that point, and that if the curves be of the mth and n^{th} degrees respectively, they will cut in $mn-1$ other points real or imaginary.

Next, suppose one of these other points (say Q) to move along one of the curves up to coincidence with P. The curves now cut in two ultimately coincident points at P, and therefore have a common tangent. There is then said to be contact *of the first order*. It will be observed that at such a point the curves *do not on the whole cross each other*.

Again, suppose another of the mn points of intersection (viz., R) to follow Q along one of the curves to coincidence with P. There are now three contiguous points on each curve

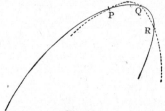

Fig. 64.

common, and therefore the curves have two contiguous tangents common, namely, the ultimate position of the chord PQ and the ultimate position of the chord QR. Contact of this kind is said to be *of the second order*, and the curves on the whole *cross each other*.

Finally, if other points of intersection follow Q and R up to P, so that ultimately k points of intersection coincide at P, there will be $k-1$ contiguous common tangents at P, and the contact is said to be of the $(k-1)^{th}$ order. And if k be odd and the contact of an *even order* the curves *will cross*, but if k be even and the contact therefore of an *odd order* they *will not cross*.

351. **Closest Degree of Contact of the Conic Sections with a Curve.**

The simplest curve which can be drawn so as to pass
through two   given points is a straight line,

do.	three	do.	circle,
do.	four	do.	parabola,
do.	five	do.	conic.

Hence, if the points be contiguous and ultimately coincident points on a given curve, we can have respectively the

Straight Line of Closest Contact (or tangent), having contact of the *first order* and cutting the curve in *two* ultimately coincident points, and therefore *not in general crossing* its curve; the

Circle of Closest Contact, having contact of the *second order* and cutting the curve in *three* ultimately coincident points, and therefore *in general crossing* its curve (this is the circle already investigated as the circle of curvature); the

Parabola of Closest Contact, having contact of the *third order* and cutting the curve in *four* ultimately coincident points, and therefore in general *not crossing;* and the

Conic of Closest Contact, having contact of the *fourth order* and cutting the curve in *five* ultimately coincident points, and therefore in general *crossing.*

It is often necessary to qualify such propositions as these by the words *in general.* Consider for instance the "circle of closest contact" at a given point on a conic section. A circle and a conic section intersect in four points real or imaginary, and since three of these are real and coincident, the circle of closest contact cuts the curve again in some one real fourth point. But *it may happen,* as in the case in which the three ultimately coincident points are at an end of one of the axes of the conic *that the fourth point is coincident with the other three,* in which case the circle of closest contact has a contact of higher order than usual, viz., of the *third* order, cutting the curve in four ultimately coincident points, and therefore on the whole *not crossing* the curve. The student should draw for himself figures of the circle of closest contact at various points of a conic section, remembering that the common chord of the circle and conic, and the tangent at the point of contact make equal angles with either axis. The conic which has the closest possible contact is said to *osculate* its curve at the point of contact, and is called the *osculating conic.* Thus the circle of curvature is called the *osculating circle,* the parabola of closest contact is called the *osculating parabola,* and so on.

352. Analytical Conditions for Contact of a given order.

We may treat this subject analytically as follows.

Let
$$y = \phi(x) \atop y = \psi(x) \Big\}$$

be the equations of two curves which cut at the point $P(x, y)$.

Consider the values of the respective ordinates at the points P_1, P_2 whose common abscissa is $x+h$.

Let $MN = h$.

Then
$$NP_1 = \phi(x+h),$$
$$NP_2 = \psi(x+h),$$

and
$$P_2P_1 = NP_1 - NP_2 = \phi(x+h) - \psi(x+h)$$
$$= [\phi(x) - \psi(x)] + h[\phi'(x) - \psi'(x)]$$
$$+ \frac{h^2}{2!}[\phi''(x) - \psi''(x)] + \dots.$$

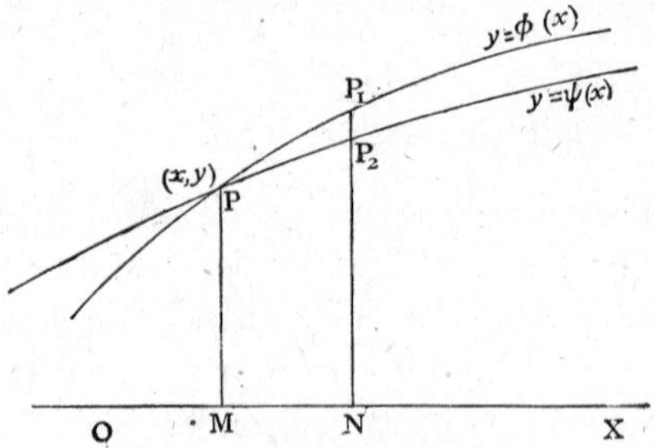

Fig. 65.

If the expression for P_2P_1 be equated to zero, the roots of the resulting equation for h will determine the points at which the curves cut.

If $\phi(x) = \psi(x)$, the equation has one root zero and the curves cut at P.

If also $\phi'(x) = \psi'(x)$ for the same value of x, the equation has two roots zero and the curves cut in *two* contiguous points at P, and therefore have a common tangent. The contact is now of the *first order*.

If also $\phi''(x) = \psi''(x)$ for the same value of x, the equation for h has three roots zero and the curves cut in *three* ultimately coincident points at P. There are now two contiguous tangents common, and the contact is said to be of the *second order*; and so on.

Similarly for curves given by their polar equations, if

$r = f(\theta)$, $r = \phi(\theta)$ be the two equations, there will be $n+1$ equations to be satisfied for the same value of θ in order that for that value there may be contact of the nth order, viz.,

$$f(\theta) = \phi(\theta), \ f'(\theta) = \phi'(\theta), \ f''(\theta) = \phi''(\theta), \ \ldots, \ f^n(\theta) = \phi^n(\theta).$$

353. Osculating Circle.

The circle of curvature may now be investigated as the circle which has contact of the second order with a given curve at a given point.

Suppose
$$y = f(x) \quad \ldots\ldots\ldots\ldots\ldots\ldots\ldots(1)$$
to be the equation of the curve.

Let
$$(x - \bar{x})^2 + (y - \bar{y})^2 = \rho^2 \quad \ldots\ldots\ldots\ldots\ldots\ldots(2)$$
be the equation of the circle of curvature.

By differentiating (2) we have
$$x - \bar{x} + (y - \bar{y})\frac{dy}{dx} = 0, \quad \ldots\ldots\ldots\ldots\ldots\ldots(3)$$
and differentiating again
$$1 + \left(\frac{dy}{dx}\right)^2 + (y - \bar{y})\frac{d^2y}{dx^2} = 0. \quad \ldots\ldots\ldots\ldots\ldots\ldots(4)$$

Now the x, y, $\dfrac{dy}{dx}$, $\dfrac{d^2y}{dx^2}$ of equations (2), (3), (4) refer to the circle. But, since there is to be contact of the second order with the curve $y = f(x)$ at the point (x, y), $\dfrac{dy}{dx}$ and $\dfrac{d^2y}{dx^2}$ *have the same value as when deduced from the equation to the curve,* i.e., we may write $f'(x)$ for $\dfrac{dy}{dx}$ and $f''(x)$ for $\dfrac{d^2y}{dx^2}$.

From equation (4)
$$y - \bar{y} = -\frac{1 + \left(\dfrac{dy}{dx}\right)^2}{\dfrac{d^2y}{dx^2}} = -\frac{1 + \{f'(x)\}^2}{f''(x)},$$

whence
$$x - \bar{x} = \frac{\dfrac{dy}{dx}\left\{1 + \left(\dfrac{dy}{dx}\right)^2\right\}}{\dfrac{d^2y}{dx^2}} = \frac{f'(x)[1 + \{f'(x)\}^2]}{f''(x)},$$

and by squaring and adding
$$\rho = \pm\frac{\left\{1 + \left(\dfrac{dy}{dx}\right)^2\right\}^{\frac{3}{2}}}{\dfrac{d^2y}{dx^2}} = \pm\frac{[1 + \{f'(x)\}^2]^{\frac{3}{2}}}{f''(x)},$$

such a sign being given to the radical as will make ρ positive, *i.e.*, if $\dfrac{d^2y}{dx^2}$ be positive we must choose the $+$ sign for the numerator, and if $\dfrac{d^2y}{dx^2}$ be negative we must choose the $-$ sign.

The values of $\bar{x}$ and $\bar{y}$ are the same as those found geometrically in Art. 339, viz.,

$$\bar{x}=x-\frac{\dfrac{dy}{dx}\left\{1+\left(\dfrac{dy}{dx}\right)^2\right\}}{\dfrac{d^2y}{dx^2}},$$

$$\bar{y}=y+\frac{1+\left(\dfrac{dy}{dx}\right)^2}{\dfrac{d^2y}{dx^2}}.$$

354. Conic having Third Order Contact at a given point.

The locus of the centres of all conics having third order contact with a given curve at a given point (*i.e.*, cutting the curve in four ultimately coincident points) is a *straight line* which passes through the point of contact.

Let P be a point on the curve and C the centre of one of the conics having third order contact with the given curve at

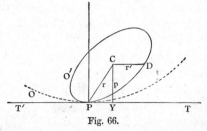

Fig. 66.

P. Let CD be the semiconjugate to CP and CY a perpendicular on the tangent at P.

Let $CP=r$, $CD=r'$, $CY=p$, and let PC make an angle ϕ with the normal at P.

Then we have $\qquad r^2+r'^2=a^2+b^2,$

and $\qquad\qquad\qquad pr'=ab,$

and therefore $\qquad rdr+r'dr'=0;$

and for a conic $\qquad \rho=\dfrac{CD^3}{ab}=\dfrac{r'^3}{ab};$ (See Ex. 5, p. 271)

therefore
$$\frac{d\rho}{ds} = \frac{3r'^2}{ab} \cdot \frac{dr'}{ds} = -\frac{3r'}{ab} \cdot \frac{rdr}{ds}$$

$$= -\frac{3r}{p} \cdot \frac{dr}{ds} = 3\frac{\sin\phi}{\cos\phi},$$

for $\dfrac{dr}{ds} = \cos CPT' = -\sin\phi$, the arcs of the curve and of the conic being measured from the points O and O' up to P, and

$$\frac{p}{r} = \cos\phi ;$$

therefore
$$\frac{d\rho}{ds} = 3\tan\phi,$$

and $\tan\phi = \dfrac{1}{3}\dfrac{d\rho}{ds}$, where $\dfrac{d\rho}{ds}$ is found for *one of the conics*.

But since the conic and the curve have contact of the third order they have the same tangent, the same $\dfrac{dr}{d\theta}$, the same $\dfrac{d^2r}{d\theta^2}$, and the same $\dfrac{d^3r}{d\theta^3}$ at the point of contact. They therefore also have *the same* ρ and *the same* $\dfrac{d\rho}{ds}$, for ρ depends on $\dfrac{d^2r}{d\theta^2}$ and $\dfrac{d\rho}{ds}$ on $\dfrac{d^3r}{d\theta^3}$.

Hence the value of ϕ found above is the same for all the conics, and depends only upon the shape of the curve at the point of contact. The locus of all such centres is therefore a straight line through the point of contact inclined in front of the normal at an angle $\tan^{-1}\left(\dfrac{1}{3}\dfrac{d\rho}{ds}\right)$, where $\dfrac{d\rho}{ds}$ *is found from the curve.*

355. This result may be established analytically as follows :—

Referring the conic to the common tangent and normal as axes, its equation takes the form $2y = ax^2 + 2hxy + by^2$.

If y be expanded in powers of x, by Maclaurin's Theorem we have

$$y = px + q\frac{x^2}{2!} + r\frac{x^3}{3!} + \dots,$$

as in Art. 329 ; p, q, and r being the values of $\dfrac{dy}{dx}$, $\dfrac{d^2y}{dx^2}$, and $\dfrac{d^3y}{dx^3}$ at the origin. Since there is contact of the third order the values of these are the same for the conic and for the curve and are therefore known quantities. Moreover, since the tangent has been chosen for the x-axis, we have

$$p = 0.$$

Substituting in the equation of the conic we have

$$2\left(q\frac{x^2}{2!}+r\frac{x^3}{3!}+...\right)\equiv ax^2+2hx\left(q\frac{x^2}{2!}+...\right)+b\left(q\frac{x^2}{2!}+...\right)^2,$$

giving
$$a=q,$$
$$qh=\frac{r}{3},$$

and thus determining a and h in terms of the known quantities q and r.

Also the centre of the conic lies on the line

$$ax+hy=0,$$

or
$$3q^2x+ry=0,$$

which is a straight line through the point of contact inclined in front of

the normal at an angle $\tan^{-1}\left(-\dfrac{r}{3q^3}\right)$.

Also since $\rho=(1+p^2)^{\frac{3}{2}}q^{-1}$

$$\frac{d\rho}{ds}=\{3(1+p^2)^{\frac{1}{2}}p-(1+p^2)^{\frac{3}{2}}q^{-2}r\}\frac{dx}{ds},$$

which, when $p=0$ and $\dfrac{dx}{ds}=1,$

becomes $\dfrac{d\rho}{ds}=-\dfrac{r}{q^2}.$

Hence the above angle may be written

$$\tan^{-1}\left(\frac{1}{3}\frac{d\rho}{ds}\right)$$

as in the preceding article.

356. Osculating Conic.

We can now pick out the particular conic which has *fourth order* contact with the given curve at the given point.

Let O be the centre of curvature of the point considered and C the required centre of the conic of closest contact. Let P_1

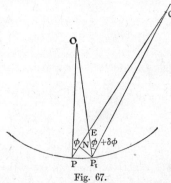

Fig. 67.

be a point on the curve adjacent to the given point P.   Join $CP,\ CP_1$ and draw P_1N at right angles to CP.

Let $\quad O\hat{P}C=\phi, \quad O\hat{P_1}C=\phi+\delta\phi, \quad PC=R.$

Then $\qquad\qquad P\hat{E}P_1=P\hat{O}E+\phi,$

and also $\qquad\qquad\quad =P_1\hat{C}E+\phi+\delta\phi,$

whence $\qquad\quad P\hat{O}E=P_1\hat{C}E+\delta\phi.$

Also, neglecting infinitesimals of higher order than the first,

$$PP_1=\delta s,$$

$$P\hat{O}E=\frac{\delta s}{\rho},$$

and $\qquad\quad P_1\hat{C}P=\frac{P_1N}{P_1C}=\frac{\delta s\cos\phi}{R}.$

Hence $\qquad\qquad \frac{\delta s}{\rho}=\frac{\delta s\cos\phi}{R}+\delta\phi,$

or, proceeding to the limit,

$$\left.\begin{array}{c}\dfrac{\cos\phi}{R}=\dfrac{1}{\rho}-\dfrac{d\phi}{ds},\\[2mm] \phi=\tan^{-1}\dfrac{1}{3}\dfrac{d\rho}{ds}\end{array}\right\}.$$

where

And since the contact is of the fourth order, $\dfrac{d\phi}{ds}$ is the same for *the curve as for the conic,* and may therefore be *supposed derived from the equation of the curve.*

These equations determine the position of C.

357. **Tangent and Normal as Axes. Co-ordinates of a Point near the Origin in terms of the Arc.**

When the tangent and normal at any point of a curve are taken as the axes of x and y it is sometimes requisite to express the co-ordinates of a point on the curve near the origin in terms of the length of the arc measured from the origin up to that point.

Assume $\qquad x=a+a_1s+a_2\dfrac{s^2}{2!}+a_3\dfrac{s^3}{3!}+\ldots,$

$$y=b+b_1s+b_2\frac{s^2}{2!}+b_3\frac{s^3}{3!}+\ldots,$$

the letters a, $a_1\ldots$, b, $b_1\ldots$ denoting constants whose values are to be determined, and s being the length of the arc. Then, when $s=0$, x and y both vanish, and therefore

$$a=b=0.$$

Again, by Maclaurin's Theorem

$$a_1 = \left(\frac{dx}{ds}\right)_0 = (\cos \psi)_0 = 1,$$

$$b_1 = \left(\frac{dy}{ds}\right)_0 = (\sin \psi)_0 = 0,$$

[the suffix zero denoting the values at the origin]

$$a_2 = \left(\frac{d^2x}{ds^2}\right)_0 = -\left(\sin \psi \frac{d\psi}{ds}\right)_0 = -\left(\frac{\sin \psi}{\rho}\right)_0 = 0,$$

$$b_2 = \left(\frac{d^2y}{ds^2}\right)_0 = \left(\cos \psi \frac{d\psi}{ds}\right)_0 = \left(\frac{\cos \psi}{\rho}\right)_0 = \frac{1}{\rho},$$

$$a_3 = \left(\frac{d^3x}{ds^3}\right)_0 = -\left(\frac{\cos \psi}{\rho^2} - \frac{\sin \psi}{\rho^2} \frac{d\rho}{ds}\right)_0 = -\frac{1}{\rho^2},$$

$$b_3 = \left(\frac{d^3y}{ds^3}\right)_0 = \left(-\frac{\sin \psi}{\rho^2} - \frac{\cos \psi}{\rho^2} \frac{d\rho}{ds}\right)_0 = -\frac{1}{\rho^2} \frac{d\rho}{ds},$$

etc.,

whence $\quad x = s - \dfrac{s^3}{6\rho^2} + \cdots,$

$$y = \frac{s^2}{2\rho} - \frac{s^3}{6\rho^2} \frac{d\rho}{ds} - \cdots.$$

EXAMPLES.

1. Determine the curvature of the curve

$$ay^3 = x^4$$

at the origin.   [COLL. EXAM.]

2. Find the radii of curvature of the two branches of the curve

$$(x-y)^2(x-2y)(x-3y) - 2a(x^3 - y^3) - 2a^2(x+y)(x-2y) = 0$$

at the origin.   [OXFORD, 1888.]

3. For the curve $\quad y^{\frac{1}{m}} \dfrac{dy}{dx} = \sqrt{a^{\frac{2}{m}} - y^{\frac{2}{m}}},$

prove that the radius of curvature is m times the normal.

4. Establish the formula

$$\rho = r\frac{d\theta}{ds} \bigg/ \left[r\left(\frac{d\theta}{ds}\right)^2 - \frac{d^2r}{ds^2} \right].$$

5. Find the equation of the circle of curvature at any point of the curve $\quad y/a = \text{vers}^{-1}x/a.$

6. If ρ be the radius of curvature of a parabola at a point whose distance, measured along the curve, from a fixed point is s, prove that

$$3\rho\frac{d^2\rho}{ds^2} - \left(\frac{d\rho}{ds}\right)^2 - 9 = 0.$$

            [OXFORD, 1889.]

7. A curve is such that the normal at any point passes through the centre of curvature of the corresponding point on the pedal with respect to a given point. Show that the curve is an equiangular spiral. [OXFORD, 1890.]

8. If ρ and ρ' be the radii of curvature at corresponding points of a curve and its evolute, and p, q, r are the first, second, and third differential coefficients of y with respect to x, prove that

$$\rho'/\rho = \{3pq^2 - r(1+p^2)\}/q^2.$$

9. The projections on the x-axis of the radii of curvature at corresponding points of $y = \log \sec x$ and its evolute are equal. [COLL. EXAM.]

10. Show that the radius of curvature of the point of the evolute of the curve $r^n = a^n \cos n\theta$

corresponding to r, θ is $\dfrac{n-1}{(n+1)^2} r \sec n\theta \tan n\theta$. [OXFORD, 1889.]

11. A tangent to the evolute of a parabola at the point where it meets the parabola is also a normal to the evolute at the point where it again meets the evolute. [COLL. EXAM.]

12. If ρ_1 be the radius of curvature at any point of a parabola, ρ_2 the radius of curvature of the corresponding point of its first negative pedal with respect to the focus, show that

$$27\rho_1{}^4 = 32l\rho_2{}^3$$

where l is the latus rectum. [OXFORD, 1889.]

13. P, Q, R, S, T are five points on a curve of continuous curvature whose abscissae are in arithmetical progression, the common difference being δx; show that as δx diminishes without limit, PT, QS, and the tangent at R ultimately intersect in the same point, and that in the parabola $y^2 = mx$ the locus of this point is a parabola with the same vertex and axis. [COLL. EXAM.]

14. The radius of curvature at the point t on the curve

$$\left.\begin{array}{l} r = f(t) \\ \theta = F(t) \end{array}\right\}$$

is given by the equation

$$\dot{s}^3\rho^{-1} = 2\dot{r}^2\dot{\theta} + r\dot{r}\ddot{\theta} - r\ddot{r}\dot{\theta} + r^2\dot{\theta}^3$$

where $$\dot{s} = \frac{ds}{dt}, \quad \ddot{r} = \frac{d^2r}{dt^2}, \text{ etc.}$$ [OXFORD, 1888.]

15. Show that the parabola whose axis is parallel to the axis of y, and which has the closest possible contact with the curve

$$a^{n-1}y = x^n$$

at the point (a, a), has for its equation

$$n(n-1)x^2 = 2ay + 2n(n-2)ax - (n-1)(n-2)a^2.$$

16. If x, y be the co-ordinates of a point P of a curve OP passing through the origin O, then the radius of curvature at O

$$= \tfrac{1}{2} Lt \frac{x^2 + y^2}{x \sin a - y \cos a},$$

where $y = x \tan a$ is the equation of the tangent at the origin.

Hence show that the radius of curvature of the curve

$$x^4 + y^2 = 2a(x + y)$$

at the origin is $2a\sqrt{2}$.

17. Show that the arcs of the two curves

$$xy = a^2, \quad x^3 = 3a^2 y$$

turn through the same angle between any the same pair of ordinates. Also show that the ratio of the radii of curvature at points on the two curves which have the same abscissa varies as the square root of the ratio of the ordinates.   [OXFORD, 1887.]

18. The radius of curvature of the first negative pedal of $p = f(r)$ at a point corresponding to $(p,\ r)$ on the original curve is

$$\frac{2r^3}{p^2} - \frac{r^4}{p^3} \frac{dp}{dr}.$$

19. Show that the curvature at any point of the pedal of an epi- or hypo-cycloid is $\dfrac{p(r^4 + a^2 p^2)}{r^6}$,

where a is the radius of the fixed circle and r and p refer to the pedal curve.   [SIDNEY COLL., CAMB.]

20. If r, p, ρ be respectively the radius vector, perpendicular from the origin on the tangent and the radius of curvature at any point of a curve, prove that the radius of curvature at the corresponding point of the reciprocal polar with regard to the origin is

$$\frac{k^2 r^3}{p^3 \rho},$$

where k^2 is the constant of reciprocation.

Hence show that the reciprocal of a circle is a conic with the origin as focus.

21. If r, p, ρ be the same as in the last question, show that the radius of curvature at the corresponding point of the inverse with regard to the origin is $\dfrac{k^2 \rho}{2p\rho - r^2}$,

k^2 being the constant of inversion.

22. Find the radii of curvature of the confocal orthogonal Limaçons

$$r \sin^2 a = a(\cos \theta - \cos a),$$
$$r \sinh^2 \beta = a(\cosh \beta - \cos \theta)$$

at a point of intersection, in terms of a and β.   [MATH. TRIPOS, 1884.

23. Show that the intrinsic equation of the curve

$$e^{\frac{y}{i}} = \sec \frac{x}{a} \text{ is } \frac{s}{a} = \text{gd}^{-1}\psi.$$

24. If λ^{-1}, μ^{-1} be the ratios of any arc of the curve

$$s = c \tan \psi$$

measured from the point $\psi = 0$, to the corresponding arcs of the evolute, and of that involute which meets the curve at the point $\psi = 0$, find the relation between λ and μ. [OXFORD, 1888.]

25. An inextensible wire in the form of a plane curve is bent so that each point of the wire moves a distance u in the direction of the normal to the curve at that point; prove that

$$\frac{\rho}{u}\left(\frac{du}{ds}\right)^2 + \frac{u}{\rho} = 2. \qquad \text{[CAMBRIDGE, 1883.]}$$

26. Show that the locus of the centre of the rectangular hyperbola, having contact of the third order with the conic

$$Ax^2 + By^2 = 1,$$

has for its equation $\quad x^2 + y^2 = \left(\dfrac{1}{A} + \dfrac{1}{B}\right)\sqrt{Ax^2 + By^2}.$

27. Show that the locus of the centres of the rectangular hyperbolae, having contact of the third order with the parabola

$$y^2 = 4ax,$$

is the equal parabola $\quad y^2 + 4a(x + 2a) = 0.$

28. If the equation to a curve passing through the origin be

$$u_1 + u_2 + u_3 + \ldots = 0,$$

where u_n is a homogeneous function of x, y of n dimensions, show that the general equation to all conics having the same curvature at the origin as the given curve is

$$u_1 + u_2 + (lx + my)u_1 = 0.$$

Thence find the circle of curvature.

29. Show that the circle of curvature at the origin for the curve

$$x + y = ax^2 + by^2 + cx^3$$

is $\qquad (a+b)(x^2 + y^2) = 2x + 2y.$

30. Obtain the equation of the conic which osculates the curve

$$ay = x^2 + a_1xy + a_2y^2 + b_0x^3 + b_1x^2y + b_2xy^2 + b_3y^3$$

at the origin.

PQ is the common chord of a parabola

$$y^2 = 4ax$$

and its osculating circle at P. Prove that the locus of the point of intersection of PQ with the perpendicular drawn on it from the vertex is the cissoid $\quad y^2(3a - x) = x^3.$ [OXFORD, 1890.]

31. Show that when the osculating circle has third order contact with its curve the curvature is measured by

$$\frac{d^2p}{dr^2}.$$

32. A line is drawn through the origin meeting the cardioide

$$r = a(1 - \cos\theta)$$

in the points P, Q, and the normals at P and Q meet in C. Show that the radii of curvature at P and Q are proportional to PC and QC.

33. If PQ be an arc not containing a point of maximum or minimum curvature, the circles of curvature at P, Q will lie one entirely within the other. [Math. Tripos.]

34. Determine the equation of the circle which touches the curve

$$r = f(\theta)$$

at the point (r_1, θ_1) and goes through another point (r_2, θ_2) on the curve; and hence derive the expression for the radius of curvature in polars. [Math. Tripos, 1884.]

35. Show that the osculating conic of the catenary

$$y = c\cosh\frac{x}{c}$$

at a point whose ordinate is $\frac{c}{2}\sqrt{10}$ is a parabola. [Oxford, 1889.]

36. An equiangular spiral has contact of the second order with a given curve at a given point; prove that its pole lies on a certain circle, and that, if the contact be the closest possible, the distance of the pole from the point of contact is

$$\frac{\rho}{\sqrt{1 + \left(\dfrac{d\rho}{ds}\right)^2}}.$$

[Math. Tripos.]

37. If accented letters refer to a point on a curve and unaccented letters to the corresponding point on the involute, prove

$$x = x' \mp \rho\frac{dx}{ds'},$$

$$y = y' \mp \rho\frac{dy'}{ds'}.$$

Show how, by means of these equations and

$$s' \mp \rho = l,$$

the equation of an involute of a given curve may be found; s' being supposed known in terms of the co-ordinates of the extremities of the arc.

38. If a right line move in any manner in a plane, the centres of curvature of the paths described by the different points in it in any position lie on a conic.

39. If, on the tangent at each point of a curve, a constant length be measured from the point of contact, prove that the normal to the locus of the points so found passes through the corresponding centre of curvature of the given curve. [BERTRAND.]

40. If through each point of a curve a line of given length be drawn, making a constant angle with the normal to the curve, the normal to the locus of the extremity of this line passes through the corresponding centre of curvature of the proposed curve. [BERTRAND.]

41. If on the tangent at each point of a curve a constant length c be measured from the point of contact, show that the radius of curvature of the curve locus of its extremity is given by

$$\rho' = \frac{(\rho^2 + c^2)^{\frac{3}{2}}}{\rho^2 + c^2 - c\dfrac{d\rho}{d\psi}},$$

where ρ and ψ refer to the corresponding point of the original curve.

42. If through each point of a curve a line of given length c be drawn, making a constant angle a with the normal at that point, the radius of curvature of the locus of its extremity is given by

$$\rho' = \frac{(\rho^2 + c^2 - 2\rho c \cos a)^{\frac{3}{2}}}{\rho^2 + c^2 - 2\rho c \cos a - c \sin a \dfrac{d\rho}{d\psi}},$$

where ρ and ψ refer to the corresponding point of the original curve.

43. Prove that in the curve whose intrinsic equation is

$$s = a \log \operatorname{cosec} \psi$$

the product of the radius of curvature and the normal is constant, the normal being terminated by the asymptote of the curve.

[MATH. TRIPOS, 1897.]

What relation does this curve bear to the catenary $y = c \cosh \dfrac{x}{c}$?

44. Show that the equation of the involute of the catenary

$$y = c \cosh \frac{x}{c}$$

which begins at the point where $x = 0, \quad y = c,$

is the Tractrix $\qquad x = c \cosh^{-1} \dfrac{c}{y} - \sqrt{c^2 - y^2}.$

45. If a straight line be drawn through the pole perpendicular to the radius vector of a point on the equiangular spiral

$$r = a e^{\theta \cot a}$$

to meet the corresponding tangent, show that the distance between the point of intersection and the point of contact of the tangent is equal to the arc of the curve measured from the pole to the point of contact. Hence prove that the locus of this point of intersection is one of the involutes of the spiral, and show that it is an equal equiangular spiral.

46. A fixed oval curve on a smooth horizontal plane is surrounded by a smooth endless string, and a particle is projected inside the string so as to move round, keeping the string stretched. If t and t' are the lengths of the straight portions of the string at any time; ϕ, ϕ' the inclinations of these lengths to a fixed line; and ρ, ρ' the radii of curvature at the points of contact; prove that

$$t'\frac{dt}{d\phi} + t\frac{dt'}{d\phi'} = \rho't - \rho t'.$$

[MATH. TRIPOS, 1885.]

47. A curve is given by the equation

$$\phi(r_1, r_2, r_3, \ldots, r_n) = 0$$

connecting the distances of a point on the curve from n fixed points in its plane, and ψ_s denotes the angle which r_s makes with the tangent to the curve; prove that the curvature at any point is given

by $\quad \dfrac{1}{\rho}\Sigma \sin \psi \dfrac{\partial \phi}{\partial r} = \Sigma \dfrac{1}{r}\sin^2\psi\dfrac{\partial \phi}{\partial r} + \Sigma \cos^2\psi\dfrac{\partial^2\phi}{\partial r^2} + 2\Sigma \cos\psi\cos\psi'\dfrac{\partial^2\phi}{\partial r\partial r'}.$

[MATH. TRIPOS, 1889.]

48. Prove that in the Cartesian oval

$$l_1 r_1 + l_2 r_2 = \text{constant}$$

where r_1 and r_2 are the distances of a point P from two fixed points A and B, the curvature at P is

$$\frac{l_1(l_1 + l_2\cos \chi)^2 r_2 + l_2(l_2 + l_1\cos \chi)^2 r_1}{r_1 r_2(l_1^2 + 2l_1 l_2\cos \chi + l_2^2)^{\frac{3}{2}}}$$

where χ is the angle APB. [MATH. TRIPOS, 1886.]

49. Prove that the radius of curvature at any point of the curve

$$mr + lr' = lc$$

is $\quad \dfrac{4l\sqrt{c}}{l^2 - m^2} \cdot \dfrac{\{l^2 c - m(lr + mr')\}^{\frac{3}{2}}}{(4l^2 - m^2)c - 3m(rl + r'm)}$

where r and r' are the distances of a point from two fixed points, and c is the distance between these two points. [COLL. EXAM.]

50. Two equal circular discs of radius a with their planes parallel are fastened at their centres to a bar, the discs being inclined to the bar at an angle a. The two wheels thus formed being rolled along a plane, prove that the intrinsic equation to the track of either wheel

on the plane is $\quad \sin \psi = \cos a \sin \dfrac{s}{a}.$

Prove that in this curve the product of the radius of curvature and the normal is constant, the normal being terminated by the straight line which divides the curve symmetrically.　　[MATH. TRIPOS, 1878.]

51. If the tangent and normal to a curve at any point be taken as the axes of x and y respectively, and if s be the distance, measured along the arc, of a point very near to the origin, show that the Cartesian co-ordinates of that point are approximately

$$x = s - \frac{s^3}{6\rho^2} + \frac{s^4}{8\rho^3}\frac{d\rho}{ds}\cdots,$$

$$y = \frac{s^2}{2\rho} - \frac{s^3}{6\rho^2}\frac{d\rho}{ds} - \frac{s^4}{24\rho^3}\left\{1 - 2\left(\frac{d\rho}{ds}\right)^2 + \rho\frac{d^2\rho}{ds^2}\right\}\cdots,$$

the values of ρ, $\dfrac{d\rho}{ds}$, and $\dfrac{d^2\rho}{ds^2}$ being those at the origin.

52. If a line be drawn parallel to the common tangent of a curve and its circle of curvature, and so near to it as to intercept on the curve a small arc of length s measured from the point of contact, of the first order of small quantities, show that the distance between the two points on the same side of the common normal in which the line cuts the curve and the circle of curvature is $\dfrac{s^2}{6\rho}\dfrac{d\rho}{ds}$, *i.e.*, is of the second order of small quantities, the values of ρ and $\dfrac{d\rho}{ds}$ being those at the point of contact; and again, if a line be drawn parallel to the common normal, the distance between the points of intersection with the curve and the circle is $\dfrac{s^3}{6\rho^2}\dfrac{d\rho}{ds}$ and is of the third order of small quantities.

53. Prove that the circle

$$\sqrt{2}(x^2 + y^2 + 2) = 3(x + y)$$

has contact of the third order with the conic

$$5x^2 - 6xy + 5y^2 = 8.$$

54. Show that for the portion of the curve

$$a^5 y^2 = x^7$$

very near the origin the shape of the evolute is approximately given by
$$1225 x^3 y^2 = 16a^5.$$

55. The conic whose focus is at the pole and which has second order contact with $u = f(\theta)$ at the point $\theta = a$ has for its equation

$$u + \cos^2(\theta - a)\frac{d}{da}\left\{\frac{f'(a)}{\cos(\theta - a)}\right\} = f(a) + f''(a).$$

56. If a chord of an ellipse be drawn to cut the evolute of the ellipse at right angles, three times the difference between its segments intercepted between the evolute and the ellipse is equal to the diameter of curvature of the evolute at the point of intersection.

[MATH. TRIPOS, 1878.]

57. If in the plane curve $\phi(x, y) = 0$,

we have at any point $\dfrac{\partial \phi}{\partial x} = 0$, $\dfrac{\partial \phi}{\partial y} = 0$, $\dfrac{\partial^2 \phi}{\partial x^2} = 0$

prove that the curvature of one of the branches of the curve which passes through that point is

$$\frac{1}{3} \frac{\partial^3 \phi}{\partial x^3} \left(\frac{\partial^2 \phi}{\partial x \partial y} \right)^{-1}.$$

[CAIUS COLL., CAMB.]

58. If θ be the angle between the normal at any point P of a plane curve $\phi(x, y) = 0$,

and the line drawn from P to the centre of the chord parallel and indefinitely near to the tangent at P, prove that

$$\cos \theta = \frac{bp^2 - 2hpq + aq^2}{\sqrt{p^2 + q^2} \sqrt{\{ (b^2 + h^2)p^2 - 2(a + b)hpq + (a^2 + h^2)p^2 \}}},$$

where $\quad p = \dfrac{\partial \phi}{\partial x}, \quad q = \dfrac{\partial \phi}{\partial y}, \quad a = \dfrac{\partial^2 \phi}{\partial x^2}, \quad h = \dfrac{\partial^2 \phi}{\partial x \partial y}, \quad$ and $\quad b = \dfrac{\partial^2 \phi}{\partial y^2}.$

[TOWNSEND.]

59. A curve is such that any two corresponding points of its evolute and an involute are at a constant distance. Prove that the line joining the two points is also constant in direction.

60. Prove that at corresponding points of a plane curve traced on a cylinder and its development when the surface of the cylinder is developed into a plane, the ordinates drawn to corresponding axes which are perpendicular to the generating lines of the cylinder are in a constant ratio; prove also that the product of the radius of curvature and the normal intercepted by the axis is the same at corresponding points of the curve and its development.

[MATH. TRIPOS, 1878.]

CHAPTER XI.

ENVELOPES.

358. Families of Curves.

If in the equation $\phi(x, y, c) = 0$ we give any arbitrary numerical values to the constant c, we obtain a number of equations representing a certain family of curves; and any member of the family may be specified by the particular value assigned to the constant c. The quantity c, which is constant for the same curve but different for different curves, is called the *parameter* of the family.

359. Envelope. Definition.

Let all the members of the family of curves $\phi(x, y, c) = 0$ be drawn which correspond to a system of infinitesimally close values of the parameter, supposed arranged in order of magnitude. We shall designate as consecutive curves any two curves which correspond to two consecutive values of c from the list. Then the locus of the ultimate points of intersection of consecutive members of this family of curves is called the ENVELOPE of the family.

360. The Envelope touches each of the Intersecting Members of the Family.

Let A, B, C represent three consecutive intersecting mem-

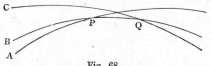

Fig. 68.

bers of the family   Let P be the point of intersection of A and B, and Q that of B and C.

Now, by definition, P and Q are points on the envelope. Thus the curve B and the envelope have two contiguous points common, and therefore have ultimately a common tangent, and therefore touch each other. Similarly, the envelope may be shown to touch any other curve of the system.

361. To find the Equation of an Envelope.

To find the equation of the envelope of the family of curves of which $\phi(x, y, c) = 0$ is the typical equation.

Let
$$\left.\begin{array}{l} \phi(x,\, y,\, c) = 0, \\ \phi(x,\, y,\, c + \delta c) = 0, \end{array}\right\} \quad \dots\dots\dots\dots\dots\dots (A)$$

be two consecutive members of the family. Expanding the latter we have

$$\phi(x,\, y,\, c) + \delta c \frac{\partial}{\partial c}\phi(x,\, y,\, c) + \dots = 0.$$

Hence in the limit, when δc is infinitesimally small, we obtain

$$\frac{\partial}{\partial c}\phi(x,\, y,\, c) = 0$$

as the equation of a curve passing through the ultimate point of intersection of the curves (A).

If we eliminate c between the equations

$$\phi(x,\, y,\, c) = 0$$

and
$$\frac{\partial}{\partial c}\phi(x,\, y,\, c) = 0$$

we obtain the locus of that point of intersection for all values of the parameter c. That is, we obtain the equations of the envelope of the family of curves of which $\phi(x, y, c) = 0$ is the type.

The polar curves $\phi(r, \theta, c)$ may be treated in the same manner.

Ex. *Find the envelope of the system of straight lines of which* $y = cx + \dfrac{a}{c}$ *is the type, c being the parameter and (a) constant for all lines of the system.*

Here
$$\phi(x, y, c) = y - cx - \frac{a}{c} = 0,$$

and
$$\frac{\partial}{\partial c}\phi(x, y, c) = -x + \frac{a}{c^2} = 0,$$

therefore
$$c = \pm\sqrt{\frac{a}{x}}\,;$$

whence
$$y = \pm x\sqrt{\frac{a}{x}} + \frac{a}{\pm\sqrt{\dfrac{a}{x}}} = \pm 2\sqrt{ax},$$

or
$$y^2 = 4ax,$$

a parabola, which is therefore the envelope. In other words, every straight line, obtained by giving any arbitrary special value to c in the equation $y = cx + \dfrac{a}{c}$, touches the parabola $y^2 = 4ax$.

362. The Envelope of $A\lambda^2 + 2B\lambda + C = 0$ is $B^2 = AC$.

If A, B, C be any functions of x and y, and the equation of any curve be $\qquad A\lambda^2 + 2B\lambda + C = 0$,

λ being an arbitrary parameter, the envelope of all such curves is $\qquad\qquad\qquad\qquad B^2 = AC.$

For we have to eliminate λ between

$$A\lambda^2 + 2B\lambda + C = 0$$

and $\qquad\qquad\qquad\qquad 2A\lambda + 2B = 0,$

and the result is clearly $\qquad B^2 = AC.$

The result of the example of Art. 361 may be obtained in this way; for

the equation $\qquad\qquad\qquad y = mx + \dfrac{a}{m}$

may be written $\qquad\qquad m^2 x - my + a = 0,$

and therefore the envelope is $\qquad y^2 = 4ax.$

363. Another Mode of Establishing the Rule.

The equation $A\lambda^2 + 2B\lambda + C = 0$ may be regarded as a quadratic equation to find the values of λ for the two particular members of the family which pass through a given point (x, y). Now, if (x, y) be supposed to be a point on the envelope, these members will be coincident. Hence for such values of x, y the quadratic for λ must have two equal roots, and the locus of such points is therefore $\qquad B^2 = AC.$

The envelope of the system $\phi(x, y, c) = 0$ might be considered in a similar manner. And it is proved in Theory of Equations that if $f(c) = 0$ is a rational algebraic equation for c, the condition that it should have a pair of equal roots is obtained by eliminating c between the equations

$$f(c) = 0,$$
$$f'(c) = 0,$$

a result agreeing with that of Art. 361.

EXAMPLES.

1. Show that the envelope of the line $\dfrac{x}{a} + \dfrac{y}{b} = 1$, where $ab = c^2$, a constant, is $4xy = c^2$.

2. Find the equation of the curve whose tangent is of the form

$$y = mx + m^4,$$

m being independent of x and y.

3. Find the envelope of the curves

$$\frac{a^2\cos\theta}{x} - \frac{b^2\sin\theta}{y} = \frac{c^2}{a}$$

for different values of θ.

4. Find the envelope of the family of trajectories

$$y = x\tan\theta - \tfrac{1}{2}g\frac{x^2}{u^2\cos^2\theta},$$

θ being the arbitrary parameter.

5. Find the envelopes of straight lines drawn at right angles to tangents to a given parabola and passing through the points in which those tangents cut   (1) the axis of the parabola,

                           (2) a fixed line parallel to the directrix.

6. Find the envelope of straight lines drawn at right angles to normals to a given parabola and passing through the points in which those normals cut the axis of the parabola.

7. A series of circles have their centres on a given straight line, and their radii are proportional to the distances of their corresponding centres from a given point in that line. Find the envelope.

8. P is a point which moves along a given straight line. PM, PN are perpendiculars on the co-ordinate axes supposed rectangular. Find the envelope of the line MN.

9. A straight line has its extremities on two fixed straight lines and forms with them a triangle of constant area. Find its envelope.

10. Show that the envelope of the lines whose equations are

$$x\sec^2\theta + y\cosec^2\theta = c$$

is a parabola touching the axes of co-ordinates.

11. Show that the system of conics obtained by varying λ in the equation

$$\frac{x^2}{a^2} + 2\lambda\frac{xy}{ab} + \frac{y^2}{b^2} = 1 - \lambda^2$$

have for their envelope the parallelogram whose sides are

$$x = \pm a, \quad y = \pm b.$$

12. Show that the envelope of the line

$$lx + my + 1 = 0,$$

where the parameters l, m are connected by the quadratic relation

$$al^2 + 2hlm + bm^2 + 2gl + 2fm + c = 0,$$

is the conic $Ax^2 + 2Hxy + By^2 + 2Gx + 2Fy + C = 0,$

A, B, C, F, G, H being minors of the determinant

$$\begin{vmatrix} a, & h, & g \\ h, & b, & f \\ g, & f, & c \end{vmatrix}.$$

364. The c-Discriminant.

The function of x and y, whose vanishing expresses that $\phi(x, y, c) = 0$ has equal roots for c, is, when expressed in its simplest rational integral form, called the c-discriminant of ϕ, and may be denoted by $\Delta_c\phi$.

Hence the envelope for different values of c will be given in the equation $\qquad \Delta_c\phi = 0$.

365. Singularities.

The equation $\Delta_c\phi = 0$ may contain loci other than the true envelope.

Imagine a curve with a double point N to be made to move in a given manner altering its shape as it travels but retaining the same general characteristics. Take a point P near the locus of the double point. First one and then the other of the branches which form the node pass through P, and when P is ultimately on the locus of the node the two positions of the curve in which a branch passes through P ultimately coincide.

We can now generalize this idea. When fixed values are assigned to x and y the equation $\phi(x, y, c) = 0$ may be regarded as giving the several values of c, corresponding to the several members of the family which pass through a specified point. If this equation be of the nth degree in c, there will be n real or imaginary solutions and therefore n members of the family each passing through this point.

When successive values of c give a locus of multiple points of the rth order for the family $\phi(x, y, c) = 0$ and the chosen point (x, y) happens to lie upon this locus, r of these members will coincide, and therefore the equation $\phi(x, y, c) = 0$ will give for such a point r equal values of c.

Hence it may be expected that the equation $\Delta_c\phi = 0$ will contain, besides the true envelope solution, the loci of any nodes, cusps or conjugate points which the members of the family may possess.

366. The more advanced student is referred for further information to Papers by Cayley, *Messenger of Mathematics*, vols. II. and XII.; Henrici, vol. II., *Proc. Lond. Math. Soc.*; and M. J. M. Hill, vol. XIX., *Proc. Lond. Math. Soc.*; where it has been shown that the c-discriminant in general contains the

envelope locus as a factor once, the node locus twice, and the cusp locus thrice.

Ex. 1. $\qquad\qquad\qquad\qquad c(y+c)^2 = x^3.$

Here differentiating with regard to c

$$(y+c)^2 + 2c(y+c) = 0,$$

giving $\qquad\qquad\qquad\qquad\qquad y + c = 0,$ ....(i.)

or $\qquad\qquad\qquad\qquad\qquad y + 3c = 0.$ ....(ii.)

Substituting from (i.) in the curve we get

$$x^3 = 0 \qquad\qquad\qquad\qquad\qquad\qquad\qquad$$ ....(iv.)

Substituting from (ii.) we get $\qquad -\dfrac{4y^3}{27} = x^3$ ....(v.)

Of these $\qquad\qquad$ (iv.) is a cusp locus

and $\qquad\qquad\qquad$ (v.) is a true envelope $3x = -4^{\frac{1}{3}}y.$

This is exhibited in the accompanying figure.

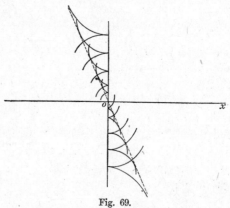

Fig. 69.

Ex. 2. It may happen accidentally that the node or cusp locus is the true envelope locus.

Thus in the family of semicubical parabolas

$$ay^2 = (x-c)^3$$

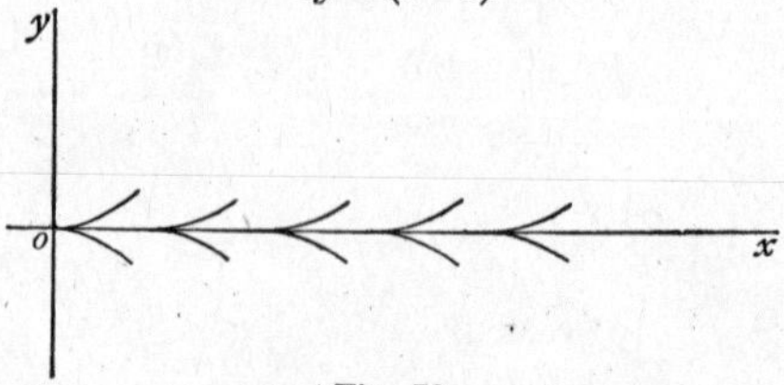

Fig. 70.

the c-discriminant is $y = 0$ or the x-axis, and as this line touches each member of the family it may be regarded as a true envelope. The cusps are now arranged as shown in Fig. 70.

Ex. 3. $$c(y+c)^2 = x^2(x+1).$$

Here there is a node or conjugate point at $(0, -c)$ according as c is positive or negative.

Differentiating we have

$$(y+c)(y+3c) = 0.$$

Eliminating c we have the results

$$x^2(x+1) = 0,$$

or $$-\frac{4y^3}{27} = x^2(x+1).$$

Of these $x = 0$ is the node locus for the portion of the y-axis below the origin, and the conjugate point locus for the portion above the origin.

The line $x+1 = 0$ is a true envelope solution, as also the cubic

$$4y^3 + 27x^2(x+1) = 0.$$

Ex. 4. Examine the cases of

$$\text{(i.)} \quad (y+c)^2 = x^2(x+1),$$
$$\text{(ii.)} \quad y = c(x+c)^2,$$
$$\text{(iii.)} \quad y^2 = c(x-c)^3.$$

367. It may happen that the consecutive members of the family $\phi(x, y, c) = 0$ do not *all* intersect in real points. In this case the curve $$\Delta_c\phi = 0$$ does not touch all the members of the family at real points.

Ex. Let circles be described having for their diameters the double ordinates of the parabola $y^2 = 4ax$. Find their envelope.

If $2c$ be the double ordinate, the typical equation of such a circle is

$$\left(x - \frac{c^2}{4a}\right)^2 + y^2 = c^2.$$

or $$c^4 - 8ac^2(x+2a) + 16a^2(x^2+y^2) = 0,\dots\dots\dots\dots\dots\dots\dots(1)$$

and the envelope is $$(x+2a)^2 = x^2 + y^2$$

or $$y^2 = 4a(x+a),\dots\dots\dots\dots\dots\dots\dots(2)$$

i.e., an equal parabola whose focus is at the vertex of the original curve.

To find where the circle (1) touches the envelope solve for x between (1) and (2). We obtain $$c^2 = 4a(x+2a)$$
$$= y^2 + 4a^2,$$

which gives an imaginary ordinate for the point of contact if $c < 2a$; *i.e.*, if the centre of the circle lies between the focus and the vertex of the original parabola. The student will be able to illustrate this result by a figure.

368. Case of Two Parameters.

Next, suppose the typical equation of the family of curves to involve two parameters a, β connected by a given equation. Then two courses are open to us. We may *eliminate one of the parameters* by means of the connecting equation and thus reduce the problem to that solved in Art. 361, *or*, as is frequently better from considerations of symmetry, *consider one of the parameters capable of independent variation and the other dependent upon it.* We then proceed as follows.

Let
$$\phi(x,\ y,\ a,\ \beta) = 0 \ \dots\dots\dots\dots\dots\dots(1)$$
be the typical equation of the curves whose envelope is to be investigated, and
$$f(a,\ \beta) = 0 \ \dots\dots\dots\dots\dots\dots(2)$$
the relation connecting a and β.

Then, supposing a the independent parameter, we have

$$\frac{\partial \phi}{\partial a} + \frac{\partial \phi}{\partial \beta} \cdot \frac{d\beta}{da} = 0, \dots\dots\dots\dots\dots\dots(3)$$

where
$$\frac{\partial f}{\partial a} + \frac{\partial f}{\partial \beta} \cdot \frac{d\beta}{da} = 0. \dots\dots\dots\dots\dots\dots(4)$$

We thus have four equations and three quantities to eliminate, viz., a, β, $\dfrac{d\beta}{da}$. The result of elimination is the equation of the envelope.

The parameters a, β, connected by the relation $f(a,\ \beta) = 0$, may be regarded as the co-ordinates of a parametric point which lies on the curve $f(x,\ y) = 0$.

369. Indeterminate Multipliers.

The equations (3) and (4) may be written

$$\frac{\partial \phi}{\partial a} da + \frac{\partial \phi}{\partial \beta} d\beta = 0 \ \ (\text{Art. 158}),$$

$$\frac{\partial f}{\partial a} da + \frac{\partial f}{\partial \beta} d\beta = 0.$$

The result of eliminating da, $d\beta$ between these equations is

$$\frac{\dfrac{\partial \phi}{\partial a}}{\dfrac{\partial f}{\partial a}} = \frac{\dfrac{\partial \phi}{\partial \beta}}{\dfrac{\partial f}{\partial \beta}}.$$

Call each of these ratios λ. We then have

$$\frac{\partial \phi}{\partial a} = \lambda \frac{\partial f}{\partial a}, \quad\quad\quad\quad\quad (5)$$

$$\frac{\partial \phi}{\partial \beta} = \lambda \frac{\partial f}{\partial \beta}. \quad\quad\quad\quad\quad (6)$$

This quantity λ is called an "Indeterminate Multiplier."

It remains to eliminate a, β, and λ between equations (1), (2), (5), and (6).

This method is peculiarly adapted to the case in which

$$\phi(x, y, a, \beta) \equiv \phi_1(x, y, a, \beta) - a_1 = 0,$$

and $$f(a, \beta) \equiv f_1(a, \beta) - a_2 = 0,$$

where ϕ_1 and f_1 are homogeneous in a and β, and of the pth and q^{th} degrees respectively, a_1 and a_2 being absolute constants. Multiply equation (5) by a and (6) by β, and add. Then by Euler's Theorem $$pa_1 = qa_2\lambda,$$ so that in such cases λ is easily found.

Ex. *Find the envelope of* $\dfrac{x}{a} + \dfrac{y}{b} = 1$, *where a and b are connected by the relation* $$a^2 + b^2 = c^2,$$
c being an absolute constant; i.e., the envelope of a line of constant length which slides with its extremities upon two fixed rods at right angles to each other.

Here $$\frac{x}{a^2}da + \frac{y}{b^2}db = 0,$$

$$a\,da + b\,db = 0,$$

and therefore $$\frac{x}{a^2} = \lambda a,$$

$$\frac{y}{b^2} = \lambda b.$$

Multiplying by a and b respectively, and adding,

$$\frac{x}{a} + \frac{y}{b} = \lambda(a^2 + b^2),$$

or $$1 = \lambda c^2.$$

Hence $$\left.\begin{array}{c} a^3 = c^2 x \\ b^3 = c^2 y \end{array}\right\},$$

and since $$a^2 + b^2 = c^2$$

we have $$(c^2 x)^{\frac{2}{3}} + (c^2 y)^{\frac{2}{3}} = c^2,$$

or $$x^{\frac{2}{3}} + y^{\frac{2}{3}} = c^{\frac{2}{3}}.$$

1. Find the envelopes of the line

$$\frac{x}{a} + \frac{y}{b} = 1$$

under the following conditions :—

$$(1) \quad a + b = k,$$
$$(2) \quad a^n + b^n = k^n,$$
$$(3) \quad a^m b^n = k^{m+n},$$

k being a constant in each case.

2. Find the envelopes of the systems of coaxial ellipses whose semiaxes a and b are connected by the equations

$$(1) \quad a + b = k,$$
$$(2) \quad \sqrt{a} + \sqrt{b} = \sqrt{k},$$
$$(3) \quad a^m + b^m = k^m,$$
$$(4) \quad ab = k^2,$$

k being a constant in each case.

3. Find the envelopes of the parabolas which touch the co-ordinate axes and are such that the distances (a, β) from the origin to the points of contact are connected by the relations

$$(1) \quad a + \beta = k,$$
$$(2) \quad a^m + \beta^m = k^m,$$
$$(3) \quad a\beta = k^2,$$

k being a constant in each case.

370. Case of Three Parameters connected by Two Equations.

Next, suppose the equation of a curve to contain *three* parameters connected by *two* equations.

Let the equation of the curve be

$$\phi(x, y, a, \beta, \gamma) = 0, \quad\text{.........................(1)}$$

and let

$$f_1(a, \beta, \gamma) = 0, \quad\text{.....................(2)}$$
$$f_2(a, \beta, \gamma) = 0, \quad\text{.....................(3)}$$

be the two connecting equations. Then we have

$$\frac{\partial\phi}{\partial a}da + \frac{\partial\phi}{\partial\beta}d\beta + \frac{\partial\phi}{\partial\gamma}d\gamma = 0, \quad\text{.......................(4)}$$

$$\frac{\partial f_1}{\partial a}da + \frac{\partial f_1}{\partial\beta}d\beta + \frac{\partial f_1}{\partial\gamma}d\gamma = 0, \quad\text{.......................(5)}$$

$$\frac{\partial f_2}{\partial a}da + \frac{\partial f_2}{\partial\beta}d\beta + \frac{\partial f_2}{\partial\gamma}d\gamma = 0. \quad\text{.......................(6)}$$

The result of eliminating da, $d\beta$, $d\gamma$ between these three equations is

$$\begin{vmatrix} \dfrac{\partial \phi}{\partial a} & \dfrac{\partial \phi}{\partial \beta} & \dfrac{\partial \phi}{\partial \gamma} \\[2ex] \dfrac{\partial f_1}{\partial a} & \dfrac{\partial f_1}{\partial \beta} & \dfrac{\partial f_1}{\partial \gamma} \\[2ex] \dfrac{\partial f_2}{\partial a} & \dfrac{\partial f_2}{\partial \beta} & \dfrac{\partial f_2}{\partial \gamma} \end{vmatrix} = 0. \dots\dots\dots\dots\dots(7)$$

If a, β, γ be eliminated between the four equations (1), (2), (3) and (7), the result will be the equation of the envelope.

It is to be noted that the same determinant would arise from the elimination of the "indeterminate multipliers" λ_1 and λ_2 from the equations

$$\frac{\partial \phi}{\partial a} + \lambda_1 \frac{\partial f_1}{\partial a} + \lambda_2 \frac{\partial f_2}{\partial a} = 0, \dots\dots\dots\dots\dots(8)$$

$$\frac{\partial \phi}{\partial \beta} + \lambda_1 \frac{\partial f_1}{\partial \beta} + \lambda_2 \frac{\partial f_2}{\partial \beta} = 0, \dots\dots\dots\dots\dots(9)$$

$$\frac{\partial \phi}{\partial \gamma} + \lambda_1 \frac{\partial f_1}{\partial \gamma} + \lambda_2 \frac{\partial f_2}{\partial \gamma} = 0, \dots\dots\dots\dots(10)$$

and it is often advantageous to use these latter equations in place of (4), (5), (6), involving da, $d\beta$, $d\gamma$.

The result of eliminating a, β, γ, λ_1, λ_2 between the six equations (1), (2), (3), (8), (9), (10) will then be the equation to the envelope.

371. The *general* investigation of the envelope of a curve whose equation contains r parameters connected by $r-1$ equations proceeds in exactly the same way, and is the result of the elimination of the r parameters and $r-1$ indeterminate multipliers between $2r$ equations.

372. Converse Problem. Given the Family and the Envelope to find the relation between the Parameters.

Suppose we are given the equation of a curve

$$\phi(x, y, a, \beta) = 0 \dots\dots\dots\dots\dots(1)$$

containing two parameters. Suppose also the envelope given, viz.,

$$F(x, y) = 0 \dots\dots\dots\dots\dots(2)$$

Required the relation between a and β.

Eliminate y between (1) and (2). We obtain an equation of the form

$$f(x, a, \beta) = 0, \dots\dots\dots\dots\dots(3)$$

giving the abscissa of the point of contact of the curve with its envelope. Since the curve touches its envelope, equation (3) must also be true for a contiguous value of x, viz., $x + \delta x$ (unless the tangent at the point of contact be parallel to the axis of y, in which case we could have eliminated x between (1) and (2) and proceeded in the same way with y). Hence

$$f(x,\, a,\, b) = 0, \Big\} \dots\dots\dots\dots\dots\dots(4)$$
$$f(x + \delta x,\, a,\, b) = 0. \Big/ \dots\dots\dots\dots\dots\dots(5)$$

The latter may be expanded in powers of δx, when it becomes

$$f(x,\, a,\, b) + \frac{\partial f}{\partial x}\delta x + \dots = 0, \dots\dots\dots\dots\dots(6)$$

and therefore in the limit

$$\frac{\partial f}{\partial x} = 0. \dots\dots\dots\dots\dots\dots\dots(7)$$

If, then, x be eliminated between

$$f(x,\, a,\, \beta) = 0,$$
$$\frac{\partial}{\partial x} f(x,\, a,\, \beta) = 0,$$

we obtain the relation sought.

It will be observed that this is precisely the same process as finding the envelope of

$$\phi(x,\, y,\, a,\, \beta) = 0,$$

considering a, β as the current co-ordinates and x, y as parameters connected by the relation

$$F(x,\, y) = 0.$$

Ex. *Given that $x^{\frac{2}{3}} + y^{\frac{2}{3}} = c^{\frac{2}{3}}$ is the envelope of $\dfrac{x}{a} + \dfrac{y}{b} = 1$, find the necessary relation between a and b.*

We have

$$\frac{dx}{x^{\frac{1}{3}}} + \frac{dy}{y^{\frac{1}{3}}} = 0,$$
$$\frac{dx}{a} + \frac{dy}{b} = 0;$$

therefore

$$x^{\frac{1}{3}} = \lambda a,$$
$$y^{\frac{1}{3}} = \lambda b.$$

Hence

$$\frac{x}{a} = \lambda x^{\frac{2}{3}}, \quad \frac{y}{b} = \lambda y^{\frac{2}{3}},$$

and by addition

$$1 = \lambda c^{\frac{2}{3}}.$$

This gives

$$a = c^{\frac{2}{3}} x^{\frac{1}{3}}, \quad b = c^{\frac{2}{3}} y^{\frac{1}{3}},$$

and by squaring and adding

$$a^2 + b^2 = c^2,$$

the relation required. (See Ex., Art. 369.)

373. Evolutes considered as Envelopes.

The evolute of a curve has been defined as the locus of the centre of curvature, and it has been shown (Art. 341) that the centre of curvature is the ultimate point of intersection of two consecutive normals. Hence the evolute is the *envelope of the normals* to a curve. It is from this point of view that the equation of the evolute of a given curve is in general most easily obtained.

Ex. *To find the evolute of the ellipse*

$$\frac{x^2}{a^2} + \frac{y^2}{b^2} = 1.$$

The equation of the normal at the point whose eccentric angle is ϕ is

$$\frac{ax}{\cos \phi} - \frac{by}{\sin \phi} = a^2 - b^2 \dots\dots\dots\dots\dots\dots\dots(1)$$

We have to find the envelope of this line for different values of the parameter ϕ.

Differentiating with regard to ϕ,

$$ax\frac{\sin \phi}{\cos^2\phi} + by\frac{\cos \phi}{\sin^2\phi} = 0,\dots\dots\dots\dots\dots\dots\dots\dots(2)$$

or

$$\frac{\sin^3\phi}{by} + \frac{\cos^3\phi}{ax} = 0.$$

Hence

$$\frac{\sin \phi}{-\sqrt[3]{by}} = \frac{\cos \phi}{\sqrt[3]{ax}} = \frac{1}{\sqrt{(ax)^{\frac{2}{3}} + (by)^{\frac{2}{3}}}} . \dots\dots\dots\dots\dots(3)$$

Substituting these values of $\sin \phi$ and $\cos \phi$ in equation (1) we obtain, after reduction

$$(ax)^{\frac{2}{3}} + (by)^{\frac{2}{3}} = (a^2 - b^2)^{\frac{2}{3}}.$$

374. Pedal Curves as Envelopes.

It has already been pointed out (Art. 223) that if circles be described on radii vectores of a given curve as diameters they all touch the *first positive pedal* of the curve with regard to the origin. It is obvious, therefore, that the problem of finding the first positive pedal of a given curve is identical with that of finding the *envelope of circles described on the radii vectores as diameters.*

Again, the *first negative pedal* is the envelope of a *straight line drawn through any point of the curve and at right angles to the radius vector to the point.*

Ex. 1. *Find the first positive pedal of the circle $r = 2a \cos \theta$ with regard to the origin.*

Let d, a be the polar co-ordinates of any point on the circle, then

$$d = 2a \cos a.$$

Again, the equation of a circle on the radius vector d for diameter is

$$r = d \cos(\theta - a), \dotfill (1)$$

or

$$r = 2a \cos a \cos(\theta - a). \dotfill (2)$$

Here a is the parameter.

Differentiating with regard to a,

$$-\sin a \cos(\theta - a) + \cos a \sin(\theta - a) = 0,$$

whence

$$\sin(\theta - 2a) = 0,$$

or

$$a = \frac{\theta}{2} \dotfill (3)$$

Substituting this value of a in equation (2)

$$r = 2a \cos^2 \frac{\theta}{2},$$

or

$$r = a(1 + \cos \theta),$$

the equation of a cardioide.

Ex. 2. *Find the equation of the first negative pedal of the cardioide*

$$r = a(1 + \cos \theta)$$

with regard to the origin.

Here we have to find the envelope of the line

$$x \cos a + y \sin a = d,$$

where d, a are the polar co-ordinates of any point on the cardioide; *i.e.*, where

$$d = a(1 + \cos a).$$

The equation of the line is therefore

$$x \cos a + y \sin a = a(1 + \cos a),$$

or

$$(x - a)\cos a + y \sin a = a,$$

a line which, from its form, is easily seen to be a tangent to

$$(x - a)^2 + y^2 = a^2,$$

or

$$r = 2a \cos \theta,$$

which is therefore its envelope.

375. Envelope of a Line regarded as a Negative Pedal.

If a straight line be in motion in any manner, suppose O to be any arbitrary origin and OY a perpendicular on the moving line. It is evident that the envelope of the moving line is the first negative pedal of the locus of Y.

As several curves have well-known first negative pedals, the envelope may in this manner often be inferred.

The following results frequently recur and may be found useful.

Original Curve.	The Given Point.	First Negative Pedal.
Straight line,	{ any point not upon the line, }	Parabola.
Circle,	any point within,	{ Ellipse with pole for focus.
Circle,	any point without,	{ Hyperbola pole for focus.
Circle,	any point upon it,	Point.
Cardioide $[r=a(1\pm\cos\theta)]$,	pole,	Circle through pole.
Limaçon $[r=a+b\cos\theta]$,	pole,	Circle.
$r^n=a^n\cos n\theta$,	pole,	$r^{\frac{n}{1-n}}=a^{\frac{n}{1-n}}\cos\frac{n}{1-n}\theta$.
Bernoulli's Lemniscate,	pole,	Rectangular hyperbola.
Equiangular spiral,	pole,	Equiangular spiral.
$r=a\sin n\theta$,	pole,	{ Epi-cycloid or hypo-cycloid.

Ex. 1. If a lamina have three straight lines traced upon it and is moved so that two of the straight lines pass through fixed points, find the envelope of the third carried line.

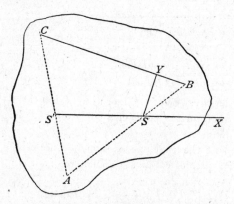

Fig. 71.

Let S and S' be the fixed points, AB, AC the lines fixed in the lamina and passing through S and S', SY a perpendicular from S on the carried line BC.

Let $\qquad SY=r,\quad YSX=\theta,\quad SS'=\lambda,\quad$ and $\quad AB=c.$

Then $\qquad A\widehat{S}S'=\theta-(90-B),$

and $\qquad r=SB\sin B=(c-AS)\sin B$

$$=[c-\frac{\lambda}{\sin A}\sin(A+B+\theta-90)]\sin B$$

This is of the form
$$r = a + \beta \cos(\theta - \gamma)$$
where a, β, γ are constants and the locus of Y is a limaçon with S for pole. Hence the envelope of any carried line BC is a circle.

Cor. Thus if two of the sides of a polygon pass through fixed points, all other sides, diagonals, or carried lines envelope circles or pass through fixed points.

Ex. 2. If a lamina with a curve traced upon it be in motion in any manner, to find the envelope of the instantaneous directions of motion of all points upon the carried curve.

Let A, B be two of the points of the curve. Draw lines AO, BO at right angles to the instantaneous directions of motion of A and B respectively. Then O is the "instantaneous centre"; and if P be any other point of the curve, PO is a normal to the path of P. Hence the envelope of all the directions of motion at any instant is the first negative pedal of the given curve with regard to the instantaneous centre.

EXAMPLES.

1. Find the envelope of the line $y = mx - 2am - am^3$ for different values of m; *i.e.*, find the equation of the evolute of the parabola $y^2 = 4ax$.

2. Show that the envelope of the family of curves
$$A\lambda^3 + 3B\lambda^2 + 3C\lambda + D = 0,$$
where λ is the arbitrary parameter and A, B, C, D are functions of x and y, is $\quad (BC - AD)^2 = 4(BD - C^2)(AC - B^2)$.

3. Find the envelope of the line which joins the feet of the two perpendiculars from any point of a circle upon a given pair of perpendicular diameters.

4. Show that the envelope of straight lines which join the extremities of a pair of conjugate diameters of an ellipse is a similar ellipse.

5. Show that if PM, PN be perpendiculars from any point P of the curve $y = mx^3$ upon the axes the envelope of MN is
$$27y + 4mx^3 = 0.$$

6. Find the envelope of circles described on the radii vectores of an ellipse drawn from the centre as diameters.

7. Show that the envelope of the family of curves
$$A \cos^n\theta + B \sin^n\theta = C,$$
where θ is the arbitrary parameter and A, B, C are functions of x and y, is $\quad A^{\frac{2}{2-n}} + B^{\frac{2}{2-n}} = C^{\frac{2}{2-n}}$.

8. Show that the envelope of a circle whose centre lies on the parabola $y^2 = 4ax$ and which passes through its vertex is

$$2ay^2 + x(x^2 + y^2) = 0.$$

9. Show that the envelope of a circle whose centre lies on the parabola $y^2 = 4ax$ and whose radius = the abscissa of the centre is made up of the tangent at the vertex and a circle with centre at the focus.

✓ 10. Two particles move along parallel straight lines, the one with uniform velocity and the other with the same initial velocity but with uniform acceleration. Show that the line joining them always touches a fixed hyperbola.

11. A series of circles is described having their centres on an equilateral hyperbola and passing through its centre. Show that the locus of their ultimate points of intersection is a lemniscate.

12. Find the envelope of the lines

$$x(\sin \theta)^{-\frac{1}{2}} + y(\cos \theta)^{-\frac{1}{2}} = a. \qquad \text{[Oxford, 1889.]}$$

13. Prove that the equation of the normal to the curve

$$x^{\frac{2}{3}} + y^{\frac{2}{3}} = a^{\frac{2}{3}}$$

may be written in the form

$$y \cos \phi - x \sin \phi = a \cos 2\phi.$$

Hence show that the evolute of the curve is

$$(x + y)^{\frac{2}{3}} + (x - y)^{\frac{2}{3}} = 2a^{\frac{2}{3}}.$$

14. Show that the envelope of the lines

$$x \cos ma + y \sin ma = a(\cos na)^{\frac{m}{n}},$$

where a is the arbitrary parameter, is

$$r^{\frac{n}{m-n}} = a^{\frac{n}{m-n}} \cos \frac{n}{m-n}\theta.$$

15. Circles are described having for diameters the radii vectores from the origin to the curve $x^3 + y^3 = 3ax^2$. Prove that their envelope is the inverse of a semicubical parabola. [Oxford, 1889.]

16. The tangent at any point P on a parabola meets the tangent at the vertex in Q, and the normal at P meets the axis in R, find the envelope of QR. [Oxford, 1888.]

17. Show that the radius of curvature of the envelope of the line

$$x \cos a + y \sin a = f(a)$$

is

$$f(a) + f''(a)$$

and that the centre of curvature is at the point

$$\left.\begin{array}{l} x = -f'(a)\sin a - f''(a)\cos a \\ y = f'(a)\cos a - f''(a)\sin a \end{array}\right\}.$$

18. If O be the pole and P any point of the curve

$$r = a \cos m\theta,$$

and if with O for pole and P for vertex a similar curve be described, the envelope of all such curves is

$$r^{\frac{1}{2}} = a^{\frac{1}{2}}\cos\frac{m\theta}{2}.$$

19. If O be the pole and P any point of the curve

$$\widehat{r^m} = a^m\cos m\theta,$$

and if with O for pole and P for vertex a curve similar to

$$r^n = a^n\cos n\theta$$

be described, the envelope of all such curves is

$$r^{\frac{mn}{m+n}} = a^{\frac{mn}{m+n}}\cos\frac{mn}{m+n}\theta.$$

20. If O be the pole and Y the foot of the perpendicular from O on any tangent to the curve

$$r^m = a^m\cos m\theta,$$

and if with O for pole and Y for vertex a curve similar to

$$r^n = a^n\cos n\theta$$

be described, the envelope of all such curves is

$$r^p = a^p\cos p\theta, \text{ where } p = \frac{mn}{m+n+mn}.$$

21. If a point on the circumference of a given circle be taken as pole, and circles be described on radii vectores of the given circle as diameters, the envelope of these circles is a cardioide.

22. Show that the envelope of all cardioides on radii vectores of the circle $r = a \cos \theta$ for axes, and having their cusps at the pole, is

$$r^{\frac{1}{3}} = a^{\frac{1}{3}} \cos \tfrac{1}{3}\theta.$$

23. Show that the envelope of all cardioides described on radii vectores of the cardioide $r = a(1 + \cos \theta)$ for axes, and having their cusps at the pole, is

$$r^{\frac{1}{4}} = (2a)^{\frac{1}{4}} \cos \frac{\theta}{4}.$$

24. On radii vectores of $r^{2n} = a^{2n} \cos 2n\theta$ as axes, curves similar to it are described, the curves being all concentric. Show that the envelope of all these is $\quad r^n = a^n\cos n\theta$.

25. A and B are two polar curves $[r = af(\theta)$ and $r = bF(\theta)]$. If curves similar to A be similarly described upon radii of B as initial lines, their envelope will be similar to that of curves similar to B similarly described on radii vectores of A as initial lines.

26. A variable parabola is drawn having its vertex on a given parabola, the two curves having the same focus ; prove that the envelope of its directrix is the curve

$$r \cos^3\frac{\theta}{3} = l,$$

referred to the common focus as pole ; and trace this curve.

[OXFORD, 1890.]

27. Prove that the pedal equation of the envelope of the line

$$x \cos 2\theta + y \sin 2\theta = 2a \cos \theta,$$

is $\qquad p^2 = \frac{4}{3}(r^2 - a^2).$

28. Prove that the pedal equation of the envelope of the line

$$x \cos m\theta + y \sin m\theta = a \cos n\theta,$$

is $\qquad m^2r^2 = (m^2 - n^2)p^2 + n^2a^2.$

29. Two central radii vectores of a circle of radius a rotate from coincidence in a given initial position with uniform angular velocities ω and ω'. Show that the pedal equation of the envelope of a line joining their extremities is

$$(\omega + \omega')^2 r^2 = 4\omega\omega' p^2 + (\omega - \omega')^2 a^2.$$

30. The envelope of polars with respect to the circle

$$x^2 + y^2 = 2ax$$

of points which lie on the circle

$$x^2 + y^2 = 2bx$$

is $\qquad \{(a - b)x + ab\}^2 = b^2\{(x - a)^2 + y^2\}.$

31. A square slides with two of its adjacent sides passing through fixed points. Show that its remaining sides touch a pair of fixed circles, one diagonal passes through a fixed point, and that the envelope of the other is a circle.

32. An equilateral triangle moves so that two of its sides pass through two fixed points. Prove that the envelope of the third side is a circle.

33. Prove that the envelope of the circles obtained by varying the arbitrary parameter a in the equation

$$c^2(y - a)^2 + (cx - a^2)^2 = (a^2 + c^2)^2$$

consists of a straight line and a circle.

34. Two points are taken on an ellipse on the same side of the major axis and such that the sum of their abscissae is equal to the semi-major axis. Show that the line joining them envelopes a parabola which goes through the extremities of the minor axis and whose latus rectum is equal to that of the ellipse.

35. Given the centre and directrices of an ellipse, show that the envelope of the normals at the ends of the latera recta is

$$27y^4 \pm 256cx^3 = 0.$$

36. Prove that the envelope of a circle which passes through a fixed point F and subtends a constant angle at another fixed point F' is a limaçon.

37. Find the envelope of a parabola of which the directrix and one point are given.

38. Show that the envelope of the common chords of the ellipse

$$x^2/a^2 + y^2/b^2 = 1$$

and its circles of curvature is the curve

$$\left(\frac{x}{a} + \frac{y}{b}\right)^{\frac{2}{3}} + \left(\frac{x}{a} - \frac{y}{b}\right)^{\frac{2}{3}} = 2. \qquad \text{[Math. Tripos, 1884.]}$$

39. Find the condition between a and b that the envelope of the

line $\qquad\qquad \dfrac{x}{a} + \dfrac{y}{b} = 1$

may be the curve $\qquad\qquad x^p y^q = k^{p+q}.$

40. S is a fixed point, and with any point P of a curve for centre and with radius $PS + k$ a circle is described. Show that the envelopes for different values of k consist of two sets of parallel curves, one set being circles; and find what the original curve must be that both sets may be circles.

41. Rays emanate from a luminous point O and are reflected at a plane curve. OY is the perpendicular from O on the tangent at any point P, and OY is produced to a point Q, such that $YQ = OY$. Show that the caustic curve is the evolute of the locus of Q. Show that the caustic curve may also be regarded as the evolute of the envelope of a circle whose centre is P and radius OP.

[If a ray of light in the plane of a given bright curve be incident upon the curve, the reflected ray and the incident ray make equal angles with the normal to the curve at the point of incidence, and the reflected ray lies in the plane of the curve. If a given system of rays be incident upon the curve, the envelope of the reflected rays is called the caustic by reflection.]

42. Parallel rays are incident on a bright semicircular wire (radius a) and in its plane. Show that the caustic curve is the epicycloid formed by a point attached to a circle of radius $\frac{a}{4}$ rolling upon the circumference of a circle of radius $\frac{a}{2}$.

43. Rays emanate from a point on the circumference of a reflecting circular arc. Show that the caustic after reflection is a cardioide.

44. Show that if rays emanate from the pole of an equiangular spiral and are reflected by the curve the caustic is a similar equiangular spiral.

45. Rays of light parallel to the y-axis fall upon the reflecting curve $y = f(x)$. Show that the equation of the reflected ray is

$$(Y - y)2p + (1 - p^2)(X - x) = 0$$

where $p = f'(x)$. Also that the length of the reflected ray between the point of reflection and the caustic is one quarter of the chord of curvature parallel to the y-axis.

46. If rays of light emanating from the pole fall upon a reflecting curve, show that the length (l) of the reflected ray is given by

$$\frac{1}{l} = \frac{d}{dr}\left(\log \frac{p^2}{r}\right).$$

47. A straight line meets one of a system of confocal conics in P, Q, and RS is the line joining the feet of the other two normals drawn from the point of intersection of the normals at P and Q. Prove that the envelope of RS is a parabola touching the axes.

[MATH. TRIPOS, 1884.]

48. Show that the tangents to a system of conics inscribed in a given quadrilateral, at the points where a fixed straight line meets them, envelope a curve of the third class touching the given line and the sides of the given quadrilateral. [MATH. TRIPOS, 1885.]

49. Show that the vanishing of the c-discriminant of the eliminant of p from the equations $\left.\begin{array}{r} xp^2 - 2yp + a = 0 \\ cp^3 - xp^2 + \dfrac{a}{3} = 0 \end{array}\right\}$

and

gives exactly the same locus as the vanishing of the p-discriminant of the first equation. Show that this is not a true envelope but a cusp locus. [MATH. TRIPOS, 1878.]

50. Find the condition that every curve of the family $f(x, y, c) = 0$ may have a double point, i.e. that there may be a node locus.

[PROF. M. J. M. HILL.]

CHAPTER XII.

CURVE TRACING.

376. Nature of the Problem.   Cartesian Equations.

If in the Cartesian equation of any algebraic curve, various values of x be assigned, we obtain a number of equations whose roots give the corresponding values of the ordinates.   The real roots of these equations can always be either found exactly or approximated closely to by methods explained in the Theory of Equations.   We can by this means, laborious though it will in most cases be, find as many points as we like which satisfy the given equation of the curve ; and by joining these points by a curved line drawn freely through them we can form a fairly good idea as to its shape.   The experience, however, which we have gained in previous chapters will in general obviate any necessity of resort to the usually tedious process of approximating to the roots of equations of high degree ; and we propose to give a list of suggestions for guidance in curve tracing which in most cases will enable us to form, without much difficulty, a sufficiently exact notion of the character of the curve represented by any specified equation.

377. Order of Procedure.

1. A glance will suffice to detect *symmetry* in a curve.

(a) If no odd powers of y occur, the curve is symmetrical with respect to the axis of x.   Similarly for symmetry about the axis of y.

(b) If all the powers of both x and y which occur be even, the curve is symmetrical about both axes, as, for instance, in the case of the ellipse $\dfrac{x^2}{a^2}+\dfrac{y^2}{b^2}=1$.

314

(*c*) Again, if on changing the signs of x and y the equation of the curve remain unchanged, there is symmetry in opposite quadrants, as in the case of the hyperbola $xy = k^2$. The origin is then said to be a *centre* of the curve.

(*d*) If the equation remain unchanged when x and y are inter-changed there is symmetry about the line $y = x$.

If the curve be not symmetrical with regard to either axis, consider whether any obvious transformation of co-ordinates could make it so.

2. Notice whether the curve passes through the origin; also the points *where it crosses the co-ordinate axes;* or, in fact, any points whose co-ordinates present themselves as obviously satisfying the equation to the curve.

3. *What linear asymptotes are there?* First find those parallel to the co-ordinate axes; next, the oblique ones (Art. 237). These results point out in what directions the curve extends to infinity.

Find also *on which side of each asymptote the curve lies* (Art. 260).

If there be a parabolic branch it is useful to obtain a para-bolic asymptote and to ascertain on which side of this parabola the curve lies (Art. 263).

4. If the curve pass through the origin, equate to zero the terms of lowest degree. These terms will give the *tangent or tangents at the origin* (Art. 291), and thus tell the direction in which the curve passes through the origin. A more complete method of finding the *shape of the curve near to and at a great distance from the origin* is to follow in Art. 382.

5. If there be a *node, cusp,* or *conjugate point* at the origin, or a multiple point of higher order than the second, take note of the fact. If there be a cusp, *test its species* (Art. 295).

6. Find *what other multiple points* the curve has (Art. 294), and ascertain the position and character of each.

7. *Find* $\dfrac{dy}{dx}$; and for what points it *vanishes* or *becomes infinite.* These results will indicate the points at which the tangent is parallel or perpendicular to the axis of x. The

direction of the tangent at other points may also be ascertained if desirable.

8. Find, if convenient, the *points of inflexion*.

9. A straight line will cut a curve of the nth degree *in n points* real or imaginary, and imaginary intersections *occur in pairs.* These facts are often useful in detecting a false notion of the shape of a curve.

10. If we can solve the equation for one of the variables, say y, in terms of the other, x, it will be frequently found that radicals occur in the solution, and that the range of admissible values of x which give real values for y *is thereby limited.* The *existence of loops* upon a curve is frequently detected thus.

11. It sometimes happens that the equation is much simplified upon *reduction to the polar form.* This is especially the case when the origin is a multiple point on the curve.

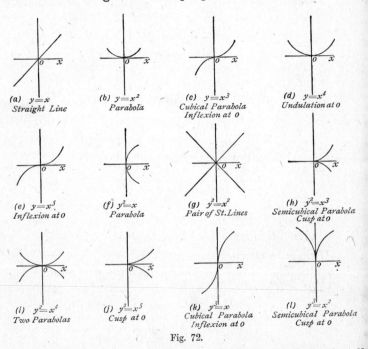

(a) $y=x$
Straight Line

(b) $y=x^2$
Parabola

(c) $y=x^3$
Cubical Parabola
Inflexion at o

(d) $y=x^4$
Undulation at o

(e) $y=x^5$
Inflexion at o

(f) $y^2=x$
Parabola

(g) $y^2=x^2$
Pair of St. Lines

(h) $y^2=x^3$
Semicubical Parabola
Cusp at o

(i) $y^2=x^4$
Two Parabolas

(j) $y^2=x^5$
Cusp at o

(k) $y^3=x$
Cubical Parabola
Inflexion at o

(l) $y^3=x^2$
Semicubical Parabola
Cusp at o

Fig. 72.

378. It is not necessary of course in every case to take all the steps indicated above, or to keep to the order laid down, but the student is advised in any curve he may attempt to trace to note down the result of each investigation he may make. For instance, he should remark, the absence just as much as the existence of symmetry, asymptotes, or singular points, and the total information gained will generally be sufficient to give a tolerably good diagram of the curve.

379. It will be useful to be able to draw at once a graph of any of the cases which come under the head

$$x^p = y^q.$$

Accordingly the student should carefully consider the figures of diagram 72 and verify the drawing in each case.

380. We add a few examples to illustrate the points enumerated.

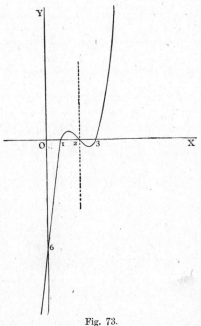

Fig. 73.

I. *To trace the curve* $y = (x-1)(x-2)(x-3)$.

(a) This curve is not symmetrical about either axis; but if the origin be transferred to the point (2, 0) the equation becomes

$$y = x(x^2 - 1),$$

showing symmetry in opposite quadrants when referred to the new axes, and that the tangent at the new origin is inclined at an angle 135° to the axis of x.

(β) Recurring to the original equation,

If	$y=0$,	$x=1,\ 2,$ or 3;
If	$x=0$,	$y=-6$;
If	$x=\infty$,	$y=\infty$;
If	$x=-\infty$,	$y=-\infty$.
When	x is >3	y is positive,
	$x<3$ but >2	y is negative,
	$x<2$ but >1	y is positive,
	$x<1$	y is negative.

(γ) The curve does not go through the origin, and, although extending to infinity, it has no rectilineal asymptote.

(δ) Since $$y=x^3-6x^2+11x-6$$

we have $$\frac{dy}{dx}=3x^2-12x+11,$$

which vanishes when $$x=2\pm\frac{1}{\sqrt{3}}.$$

(ϵ) Also $\dfrac{d^2y}{dx^2}=6(x-2)$, which shows that there is a point of inflexion at the point where $x=2$.

The shape of the curve is therefore that shown in Fig. 73.

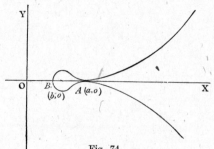

Fig. 74.

II. *To trace the curve* $$y=\pm\frac{(x-a)^2\sqrt{x-b}}{a^{\frac{3}{2}}}.$$

CASE 1. Suppose $a>b$ (Fig. 74).

(a) The curve is symmetrical with regard to the axis of x.

(β) While $x<b$, y is imaginary,

and y is real for all values of x from b to ∞, and the curve meets the axis of x when $x=a$ and when $x=b$.

(γ) $\dfrac{dy}{dx}=0$ when $x=a$, and $=\infty$ when $x=b$, so that the curve touches the axis x at the point $(a,0)$, and cuts it at right angles at $(b,0)$.

(δ) There is no asymptote; but, when $x=\infty$, y and $\dfrac{dy}{dx}$ are both ∞ in the limit, the curve ultimately taking the shape of

$$y=\pm\frac{x^{\frac{5}{2}}}{a^{\frac{3}{2}}}.$$

CASE 2. Next consider $a<b$ (Fig. 75).

(a') There is in this case also symmetry about the axis of x.

(β') The equation to the curve is satisfied by the point $(a, 0)$, but by no other point in its vicinity, for if x be $<b$, y is imaginary except when $x=a$. The point $(a, 0)$ is therefore a conjugate point.

(γ') Moreover $\dfrac{dy}{dx}=\infty$ when $x=b$, and the curve cuts the axis of x at right angles at this point.

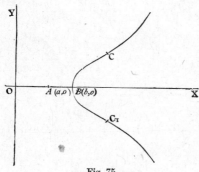

Fig. 75.

(δ') Also, when $x=\infty$, $\dfrac{dy}{dx}=\infty$; so the curve in departing from $(b, 0)$ (the point B in Fig. 75) must bend towards the positive direction of the axis of x, and, finally, $\dfrac{dy}{dx}$ again becomes infinite, showing that there must be a point of inflexion at some point C between B and ∞. Its exact position is of course given by the equation

$$\frac{d^2y}{dx^2}=0.$$

The shapes of the curves in the two cases are given in Figs. 74 and 75 respectively.

EXAMPLES.

1. Trace the curve $y=x^2(x-1)$,

showing that its tangent is parallel to the axis of x at the origin and at the point $x=\frac{2}{3}$.

2. Trace the curve $a^2(y-b)+x^3=0$.

3. Trace the curve $(x-a)^2+(y-b)^3=0$.

4. Trace the curve $ay^2=(x-a)(x-b)(x-c)$,

where a, b, c are in descending order of magnitude, and examine the cases

         (1) $a=b$.

         (2) $b=c$.

         (3) $a=b=c$.

III. *To trace the curve* $\quad y=\dfrac{x^3+ax^2+a^3}{x^2-a^2},$

a being positive.

(a) There is no symmetry about either axis and the curve does not pass through the origin.

(β) The curve cuts the axis of y at the point $(0,\ -a)$ and the axis of x at the point given by the real root of

$$x^3+ax^2+a^3=0.$$

(It is clear that two roots of this equation are imaginary, for the sum of the squares of the reciprocals of its roots is negative.) Also, the real root is obviously negative and numerically greater than a.

(γ) When $\quad x$ is $>a,\qquad\qquad\qquad y$ is positive.

When $\quad x$ lies between a and $-a$, y is negative.

When x is $<-a$, y is positive until x passes the negative root above referred to, and then is negative afterwards.

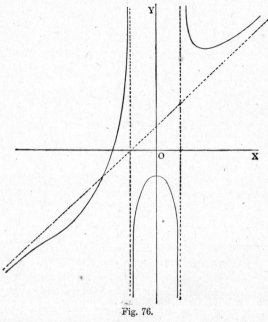

Fig. 76.

(δ) The asymptotes parallel to the axes are $x=\pm a$. To find the oblique asymptote we have

$$y=x\frac{1+\dfrac{a}{x}+\dfrac{a^3}{x^3}}{1-\dfrac{a^2}{x^2}}=x\left(1+\frac{a}{x}+\frac{a^3}{x^3}\right)\left(1+\frac{a^2}{x^2}+\dots\right),$$

or $\qquad\qquad y=x+a+\dfrac{a^2}{x}+\dots.$

Hence $y = x + a$ is the oblique asymptote, and, if x be positive, the ordinate of the curve is obviously greater than that of the asymptote, and the curve lies above the oblique asymptote. If x be negative, the curve lies below it.

(ϵ) $$\frac{dy}{dx} = \frac{x(x^3 - 3a^2x - 4a^3)}{(x^2 - a^2)^2},$$

which gives $\frac{dy}{dx} = 0$, when $x = 0$ or when $x^3 - 3a^2x - 4a^3 = 0$, which clearly has a positive root lying between $x = 2a$ and $x = 3a$, and which can be shown to have only this one real root. Also, $\frac{dy}{dx} = \infty$ only when $x = \pm a$.

(ζ) A point of inflexion lies between $x = -5a$ and $x = -6a$ (Ex. 13, p. 248).

The shape is therefore that given in Fig. 76.

IV. *To trace the curve* $\qquad y^2 + 2x^3y + x^7 = 0$.

(a) The curve is not symmetrical about either axis and there are no asymptotes.

(β) The curve passes through the origin, but cuts neither axis again.

(γ) There is a cusp at the origin, the equation of the tangent being

$$y = 0.$$

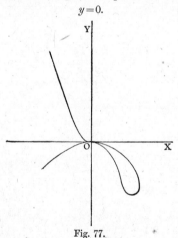

Fig. 77.

Proceeding according to Art. 295 the quadratic for P is

$$P^2 + 2Px^3 + x^7 = 0,$$

an equation whose roots are real if x be very small, positive or negative; for the criterion for real roots is that $x^6 - x^7$ should be > 0. This condition is fulfilled until x is > 1, when P or y becomes imaginary.

Moreover, the product of the roots $= x^7$ and is positive or negative according as x is positive or negative. There is therefore a double cusp at the origin, and on the positive side of the axis of y it is of the second species, while on the negative side it is of the first species. The point is therefore a point of oscul-inflexion (Fig. 50).

E.D.C. X

(δ) $$y = -x^3 \pm x^3\sqrt{1-x},$$

so that $\frac{dy}{dx} = \infty$ if $x=1$. Also, one value of $\frac{dy}{dx}$ is zero when $x = \frac{48}{49}$.

The shape of the curve is now readily seen to be that shown in Fig. 77.

381. The following curve illustrates a particular artifice which may be occasionally employed, namely to express the ordinate of the curve as the sum or difference of the ordinates of two known or easily traceable curves.

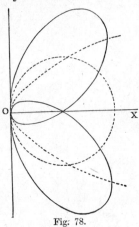

Fig. 78.

V. *To trace* $$(x^2 + y^2 - 3ax)^2 = 4ax^2(2a - x).$$

Here
$$y^2 = 2ax - x^2 \pm 2\sqrt{ax}\sqrt{2ax - x^2} + ax$$
$$= (\sqrt{2ax - x^2} \pm \sqrt{ax})^2 ;$$

therefore
$$y = \pm\sqrt{2ax - x^2} \pm \sqrt{ax},$$

or
$$y = \pm y_1 \pm y_2,$$

where y_1 and y_2 are corresponding ordinates of the circle $x^2 + y^2 = 2ax$ and of the parabola $y^2 = ax$. Hence the ordinate of the curve is the sum or difference of the corresponding ordinates of these curves. The circle and the parabola are shown by dotted lines in the accompanying figure, and the resultant curve by the continuous line.

EXAMPLES.

1. Trace the curve $$(x + y + 1)^2 = (1 - x)^5,$$
showing that there is a cusp of the first species at $(1, -2)$; also that all chords parallel to the axis of y are bisected by the line
$$x + y + 1 = 0.$$

2. Trace the curve $$r = a\sec\theta \pm a\cos\theta,$$
the radius vector being the sum or difference of the radii vectores of a straight line and a circle.

382. Newton's Diagram of Squares.

When a curve whose equation is algebraic and rational passes through the origin, it is frequently desirable to ascertain the shape of the curve in the immediate neighbourhood of the origin more accurately than can be predicted from a mere knowledge of the direction of the tangents, and also to form some idea of the limiting form of the curve at a great distance from the origin.

The following is a graphical method of determining what terms of an equation are to be retained or rejected in such cases :—

Let $Ax^p y^q$, $Bx^r y^s$ be any two terms of the equation of the curve ; and let us suppose them to be such that they are of the same order of magnitude. Take a pair of co-ordinate axes and mark down the positions of the points (p, q) (r, s), which we shall call P and R respectively. Then, since $x^p y^q$ and $x^r y^s$ are of the same order of magnitude, x^{p-r} and y^{s-q} are also of the same order, and therefore the order of x is that of $y^{\frac{s-q}{p-r}}$.

Now $\dfrac{s-q}{r-p} = \tan \theta$, where θ is the angle which the line PR makes with OX. So that the order of x is that of $y^{-\tan \theta}$, and therefore the order of the term $Ax^p y^q$ is that of $y^{q-p\tan \theta}$. Now

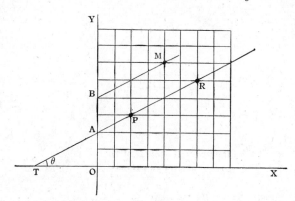

Fig. 79.

$q - p \tan \theta =$ the intercept OA made by the line PR upon OY, so that the order of the terms $Ax^p y^q$ and $Bx^r y^s$ is that of y^{OA} and is measured by the intercept OA.

Consider next any other term $Cx^m y^n$ in the equation. Let its graphical point (m, n) be denoted by M in the figure. Then the order of this term is that of

$$y^{n - m \tan \theta} \text{ or } y^{OB},$$

the line MB being drawn parallel to RP, cutting off the intercept OB on the axis of y. OB therefore graphically marks the order of this term, which may therefore be rejected in tracing near the origin in comparison with the terms denoted by the points P and R if OB be greater than OA; and in tracing the curve at a great distance from the origin it may be rejected if OB be less than OA. Thus if all the terms of the equation be represented graphically by the series of points $P, Q, R, S \ldots$ in the manner above described, and if when any two, say P and R, are chosen all the other points lie on the side of the line PR remote from the origin, they may all be rejected in tracing the portion of the curve in the immediate proximity of the origin; but if they all lie on the origin side of the line PR they may all be rejected in tracing the curve at an infinite distance from the origin.

Ex. If the equation be
$$x^2 y^3 + 2xy + 3x^4 y + x^2 y^2 + y^4 = 0,$$
the points A, B, C, D, E represent the 1st, 2nd, etc., terms respectively,

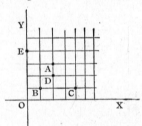

Fig. 80.

and a glance at the diagram will show that the

second and third ⎫ BC
and the   second and fifth ⎰ BE

are pairs which may be taken together in tracing near the origin, whilst the

first and third ⎫ AC
and the   first and fifth ⎰ AE

are pairs which may be taken together in approximating to the form of the curve at an infinite distance from the origin.

383. The above method is a modification of the one adopted in such cases by Newton, and is known as Newton's Parallelogram. A further slight variation on the same method is due to De Gua, and is known as De Gua's *Analytical Triangle*. [De Gua's *Usage de l'Analyse de Descartes*, Paris, 1740.]

VI. *To trace* $\qquad x^5 + y^5 - 5a^2x^2y = 0.$

(a) Newton's diagram shows at once that near the origin the first and third of these terms, or the second and third, may be taken together,

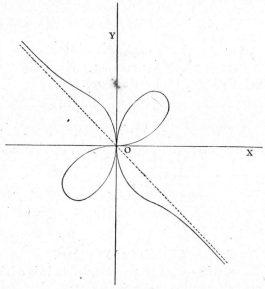

Fig. 81.

whilst at a great distance from the origin the first and second may be taken together. This indicates that at the origin the curve assumes the parabolic forms $\qquad y^2 = \pm ax\sqrt{5},$

$$x^3 = 5a^2y,$$

and that at infinity it approximates to the straight line $x + y = 0$, which is obviously the only asymptote.

(β) Moreover, the equation may be written

$$y = -x\left(1 - 5a^2\frac{y}{x^3}\right)^{\frac{1}{5}}$$

$$= -x + \frac{a^2y}{x^2} + \dots$$

$$= -x - \frac{a^2}{x} + \dots,$$

when in the limit $\qquad y = -x =$ a very large quantity.

Hence again $y = -x$ is an asymptote, but we gain the additional information that if x be negative and very large the ordinate of the curve is greater than the ordinate of the asymptote.

(γ) Since when the signs of x and y are both changed the equation remains of the same form there is symmetry in opposite quadrants.

(δ) Since

$$\frac{dy}{dx} = \frac{x(2a^2y - x^3)}{y^4 - a^2x^2},$$

we have

$$\frac{dy}{dx} = 0$$

at the points where the curve is intersected by the cubical parabola $2a^2y = x^3$ (which is easily traced), and by the axis of y; and

$$\frac{dy}{dx} = \infty,$$

where the curve is cut by either of the parabolas $y^2 = \pm ax$. The form of the equation is therefore that shown in Fig. 81.

EXAMPLES.

1. Trace $\qquad\qquad x^5 + y^5 = 5ax^2y^2,$

showing that at the origin there are two cusps of the first species, an asymptote $x + y = a$, two infinite branches below the asymptote, and a loop in the first quadrant.

2. Show that the curve $\quad y^6 - a^2x^2y^2 + x^6 = 0$

consists of four equal loops, one in each of the four quadrants and lying entirely within the circle $r = a$.

384. Polar Equations.   Order of Procedure.

In tracing a curve from its polar equation it is advisable to follow some such routine as the following :—

1. If possible *form a table* of corresponding values of r and θ which satisfy the equation of the curve. Consider both positive and negative values of θ.

2. Examine whether there be symmetry. If a change of sign of θ leaves the equation unaltered the curve is symmetrical about the initial line. If only even powers of r occur the curve is symmetrical about the origin and the pole is a "centre."

3. Obtain the *value of tan ϕ*, Art. 202. This will indicate the direction of the tangent at any point. The length of the polar subtangent is often useful, Art. 203.

4. Examine whether any values of θ exist which give an infinite value of r. If so, find whether the curve has *asymptotes* in such directions (Art. 265) and find their equations.

5. Examine whether there be an *asymptotic circle* (Art. 270).

6. Find the positions of the *points of inflexion* (Art. 283).

7. It will frequently be obvious from the equation of the curve that the values of r or θ are *confined between certain limits.* If such exist they should be ascertained.

E.g., if $r = a \sin n\theta$, it is clear that r must lie in magnitude between the limits 0 and a, and the curve lie wholly within the circle $r = a$.

8. It may be useful to know too whether the curve is convex or concave to the pole at certain points. This can be tested by Art. 282.

385. Curves of the Class $r = a \sin n\theta$.

These curves were called Rhodoneae by the Abbé Grandi from a fancied resemblance to rose-petals.*

VII. *To trace* $\qquad r = a \sin 5\theta$.

(a) We have the following table of corresponding values of r and θ:—

Values of θ	0	Intermed. Values.	$\dfrac{\pi}{10}$	Intermed. Values.	$\dfrac{2\pi}{10}$	Intermed. Values.	$\dfrac{3\pi}{10}$	Intermed. Values.	$\dfrac{4\pi}{10}$	Intermed. Values.
Corresponding Values of r	0	Pos. and Incr.	a	Pos. and Decr.	0	Neg.	$-a$	Neg.	0	Pos.

Values of θ	$\dfrac{5\pi}{10}$		$\dfrac{6\pi}{10}$		$\dfrac{7\pi}{10}$		$\dfrac{8\pi}{10}$	etc.
Corresponding Values of r	a	Pos.	0	Neg.	$-a$	Neg.	0	etc.

(β) r is never greater than a, and there is no asymptote.

(γ) $\tan \phi = \frac{1}{5} \tan 5\theta$, and therefore vanishes whenever r vanishes and $= \infty$ whenever $r = \pm a$. The curve therefore consists of a series of similar loops as shown in Fig. 82, all being arranged symmetrically about the origin and lying entirely within a circle whose centre is at the pole and radius a.

386. Any other curve of the class

$$r = a \sin n\theta$$

may be traced in a similar manner.

---

* *Flores Geometrici* and *Phil. Trans.* for 1723, referred to by D. F. Gregory, *Examples*, p. 185.

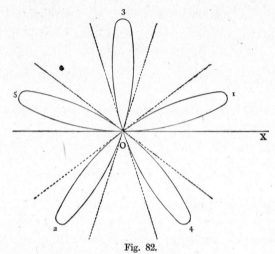

Fig. 82.

We annex a figure of the curve

$$r = a \sin 6\theta \text{ (fig. 83)}.$$

It will be noticed for this class of curves that if *n be odd there are n loops*, whilst if *n be even there are 2n loops.*   This will

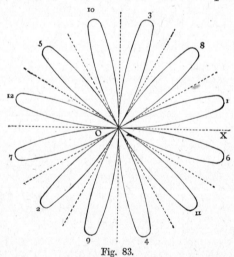

Fig. 83.

be easily seen from the *order of description* of the loops, which we have denoted by the numerals 1, 2, 3 ..., in the figures.

387. Curves of the class

$$r \sin n\theta = a$$

belong to a group of curves known as Cotes's Spirals and are inverse to the above species. Their forms are therefore obvious, going to ∞ along an asymptote whenever the radius of the companion curve $r = a \sin n\theta$ vanishes, and touching $r = a \sin n\theta$

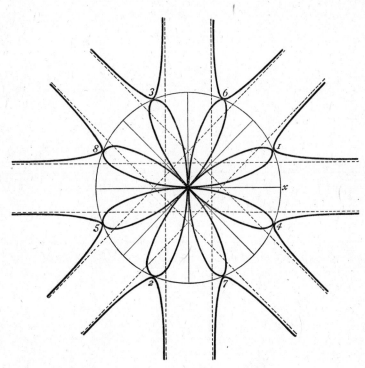

Fig. 84.

at the extremity of each loop. Since the polar subtangents corresponding to the values of θ for which r becomes infinite (viz. $n\theta = \kappa\pi$) are given by

$$-\frac{d\theta}{du} = -\frac{a}{n \cos \kappa\pi},$$

the asymptotes are not radial but can at once be drawn. We give in illustration a tracing of the curves

$$r = a \sin 4\theta,$$
$$a = r \sin 4\theta,$$

with the asymptotes of the latter in one figure (Fig. 84).

388. Class $r^n = a^n \cos n\theta.$

The class of curves of which
$$r^n = a^n \cos n\theta$$
is the type, embraces, as has been previously noticed, several important and well known curves. For instance, we get Bernoulli's lemniscate ($n=2$), the circle ($n=1$), the cardioide ($n=\frac{1}{2}$), the parabola ($n=-\frac{1}{2}$), the straight line ($n=-1$), the rectangular hyperbola ($n=-2$).

VIII. *To trace* $\qquad\qquad r^2 = a^2 \cos 2\theta$ (*Bernoulli's Lemniscate*).

(α) Negative values of $\cos 2\theta$ give imaginary values of r. Hence the only real portions of the curve lie in the two quadrants bounded by $\theta = -\dfrac{\pi}{4}$ and $\theta = +\dfrac{\pi}{4}$, and by $\theta = \dfrac{3\pi}{4}$ and $\theta = \dfrac{5\pi}{4}.$

(β) $\qquad\qquad\qquad r=0$ when $\theta = \pm\dfrac{\pi}{4}$ or $\dfrac{3\pi}{4}$ or $\dfrac{5\pi}{4},$

and $\qquad\qquad\qquad\quad = \pm a$ when $\theta = 0$ or $\pi.$

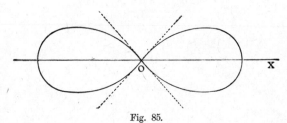

Fig. 85.

(γ) Since the only power of r occurring is even, the curve is symmetrical about the origin. Again, since the equation is unaltered by writing $-\theta$ for θ, the curve is obviously symmetrical about the initial line.

Also, r increases from $\theta = -\dfrac{\pi}{4}$ to 0 and decreases again from $\theta = 0$ to $\dfrac{\pi}{4}$ and is nowhere infinite or in fact greater than a.

The curve therefore consists of two similar loops as shown in Fig. 85.

Other curves of this species may be treated in a similar manner. It will be easily seen that if n be fractional $\left(=\dfrac{p}{q}\right)$, the curve will have p portions arranged symmetrically about the origin.

For example, in the curve $\qquad r^{\frac{3}{5}} = a^{\frac{3}{5}} \cos\dfrac{3}{5}\theta$

we have the following scheme of values for r and θ :—

θ	0	$\dfrac{5\pi}{6}$	$\dfrac{10\pi}{6}$	$\dfrac{15\pi}{6}$	$\dfrac{20\pi}{6}$	$\dfrac{25\pi}{6}$	$\dfrac{30\pi}{6}$	etc.
r	a	0	$-a$	0	a	0	$-a$	etc.

whence we obtain a figure with three equal loops, the whole lying within a circle whose radius is a and centre at the origin (Fig. 86).

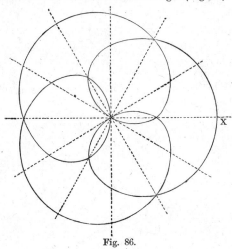

Fig. 86.

EXAMPLES.

1. Trace the curves $\quad r=a\cos 2\theta, \quad r\cos 2\theta=a,$
$$r=a\cos 3\theta, \qquad\qquad r=a\cos 4\theta.$$

2. Trace $\qquad\qquad r^3=a^3\cos 3\theta, \quad r^3\cos 3\theta=a^3,$
$$r^{\frac{1}{3}}=a^{\frac{1}{3}}\cos\tfrac{1}{3}\theta, \quad r^{\frac{1}{3}}\cos\tfrac{1}{3}\theta=a^{\frac{1}{3}},$$
$$r^{\frac{3}{4}}=a^{\frac{3}{4}}\cos\tfrac{3}{4}\theta, \quad r^{\frac{3}{4}}\cos\tfrac{3}{4}\theta=a^{\frac{3}{4}}.$$

3. Trace the curve $\qquad y^2(x^2+a^2)=x^2(a^2-x^2).$ [I. C. S., 1885.]

Show that the abscissa corresponding to any given central radius vector is equal to the corresponding radius vector in Bernoulli's Lemniscate, and hence that the curve consists of two loops passing through the origin and resembling those of the Lemniscate.

IX. *To trace* $\qquad\qquad r=\dfrac{a\theta}{1+\theta}.$

(*a*) By giving a set of values to θ we have the following table :—

Values of θ in Circular Measure	∞	4	3	2	1	$\frac{1}{2}$	$\frac{1}{4}$	0	$-\frac{1}{4}$	$-\frac{1}{2}$
Values of r	a	$\frac{4a}{5}$	$\frac{3a}{4}$	$\frac{2a}{3}$	$\frac{a}{2}$	$\frac{a}{3}$	$\frac{a}{5}$	0	$-\frac{a}{3}$	$-a$

Values of θ in Circular Measure	$-\frac{3}{4}$	-1	$-\frac{5}{4}$	$-\frac{4}{3}$	$-\frac{3}{2}$	-2	-3	-4	-10	$-\infty$
Values of r	$-3a$	∞	$5a$	$4a$	$3a$	$2a$	$\frac{3a}{2}$	$\frac{4a}{3}$	$\frac{10a}{9}$	a

(β) Since we may write the equation

$$r = \frac{a}{1 + \dfrac{1}{\theta}},$$

when θ becomes very large, either positively or negatively, the form of the curve approximates to that of an asymptotic circle $r = a$, which it approaches both from within and without.

(γ) Art. 265 shows that $\quad r \sin(\theta + 1) + a = 0$

is an asymptote to the curve. This line touches the asymptotic circle and is shown by the dotted straight line in the figure.

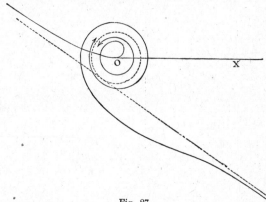

Fig. 87.

(δ) The points of inflexion (Art. 283) are given by the equation

$$\theta^3 + \theta^2 + 2 = 0,$$

an equation which has one real root which lies between $\theta = -1$ and $\theta = -2$. The curve is therefore that shown in Fig. 87.

EXAMPLES.

1. Trace $\qquad\qquad r = \dfrac{a\theta^2}{\theta^2 + 1},$

showing that it lies entirely within the circle $r = a$, which is an asymptotic circle; also, that there is a cusp of the first species at the origin.

2. Trace $\qquad\qquad r = \dfrac{a\theta^2}{\theta^2 - 1}.$

Show that there are two linear asymptotes and an asymptotic circle; also a cusp of the first species at the origin and a point of inflexion when $\theta^2 = 3$.

EXAMPLES.

1. Show that the curve $\quad y^2 = x^2 \dfrac{a^2 + x^2}{a^2 - x^2}$

consists of two branches each passing through the origin and extending to infinity, and that the whole curve is contained between two asymptotes parallel to the axis of y.

2. Show that the curve $\quad y^2 = x^2 \dfrac{x^2 - 4a^2}{x^2 - a^2}$

has two infinite branches passing through the origin and lying between the asymptotes $x = \pm a$, and that there are in addition two other infinite branches resembling those of the hyperbola

$$x^2 - y^2 = 4a^2.$$

3. Show that the curve $\quad x^3 + y^3 = a^3$

consists of one infinite branch running to the asymptote $x + y = 0$ at each end and cutting the axes at right angles at the points $(a, 0)$, $(0, a)$ at which there are points of inflexion.

4. Show that the curve $\quad x^3 + y^3 = 3axy$

consists of one infinite branch running to the asymptote $x + y + a = 0$ at each end and lying on the upper side of that line. Also, that the axes of co-ordinates are tangents at the origin, and that there is a loop in the first quadrant. This curve is called the Folium of Descartes.

5. Trace the curves

$\qquad$ (a) $x^3 + y^3 = a^2 x.$

$\qquad$ (β) $x^3 + y^3 = 2ax^2.$

$\qquad$ (γ) $ay^2 = x(a^2 - x^2).$

6. Show that the curve

$$ay^2 = x^2 y + x^3$$

has a cusp of the first species at the origin and an asymptote $x + y = a$ cutting the curve at $\left(\dfrac{a}{2}, \dfrac{a}{2}\right)$. Trace the curve.

7. Trace the curves

$\qquad$ (a) $ay^2 - 2axy + x^3 = 0,$

$\qquad$ (β) $y^3 + axy + bx^2 = 0,$

a and b both being positive quantities.

8. Trace $\qquad xy^2 = 4a^2(2a - x).$ (The Witch.)

9. Trace the curve $\qquad y^2(2a - x) = x^3.$ (Cissoid of Diocles.)

10. Trace $\qquad \left(\dfrac{y}{x+a}\right)^3 = \dfrac{x - a}{x + 2a},$

and show that the oblique asymptote cuts the curve at an angle $\tan^{-1} 8$

11. Trace $$2x(x^2+y^2)=a(2x^2+y^2)$$

and find by polars the co-ordinates of the points of inflexion.

12. Trace $$y(a^2+x^2)=a^2x,$$

showing that there are points of contrary flexure where $x=0$ or $\pm a\sqrt{3}$, that the tangent is parallel to the axis of x where $x=\pm a$, and that the axis of x is an asymptote.

13. Trace $$x^2y^2=a^2(x^2-y^2),$$

showing that the curve lies entirely between its asymptotes $y=\pm a$, and that its tangents at the origin are $y=\pm x$.

14. Trace the curve $(x^2-a^2)(y^2-b^2)=a^2b^2$.

15. Trace $$x^4=a^2(x^2-y^2).$$

16. Trace $$(y^2-a^2)^2=x^2(x^2-2a^2).$$

17. Trace $$axy=x^3-a^3.\quad\text{(The Trident.)}$$

18. Trace the curve $x^4-2mx^2y^2+y^4=a^4$

when m is respectively greater than, equal to, and less than unity, and also when m is zero.   [LONDON, 1880.]

19. Trace $$y^2=x^2\frac{x+a}{x-a}.$$

20. Trace $$y^2=x^2\frac{x^2+a^2}{x^2-a^2}.$$

21. Trace $$x(x+y)^2=a(x-y)^2.\qquad\text{[I. C. S., 1879.]}$$

22. Trace $$x^3=y(x-a)^2.\qquad\text{[OXFORD, 1876.]}$$

23. Trace $$\left(\frac{x}{y-a}\right)^2=\frac{y-a}{y+a}.\qquad\text{[H. C. S., 1881.]}$$

24. Find the multiple points on the curve

$$2(x^4+y^4)+5x^2y^2+4a^4=6a^2(x^2+y^2)$$

and the directions of the tangents at those points.   [H. C. S., 1881.] Also trace the curve.

25. Trace the curve $x^3+y^3+3cxy=a^3$,

and prove that as c diminishes to a the ultimate form of the loop is that of an ellipse whose eccentricity $=\sqrt{\frac{2}{3}}$.   [MATH. TRIPOS.]

26. Trace $$(x-y)^2(x+y)(2x+y)=a^2y^2.\qquad\text{[CAMB., 1879.]}$$

27. Trace the curve $r=a(1+\cos\theta)$.   (Cardioide.)

28. Trace $r = a + b \cos \theta$. (The Limaçon of Pascal.)

29. Trace $r = a(2 \cos \theta \pm 1)$. (The Trisectrix.)

30. Trace the following spirals :—

    (a) $r = a\theta$. (Spiral of Archimedes.)

    (β) $r\theta = a$. (The Hyperbolic or Reciprocal Spiral.)

    (γ) $r^2\theta = a^2$. (The Lituus.)

    (δ) $r = ae^{m\theta}$. (The Logarithmic or Equiangular Spiral.)

Show that in each case there is an infinite number of convolutions round the pole, and that $r \sin \theta = a$ is an asymptote to (β) and the initial line an asymptote to (γ).

31. Trace the curves

$$r = a \cos 5\theta, \quad r \cos 5\theta = a, \quad r = a \cos \tfrac{1}{5}\theta.$$

32. Trace the curves

$$r^{\frac{2}{3}} = a^{\frac{2}{3}} \cos \tfrac{2}{3}\theta, \quad r^{\frac{2}{3}} = a^{\frac{2}{3}} \sec \tfrac{2}{3}\theta, \quad r^{\frac{2}{5}} = a^{\frac{2}{5}} \cos \tfrac{2}{5}\theta.$$

What is the relation between them ?   [CAMB., 1876.]

33. Trace the curve $\theta = \dfrac{a}{r - a}$,

showing that a line parallel to the initial line at a distance a above it is an asymptote. Show also that there is an asymptotic circle $r = a$.

34. Trace $r = a\dfrac{\theta + \sin \theta}{\theta - \sin \theta}$.

Show that this curve has an asymptotic circle ; also that as each branch of the curve comes from infinity it approaches the asymptotic circle from the outside on one side of the initial line and from the inside upon the other.

35. Trace $r = 2a\dfrac{\sin^2\theta}{\cos \theta}$ (The Cissoid)

from the polar equation.

36. Trace $r = a\dfrac{\theta - a}{\theta + a}$.

37. Trace $r\theta^2 = \tan \theta$, from $\theta = 0$ to $\theta = 2\pi$.   [OXFORD, 1876.]

38. Trace $r^3 \sin 3(\theta - a) = \sin \theta - \sin a$.   [CAMB., 1879.]

39. Trace the " curve of sines "

$$y = b \sin \frac{x}{a}.$$

40. Trace $y = e^{-\lambda x} \tan \mu x.$

41. Trace $r = \dfrac{a}{\theta^5 - 1}$

for positive values of θ.

                    [TRIN. COLL. CAMB., 1873.]

42. Trace
$$r = \frac{a}{1 - \sin 2\theta}.$$
[OXFORD.]

43. Trace $\quad (x+a)^2(y-a) + (y+a)^2(x-a) = 0.$ [OXFORD.]

44. Trace
$$y^2 = c^2 \frac{(x+a)(x+b)}{(x-a)(x-b)}.$$

45. Trace
$$\left.\begin{array}{l} x = a(1 - \cos \theta) \\ y = a\theta \end{array}\right\}.$$

(The companion to the Cycloid.)

46. Trace
$$y = c \cosh \frac{x}{c}. \quad \text{(The Catenary.)}$$

47. Trace
$$y = x^2 + \cosh x.$$

48. Trace
$$x^2 y^2 = (a + y)^2 (b^2 - y^2),$$
or
$$r = a \operatorname{cosec} \theta \pm b.$$

(The Conchoid of Nicomedes.)

49. Trace $\quad \{y^2 + (a+x)^2\}\{y^2 + (a-x)^2\} = a^2 b^2,$

examining the cases   (1) $a < b.$

       (2) $a = b.$ (Lemniscate of Bernoulli.)

       (3) $a > b.$ (Cassini's Ovals.)

50. Trace $\quad\quad y^4 + x^2 y^2 + 2y^3 - x^3 = 0.$ [CRAMER.]

51. Trace

$r = a(\cos a \cos \theta - \frac{1}{3} \cos 3a \cos 3\theta + \frac{1}{5} \cos 5a \cos 5\theta - \ldots).$

[MATH. TRIPOS, 1878.]

52. Trace $\quad\quad\quad y = e^{-x^2}.$ (The Probability Curve.)

53. Trace the curves

    (a) $y^4 - axy^2 + x^4 = 0.$

    (β) $a^3 y^2 - 2abx^2 y - x^5 = 0.$

    (γ) $y^5 + ax^4 - b^2 xy^2 = 0.$ [CRAMER.]

54. Trace $\quad\quad x^4 - ax^2 y + by^3 = 0.$ [DE GUA.]

55. Trace   (a) $\; x^5 + y^5 = 2a^3 xy.$

    (β) $\; x^5 + y^5 = xy(a^2 x + b^2 y).$ [FROST.]

CHAPTER XIII.

ON SOME WELL-KNOWN CURVES.

389. The present chapter is devoted to a short description of some special curves whose properties have been investigated and which have acquired historical importance, being associated for the most part with the names of some of the greatest Geometers of past ages. It has been considered advisable to introduce at this point an enumeration of their principal properties for the sake of reference, though unnecessary to give in all cases full proofs of the results stated as the student will be readily able to supply them. In some cases several of these properties will be found to have been already proved or suggested for proof for the student in earlier pages.

ʼ THE CYCLOID.

390. This curve appears to have been discovered in the fifteenth century, and is associated with the names of Galileo, Descartes, Wren, Pascal, Huyghens, and many others. It derives its principal interest from its importance in Mechanics.

391. DEF. *When a circle rolls in a plane along a given straight line, the locus traced out by any point on the circumference of the rolling circle is called a* CYCLOID.

392. Description of the Curve.

The nature of the motion shows that there is an infinite number of cusps arranged at equal distances along the given straight line. It is usual to confine the name cycloid to the portion of the curve lying between two consecutive cusps.

Let A, B be two consecutive cusps, ACB the arc of the cycloid lying between them. The line AB along which the circle rolls is called the *base*. Let GPT be the rolling circle, G the point of contact, GT the diameter through G, and P the point attached to the circumference, which by its motion traces the cycloid. The circle GPT is called the *generating circle*. Let C be the point of the curve at greatest distance from AB; this point is called the *vertex*. Let CX be the tangent at C,

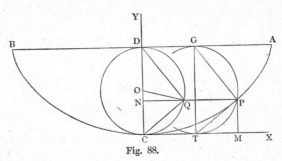

Fig. 88.

and CY the normal, obviously bisecting the base AB in the point D. We shall take these lines as co-ordinate axes. It is clear that the curve is symmetrical about CY.

393. Tangent and Normal.

Since a circle may be considered as the limit of an inscribed regular polygon with an indefinitely large number of sides, the circle GPT may be supposed to be for the instant turning about an angular point of this polygon situated at G. Hence the motion of the point P is instantaneously perpendicular to the line PG, which is therefore the direction of the normal at P. Moreover, since this motion is in the direction of PT, PT is the tangent at P to the locus of P.

394. Equations of the Cycloid.

Let DQC be the circle described upon DC for diameter and let O be its centre. Draw PM, PN perpendicular to CX and CY respectively, the latter cutting the circle DQC in Q. Join DQ, OQ, CQ.

Now, since the circle rolls *without sliding* along the line AB, every point of the circle comes successively into contact with the straight line, so that the length of AD is half of the circumference of the circle, and the portion

$$GA = \text{arc } GP = \text{arc } DQ.$$

Hence the remainder $DG = \text{arc } CQ.$

Now, $PQCT$, $PQDG$ are parallelograms; whence, if a be the radius of the generating circle and θ the angle COQ,

$$PQ = DG = \text{arc } CQ = a\theta.$$

Hence, if x, y be co-ordinates of P,

$$\left. \begin{aligned} x &= CM = NQ + QP = a(\theta + \sin \theta) \\ y &= CN = CO - NO = a(1 - \cos \theta) \end{aligned} \right\} \quad \dots\dots\dots\dots (\text{A})$$

From these equations the Cartesian equation may be at once obtained by eliminating θ; the result being

$$x = a \text{ vers}^{-1}\frac{y}{a} + \sqrt{2ay - y^2}, \dots\dots\dots\dots\dots (\text{B})$$

but from the form of the result the equation is not so useful as the two equations marked (A).

395. Length of the arc CP.

Since

$$\left. \begin{aligned} x &= a(\theta + \sin \theta) \\ y &= a(1 - \cos \theta) \end{aligned} \right\},$$

we obtain

$$\left. \begin{aligned} dx &= a(1 + \cos \theta)d\theta \\ dy &= a \sin \theta d\theta \end{aligned} \right\},$$

squaring and adding, $ds^2 = dx^2 + dy^2 = 2a^2(1 + \cos \theta)d\theta^2$

$$= 4a^2\cos^2\frac{\theta}{2}d\theta^2,$$

or

$$ds = 2a \cos \frac{\theta}{2}d\theta,$$

and upon integration $\quad s = 4a \sin \frac{\theta}{2}, \dots\dots\dots\dots\dots (\text{C})$

the constant of integration vanishing if s be measured from C, so that s and θ vanish together.

Again, since chord $CQ = 2a \sin \frac{\theta}{2}$,

we have $\quad\quad$ arc $CP = 2$ chord CQ. $\dots\dots\dots\dots\dots (\text{D})$

Further, since $\quad\quad y = 2a \sin^2\frac{\theta}{2}$,

$$s = 4a\sqrt{\frac{y}{2a}} = \sqrt{8ay}. \dots\dots\dots\dots\dots (\text{E})$$

396. Geometrical Proofs.

These results may be established by geometry as follows:—

Let TPG be any position of the generating circle, G being the point of contact, GT the diameter through G, and P the tracing point. Let the circle roll through an infinitesimal distance till the point of contact comes to G'. Let the circle in rolling turn through an infinitesimal angle equal to POQ, OQ being a radius of the circle, and let P come to P'. Then QP' is parallel and equal to GG', and therefore to the arc QP. PP'

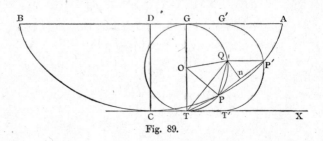

Fig. 89.

is ultimately the tangent at P and therefore ultimately in a straight line with TP. Draw Qn at right angles to PP'; then Tn and TQ are ultimately equal, and Pn is therefore the increase in the chord TP in rolling from G to G'. Moreover PP' is ultimately the increase of arc, and since in the limit $QP' =$ arc $QP =$ chord QP, and Qn is drawn perpendicularly to PP', n is the middle point of PP', and therefore the rate of growth of the arc CP is double that of the chord TP, and they begin their growth together at C. Hence arc $CP = 2$ chord TP.

397. Intrinsic Equation.

If in Fig. 88 $PTX = \psi$, we have $\psi = \dfrac{\theta}{2}$; whence the intrinsic equation of the cycloid is $s = 4a \sin \psi$.

398. Radius of Curvature.

The formula of Art. 322 gives

$$\rho = \frac{ds}{d\psi} = 4a \cos \psi = 4a \cos \frac{\theta}{2} = 2PG,$$

i.e.,   radius of curvature $= 2$. normal.

399. Evolute.

By Art. 347 the intrinsic equation of the evolute of the curve $s = f(\psi)$ is $\qquad s = f'(\psi)$.

Applying this, we have for the evolute of the above cycloid

$$s = 4a \cos \psi,$$

which clearly represents an equal cycloid (see Art. 349).

400. Geometrical Proofs.

These results may also be established geometrically as follows :—

Let AD be half the base and CD the axis of a given cycloid APC. Produce CD to F, making DF equal to CD, and through F draw FE parallel to DA. Through any point G on the base draw TGG' parallel to CD and cutting the tangent at C in

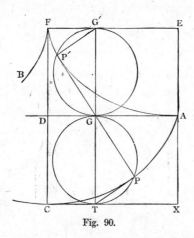

Fig. 90.

T and the line FE in G'. On GT and $G'G$ as diameters describe circles, the former cutting the cycloid in the tracing point P. Join PT, PG and produce PG to meet the circle $GP'G'$ in P' and join $P'G'$. Then obviously the arc $G'P' =$ arc $PT = DG = FG'$, and therefore the point P' lies on a cycloid, equal to the original cycloid, with cusp at F and vertex at A. Moreover $P'G$ is a tangent to this cycloid and $P'G'$ a normal. The cycloid FA is therefore the envelope of the normals of the cycloid AC and therefore its *evolute ;* and P' is the *centre of curvature* corresponding to the point P on the original cycloid.

If, therefore, a string of length equal to the arc $FP'A$ have one extremity attached to a fixed point at F the other end, when the string is unwound from the curve $FP'A$, will trace out the cycloidal arc APC. Thus a heavy particle may be made to *oscillate along a cycloidal arc*, by allowing the suspending string to wrap alternately upon two rigid cycloidal cheeks such as FA, FB.

Moreover, since PP' is obviously by its construction bisected at G, the radius of curvature at any point of a cycloid is *double the length of the normal*.

401. Area bounded by the Cycloid and its Base.

Let PGP', $QG'Q'$ be two contiguous normals. Then G, G' are their middle points, and therefore ultimately the elementary area $GPQG'$ is treble the elementary area $P'GG'Q'$. Hence, summing all such elements, the area $APCD$ is treble the area

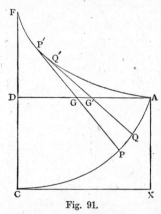

Fig. 91.

$ADFP'$; *i.e.*, the area of the cycloid is three-fourths of the circumscribing rectangle, for the area of $ADFP'$ is equal to the area $CXAP$.

Now the length of $AD =$ half the circumference of the circle

$$= \pi a.$$

Hence the rectangle $AXCD = \pi a . 2a = 2\pi a^2$, and therefore the

semicycloidal area $APCD = \frac{3}{4} . 2\pi a^2 = \frac{3}{2}\pi a^2$,

and the area bounded by the whole cycloid and its base $= 3\pi a^2$, and is therefore *three times the area of the generating circle*.

THE TROCHOIDS.

402. If the point P (in Art. 392) be attached to the rolling circle at a point not upon the circumference, but at a distance b from the centre, the curve traced is called a *curtate* or a *prolate* cycloid according as b is greater or less than the radius a.

These curves as a class are called Trochoids.

It will be obvious from the mode of description that if $b > a$ the series of cusps which characterize the ordinary cycloid are replaced by a series of nodes and loops.

403. The equations of a trochoid referred to the same axes as the cycloid in Art. 394 will obviously be

$$\left. \begin{array}{l} x = a\theta + b \sin \theta \\ y = a - b \cos \theta \end{array} \right\}.$$

EPI- AND HYPO-CYCLOIDS AND EPI- AND HYPO-TROCHOIDS.

404. When a circle rolls without sliding upon the circumference of a fixed circle, the path of a point attached to the circumference of the rolling circle is called an epi- or a hypo-cycloid according as the moving circle rolls upon the exterior or the interior of the other.

The path of any other carried point is called an epi- or a hypo-trochoid.

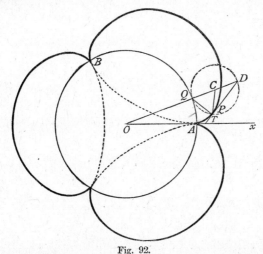

Fig. 92.

405. The figure (92) represents the three-cusped epi- and hypo-cycloids formed when the ratio of the radius of the rolling circle to that of the fixed one is $1:3$.

406. Let the radii be respectively b and a. In the figure the rolling circle with its carried point P is represented as tracing the epi-cycloid. Let O be the fixed centre, Q the point of contact, A the point with which P is originally in contact, C the centre of the moving circle. Join OC, cutting the rolling circle in D. Join QP, CP, and DP, the latter cutting the initial radius OA, which we choose for x-axis, in T.

Then, as in Art. 393, PQ is the normal and PT the tangent to the path of P.

Let $$Q\hat{O}A = \theta \text{ and } Q\hat{C}P = \phi.$$

Then, since $$\text{arc } QP = \text{arc } QA,$$

we have $$b\phi = a\theta.$$

Hence $$C\hat{D}P = \frac{\phi}{2} = \frac{a\theta}{2b}$$

and $$\psi = P\hat{T}x = \theta + \frac{\phi}{2} = \frac{a+2b}{2b}\theta.$$

407. Again, CP makes with the x-axis the angle

$$\theta + \phi = \frac{a+b}{b}\theta.$$

Hence the equations of the curve are

$$\left. \begin{aligned} x &= (a+b)\cos\theta - b\cos\frac{a+b}{b}\theta \\ y &= (a+b)\sin\theta - b\sin\frac{a+b}{b}\theta \end{aligned} \right\} \quad \ldots\ldots\ldots\ldots\ldots\text{(A)}$$

408. If the carried point P be not upon the circumference but at a distance mb from C it is plain that the corresponding equations for the epitrochoid will be

$$\left. \begin{aligned} x &= (a+b)\cos\theta - mb\cos\frac{a+b}{b}\theta \\ y &= (a+b)\sin\theta - mb\sin\frac{a+b}{b}\theta \end{aligned} \right\} \quad \ldots\ldots\ldots\ldots\ldots\text{(B)}$$

409. The path of the carried point when the moving circle rolls upon the interior of the circumference is obtained from equations (A) or (B) respectively by changing the sign of b.

410. If p be the perpendicular from O upon the tangent PT to the epicycloid (Fig. 92) we have

$$p = OD \sin \frac{\phi}{2} = (a+2b) \sin \frac{a\psi}{a+2b}.$$

This furnishes us with the tangential-polar equation.

411. From the triangle OCP (or otherwise)

$$r^2 = (a+b)^2 + b^2 - 2(a+b)b \cos \phi$$
$$= (a+b)^2 + b^2 - 2(a+b)b\left(1 - 2\sin^2\frac{\phi}{2}\right)$$
$$= a^2 + 4(a+b)b\left(\frac{p}{a+2b}\right)^2,$$

the pedal equation.

412. Differentiating equations (A)

$$\frac{dx}{d\theta} = -(a+b)\sin\theta + (a+b)\sin\frac{a+b}{b}\theta,$$

$$\frac{dy}{d\theta} = (a+b)\cos\theta - (a+b)\cos\frac{a+b}{b}\theta.$$

Hence, squaring, adding, and extracting the root,

$$\frac{ds}{d\theta} = \pm 2(a+b)\sin\frac{a}{2b}\theta,$$

Hence
$$s = \frac{4b(a+b)}{a}\cos\frac{a}{2b}\theta,$$

s being measured from the vertex, where $\theta = \pi b/a$.

Thus
$$s = \frac{4b(a+b)}{a}\cos\frac{a}{a+2b}\psi$$

is the intrinsic equation to the curve.

This may also be obtained quickly by applying the formula $\frac{ds}{d\psi} = p + \frac{d^2p}{d\psi^2}$ and integrating.

These results will (as in Art. 409) all remain true for the hypocycloid when the sign of b is changed; or they may be obtained independently.

413. Thus any epi- or hypo-cycloid may be represented by any of the equations, $p = A \sin B\psi$, or $A \cos B\psi$,

$$s = A \sin B\psi, \text{ or } A \cos B\psi,$$
$$r^2 = A + Bp^2,$$

the constants A and B being readily determinable in any particular case by aid of the preceding Articles.

414. Any of these formulae give the radius of curvature. For example, taking $p = A \sin B\psi$, we have

$$\rho = p + \frac{d^2 p}{d\psi^2} = A(1 - B^2)\sin B\psi \propto p,$$

i.e., the radius of curvature varies as the central perpendicular.

415. The evolute of any epi- or hypo-cycloid is a similar epi- or hypo-cycloid. (See Art. 349.)

416. The equations of the tangent and normal at any point on the curve where $\theta = a$ may be written

$$\left. \begin{aligned} x \sin \frac{a+2b}{2b}a - y \cos \frac{a+2b}{2b}a &= (a+2b)\sin \frac{a}{2b}a \\ x \cos \frac{a+2b}{2b}a + y \sin \frac{a+2b}{2b}a &= a \cos \frac{a}{2b}a \end{aligned} \right\}.$$

417. The polar equations of the tangent and normal with O for pole and OA for initial line are therefore

$$\left. \begin{aligned} r \sin\left(\frac{aa}{2b} + a - \theta\right) &= (a+2b)\sin \frac{a}{2b}a \\ r \cos\left(\frac{aa}{2b} + a - \theta\right) &= a \cos \frac{a}{2b}a \end{aligned} \right\}.$$

If the initial line were chosen to bisect the arc joining two consecutive cusps A, B, we should have to change a to $a' + \dfrac{\pi b}{a}$ and θ to $\theta' + \dfrac{\pi b}{a}$. If this change be made, the equation of the normal becomes

$$r \sin\left(\frac{aa'}{2b} + a' - \theta'\right) = a \sin \frac{a}{2b}a',$$

which shows by comparison with the tangent that the normal touches another epicycloid formed by the rolling of a circle of radius B upon another of radius A where

$$A + 2B = a, \qquad \frac{A}{2B} = \frac{a}{2b},$$

i.e.,
$$A = \frac{a}{a+2b} \cdot a, \qquad B = \frac{a}{a+2b} \cdot b.$$

This also follows from Art. 341 and verifies the result of Art. 349.

418. Double method of generating Hypocycloids.

Changing the sign of b in Equations (A) the equations of the hypocycloid are

$$x = (a-b)\cos\theta + b\cos\frac{a-b}{b}\theta$$
$$y = (a-b)\sin\theta - b\sin\frac{a-b}{b}\theta$$ ....(C)

Writing $\dfrac{a+c}{2}$ for b and $\dfrac{a+c}{c}\theta'$ for θ, we have

$$x = \frac{a-c}{2}\cos\frac{a+c}{c}\theta' + \frac{a+c}{2}\cos\frac{a-c}{c}\theta'$$
$$y = \frac{a-c}{2}\sin\frac{a+c}{c}\theta' - \frac{a+c}{2}\sin\frac{a-c}{c}\theta'$$,

and it is evident that a change in the sign of c does not alter these equations. It follows therefore that the same hypocycloid can be generated by the rolling of either of the circles whose radii are $\dfrac{a \pm c}{2}$ upon a circle of radius a.

And if we write $a+c$ for b and make the same change for θ as above, the equations of the hypocycloid become

$$x = (a+c)\cos\theta' - c\cos\frac{a+c}{c}\theta',$$

$$y = (a+c)\sin\theta' - c\sin\frac{a+c}{c}\theta'.$$

These are the equations of an epicycloid. It appears then that the hypocycloid formed when the radius of the rolling circle is greater than that of the fixed circle may be regarded as an epicycloid generated by the rolling of a circle whose radius is the difference of the original radii.* This can also be shown geometrically.

419. If the ratio of $a:b$ be commensurable, there will be a finite number of cusps, the curve returning into itself.

The equations

$$x = (a-b)\cos\theta + b\cos\frac{a-b}{b}\theta$$
$$y = (a-b)\sin\theta - b\sin\frac{a-b}{b}\theta$$

---

* Peacock, *Examples*. Citing Euler, *Acta Petrop.*, 1784.

of the hypocycloid become, when $b = \frac{1}{2}a$,

$$\left.\begin{aligned} x &= a \cos \theta \\ y &= 0 \end{aligned}\right\},$$

indicating that the curve degenerates into a diameter of the fixed circle. This admits of easy geometrical proof.

If $b = \frac{1}{4}a$, we have

$$\left.\begin{aligned} x &= \frac{a}{4}(3 \cos \theta + \cos 3\theta) = a \cos^3\theta \\ y &= \frac{a}{4}(3 \sin \theta - \sin 3\theta) = a \sin^3\theta \end{aligned}\right\},$$

giving $$x^{\frac{2}{3}} + y^{\frac{2}{3}} = a^{\frac{2}{3}}$$

the four-cusped hypocycloid.

When $a = b$ the equations of the epicycloid reduce to

$$x = a(2 \cos \theta - \cos 2\theta),$$
$$y = a(2 \sin \theta - \sin 2\theta),$$

and after elimination of θ we obtain

$$(x^2 + y^2 - a^2)^2 = 4a^2\{(x-a)^2 + y^2\}.$$

If now the origin be transferred to the point $(a, 0)$ and the resulting equation transformed to polars, it will be apparent that the epicycloid becomes a cardioide (Art. 424).

The trochoidal curves corresponding to this case become limaçons.

It follows from Art. 415 that the evolute of a cardioide is also a cardioide.

420. The portion of the tangent to $x^{\frac{2}{3}} + y^{\frac{2}{3}} = a^{\frac{2}{3}}$ intercepted between the co-ordinate axes is of constant length.

The portion of the tangent of the three-cusped hypocycloid intercepted by the curve itself is of constant length.

421. It may be observed that the envelope of any line whose equation can be thrown into the form

$$x \cos a + y \sin a = c \sin na (= p),$$

being obtained by the elimination of a between this equation and $\qquad -x \sin a + y \cos a = nc \cos na,$

has for its pedal equation

$$r^2 = c^2\sin^2 na + n^2 c^2 \cos^2 na$$
$$= p^2 + n^2(c^2 - p^2),$$

or $\qquad r^2 = (1 - n^2)p^2 + n^2 c^2,$

and is therefore an epi- or hypo-cycloid.

422. The equation of the pedal of this curve is obviously

$$r = c \sin n\theta,$$

and therefore the polar reciprocal, which is the inverse of the pedal, is the Cotes's spiral

$$r \sin n\theta = \text{constant} \quad \text{(Art. 454)}.$$

423. The student is referred to Dr. Heath's *Optics*, Arts. 100 to 103, where epicycloids are shown to occur in certain cases as caustics by reflection from a bright circular arc.

The Limaçon of Pascal, the Cardioide, and the Trisectrix.

424. Take a circle OQD of which OD $(=b)$ is the diameter and E the centre. Let a straight rod PP' of any length $(2a)$ move in such a manner that its mid-point Q describes the given circle whilst the rod is constrained to pass through a fixed point O on the circumference. Its ends trace out the Limaçon.

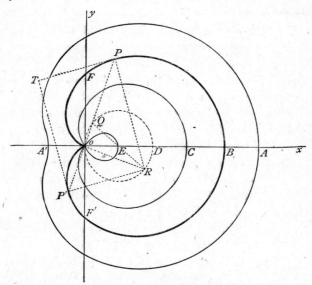

Fig. 93.

Obviously this rod can be constrained to move as described above by a simple mechanical contrivance.

Taking OD for initial line let r, θ be the polar co-ordinates of P, then evidently

$$r = QP + OQ = a + b \cos \theta \ldots\ldots\ldots\ldots\ldots\ldots(1)$$

Similarly $\qquad OP' = r' = a - b \cos \theta.$

This however is obtained at once from equation (1) by increasing θ by π. Hence P and P' describe the same curve. Evidently also any "focal chord" PP' is of constant length.

When $a = b$, the limaçon is called a cardioide from its heart-like shape. The curve then has a cusp at O. Other limaçons are of two classes according as a is $>$ or $< b$. The outer curve in the figure typifies the class for which a is $> b$. The dark curve on OB for diameter is the cardioide. The inner curve is a limaçon for which a is $< b$. There is on this class a node at O. The dotted curve is the circular locus of Q. The point P is shown in the figure as tracing the cardioide. The equations of the particular curves drawn in the figure are

$r = 2 \cos \theta$, $r = 1 + 2 \cos \theta$, $r = 2 + 2 \cos \theta$, $r = 3 + 2 \cos \theta$.

425. Considering the motion of the rod the following facts will be clear :—

(a) Since Q is moving along the tangent to the circle the instantaneous centre for the motion of the rod must lie somewhere in the normal QER.

(b) The motion of the point of the rod which is just passing through O can only be in the direction of the rod itself. Therefore the instantaneous centre must lie somewhere in a line OR drawn at right angles to the rod.

(c) The instantaneous centre must therefore be at R, the point on Q's circular locus which is diametrically opposite to Q.

(d) The motion of P and of P' is therefore at right angles to RP and RP' respectively. These lines are therefore the normals at P and P'.

(e) Thus in any limaçon the normals at the extremities of any focal chord intersect on a fixed circle.

(f) In the case of the cardioide $QP = QR = QP'$ and the normals at P and P' intersect at right angles.

(g) The tangents at the ends of the focal chord PP' (of the cardioide) also intersect at right angles, the figure $TPRP'$ forming a rectangle.

(*h*) Also in this case, since RQ if produced passes through T and $ET = 3ER =$ constant, the locus of intersection of ortho-tomic tangents (or "orth-optic" points) is a circle whose centre is E and radius three times that of the Q-circle.

426. The cardioide and the limaçon may also be generated as an epicycloid or an epitrochoid by the rolling of one circle upon another of equal radius. (Art. 419.)

427. These curves are also the first positive pedals of a circle with regard to an arbitrary point.

Take a circle, centre C and radius a. Let OP be a perpendicular from the pole upon the tangent at any point Q. Let $CO = b$, $OP = r$, $POC = \theta$. Draw CR at right angles to OP.

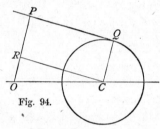

Fig. 94.

Then $$r = OR + RP = a + b\cos\theta.$$
When O lies upon the circumference of the circle we have $a = b$ and the pedal becomes a cardioide.

428. The equation $r = a + b\cos\theta$ shows that a limaçon is the inverse of a central conic with regard to the focus, and that a cardioide is the inverse of a parabola.

429. For some purposes it is a little more convenient to call the angle $POA' = \theta$ (Fig. 93), and the equation of the cardioide then becomes $r = a(1 - \cos\theta)$.
We have at once
$$\tan\phi = r\frac{d\theta}{dr} = \frac{1 - \cos\theta}{\sin\theta} = \tan\frac{\theta}{2},$$
or
$$\phi = \frac{\theta}{2},$$
i.e.,
$$O\widehat{P}T = \tfrac{1}{2}P\widehat{O}A'.$$

430. This property shows that the curves
$$r = a(1 - \cos\theta),$$
$$r = b(1 + \cos\theta),$$

whose axes are turned in opposite directions cut at right angles for all values of a and b.

Thus the "Orthogonal Trajectories" (*i.e.*, curves which cut at right angles) of the system of cardioides obtained by giving a different values in the first equation is the system of cardioides obtained by giving b different values in the second. This result may be obtained by inversion of the corresponding property for parabolas.

431. The particular limaçon shown with a node in Fig. 93, and whose equation is $\quad r = 1 + 2 \cos \theta$, is called the Trisectrix.

With centre at O (Fig. 93) and radius OE describe a circle. Lay off from OE any angle $E\hat{O}S$ less than four right angles, and let the bounding radius cut the circle (centre O) at S, and the chord ES cut the limaçon at J. Then it is easy to show that OJ trisects $E\hat{O}S$.*

The Curve of Sines, Harmonic Curve, Companion to the Cycloid.

432. Figure 95 is a graph of the equation
$$y = \sin x.$$

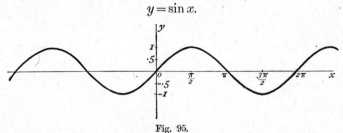

Fig. 95.

There are points of inflexion whenever the curve cuts the x-axis; also the curve lies entirely between the lines $y = \pm 1$.

433. The curve $y = m \sin x$ (sometimes referred to as the Harmonic Curve) only differs from the above in that its ordinates are each m times the corresponding ordinates of the Curve of Sines.

434. The companion to the cycloid
$$x = a\theta,$$
$$y = a(1 - \cos \theta),$$

---

* Azemar and Garnier, *Trisection de l'Angle*, Paris, 1809.   Cited by Peacock, *Examples*, p. 173.

differs from the cycloid in that, instead of producing the abscissa NQ to P (Fig. 88) to make the *produced* part

$$QP = \text{arc } CQ,$$

we make $\qquad NP = \text{arc } CQ.$

The equation may be written

$$y - a = a \sin\left(\frac{x}{a} - \frac{\pi}{2}\right),$$

and therefore the locus is the harmonic curve.

EXAMPLES.

Trace the curves

$y = \cos x,$	$y = \tan x,$	$y = \cot x,$	$y = \operatorname{cosec} x,$
$y = \sec x,$	$y = \sin x + \cos x,$	$y = \sin 3x,$	$y = e^x \sin x,$
$y = \sin(\pi \sin x),$	$y = \sin(\pi \cos x),$	$y = \cos(\pi \sin x),$	$y = \cos(\pi \cos x).$

THE CISSOID OF DIOCLES.

435. Let APB be a semicircle whose diameter is AB, BT the tangent at B, APT a straight line through A cutting the

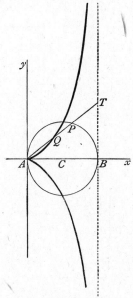

Fig. 96.

semicircle and the tangent in P and T. Take Q upon AT such that $AQ = PT$. The locus of Q is the cissoid.

436. The Cartesian equation with A for origin and AB for x-axis is
$$y^2(2a-x)=x^3.$$

The polar equation is
$$r=2a\sin^2\theta/\cos\theta.$$

437. The curve is the *first positive pedal* with regard to the vertex, of the parabola $y^2+4bx=0$, where $b=2a$.

It is also the *inverse* with regard to the vertex of the parabola $y^2=4bx$, the constant of inversion being the semi-latus rectum.

438. The curve was invented by Diocles in the sixth century for the construction of two mean proportionals between two given lines. Take BC, one extreme, as the radius and construct the cissoid. Erect a perpendicular CR to CB through the centre C equal to the other extreme. Join BR cutting the cissoid at Q; and let AQ produced if necessary cut CR at S. Then CS is the first of the mean proportionals.

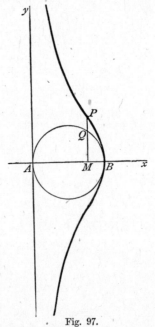

Fig. 97.

439. The curve can be mechanically constructed by an instrument invented by Newton.

Take a rod LMN bent at right angles at M, and such that $MN = AB$ (Fig. 96). Let the leg LM always pass through a fixed point O on CA produced so that $AO = CA$, and let N travel along the perpendicular to AB through C. Then Q the mid-point of MN traces out the cissoid.

THE WITCH OF AGNESI.

440. Let AQB be a semicircle whose diameter is AB. Produce MQ the ordinate of Q so that

$$MQ : MP = AM : AB,$$

the locus of P is the Witch. (Fig. 97.)

If A be the origin and AB the x-axis the equation is

$$xy^2 = 4a^2(2a - x).$$

This curve was discussed by Maria Gaetana Agnesi, Professor of Mathematics at Bologna, 1748.

THE FOLIUM OF DESCARTES.

441. The Cartesian equation is

$$x^3 + y^3 = 3axy.$$

There is symmetry about the line $y = x$. The axes of co-ordinates are tangents at the origin and there is a loop in

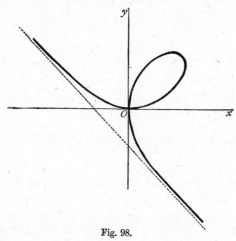

Fig. 98.

the first quadrant. The curve consists of an infinite branch running to the asymptote $x + y + a = 0$ at each end and lying on the upper side of that line.

The curve being a cubic with one node has its deficiency zero and is therefore unicursal.

Let $\qquad\qquad y = mx.$

Then $\qquad\qquad x = \dfrac{3am}{1+m^3}, \quad y = \dfrac{3am^2}{1+m^3}.$

Hence by assigning various arbitrary values to m any number of points can be discovered lying upon the curve, and the curve might be completely traced in this manner.

The Logarithmic Curve and the Curve of Frequency.

442. The equation of the logarithmic curve is

$$x = \log y \quad \text{or} \quad y = e^x.$$

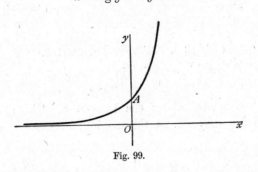

Fig. 99.

When x is negative and very large the ordinate diminishes without limit and the x-axis towards $-\infty$ becomes asymptotic. Travelling from left to right, equidistant ordinates form a geometrical progression and on the right-hand side of the y-axis rapidly increase as x increases.

The subtangent $\dfrac{y}{y_1} = 1$, and is therefore of constant length.

443. The curve $y = e^{-x^2}$ is known as the Curve of Frequency of Error or the Probability Curve.* All ordinates are positive; it cuts the y-axis perpendicularly at unit distance from the origin. The curve is symmetrical about the y-axis running asymptotically to the x-axis on its upper side at both extremities. There are points of inflexion where $x = \pm \dfrac{1}{\sqrt{2}}$.

---

* Airy, *Theory of Errors of Observation.*

The Chainette or Catenary, and its Involute the Tractory or Tractrix.

444. The chainette is the curve in which a uniform heavy string will hang under the action of gravity.

Its Cartesian equation is proved in books on **Analytical Statics** to be $y = c \cosh \dfrac{x}{c}$.[*]

Its form is that represented by the curve PCP' in Fig. 100.

It is symmetrical about a vertical axis Oy through its lowest point C. The ordinate of C is c.

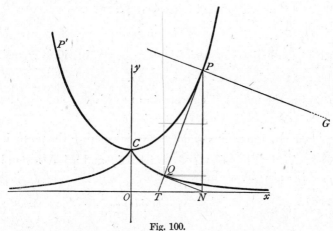

Fig. 100.

445. Let PN be an ordinate, PT the tangent, NQ a perpendicular from N upon the tangent PT, the normal cutting the x-axis in G. The x-axis is called the directrix.

(1) Then
$$\tan \psi = \frac{dy}{dx} = \sinh \frac{x}{c} \text{ or } \psi = \operatorname{gd} \frac{x}{c}.$$

(2) Also
$$\frac{y}{NQ} = \sec \psi = \sqrt{1 + \sinh^2 \frac{x}{c}} = \cosh \frac{x}{c} = \frac{y}{c}.$$

Hence $NQ = c$.

(3) Again
$$\frac{ds}{dx} = \sqrt{1 + \sinh^2 \frac{x}{c}} = \cosh \frac{x}{c},$$

whence $s = c \sinh \dfrac{x}{c}$ if s be measured from the vertex C to P so that s and x vanish together.

[*] Dr. Routh, *Analytical Statics*, vol. I, Art. 443.

(4) Also $\qquad PQ = QN \tan \psi = c \sinh \dfrac{x}{c} = s.$

(5) Hence the path of Q is an involute of the chainette. This curve is called the Tractory, and possesses as shown in (2) the geometrical property that the tangent to the path is of constant length.

(6) If a person travelling along Ox drags a stone along the ground (supposed perfectly rough) from the initial position C by means of a string of length c, the path of the stone is the tractory.

(7) From the right-angled triangle PQN we have at once
$$y^2 = c^2 + s^2.$$

(8) Since $s = c \sinh \dfrac{x}{c}$ and $\sinh \dfrac{x}{c} = \tan \psi$, the intrinsic equation of the chainette is $\quad s = c \tan \psi.$

(9) Hence the radius of curvature $= c \sec^2 \psi$.

But $\qquad\qquad PG = y \sec \psi = c \sec^2 \psi.$

Hence the radius of curvature is equal to the normal.

(10) If x', y' be the point Q of the tractory and $\psi' = Q\widehat{N}x$ and s' the arc CQ, we have
$$\frac{dy'}{ds'} = -\sin \psi' = -\frac{y'}{c},$$

giving $\qquad \log y' = \text{constant} - \dfrac{s'}{c}.$

But $\qquad\qquad y' = c$ when $s' = 0$.

Hence the constant $= \log c$.

Thus $\qquad\qquad s' = c \log \dfrac{c}{y'}.$

(11) The Cartesian equation of the tractory is
$$x = \sqrt{c^2 - y^2} + \frac{c}{2} \log \frac{c - \sqrt{c^2 - y^2}}{c + \sqrt{c^2 - y^2}}$$

(12) If a point X be taken on the tangent QN to the tractrix so that NX is of constant length, the path of X has been called by Riccati the Syntractory.[*]

* Peacock, p. 175.

THE CONCHOID OF NICOMEDES.

446. AB is a straight line and O a fixed point; V any point on the given line, and on OV and OV produced, points P', P are taken so that

$$VP' = VP = \text{a constant length.}$$

The locus of P or P' is called the Conchoid.

Let the perpendicular ON upon AB be a and let $VP = b$. Then, taking O for pole and the initial line Ox parallel to AB, the polar equation is $\qquad r = a \operatorname{cosec} \theta \pm b,$

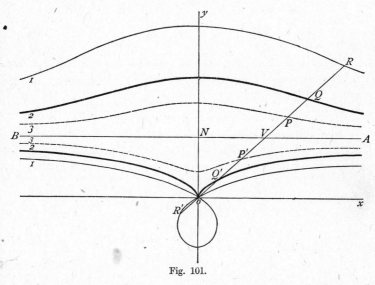

Fig. 101.

the $+$ referring to the branch more remote from A and the $-$ to the branch nearer to A. These are respectively called the superior and the inferior branches. Both branches belong to the same curve and are included in the Cartesian equation

$$x^2 y^2 = (a+y)^2 (b^2 - y^2),$$

the origin in this case being taken at N and NA for x-axis.

447. There are three classes, according as a is $<$, $=$, or $>b$. If a be $< b$, there will be a node at O and a loop below the initial line.

If $a = b$, there will be a cusp at O.

If $a > b$, the curve will be as shown by the dotted lines 3, 3 in
the figure.   As defined by the Cartesian equation, there
would also be in this case a conjugate point at O.

448. The curve was used for the trisection of an angle, and
the insertion of two mean proportionals between two given
straight lines.   It admits, as shown by Nicomedes, of a simple
mechanical construction.*   For it is easy to make a mechanical contrivance which will constrain the motion of a given rod
so as to pass always through a fixed point, whilst a given point
of the rod performs a rectilineal path.   By what precedes, any
other point of the rod describes a conchoid.

THE SPIRALS.

THE EQUIANGULAR OR LOGARITHMIC SPIRAL.

449. This curve possesses the characteristic property that
the tangent makes a constant angle with the radius vector.

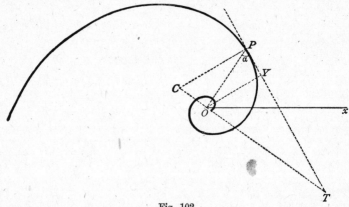

Fig. 102.

Let O be the pole, PT the tangent at P, OY the perpendicular, OT the polar subtangent cutting the normal in C.   Let
$OPT = a$.

We have the following properties:—

(1) $$p = OY = r \sin a,$$

(2) $$\rho = r\frac{dr}{dp} = r \operatorname{cosec} a = CP.$$

Hence C is the centre of curvature.

* Montucla, *Histoire des Math.*, tom. I., p. 236, referred to by Peacock ; and Newton,
App. to Arith. Univ.

(3) $$\frac{dr}{ds} = \cos \alpha.$$

Hence if the arc be measured from the pole, where $r = 0$, we have $\qquad r = s \cos \alpha.$

But $\qquad\qquad r = PT \cos \alpha.$

Therefore $\qquad PT = s.$

(4) If YY' be the tangent to the first positive pedal curve
$$Y'YO = YPO = \alpha.$$

Hence the first positive pedal is an equal equiangular spiral. Hence also all other pedals are equal spirals.

(5) Since PC is a tangent at C to the evolute, and $OCP = \alpha$, the first, and all other evolutes are equal spirals.

(6) From similar considerations the inverse, and the polar reciprocal with regard to the pole are equal spirals.

(7) Since $\frac{rd\theta}{dr} = \tan \alpha$ we have $\frac{dr}{r} = \cot \alpha \,.\, d\theta$, and the polar equation is of the form
$$r = ae^{\theta \cot \alpha}.$$

(8) If the spiral roll along a fixed line, the locus of the pole, and also of the centre of curvature of the point of contact is a straight line.

450. Of the system of " Parabolic Spirals " $r = a\theta^n$ the most remarkable are those for which

$\qquad\qquad n = 1$ (the Archimedean Spiral).

$\qquad\qquad n = -1$ (the Hyperbolic or Reciprocal Spiral).

$\qquad\qquad n = -\frac{1}{2}$ (the Lituus).

The Spiral of Archimedes.

451. The equation of the curve is $r = a\theta$.

This curve is due to Conon, who however died before he had completed his investigations of its properties. These investigations were continued and completed by Archimedes who published them in a tract on spirals still extant.

(1) If a circle of radius a be drawn with centre at the pole any radius vector of the curve is equal to the arc of this circle measured from the initial line to the point in which the radius vector cuts the circle.

(2) We have for this curve

$$p = \frac{r^2}{\sqrt{a^2 + r^2}}; \quad \tan\phi = \frac{r}{a} = \theta; \quad \text{subtangent} = \frac{r^2}{a}.$$

(3) The locus of the extremity of the polar subtangent is

$$r_1 = a\left(\theta_1 + \frac{\pi}{2}\right)^2.$$

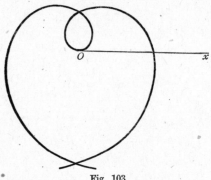

Fig. 103.

For this curve the corresponding locus is

$$r_2 = a\left(\theta_2 + \frac{2\pi}{2}\right)^3 \Big/ 2!;$$

and so on. The nth locus thus formed is

$$r_n = a\left(\theta_n + \frac{n\pi}{2}\right)^{n+1} \Big/ n!.$$

These loci thus form a series of "Parabolic Spirals" of ascending order.[*]

(4) The area bounded by any portion and its extreme radii vectores can easily be found by the Integral Calculus.

THE RECIPROCAL OR HYPERBOLIC SPIRAL.

452. The polar equation is $r\theta = a$.

This curve is the inverse of the Archimedean spiral. The name Hyperbolic is derived from the analogy between the form of its equation and that in Cartesians for a hyperbola referred to its asymptotes.

[*] Peacock, *Examples*, p. 180.

(1) If a circle be drawn with any radius and centre at the origin, the arc of this circle intercepted between the points where it is cut by the curve and by the initial line is of constant length.

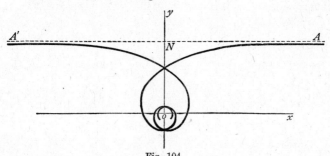

Fig. 104.

(2) We have $\tan \phi = r \dfrac{d\theta}{dr} = r \left(-\dfrac{a}{r^2} \right) = -\theta.$

(3) Subtangent $= r^2 \dfrac{d\theta}{dr} = -a = \text{constant}.$

The asymptote is at a distance a from the initial line and above it.

(4) The pedal equation is

$$\frac{1}{p^2} = \frac{1}{r^2} + \frac{1}{a^2}.$$

THE LITUUS.

453. The equation to the curve is

$$r = a\theta^{-\frac{1}{2}}.$$

The initial line is an asymptote.

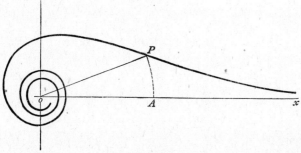

Fig. 105.

If any radius vector OP be taken and a circular sector OPA described bounded by the radius vector and the initial line, its area is

$$\tfrac{1}{2}r^2\theta = \frac{a^2}{2},$$

and is therefore constant.

COTES'S SPIRALS.

454. The group of curves included in the formula

$$\frac{1}{p^2} = \frac{A}{r^2} + B$$

are called Cotes's Spirals. They occur as the path of a particle projected in any manner under the action of a central force varying as the inverse cube of the distance.

There are five varieties.

(1) If $B = 0$, $\dfrac{p}{r}$ is constant, whence ϕ is constant and the curve is an equiangular spiral.

(2) If $A = 1$, we have

$$\frac{1}{p^2} = u^2 + \left(\frac{du}{d\theta}\right)^2 = u^2 + B,$$

giving $u = \sqrt{B}\,\theta$, θ being supposed measured from an initial line drawn parallel to the asymptote. This is the reciprocal spiral.

More generally

$$u^2 + \left(\frac{du}{d\theta}\right)^2 = Au^2 + B,$$

or

$$\left(\frac{du}{d\theta}\right)^2 = (A-1)u^2 + B.$$

The right-hand side may be put into one of the forms

$$n^2(u^2 + a^2),$$
$$n^2(u^2 - a^2),$$
$$n^2(a^2 - u^2),$$

according to the signs of $A - 1$ and B; a and n being constants.

(3) If

$$\left(\frac{du}{d\theta}\right)^2 = n^2(u^2 + a^2),$$

we have

$$\frac{du}{\sqrt{u^2 + a^2}} = nd\theta$$

and

$$u = a \sinh n\theta.$$

(4) If
$$\left(\frac{du}{d\theta}\right)^2 = n^2(u^2 - a^2),$$

we have similarly $u = a \cosh n\theta$.

(5) If
$$\left(\frac{du}{d\theta}\right)^2 = n^2(a^2 - u^2),$$

$$u = a \sin n\theta. \quad \text{(Art. 387.)}$$

Cases (3) and (4) present no difficulty in tracing.

INVOLUTE OF A CIRCLE.

455. If a thread be unwound from a circle, any point of the unwinding thread traces out an involute of a circle. Let PQ be any position of the thread, P the tracing point. Then PQ is a tangent to the circle and a normal to the involute. Let

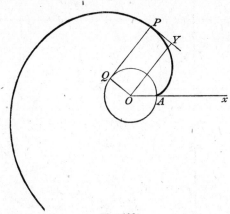

Fig. 106.

O be the centre of the circle and a its radius. Then clearly the pedal equation is $r^2 = p^2 + a^2$.

Also
$$\rho = PQ = \text{arc } AQ = a\psi,$$

giving
$$s = \frac{a\psi^2}{2},$$

s being measured from the point A at which the involute meets the circle, and OA being the initial line.

If OY be the perpendicular from O upon the tangent at P we have
$$OY = a\psi = a\left(YOX + \frac{\pi}{2}\right).$$

Hence the first positive pedal is the Archimedean spiral.

The polar equation is at once obtainable.   For

$$\cos^{-1}\frac{a}{r} = Q\widehat{O}P = Q\widehat{O}A - \theta = \frac{\operatorname{arc} AQ}{a} - \theta = \frac{QP}{a} - \theta = \frac{\sqrt{r^2 - a^2}}{a} - \theta,$$

or

$$\theta = \frac{\sqrt{r^2 - a^2}}{a} - \cos^{-1}\frac{a}{r}.$$

The Evolute of a Parabola.

456. The evolute of $y^2 = 4ax$ may be shown to be the semi-cubical parabola $27ay^2 = 4(x - 2a)^3.$

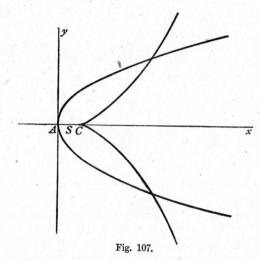

Fig. 107.

The cusp is at the point $(2a,\ 0)$, and the curve cuts the parabola again at a point whose abscissa is $8a$. The tangent to the evolute at this point cuts the parabola again upon the ordinate through the cusp.

From points on the right-hand side of the evolute three real normals can be drawn to the parabola. From points on the left side only one real normal can be drawn.

The Evolute of an Ellipse.

457. The equation of the evolute of $x^2/a^2 + y^2/b^2 = 1$ has been shown to be $(ax)^{\frac{2}{3}} + (by)^{\frac{2}{3}} = (a^2 - b^2)^{\frac{2}{3}}.$

There is a cusp at each point where the curve meets the co-ordinate axes.

From points within the evolute four real normals can be drawn to the conic. From points outside two normals can be drawn.

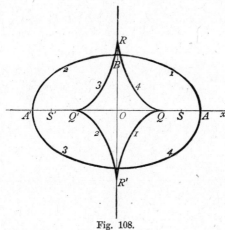

Fig. 108.

Normals from the portion of the ellipse marked (1) touch the portion of the evolute marked (1), and the correspondence is similarly denoted by numerals for the other quadrants.

The radii of curvature at A and B are respectively $\dfrac{b^2}{a}$ and $\dfrac{a^2}{b}$,

Thus $$AQ = \frac{b^2}{a} \text{ and } BR' = \frac{a^2}{b}.$$

The length of the evolute is $4\left(\dfrac{a^2}{b} - \dfrac{b^2}{a}\right)$.

CASSINI'S OVALS.

458. Let r and r' be the distances of a moveable point P from two fixed points S and S'. The locus traced out by P when $$rr' = \text{constant } (= b^2 \text{ say})$$ is called an Oval of Cassini.

Let $SS' = 2a$ and take SS' for x-axis and its mid-point O for origin. The Cartesian equation is then

$$[(x-a)^2 + y^2][(x+a)^2 + y^2] = b^4, \dots\dots\dots\dots(1)$$

or in Polars $$(r^2 + a^2)^2 - 4a^2 r^2 \cos^2\theta = b^4,$$

reducing to $$r^4 + a^4 - 2r^2 a^2 \cos 2\theta = b^4.$$

If $b = a = c/\sqrt{2}$ this further reduces to

$$r^2 = c^2 \cos 2\theta. \quad\dots\dots\dots\dots\dots\dots\dots(2)$$

This species of Cassini's oval is called the Lemniscate of Bernoulli. This is shown by the thick line in the figure.

It is the first positive pedal of a rectangular hyperbola with regard to the centre, and possesses the property that

$$SP \sim S'P = OP\sqrt{2}.$$

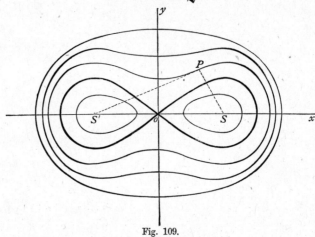

Fig. 109.

In equation (1) when b is $< a$ the curve consists of two ovals within the loops of the lemniscate.

When b is $> a$ the curve consists of one oval lying outside the lemniscate.

The curve $(x^2 + y^2)^2 = a^2x^2 + b^2y^2$, which is the pedal of a central conic with regard to the centre, has a similar shape, and becomes a Bernoulli's lemniscate when the conic is a rectangular hyperbola.

CARTESIAN OVALS.

459. If r and r' be as defined in Art. 458, the loci indicated by the equation $\quad\quad lr + mr' = n$,
are called Cartesian Ovals.

This equation in general gives rise to a quartic Cartesian equation.

The following cases will be recognized :—

      If $l = m$ we have $r + r' = $ constant ; an ellipse.
      If $l = -m$ we have $r - r' = $ constant ; a hyperbola.
      If $n = 0$ we have $r : r' = $ constant ; a circle.

Also since $l\dfrac{dr}{ds}+m\dfrac{dr'}{ds}=0$ it will be evident that in all cases the normal divides the angle between r and r' in such manner that the sines of the portions are in the ratio $m:l$. The student is referred for further information to a chapter on Cartesians in Professor Williamson's *Differential Calculus**
where several interesting properties are investigated.

THE QUADRATRICES OF DINOSTRATUS AND TSCHIRNHAUSEN.

460. Let AFA_1 be a semicircle of which AA_1 is a diameter and O the centre. Let QN be an ordinate of a point Q on the circle and P another point so related to Q that the ordinate QN travels at uniform rate from A to O in the same time that OP rotates uniformly from OA through a right angle. Let OP and NQ intersect in R, then the locus of R is the Quadratrix of Hippias or Dinostratus.

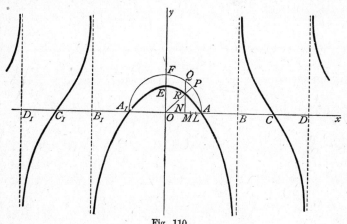

Fig. 110.

Let $NOP=\theta$ and $OA=a$, then arc $AP=a\theta$.

Also
$$\frac{AN}{AO}=\frac{\text{angle }AOP}{\text{right angle}}.$$

Hence $AN=\dfrac{2a\theta}{\pi}$ or $\theta=\dfrac{\pi}{2}\dfrac{a-x}{a}$, ($O$ being the origin).

But
$$\frac{y}{x}=\tan\theta.$$

Hence the Cartesian equation of the locus is

$$y = x \cot \frac{\pi x}{2a}.$$

The form of the equation shows that there is symmetry about the y-axis, and the curve may be seen to be as shown in the accompanying figure.

461. This curve if accurately traced could be used for the trisection of an angle. Lay off any angle AOP by a line OP cutting the quadratrix in R. Draw the perpendicular RN to OA. Trisect AN at L, M and erect perpendiculars to AN cutting the curve in X, Y. Then since

$$AL = \frac{1}{3} AN = \frac{1}{3} \cdot \frac{2a\theta}{\pi},$$

the　　　　　　angle $AOX = \dfrac{\theta}{3}.$

Similarly　　　　　$AOY = \dfrac{2\theta}{3},$

and the angle is trisected.

462. Again, since the intercept OE made on the y-axis is

$$Lt_{x=0}\, x \cot \frac{\pi x}{2a} = Lt \cos \frac{\pi x}{2a} \cdot \frac{\dfrac{\pi x}{2a}}{\sin \dfrac{\pi x}{2a}} \cdot \frac{2a}{\pi} = \frac{2a}{\pi},$$

we could (if the curve could be accurately drawn) measure OE and hence deduce the value of π. Hence the area of a circle could be found. It is from this property that the curve derives its name.

463. If a parallel to the x-axis be drawn through P cutting MQ in S, the locus of S is

$$y = a \sin \theta = a \sin \frac{\pi}{2} \frac{a - x}{a}$$

or　　　　　　　$y = a \cos \dfrac{\pi x}{2a}.$

This curve is called the Quadratrix of Tschirnhausen.

APPLICATION TO THE EVALUATION OF

SINGULAR FORMS, MAXIMA AND

MINIMA VALUES, ETC.

CHAPTER XIV.

UNDETERMINED FORMS.

464. In Chap. I. it was explained that a function may involve an independent variable in such a manner that its value for a certain assigned value of the variable cannot be found by a direct substitution of that value. And in such cases the function is said to assume a "*Singular*," "*Undetermined*," "*Illusory*," or "*Indeterminate*" form.

465. It is proposed in the present chapter to consider more fully the method of evaluation of the true limiting values of such quantities when the independent variable is made to approach indefinitely near its assigned value.

466. List of Forms occurring.

Several cases are to be considered, viz., when upon substitution of the assigned value of the independent variable, the function reduces to one of the forms

$$\frac{0}{0}, \quad 0 \times \infty, \quad \frac{\infty}{\infty}, \quad \infty - \infty, \quad 0^0, \quad \infty^0, \quad \text{or } 1^\infty.$$

It is frequently easy to treat these cases by algebraical or trigonometrical methods without having recourse to the Differential Calculus, though the latter is required for a general discussion of such forms.

By far the most important case to consider is that in which the function takes the form $\frac{0}{0}$; for, in the first place, it is the one which most frequently occurs; and, secondly, any of the other forms may be made to depend upon this one by some special artifice.

467. Algebraical Treatment.

Suppose the function to take the form $\frac{0}{0}$ when the independent variable x ultimately coincides with its assigned value a. Put $x = a + h$ and *expand both numerator and denominator* of the function. It will now become apparent that the reason why both numerator and denominator vanish is that some power of h is a common factor of each. This should now be *divided out*. Finally, put $h = 0$ so that x becomes $= a$, and the true limiting value of the function will be apparent.

In the particular case in which x is to become *zero* the expansion of numerator and denominator in powers of x should be at once proceeded with without any preliminary substitution for x.

In the case in which x is to become infinite, put $x = \frac{1}{y}$, so that when x becomes $= \infty$, y becomes $= 0$.

The method thus explained will be better understood by examining the mode of solution of the following examples.

Ex. 1. *Find* $Lt_{x=0} \dfrac{a^x - b^x}{x}.$

Here numerator and denominator both vanish if x be put equal to 0. We therefore expand a^x and b^x by the exponential theorem. Hence

$$Lt_{x=0} \frac{a^x - b^x}{x}$$

$$= Lt_{x=0} \frac{\left\{1 + x\log_e a + \frac{x^2}{2!}(\log_e a)^2 + \ldots\right\} - \left\{1 + x\log_e b + \frac{x^2}{2!}(\log_e b)^2 + \ldots\right\}}{x}$$

$$= Lt_{x=0} \left\{\log_e a - \log_e b + \frac{x}{2!}(\overline{\log_e a}|^2 - \overline{\log_e b}|^2) + \ldots\right\}$$

$$= \log_e a - \log_e b = \log_e \frac{a}{b}.$$

Ex. 2. *Find* $Lt_{x=1} \dfrac{x^7 - 2x^5 + 1}{x^3 - 3x^2 + 2}.$

This is of the form $\frac{0}{0}$ if we put $x = 1$. Therefore we put $x = 1 + h$ and expand. We thus obtain

$$Lt_{x=1} \frac{x^7 - 2x^5 + 1}{x^3 - 3x^2 + 2} = Lt_{h=0} \frac{(1+h)^7 - 2(1+h)^5 + 1}{(1+h)^3 - 3(1+h)^2 + 2}$$

$$= Lt_{h=0} \frac{(1 + 7h + 21h^2 + \ldots) - 2(1 + 5h + 10h^2 + \ldots) + 1}{(1 + 3h + 3h^2 + \ldots) - 3(1 + 2h + h^2) + 2}$$

$$= Lt_{h=0} \frac{-3h + h^2 + \ldots}{-3h + \ldots}$$

$$= Lt_{h=0} \frac{-3 + h + \ldots}{-3 + \ldots}$$

$$= \frac{-3}{-3} = 1.$$

It will be seen from these examples that in the process of expansion it is only necessary in general *to retain a few of the lowest powers of h.*

Ex. 3. *Find* $\qquad Lt_{x=0}\left(\frac{\tan x}{x}\right)^{\frac{1}{x^2}}.$

Since $\qquad\qquad \frac{\tan x}{x} = \frac{1}{\cos x} \cdot \frac{\sin x}{x},$

we have $\qquad\qquad Lt_{x=0} \frac{\tan x}{x} = 1.$

Hence the form assumed by $\left(\frac{\tan x}{x}\right)^{\frac{1}{x^2}}$ is 1^{∞} when we put $x = 0.$

Expand $\sin x$ and $\cos x$ in powers of x. This gives

$$Lt_{x=0}\left(\frac{\tan x}{x}\right)^{\frac{1}{x^2}} = Lt_{x=0}\left(\frac{x - \frac{x^3}{3!} + \ldots}{x - \frac{x^3}{2!} + \ldots}\right)^{\frac{1}{x^2}}$$

$$= Lt_{x=0}\left(1 + \frac{x^2}{3} + \text{higher powers of } x\right)^{\frac{1}{x^2}}$$

$$= Lt_{x=0}\left(1 + \frac{x^2 l}{3}\right)^{\frac{1}{x^2}},$$

where l is a series in ascending powers of x whose first term (and therefore whose limit when $x = 0$) is unity. Hence

$$Lt_{x=0}\left(\frac{\tan x}{x}\right)^{\frac{1}{x^2}} = Lt_{x=0}\left\{\left(1 + \frac{x^2 l}{3}\right)^{\frac{3}{lx^2}}\right\}^{\frac{l}{3}} = e^{\frac{1}{3}}, \text{ by Art. 20.}$$

Ex. 4. *Find* $\qquad Lt_{x=1} x^{\frac{1}{1-x}}.$

This expression is of the form $1^{\infty}.$

Put $\qquad\qquad 1 - x = y,$

and therefore, if $x = 1,$ $\qquad y = 0;$

therefore $\qquad$ Limit required $= Lt_{y=0}(1 - y)^{\frac{1}{y}} = e^{-1}$ (Art. 20).

Ex. 5. $\qquad\qquad Lt_{x=\infty} x(a^{\frac{1}{x}} - 1).$

This is of the form $\infty \times 0.$

Put $\qquad\qquad x = \frac{1}{y},$

therefore, if $x = \infty,$ $\qquad y = 0,$

and $\qquad$ Limit required $= Lt_{y=0} \frac{a^y - 1}{y} = \log_e a$ (Art. 21).

EXAMPLES.

Find the values of the following limits :—

1. $Lt_{x=0}\dfrac{a^x-1}{b^x-1}$.

2. $Lt_{x=1}\dfrac{x^{\frac{3}{2}}-1}{x^{\frac{5}{2}}-1}$.

3. $Lt_{x=1}\dfrac{x^m-1}{x^n-1}$.

4. $Lt_{x=0}\dfrac{(1+x)^{\frac{1}{n}}-1}{x}$.

5. $Lt_{x=1}\dfrac{x^4+x^3-x^2-5x+4}{x^3-x^2-x+1}$.

6. $Lt_{x=1}\dfrac{x^5-2x^3-4x^2+9x-4}{x^4-2x^3+2x-1}$.

7. $Lt_{x=0}\dfrac{e^x-e^{-x}}{x}$.

8. $Lt_{x=0}\dfrac{e^x+e^{-x}-2}{x^2}$.

9. $Lt_{x=0}\dfrac{x\cos x-\log(1+x)}{x^2}$.

10. $Lt_{x=0}\dfrac{xe^x-\log(1+x)}{x^2}$.

11. $Lt_{x=0}\dfrac{x-\sin x\cos x}{x^3}$.

12. $Lt_{x=0}\dfrac{\sin^{-1}x-x}{x^3\cos x}$.

13. $Lt_{x=0}\dfrac{\cosh x-\cos x}{x\sin x}$.

14. $Lt_{x=0}\dfrac{\sin^{-1}x}{\tan^{-1}x}$.

15. $Lt_{x=0}\dfrac{\sin^{-1}x-\sinh x}{x^5}$.

16. $Lt_{x=0}\dfrac{x\cos^3x-\log(1+x)-\sin^{-1}\frac{x^2}{2}}{x^3}$.

17. $Lt_{x=0}\dfrac{2\sin x+\tanh^{-1}x-3x}{x^5}$.

18. $Lt_{x=0}\dfrac{e^x\sin x-x-x^2}{x^2+x\log(1-x)}$.

19. $Lt_{x=0}\dfrac{x^3e^{\frac{x^4}{4}}-\sin^{\frac{3}{2}}x^2}{x^7}$.

20. $Lt_{x=0}\left(\dfrac{\tan x}{x}\right)^{\frac{1}{x}}$.

21. $Lt_{x=0}\left(\dfrac{\tan x}{x}\right)^{\frac{1}{x^3}}$.

22. $Lt_{x=0}\left(\dfrac{\sin x}{x}\right)^{\frac{1}{x}}$.

23. $Lt_{x=0}\left(\dfrac{\sin x}{x}\right)^{\frac{1}{x^2}}$.

24. $Lt_{x=0}\left(\dfrac{\sin x}{x}\right)^{\frac{1}{x^3}}$.

25. $Lt_{x=0}(\text{covers } x)^{\frac{1}{x}}$.

26. $Lt_{x=\frac{\pi}{2}}(\text{cosec } x)^{\tan^2 x}$.

APPLICATION OF THE DIFFERENTIAL CALCULUS.

468. John Bernoulli* was the first to make use of the processes of the Differential Calculus in the determination of the true values of functions assuming singular forms. We propose now to discuss each singularity in order.

469. I. FORM $\dfrac{0}{0}$.

Consider a curve passing through the origin and defined by the equations
$$x=\psi(t),$$
$$y=\phi(t).$$

* *Acta Eruditorum*, 1704.

Let x, y be the co-ordinates of a point P on the curve very near the origin, and suppose a to be the value of t correspond-

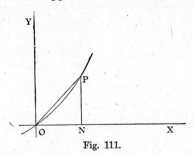

Fig. 111.

ing to the origin, so that $\phi(a) = 0$ and $\psi(a) = 0$.

Then ultimately we have

$$Lt\frac{y}{x} = Lt \tan PON = Lt_{x=0}\frac{dy}{dx} = Lt_{t=a}\frac{\phi'(t)}{\psi'(t)}.$$

Hence

$$Lt_{t=a}\frac{\phi(t)}{\psi(t)} = Lt_{t=a}\frac{\phi'(t)}{\psi'(t)};$$

and if $\dfrac{\phi'(t)}{\psi'(t)}$ be not of the form $\dfrac{0}{0}$ when t takes its assigned value a, we therefore obtain

$$Lt_{t=a}\frac{\phi(t)}{\psi(t)} = \frac{\phi'(a)}{\psi'(a)}.$$

But, if $\dfrac{\phi'(t)}{\psi'(t)}$ be also of undetermined form, we may repeat

the process; thus $\quad Lt_{t=a}\dfrac{\phi'(t)}{\psi'(t)} = Lt_{t=a}\dfrac{\phi''(t)}{\psi''(t)} = \text{etc.,}$

proceeding in this manner until we arrive at a fraction such that when the value a is substituted for t its numerator and denominator *do not both vanish*, and thus obtaining an intelligible result—zero, finite, or infinite.

470. Another Proof of the Method.

We may arrive at the same result in another way, thus :—

Let $\dfrac{\phi(x)}{\psi(x)}$ take the form $\dfrac{0}{0}$ when x approaches and ultimately

coincides with the value a. Let $x = a + h$. Then by Taylor's

Theorem $\quad \dfrac{\phi(x)}{\psi(x)} = \dfrac{\phi(a) + h\phi'(a + \theta h)}{\psi(a) + h\psi'(a + \theta_1 h)} = \dfrac{\phi'(a + \theta h)}{\psi'(a + \theta_1 h)},$

for $\phi(a)=0$ and $\psi(a)=0$ by supposition.   Hence in the limit when $x=a$ (and therefore $h=0$), we have

$$Lt_{x=a}\frac{\phi(x)}{\psi(x)}=Lt_{h=0}\frac{\phi'(a+\theta h)}{\psi'(a+\theta_1 h)}=\frac{\phi'(a)}{\psi'(a)}.$$

If it should happen that $\phi'(a)$ and $\psi'(a)$ are both zero, we can, as before, repeat the process of differentiating the numerator and denominator before substitution for x.

Ex. 1. $Lt_{\theta=0}\dfrac{\sin\theta-\theta}{\theta^3}$.

Here $\phi(\theta)=\sin\theta-\theta$, and $\psi(\theta)=\theta^3$,
which both vanish when θ vanishes.

$$\phi'(\theta)=\cos\theta-1, \text{ and } \psi'(\theta)=3\theta^2,$$

and both of these expressions vanish with θ.

Differentiating again

$$\phi''(\theta)=-\sin\theta, \text{ and } \psi''(\theta)=6\theta,$$

and still both expressions vanish with θ.   We must therefore differentiate again $\phi'''(\theta)=-\cos\theta$, and $\psi'''(\theta)=6$,
whence $\phi'''(0)=-1$,   and $\psi'''(0)=6$;

therefore $Lt_{\theta=0}\dfrac{\sin\theta-\theta}{\theta^3}=-\dfrac{1}{6}.$

Ex. 2. $Lt_{\theta=0}\dfrac{e^\theta-e^{-\theta}+2\sin\theta-4\theta}{\theta^5}$ $\left[\text{Form }\dfrac{0}{0}\right]$

$$=Lt_{\theta=0}\frac{e^\theta+e^{-\theta}+2\cos\theta-4}{5\theta^4}\qquad\left[\text{Form }\frac{0}{0}\right]$$

$$=Lt_{\theta=0}\frac{e^\theta-e^{-\theta}-2\sin\theta}{20\theta^3}\qquad\left[\text{Form }\frac{0}{0}\right]$$

$$=Lt_{\theta=0}\frac{e^\theta+e^{-\theta}-2\cos\theta}{60\theta^2}\qquad\left[\text{Form }\frac{0}{0}\right]$$

$$=Lt_{\theta=0}\frac{e^\theta-e^{-\theta}+2\sin\theta}{120\theta}\qquad\left[\text{Form }\frac{0}{0}\right]$$

$$=Lt_{\theta=0}\frac{e^\theta+e^{-\theta}+2\cos\theta}{120}=\frac{1}{30}.$$

471. The proposition of Art. 469 may also be treated as follows.

Let $\phi(a)=0$ and $\psi(a)=0$, and let the pth differential coefficient of $\phi(x)$ and the qth of $\psi(x)$ be the first which do not vanish when x is put equal to a.   Then by Taylor's Theorem, putting $x=a+h$,

$$\phi(x)=\phi(a)+h\phi'(a)+\ldots+\frac{h^{p-1}}{(p-1)!}\phi^{p-1}(a)+\frac{h^p}{p!}\phi^p(a+\theta h)$$

$$=\frac{h^p}{p!}\phi^p(a+\theta h).$$

Similarly $\quad\quad \psi(x)=\dfrac{h^q}{q!}\psi^q(a+\theta_1 h).$

Hence $\quad\quad Lt_{x=a}\dfrac{\phi(x)}{\psi(x)}=\dfrac{q!}{p!}Lt_{h=0}h^{p-q}\dfrac{\phi^p(a+\theta h)}{\psi^q(a+\theta_1 h)}$

$$=\dfrac{q!}{p!}\dfrac{\phi^p(a)}{\psi^q(a)}Lt_{h=0}h^{p-q}.$$

Now, if $\quad\quad p>q, \quad Lt_{h=0}h^{p-q}=0.$

If $\quad\quad\quad p<q, \quad Lt_{h=0}h^{p-q}=\infty .$

If $\quad\quad\quad p=q, \quad Lt_{x=a}\dfrac{\phi(x)}{\psi(x)}=\dfrac{\phi^p(a)}{\psi^p(a)};$

so that the limit is 0, $\dfrac{\phi^p(a)}{\psi^p(a)}$, or ∞, according as p is $>$, $=$, or $<q$.

472. II. Form $0\times\infty$.

Let $\phi(a)=0$ and $\psi(a)=\infty$, so that $\phi(x)\psi(x)$ takes the form $0\times\infty$ when x approaches and ultimately coincides with the value a.

Then $\quad\quad Lt_{x=a}\phi(x)\psi(x)=Lt_{x=a}\dfrac{\phi(x)}{\dfrac{1}{\psi(x)}},$

and since $\quad\quad\quad \dfrac{1}{\psi(a)}=\dfrac{1}{\infty}=0,$

the limit may be supposed to take the form $\dfrac{0}{0}$, and may be treated like Form I.

Ex. 1. $\quad\quad Lt_{\theta=0}\,\theta\cot\theta=Lt_{\theta=0}\dfrac{\theta}{\tan\theta}=Lt_{\theta=0}\dfrac{1}{\sec^2\theta}=1.$

Ex. 2. $\quad\quad Lt_{x=\infty}x\sin\dfrac{a}{x}=Lt_{x=\infty}\dfrac{\sin\dfrac{a}{x}}{\dfrac{1}{x}}=Lt_{\frac{a}{x}=0}\,a\dfrac{\sin\dfrac{a}{x}}{\dfrac{a}{x}}=a.$

473. III. Form $\dfrac{\infty}{\infty}$.

Let $\phi(a)=\infty$, $\psi(a)=\infty$, so that $\dfrac{\phi(x)}{\psi(x)}$ takes the form $\dfrac{\infty}{\infty}$ when x approaches indefinitely near the value a.

The artifice adopted in this case is to write

$$\dfrac{\phi(x)}{\psi(x)}=\dfrac{\dfrac{1}{\psi(x)}}{\dfrac{1}{\phi(x)}}.$$

Then since $\dfrac{1}{\psi(a)} = \dfrac{1}{\infty} = 0$, and $\dfrac{1}{\phi(a)} = \dfrac{1}{\infty} = 0$, we may consider this as taking the form $\dfrac{0}{0}$, and therefore we may apply the rule of Art. 469

$$Lt_{x=a}\frac{\phi(x)}{\psi(x)} = Lt_{x=a}\frac{\dfrac{1}{\psi(x)}}{\dfrac{1}{\phi(x)}} = Lt_{x=a}\frac{\dfrac{\psi'(x)}{[\psi(x)]^2}}{\dfrac{\phi'(x)}{[\phi(x)]^2}}$$

$$= Lt_{x=a}\left[\frac{\phi(x)}{\psi(x)}\right]^2 \frac{\psi'(x)}{\phi'(x)}.$$

Therefore $\qquad Lt_{x=a}\dfrac{\phi(x)}{\psi(x)} = \left[Lt_{x=a}\dfrac{\phi(x)}{\psi(x)}\right]^2 Lt_{x=a}\dfrac{\psi'(x)}{\phi'(x)}.$

Hence, *unless* $Lt_{x=a}\dfrac{\phi(x)}{\psi(x)}$ *be zero or infinite*, we have

$$1 = \left\{Lt_{x=a}\frac{\phi(x)}{\psi(x)}\right\}\left\{Lt_{x=a}\frac{\psi'(x)}{\phi'(x)}\right\},$$

or $\qquad Lt_{x=a}\dfrac{\phi(x)}{\psi(x)} = Lt_{x=a}\dfrac{\phi'(x)}{\psi'(x)}.$

If, however, $Lt_{x=a}\dfrac{\phi(x)}{\psi(x)}$ be zero, then

$$Lt_{x=a}\frac{\phi(x)+\psi(x)}{\psi(x)} = 1,$$

and therefore, by the former case (the limit being neither zero nor infinite), $\qquad = Lt_{x=a}\dfrac{\phi'(x)+\psi'(x)}{\psi'(x)}.$

Hence, subtracting unity from each side,

$$Lt_{x=a}\frac{\phi(x)}{\psi(x)} = Lt_{x=a}\frac{\phi'(x)}{\psi'(x)}.$$

Finally, in the case in which

$$Lt_{x=a}\frac{\phi(x)}{\psi(x)} = \infty, \quad Lt_{x=a}\frac{\psi(x)}{\phi(x)} = 0$$

and therefore by the last case

$$= Lt_{x=a}\frac{\psi'(x)}{\phi'(x)};$$

therefore $\qquad Lt_{x=a}\dfrac{\phi(x)}{\psi(x)} = Lt_{x=a}\dfrac{\phi'(x)}{\psi'(x)}.$

This result is therefore proved true in all cases.

474. *If any function become infinite for any finite value of the independent variable, then all its differential coefficients will also become infinite for the same value.* An algebraical function only becomes infinite by the vanishing of some factor in the denominator. Now, the process of differentiating never removes such a factor, but raises it to a higher power in the denominator. Hence all differential coefficients of the given function will contain that vanishing factor in the denominator, and will therefore become infinite when such a value is given to the independent variable as will make that factor vanish.

It is obvious too that the circular functions which admit of infinite values, viz., $\tan x$, $\cot x$, $\sec x$, $\csc x$, are really fractional forms, and become infinite by the vanishing of a sine or cosine *in the denominator*, and therefore these follow the same rule as the above.

The rule is also true for the logarithmic function $\log(x-a)$ when $x=a$, or for the exponential function $b^{\frac{1}{x-a}}$ when $x=a$, b being supposed greater than unity.*

475. From the above remarks it will appear that if $\phi(a)$ and $\psi(a)$ become infinite so also *in general* will $\phi'(a)$ and $\psi'(a)$. Hence at first sight it would appear that the formula $Lt_{x=a}\dfrac{\phi'(x)}{\psi'(x)}$ is no better than the original form $Lt_{x=a}\dfrac{\phi(x)}{\psi(x)}$. But it *generally* happens that the limit of the expression $\dfrac{\phi'(x)}{\psi'(x)}$, when $x=a$, can be more easily evaluated.

Ex. 1. Find $Lt_{\theta=\frac{\pi}{2}}\dfrac{\log\left(\theta-\dfrac{\pi}{2}\right)}{\tan\theta}$ *which is of the form* $\dfrac{\infty}{\infty}$.

Following the rule of differentiating numerator for new numerator, and denominator for new denominator, we may write the above limit

$$=Lt_{\theta=\frac{\pi}{2}}\frac{\dfrac{1}{\theta-\dfrac{\pi}{2}}}{\sec^2\theta},$$

which is still of the form $\dfrac{\infty}{\infty}$. But it can be written

$$=Lt_{\theta=\frac{\pi}{2}}\frac{\cos^2\theta}{\theta-\dfrac{\pi}{2}}\left(\text{which is of the form }\frac{0}{0}\right)$$

$$=Lt_{\theta=\frac{\pi}{2}}\frac{-2\cos\theta\sin\theta}{1}=0.$$

* For further discussion of this point the student is referred to Professor De Morgan's *Diff. and Int. Calculus.*

Ex. 2. *Evaluate* $Lt_{x=\infty}\dfrac{x^n}{e^x}$, *which is of the form* $\dfrac{\infty}{\infty}$.

$$Lt_{x=\infty}\frac{x^n}{e^x}=Lt_{x=\infty}\frac{nx^{n-1}}{e^x}=\ldots$$

$$=Lt_{x=\infty}\frac{n!}{e^x}=\frac{n!}{\infty}=0.$$

It is obvious that the same result is true when n is fractional.

Ex. 3. *Evaluate* $Lt_{x=0}x^m(\log x)^n$, m *and* n *being positive.*

This is of the form $0\times\infty$, but may be written

$$Lt_{x=0}\left\{\frac{\log x}{x^{-\frac{m}{n}}}\right\}^n \qquad\qquad \left[\text{Form } \frac{\infty}{\infty}\right]$$

and by putting $x^{\frac{m}{n}}=e^{-y}$ this expression is reduced to

$$Lt_{y=\infty}\left\{\frac{-\dfrac{n}{m}y}{e^y}\right\}^n=0 \text{ as in Ex. 2.}$$

476. IV. Form $\infty-\infty$.

Next, suppose $\phi(a)=\infty$ and $\psi(a)=\infty$, so that $\phi(x)-\psi(x)$ takes the form $\infty-\infty$, when x approaches and ultimately coincides with the value a.

Let $\qquad u=\phi(x)-\psi(x)=\psi(x)\left\{\dfrac{\phi(x)}{\psi(x)}-1\right\}.$

From this method of writing the expression it is obvious that unless $Lt_{x=a}\dfrac{\phi(x)}{\psi(x)}=1$ the limit of u becomes $\psi(a)\times$ (a quantity which does not vanish); and therefore the limit sought is ∞.

But if $Lt_{x=a}\dfrac{\phi(x)}{\psi(x)}=1$, the problem is reduced to the evaluation of an expression which takes the form $\infty\times0$, a form which has been already discussed (II.).

Ex. $\qquad Lt_{x=0}\left(\dfrac{1}{x}-\cot x\right)=Lt_{x=0}\dfrac{1}{x}(1-x\cot x)$

$$=Lt_{x=0}\frac{\sin x-x\cos x}{x\sin x}\left(\text{which is of the form } \frac{0}{0}\right)$$

$$=Lt_{x=0}\frac{x\sin x}{\sin x+x\cos x}\left(\begin{array}{c}\text{which is of the same}\\\text{form still}\end{array}\right)$$

$$=Lt_{x=0}\frac{\sin x+x\cos x}{2\cos x-x\sin x}=0.$$

477. V. Forms 0^0, ∞^0, 1^∞.

Let $y=u^v$, u and v being functions of x; then

$$\log_e y=v\log_e u.$$

Now $\log_e 1=0$, $\log_e\infty=\infty$, $\log_e 0=-\infty$; and therefore when the expression u^v takes one of the forms 0^0, ∞^0, 1^∞, $\log y$ takes the undetermined form $0 \times \infty$. The rule is therefore to *take the logarithm and proceed as in Art.* 472.

Ex. 1. *Find* $Lt_{x=0}x^x$, *which takes the undetermined form* 0^0.

$$Lt_{x=0}\log_e x^x = Lt_{x=0}\frac{\log_e x}{\frac{1}{x}} = Lt_{x=0}\frac{\dfrac{1}{x}}{-\dfrac{1}{x^2}} = Lt_{x=0}(-x) = 0,$$

whence $$Lt_{x=0}x^x = e^0 = 1.$$

Ex. 2. *Find* $Lt_{x=\frac{\pi}{2}}(\sin x)^{\tan x}$. *This takes the form* 1^∞.

$$Lt_{x=\frac{\pi}{2}}(\sin x)^{\tan x} = Lt_{x=\frac{\pi}{2}}e^{\tan x \log \sin x},$$

and $$Lt_{x=\frac{\pi}{2}}\tan x \log \sin x = Lt_{x=\frac{\pi}{2}}\frac{\log \sin x}{\cot x} = Lt_{x=\frac{\pi}{2}}\frac{\cot x}{-\operatorname{cosec}^2 x}$$
$$= Lt_{x=\frac{\pi}{2}}(-\sin x \cos x) = 0,$$

whence required limit $= e^0 = 1$.

A slightly different arrangement of the work is exemplified here.

478. The following example is worthy of notice, viz.,
$$Lt_{x=a}\{1 + \phi(x)\}^{\psi(x)},$$
given that $\phi(a) = 0$, $\psi(a) = \infty$, $Lt_{x=a}\phi(x)\psi(x) = m$.

We can write the above in the form
$$Lt_{x=a}\left[\{1 + \phi(x)\}^{\frac{1}{\phi(x)}}\right]^{\phi(x)\,.\,\psi(x)},$$
which is clearly e^m by Art. 20, Chap. I.

It will be observed that many examples take this form, such, for example, as $Lt_{x=0}\left(\dfrac{\tan x}{x}\right)^{\frac{1}{x^2}}$ on p. 375, and Exs. 20 to 26 on p. 376.

479. $\dfrac{dy}{dx}$ **of doubtful value at a Multiple Point.**

Since $\dfrac{\partial u}{\partial x} = 0$ and $\dfrac{\partial u}{\partial y} = 0$ at any multiple point on the curve $u = 0$, it will be apparent that at such a point the value of $\dfrac{dy}{dx}$ as derived from the formula

$$\frac{dy}{dx} = -\frac{\dfrac{\partial \phi}{\partial x}}{\dfrac{\partial \phi}{\partial y}}$$

will be of the undetermined form $\dfrac{0}{0}$.

The rule of Art. 469 may be applied to find the true limiting values of $\frac{dy}{dx}$ for such cases, but it is generally better to proceed otherwise.

If the multiple point be at the origin, the equations of the tangents at that point can be at once written down by inspection and the required values of $\frac{dy}{dx}$ thus found.

If the multiple point be not at the origin, the equation of the curve should be transformed to parallel axes through the multiple point and the problem is then solved as before.

Ex. Consider the value of $\frac{dy}{dx}$ at the origin for the curve

$$x^4 + ax^2y + bxy^2 + y^4 = 0.$$

The tangents at the origin are obviously

$$x = 0, \quad y = 0, \quad ax + by = 0,$$

making with the axis of x angles whose tangents are respectively

$$\infty, \quad 0, \quad -\frac{a}{b},$$

which are therefore the required values of $\frac{dy}{dx}$.

EXAMPLES.

Investigate the following limiting forms :—

1. $Lt_{x=0} \dfrac{\log(1-x^2)}{\log \cos x}$.

2. $Lt_{x=1} \dfrac{2x^3 - 3x^2 + 1}{3x^5 - 5x^3 + 2}$.

3. $Lt_{x=\frac{\pi}{4}} \dfrac{1-\tan x}{1-\sqrt{2}\sin x}$.

4. $Lt_{x=1} \dfrac{1+\cos \pi x}{\tan^2 \pi x}$.

5. $Lt_{x=a} \log\left(2 - \dfrac{x}{a}\right) \cot(x-a)$.

6. $Lt_{x=0} \dfrac{\log_{\sin x}\cos x}{\log_{\sin \frac{x}{2}}\cos \frac{x}{2}}$.

7. $Lt_{\theta=0} \dfrac{\cot \theta \tan^{-1}(m\tan\theta) - m\cos^2\frac{\theta}{2}}{\sin^2\frac{\theta}{2}}$.

8. $Lt_{x=0}(\cos x)^{\cot^2 x}$.

9. $Lt_{x=1}(1-x^2)^{\frac{1}{\log(1-x)}}$.

10. $Lt_{x=0}(\log x)^{\log(1-x)}$.

11. $Lt_{x=\infty} \dfrac{Ax^n + Bx^{n-1} + Cx^{n-2} + \ldots}{ax^m + bx^{m-1} + cx^{m-2} + \ldots}$ according as n is $>$, $=$, or $< m$.

12. $Lt_{x=0}x^{-x^m}$, m being positive.

13. $Lt_{x=\infty}\left(\dfrac{ax+1}{ax-1}\right)^x$.

14. $Lt_{x=\frac{\pi}{2}}\left(\dfrac{1+\cos x}{1-\cos x}\right)^{\frac{1}{\cos x}}$.

15. $Lt_{x=0}\{\cot(45°-x)\}^{\cot x}$.

16. $Lt_{x=\infty}\left(\dfrac{a_1^{\frac{1}{x}}+a_2^{\frac{1}{x}}+a_3^{\frac{1}{x}}+\ldots+a_n^{\frac{1}{x}}}{n}\right)^{nx}$.

17. $Lt_{x=0}\dfrac{2x^2-2e^{x^2}+2\cos x^{\frac{3}{2}}+\sin^3 x}{x^4}$.

18. $Lt_{x=1}\dfrac{\sqrt{1+x}-\sqrt{1+x^2}}{\sqrt{1-x}-\sqrt{1-x^2}}$.

19. $Lt_{x=\infty}a^x\sin\dfrac{b}{a^x}$ $\quad\begin{cases}\text{(i.) If } a \text{ be} >1.\\ \text{(ii.) If } a \text{ be} <1.\end{cases}$

20. $Lt_{x=0}\dfrac{\operatorname{cosec} x-\cot x}{x}$.

21. $Lt_{x=0}\dfrac{\sqrt{a^2+ax+x^2}-a\sqrt{1+\dfrac{x}{a}}}{\log\cos\dfrac{x}{a}}$.

22. $Lt_{x=a}\dfrac{e^{\frac{a-x}{a}}\sin^{-1}\dfrac{a-x}{a}+\log\dfrac{x}{a}-\dfrac{1}{2}\left(1-\dfrac{x}{a}\right)^2}{\left(\dfrac{3x}{a}-\dfrac{3x^2}{a^2}+\dfrac{x^5}{a^3}\right)^{-1}-1}$.

23. $Lt_{x=0}\left(\dfrac{a}{x}-\cot\dfrac{x}{a}\right)$.

24. $Lt_{x=0}\dfrac{\sqrt{a^2+ax+x^2}-\sqrt{a^2-ax+x^2}}{\sqrt{a+x}-\sqrt{a-x}}$.

25. $Lt_{x=0}\dfrac{\log(1+x+x^2)+\log(1-x+x^2)}{\sec x-\cos x}$.

26. $Lt_{x=0}\dfrac{x\sin(\sin x)-\sin^2 x}{x^6}$.

27. $Lt_{x=0}\dfrac{(1+x)^{\frac{1}{x}}-e}{x}$.

28. $Lt_{x=0}\dfrac{(1+x)^{\frac{1}{x}}-e+\dfrac{ex}{2}-\dfrac{11ex^2}{24}}{x^3}$.

29. $Lt_{x=\infty}\left[x\left(1+\dfrac{1}{x}\right)^x-ex^2\log\left(1+\dfrac{1}{x}\right)\right]$.

30. $Lt_{x=y=a} \dfrac{(x-y)a^n + (y-a)x^n + (a-x)y^n}{(x-y)(y-a)(a-x)}$.

[Put $x = a+h$, $y = a+k$, and expand in powers of h and k, and finally, after reduction, put $h = 0$, $k = 0$.]

31. $Lt_{x=y=1} \dfrac{\log x + \log y}{x+y-2}$.

32. Show that *generally*, if a function of two independent variables take one of the singular forms $\dfrac{0}{0}$, etc., for certain values of the variables, its value is truly indeterminate.

33. Given $x^3 + y^3 + a^3 = 3axy$,

find the values of $\dfrac{dy}{dx}$ when $x = y = a$.

34. Find the values of $\dfrac{dy}{dx}$ at the origin for the curve

$$x^3 + y^3 = 3axy.$$

35. For the curve $x^2 y^2 = (a^2 - y^2)(b+y)^2$

find the values of $\dfrac{dy}{dx}$ at the point $(0, -b)$.

36. For the curve $x^4 + ax^2 y = ay^3$

find the values of $\dfrac{dy}{dx}$ when $x = 0$.

37. Prove $Lt_{x=0} \dfrac{a^x - 1}{x^n \sin x} \left(\dfrac{b \sin x - \sin bx}{\cos x - \cos bx} \right)^n = \left(\dfrac{b}{3} \right)^n \log a$.

38. Prove $Lt_{x=0} \dfrac{\dfrac{d^{n+1}u}{dx^{n+1}}}{\dfrac{d^{n-1}u}{dx^{n-1}}} = n^2 - m^2$,

where $u = \dfrac{\cos my}{\cos y}$ and $x = \sin y$.

39. Find $Lt_{\theta=0} \dfrac{d^2 y}{dx^2}$, where $y = \dfrac{\theta}{\sin \theta}$ and $\theta = \cos^{-1}(1-x)$.

[I. C. S., 1884.]

40. If $y = (\sin^{-1} x)^2$, prove that

$$Lt_{x=0} \dfrac{\dfrac{d^{n+2}y}{dx^{n+2}}}{\dfrac{d^n y}{dx^n}} = n^2.$$

41. Prove that $Lt_{x=\infty} \dfrac{a^{x^m}}{b^{x^n}}$ is zero or infinite according as n is greater or less than m, a and b being both greater than unity.

42. Prove $Lt_{x=a}\left(2 - \dfrac{x}{a}\right)^{\tan\frac{\pi x}{2a}} = e^{\frac{2}{\pi}}$.

43. Prove $Lt_{x=a}\sqrt{a^2 - x^2}\cot\left\{\dfrac{\pi}{2}\sqrt{\dfrac{a-x}{a+x}}\right\} = \dfrac{4a}{\pi}$.

44. Find $Lt_{x=0}(\cos ax)^{\operatorname{cosec}^2 bx}$.

45. Find $Lt\dfrac{a^x\sin bx - b^x\sin ax}{\tan bx - \tan ax}$,
$\begin{cases} (1) \ \text{If } x = 0. \\ (2) \ \text{If } a = b. \end{cases}$

46. Find $Lt_{x=1}\dfrac{x^{\frac{3}{2}} - 1 + (x-1)^{\frac{3}{2}}}{(x^2-1)^{\frac{3}{2}} - x + 1}$.

47. Find $Lt_{x=a}\dfrac{\sqrt{x} - \sqrt{a} + \sqrt{x-a}}{\sqrt{x^2 - a^2}}$.

48. Find $Lt_{x=0}(\cos x)^{\cot x}$.

49. Prove that if, when x is infinite, $\phi(x) = \infty$, then will

$$Lt_{x=\infty}\frac{\phi(x)}{x} = Lt\{\phi(x+1) - \phi(x)\},$$

and also that $\quad Lt_{x=\infty}\{\phi(x)\}^{\frac{1}{x}} = Lt\dfrac{\phi(x+1)}{\phi(x)}$.

[TODHUNTER'S DIFF. CALC.]

50. Prove that $Lt_{x=\infty}\left\{\dfrac{x^x}{x!}\right\}^{\frac{1}{x}} = e$.

[TODHUNTER'S DIFF. CALC.]

51. Prove $\quad Lt_{n=\infty}\dfrac{1^m + 2^m + 3^m + \ldots + n^m}{n^{m+1}} = \dfrac{1}{m+1}$,

m being positive.

52. Prove $Lt_{h=0}h\{a^m + \overline{a+h}|^m + \overline{a+2h}|^m + \ldots + \overline{a+(n-1)h}|^m\}$

$$= \frac{b^{m+1} - a^{m+1}}{m+1},$$

where $\quad h = \dfrac{b-a}{n}$, and a, b are any given quantities.

CHAPTER XV.

MAXIMA AND MINIMA—ONE INDEPENDENT VARIABLE.

480. Elementary Methods.

Examples frequently occur in algebra and geometry in which it is required to find whether any limitations exist to the admissible values of certain functions for *real* values of the variable or variables upon which they depend. These investigations can sometimes be conducted in an elementary manner. A few examples follow in illustration of this.

Ex. 1. The function $x^2 - 4x + 9$ may be written in the form

$$(x-2)^2 + 5,$$

from which it is at once apparent that the least admissible value of the expression is 5, the value which it assumes when $x = 2$. For the square of a real quantity is essentially positive, and therefore any value of x other than 2 will give a greater value than 5 to the expression considered.

Ex. 2. Investigate whether any limitation exists to the values of the expression $\dfrac{x^2 - x + 1}{x^2 + x + 1}$ for real values of x.

Putting $\dfrac{x^2 - x + 1}{x^2 + x + 1} = y,$

we have $x^2(1-y) - x(1+y) + 1 - y = 0,$

an equation whose roots are real only when

$$(1+y)^2 > 4(1-y)^2,$$

i.e., when $(3y-1)(3-y)$ is positive ;

i.e., when y lies between the values 3 and $\frac{1}{3}$. It appears therefore that the given expression *always lies in value between* 3 *and* $\frac{1}{3}$. Its maximum value is therefore 3 and its minimum $\frac{1}{3}$.

Ex. 3. If a, b, c, x, y, z be all real quantities such that $a^2+b^2+c^2$ and $x^2+y^2+z^2$ are both given, then $ax+by+cz$ will have its maximum value when

$$\frac{x}{a}=\frac{y}{b}=\frac{z}{c}.$$

For the identity

$$(a^2+b^2+c^2)(x^2+y^2+z^2)=(ax+by+cz)^2+(bz-cy)^2+(cx-az)^2+(ay-bx)^2$$

shows that $(ax+by+cz)^2$ will have its maximum value when the remaining three squares on the right-hand side have their minimum values. And being squares of real quantities they cannot be negative. Their minimum is therefore when each separately vanishes, which gives the result stated.

Ex. 4. *To determine geometrically the greatest triangle inscribed in a given ellipse.*

It is obvious from elementary considerations that if the ellipse be projected orthogonally into a circle a triangle of maximum area inscribed in the given ellipse must project into a triangle of maximum area inscribed in a circle ; and such a triangle is equilateral and the tangent to the circle at each angular point of the triangle is parallel to the opposite side. This property of parallelism is a projective property, and therefore holds for a maximum triangle inscribed in the given ellipse.

Moreover
$$\frac{\text{Area of a maximum triangle inscribed in the ellipse}}{\text{Area of ellipse}}$$

$$=\frac{\text{Area of equilateral triangle inscribed in a circle}}{\text{Area of the circle}}$$

$$=\frac{3\sqrt{3}}{4\pi}.$$

Hence the area of the greatest triangle inscribed in an ellipse whose semi-axes are a, b is
$$\frac{3\sqrt{3}}{4}ab.$$

Ex. 5. If A, B, C ... be a number of fixed points and P any other point, and if G be the centroid of masses λ at A, μ at B, etc., then it is a geometrical proposition that

$$(\Sigma\lambda PA^2)=(\Sigma\lambda GA^2)+(\Sigma\lambda).PG^2.$$

Hence, since $\Sigma\lambda GA^2$ is a fixed quantity for all positions of P, $\Sigma\lambda PA^2$ has its minimum value when P is at G.

Ex. 6. In any triangle the maximum value of $\cos A \cos B \cos C$ is $\frac{1}{8}$.

For
$$2\cos A \cos B \cos C=\cos A(\cos \overline{B-C}-\cos A),$$

and therefore as long as B and C are unequal we may increase the expression by making them more nearly equal and keeping their sum constant. Thus $\cos A \cos B \cos C$ does not attain its maximum value until

$$A=B=C=\frac{\pi}{3},$$

and then its value $=(\frac{1}{2})^3$.

EXAMPLES.

1. Show algebraically that the expression $x+\dfrac{1}{x}$ cannot lie between 2 and -2 for real values of x. Illustrate this geometrically by tracing the hyperbola $$xy-x^2=1.$$

2. Prove that, if x be real, $\dfrac{x^2-4x+9}{x^2+4x+9}$ must lie between 5 and $\frac{1}{5}$.

3. Show that, if x be real, $\dfrac{x+a}{x-a}\cdot\dfrac{x+b}{x-b}$ cannot lie between the values

$$-\left(\frac{\sqrt{a}+\sqrt{b}}{\sqrt{a}-\sqrt{b}}\right)^2 \text{ and } -\left(\frac{\sqrt{a}-\sqrt{b}}{\sqrt{a}+\sqrt{b}}\right)^2.$$

4. Show that the triangle of greatest area with given base and vertical angle is isosceles.

5. If A, B be two given points on the same side of a given straight line and P be a point in the line, then $AP+BP$ will be least when AP and BP are equally inclined to the straight line.

6. Show that the triangle of least perimeter inscribable in a given triangle is the pedal triangle.

7. Show that the greatest chord passing through a point of intersection of two given circles is that which is drawn parallel to the line joining the centres.

8. Determine the maximum triangle of given species whose sides pass through given points.

9. Find the least isosceles triangle which can be described about an ellipse with its base parallel to one of the axes, and show that it has its sides parallel to those of the greatest isosceles triangle which can be inscribed in the same ellipse with its vertex at one extremity of the other axis.   [I. C. S., 1884.]

10. The diagonals of a maximum parallelogram inscribed in an ellipse are conjugate diameters of the ellipse.

11. If the sum of two varying positive quantities be constant, show that their product is greatest when the quantities are equal. Extend this to the case of any number of positive quantities.

12. If $a^2x^4+b^2y^4=c^4$, find the maximum value of xy.   [I. C. S., 1889.]

13. If A, B, C be the angular points of a triangle and P any other point, then $AP+BP+CP$ will be a minimum when each of the angles at P is $120°$. [AP is a normal to the ellipse with foci B, C and passing through P.]

14. Find a point P within a triangle ABC such that $AP^2+BP^2+CP^2$ has a minimum value.

15. Prove from statical considerations, or otherwise, that if P be a point within a triangle, then

$$AP^2\tan A+BP^2\tan B+CP^2\tan C$$

has its minimum value when P is the orthocentre.

16. If a triangle be inscribed in a circle of given radius R, show that the maximum value of the sum of the squares of the sides is $9R^2$.

17. If $\theta + \phi =$ const., the maximum value of $\sin \theta \sin \phi$ is attained when
$$\theta = \phi.$$

18. Show trigonometrically that the greatest and least values of the expression $\qquad a \sin x + b \cos x$

are $\qquad \sqrt{a^2 + b^2}$ and $-\sqrt{a^2 + b^2}$.

19. Show by trigonometry that the greatest and least values of the function $\qquad a \cos^2\theta + 2h \sin \theta \cos \theta + b \sin^2\theta$

are respectively $\qquad \dfrac{a+b}{2} \pm \sqrt{\left(\dfrac{a-b}{2}\right)^2 + h^2}.$

20. Find the rectangle of maximum area whose sides pass through the angular points of a given rectangle.

21. PSP', QSQ' are focal chords of a conic intersecting at right angles. Find the positions of the chords when $PP' + QQ'$ has a maximum or minimum value.

THE GENERAL PROBLEM.

481. Suppose x to be any independent variable capable of assuming *any real value whatever*, and let $\phi(x)$ be any given function of x. Let the curve $y = \phi(x)$ be represented in the adjoining figure, and let $A, B, C, D, \ldots$ be those points on the curve at which the tangent is parallel to one of the co-ordinate axes.

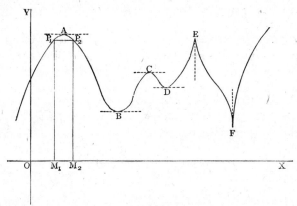

Fig. 112.

Suppose an ordinate to travel from left to right along the axis of x. Then it will be seen that as the ordinate passes such points as A, C, or E it *ceases to increase and begins to decrease;* whilst when it passes through B, D, or F it *ceases to decrease and begins to increase.* At each of the former set of points the ordinate is said to have a **maximum** value, whilst at the latter it is said to have a **minimum** value.

482. Points of Inflexion.

On inspection of Fig. 113 it will be at once obvious that at such points of inflexion as G or H, where the tangent is parallel to one of the co-ordinate axes, there is neither a maximum

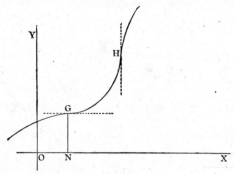

Fig. 113.

nor a minimum ordinate. Near G, for instance, the ordinate increases up to a certain value NG, and then as it passes through G it continues to increase without any prior *sensible* decrease.

This point may however be considered as a combination of two such points as A and B in Fig. 112, the ordinate increasing

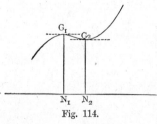

Fig. 114.

up to a certain value N_1G_1, then decreasing through an indefinitely small and negligible interval to N_2G_2, and then increasing again as shown in the magnified figure (Fig. 114), the points G_1, G_2 being ultimately coincident.

483. We are thus led to the following definition :—

DEF. *If, while the independent variable x increases contin-uously, a function dependent upon it, say $\phi(x)$, increase through any finite interval however small until $x = a$ and then decrease, $\phi(a)$ is said to be a* MAXIMUM *value of $\phi(x)$. And if $\phi(x)$ decrease to $\phi(a)$ and then increase, both decrease and increase being through a finite interval, then $\phi(a)$ is said to be a* MINIMUM *value of $\phi(x)$.*

484. Criteria for the discrimination of Maxima and Minima Values.

The criteria may be deduced at once from the aspect of $\dfrac{dy}{dx}$ as a *rate-measurer.* For $\dfrac{dy}{dx}$ is positive or negative according as y is an increasing or a decreasing function. Now, if y have a *maximum* value it is ceasing to increase and beginning to decrease, and therefore $\dfrac{dy}{dx}$ must be changing from *positive to negative;* and if y have a *minimum* value it is ceasing to decrease and beginning to increase, and therefore $\dfrac{dy}{dx}$ must be changing from *negative to positive.* Moreover, since a change from positive to negative, or *vice versa,* can only occur by passing through one of the values zero or in-finity, we must search for the maximum and minimum values among those corresponding to the values of x given by $\phi'(x) = 0$ or by $\phi'(x) = \infty$.

485. Further, since $\dfrac{dy}{dx}$ must be increasing when it changes from negative to positive, $\dfrac{d^2y}{dx^2}$ if not zero must then be positive ; and similarly, when $\dfrac{dy}{dx}$ changes from positive to negative $\dfrac{d^2y}{dx^2}$ must be negative, so we arrive at another form of the criterion for maxima and minima values, viz., that there will be a maxi-mum or minimum according as the value of x which makes $\dfrac{dy}{dx}$ zero or infinite, gives $\dfrac{d^2y}{dx^2}$ *a negative or a positive sign.*

486. Properties of Maxima and Minima Values. Criteria obtained Geometrically.

The following statements will be obvious from the figures 112 and 113 :—

(*a*) According to the definition given in Art. 483, the term maximum value does not mean the absolutely greatest nor minimum the absolutely least value of the function discussed. Moreover there may be *several maxima* values and *several minima* values of the same function, some greater and some less than others, as in the case of the ordinates at *A, B, C, ...* (Fig. 112).

(*β*) Between two equal values of a function *at least one maximum or one minimum must lie;* for whether the function be increasing or decreasing as it passes the value [M_1P_1 in Fig. 112] it must, if continuous, respectively decrease or increase again at least once before it attains its original value, and therefore must pass through at least one maximum or minimum value in the interval.

(*γ*) For a similar reason it is clear that between two maxima at least one minimum must lie; and between two minima at least one maximum must lie. In other words, maxima and minima values must occur alternately. Thus we have a maximum at *A*, a minimum at *B*, a maximum at *C*, etc.

(*δ*) In the immediate neighbourhood of a maximum or minimum ordinate two contiguous ordinates are equal, one on each side of the maximum or minimum ordinate; and these may be considered as ultimately coincident with the maximum or minimum ordinate. Moreover as the ordinate is ceasing to increase and beginning to decrease, its rate of variation is itself in general an infinitesimal. This is expressed by saying that at a maximum or minimum the function discussed has a **stationary** value. This principle is of much use in the geometrical treatment of maxima and minima problems.

(*ε*) At all points, such as *A, B, C, D, E, ...*, at which maxima and minima ordinates occur the *tangent is parallel to one or other of the co-ordinate axes*. At points like *A, B, C, D* the value of $\frac{dy}{dx}$ vanishes, whilst at the cuspidal points *E, F*, $\frac{dy}{dx}$ becomes infinite. The positions of maxima and minima ordinates are therefore given by the roots of the equations

$$\left.\begin{array}{l} \phi'(x)=0 \\ \phi'(x)=\infty \end{array}\right\}.$$

(ζ) That $\dfrac{dy}{dx} = 0$, or $\dfrac{dy}{dx} = \infty$, are not in themselves *sufficient* conditions for the existence of a maximum or minimum value is clear from observing the points G, H of Fig. 113, at which the tangent is parallel to one of the co-ordinate axes, but at

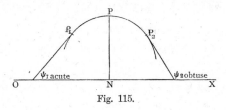

Fig. 115.

which the ordinate has not a maximum or minimum value. But in passing a *maximum* value of the ordinate the angle ψ which the tangent makes with OX changes from acute to obtuse (Fig. 115), and therefore $\tan \psi$, or $\dfrac{dy}{dx}$, changes from *positive to negative;* while in passing a *minimum* value ψ changes from obtuse to acute (Fig. 116), and therefore $\dfrac{dy}{dx}$ changes from *negative to positive.*

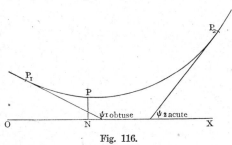

Fig. 116.

487. Working Rule.

We can therefore make the following rule for the **detection and discrimination** of maxima and minima values. First *find* $\dfrac{dy}{dx}$ and by equating it to zero find for what values of x it *vanishes;* also observe if any values of x will make it become *infinite.* Then test for each of these values whether the sign of $\dfrac{dy}{dx}$ *changes from + to − or from − to +* as x increases

through that value. If the former be the case y has a **maximum**
value for that value of x; but if the latter, a **minimum**. If no
change of sign take place the point is **a point of inflexion** at
which the tangent is parallel to one of the co-ordinate axes;
or, in some cases it may be more convenient to discriminate by
applying the test of Art. 485. Find the sign of $\dfrac{d^2y}{dx^2}$ corresponding to the value of x under discussion. A *positive* sign
indicates a *minimum* value for y; a *negative* sign, a *maximum*.
When $\dfrac{d^2y}{dx^2}=0$ this test fails and there is need of further investigation (Art. 488).

EXAMPLES.

1. Find the maximum and minimum values of y where
$$y=(x-1)(x-2)^2.$$
Here
$$\frac{dy}{dx}=(x-2)^2+2(x-1)(x-2)$$
$$=(x-2)(3x-4).$$

Putting this expression $=0$ we obtain for the values of x which give
possible maxima or minima values
$$x=2 \quad \text{and} \quad x=\frac{4}{3}.$$

To test these : we have

if x be a little less than 2, $\dfrac{dy}{dx}=(-)(+)=$ negative,

if x be a little greater than 2, $\dfrac{dy}{dx}=(+)(+)=$ positive.

Hence there is a change of sign, viz., from negative to positive as x passes
through the value 2, and therefore $x=2$ gives y a *minimum* value.

Again,   if x be a little less than $\dfrac{4}{3}$, $\dfrac{dy}{dx}=(-)(-)=$ positive,

and   if x be a little greater than $\dfrac{4}{3}$, $\dfrac{dy}{dx}=(-)(+)=$ negative,

showing that there is a change of sign in $\dfrac{dy}{dx}$, viz., from positive to negative,
and therefore $x=\dfrac{4}{3}$ gives a *maximum* value for y.

Otherwise : $\dfrac{dy}{dx}=(x-2)(3x-4),$

so that when $\dfrac{dy}{dx}$ is put $=0$ we obtain $x=2$ or $\dfrac{4}{3}.$

And $\dfrac{d^2y}{dx^2}=6x-10,$

so that, when $x=2$, $\dfrac{d^2y}{dx^2}=2,$

a positive quantity, showing that, when $x=2$, y assumes a minimum value, whilst, when $x=\frac{4}{3}$, $\frac{d^2y}{dx^2}=-2$,

which is negative, showing that, for this value of x, y assumes a maximum value.

2. If
$$\frac{dy}{dx}=(x-a)^{2n}(x-b)^{2p+1},$$

where n and p are positive integers, show that $x=a$ gives neither maximum nor minimum values of y, but that $x=b$ gives a minimum.

It will be clear from this example that neither maxima nor minima values can arise from the vanishing of such factors of $\frac{dy}{dx}$ as have even indices.

3. Show that $\frac{x^2-7x+6}{x-10}$ has a maximum value when $x=4$ and a minimum when $x=16$.

4. If
$$\frac{dy}{dx}=x(x-1)^2(x-3)^3,$$

show that $x=0$ gives a maximum value to y

and $x=3$ gives a minimum.

5. Find the maximum and minimum values of
$$2x^3-15x^2+36x+6.$$

6. Show that the expression
$$(x-2)(x-3)^2$$

has a maximum value when $x=\frac{7}{3}$, and a minimum value when $x=3$.

7. Show that the expression
$$x^3-3x^2+6x+3$$

has neither a maximum nor a minimum value.

8. Investigate the maximum and minimum values of the expression
$$3x^5-25x^3+60x.$$

9. For a certain curve
$$\frac{dy}{dx}=(x-1)(x-2)^2(x-3)^3(x-4)^4\ ;$$

discuss the character of the curve at the points $x=1$, $x=2$, $x=3$, $x=4$.

10. Find the positions of the maximum and minimum ordinates of the curve for which $\frac{dy}{dx}=(x-2)^3(2x-3)^4(3x-4)^5(4x-5)^6.$

11. *To show that a triangle of maximum area inscribed in any oval curve is such that the tangent at each angular point is parallel to the opposite side.*

If PQR be a maximum triangle inscribed in the oval, its vertex P lies between the vertices L, M of two equal triangles LQR, MQR inscribed in

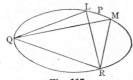

Fig. 117.

the oval. Now, the chord LM is parallel to QR and the tangent at P is the limiting position of the chord LM, which proves the proposition.

It follows that, if the oval be an ellipse, the medians of the triangle are diameters of the curve, and therefore the centre of gravity of the triangle is at the centre of the ellipse.

12. *Show that the sides of a triangle of minimum area circumscribing any oval curve are bisected at the points of contact ; and hence that, if the oval be an ellipse, the centre of gravity of such a triangle coincides with the centre of the ellipse.*

Let ABC be a triangle of minimum area circumscribing the oval. Suppose P the point of contact of BC. Let AB_1C_1, AB_2C_2 be two equal

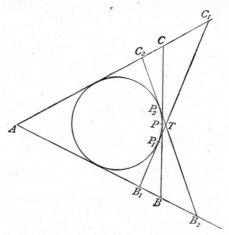

Fig. 118.

circumscribing triangles such that B_1C_1, B_2C_2 touch the oval at P_1, P_2 on opposite sides of P and intersect in T. Then

$$\text{triangle } TB_1B_2 = \text{triangle } TC_1C_2$$

or $\tfrac{1}{2}TB_1 . TB_2\sin B_1TB_2 = \tfrac{1}{2}TC_1 . TC_2\sin C_1TC_2.$

If we bring P_1 and P_2 nearer and nearer to P so as to entrap the minimum triangle, the above equation ultimately becomes

$$TB^2 = TC^2 ;$$

and T being ultimately the point of contact P, the side BC is bisected at its point of contact. The remainder follows as in Ex. 11.

13. *To show that a triangle of maximum perimeter inscribed in any oval is such that the tangent at any angular point makes equal angles with the sides which meet at that point.*

For, with Fig. 117, let PQR be a triangle of maximum perimeter inscribed in the oval; its vertex P lies between the vertices L, M of two inscribed triangles LQR, MQR of equal perimeter. Now since

$$QL + LR = QM + MR,$$

L and M lie upon an ellipse whose foci are Q and R. When we proceed to the limit where L and M approach indefinitely near P the curve and the ellipse have the same tangent at P. Hence the result. Also if the oval be an ellipse it is clear that the sides will touch a confocal.

14. *If a triangle of minimum perimeter circumscribe an oval, the points of contact of the sides are also the points where they are touched by the e-circles of the triangle.*

Let ABC be a triangle of minimum perimeter circumscribing an oval. Suppose P the point of contact of BC. Let AB_1C_1, AB_2C_2 be two circumscribing triangles of equal perimeter such that B_1C_1, B_2C_2 touch the curve at P_1, P_2 on opposite sides of P and intersect in T. Then

$$B_2B_1 + B_1C_1 = B_2C_2 + C_2C_1.$$

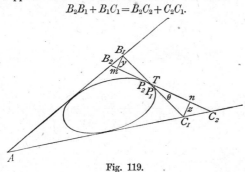

Fig. 119.

Let perpendiculars $B_1m(=y)$ and $C_1n(=z)$ be drawn upon B_2C_2, and let $B_1TB_2 = \theta$ an infinitesimal of the first order; y and z are therefore also first order infinitesimals. The above equation then becomes

$$y \operatorname{cosec} B_2 + (y+z)\operatorname{cosec} \theta = y \cot(\pi - B_2) + (y+z)\cot \theta + z \cot C_2 + z \operatorname{cosec} C_2$$

or
$$\left(y \cot \frac{B_2}{2} - z \cot \frac{C_2}{2}\right)\sin \theta + (y+z)(1 - \cos \theta) = 0.$$

Now $1 - \cos \theta$ is a second order infinitesimal, and rejecting third and higher orders we obtain

$$Lt \frac{y}{z} = \frac{\tan \dfrac{B}{2}}{\tan \dfrac{C}{2}}.$$

Now
$$Lt \frac{y}{z} = Lt \frac{B_1T}{C_1T} = \frac{BP}{CP}.$$

Thus the side BC is divided at the point of contact in the ratio

$$\tan \frac{B}{2} : \tan \frac{C}{2}.$$

These points are the points of contact also with the escribed circles of the triangle.

15. *To find the path of a ray of light from a point A in one medium to a point B in another medium, supposing the path to be such that the least possible time is occupied in passing from A to B, and that the velocity of propagation of light changes from v to v' on passing the boundary separating the media.*   [FERMAT'S PROBLEM.]

We shall, for simplicity, consider A and B to lie in the plane of the paper, and the separating surface of the media to be cylindrical with its generators perpendicular to the plane of the paper.

Let OPP' be the section of the separating surface by the plane of the paper, and let APB, $AP'B$ be two contiguous paths from A to B.   Then,

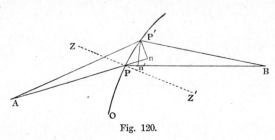

Fig. 120.

if the times in these two paths be equal, the quickest path lies between them.   Let fall perpendiculars $P'n$, $P'n'$ from P' upon AP and BP, and draw the normal ZPZ' at the point P.

Then, since the time in APB=time in $AP'B$,

$$\frac{AP}{v}+\frac{PB}{v'}=\frac{AP'}{v}+\frac{BP'}{v'},$$

or in the limit

$$\frac{Pn}{v}=\frac{Pn'}{v'},$$

whence

$$Lt\frac{\sin nPZ'}{\sin n'PZ'}=Lt\frac{Pn}{Pn'}=\frac{v}{v'}\ ;$$

and therefore, if in the limit the incident ray AP and the refracted ray PB make angles i, i' respectively with the normal at P, we obtain

$$\frac{\sin i}{\sin i'}=\frac{v}{v'},$$

thus proving Snell's well known law of refraction.

16. Another example of the power of this geometrical method is to be found in the following dynamical problem.

To find the nature of the curve along which a particle can slide from one given point to a second not in the same vertical line under the action of gravity in the shortest time.*

It may be taken as obvious that the path between any two points lies entirely in the vertical plane joining them.

Let A and B be two points of the path very near to each other.   Let APB, $AP'B$ be two contiguous broken rectilineal paths, which may be regarded as so short that the velocity through AP and AP' may be regarded as constant and equal to that at A (v say), and that the velocities in PB and $P'B$ are constant and equal to that at B (v').   And suppose

---

* Woodhouse, *Isoperimetrical Problems,* referred to by Tait and Steel, *Dynamics of a Particle.*   App. C.

that the points P, P' are in a horizontal line (Px), and that the times down these paths are equal. If Q be another point in Px such that the time down AQ, QB is a minimum, Q lies between P and P'.

Constructing as in Ex. 15 we have in the same way

$$v \propto \cos \psi, \text{ where } \psi = AQx.$$

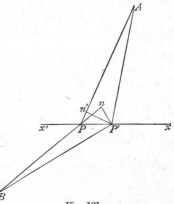

Fig. 121.

Now it is known from elementary dynamics that $v^2 \propto$ vertical distance fallen through. Hence the curve is such that the vertical distance of the particle at any instant from the horizontal through the starting-point $\propto \cos^2\psi$. Thus the path is identified with the cycloid, Arts. 394 and 397.

This curve has therefore been called a Brachistochrone for particles sliding down it under the action of gravity.

17. Extend the results of Examples 11, 12, 13, 14 to polygons inscribed in or circumscribing an oval.

18. Show that the chord of a given curve which passes through a given point and cuts off a maximum or minimum area is bisected at the point.

19. Find the area of the greatest triangle which can be inscribed in a given parabolic segment having for its base the bounding chord of the segment.

20. In any oval curve the maximum or minimum chord which is normal at one end is either a radius of curvature at that end, or normal at both ends.

21. In the axis of a given parabola and within the curve are taken two fixed points P, Q; find the point on the curve at which the line PQ subtends the greatest angle, and show that, if the semi-latus rectum is an Arithmetic mean between the distances of P, Q from the vertex, the abscissa of the point is to the geometric mean between the distances as $1 : \sqrt{3}$. [OXFORD, 1889.]

488. Analytical Investigation.

We now proceed to investigate the conditions for the existence of maxima and minima values from a purely analytical point of view.

It appears from the definition given of maxima and minima values that as x increases or decreases from the value a through any small but finite interval h, if $\phi(x)$ be always less than $\phi(a)$, then $\phi(a)$ is a maximum value of $\phi(x)$; and that if $\phi(x)$ be always greater than $\phi(a)$, then $\phi(a)$ is a minimum value of $\phi(x)$.

We shall assume in the present article that none of the derived functions we find it necessary to employ become infinite or discontinuous for the particular values discussed of the independent variable. We then have by Lagrange's modification of Taylor's Theorem

$$\left. \begin{aligned} \phi(x+h)-\phi(x) &= h\phi'(x)+\frac{h^2}{2!}\phi''(x+\theta h) \\ \text{and} \qquad \phi(x-h)-\phi(x) &= -h\phi'(x)+\frac{h^2}{2!}\phi''(x-\theta'h) \end{aligned} \right\} \dots\dots\dots\text{(A)}$$

And when h is made sufficiently small the sign of the right-hand side of each equation, and therefore also of the left-hand side, is ultimately dependent upon that of $h\phi'(x)$, that being the term of lowest degree in h.

Hence
$$\left. \begin{aligned} \phi(x+h)-\phi(x) \\ \text{and} \qquad \phi(x-h)-\phi(x) \end{aligned} \right\}$$

have in general *opposite signs*.

For a maximum or minimum value, however, it has been explained above that these expressions must, when h is taken small enough, have the *same sign*. It is therefore necessary that $\phi'(x)$ should *vanish*, so that the lowest terms of the right-hand sides of the equations (A) should depend upon an even power of h. $\phi'(x)=0$ is therefore an *essential* condition for the occurrence of a maximum or minimum value. Let the roots of this equation be a, b, c, ...

Consider the root $\qquad x=a.$

We may now replace equations (A) by the two equations

$$\left. \begin{aligned} \phi(a+h)-\phi(a) &= \frac{h^2}{2!}\phi''(a)+\frac{h^3}{3!}\phi'''(a+\theta_1 h) \\ \phi(a-h)-\phi(a) &= \frac{h^2}{2!}\phi''(a)-\frac{h^3}{3!}\phi'''(a-\theta'_1 h) \end{aligned} \right\} \dots\ \dots\dots\text{(B)}$$

It is obvious now as before that the term $\frac{h^2}{2!}\phi''(a)$, being that of lowest degree, governs the sign of the right and therefore also of the left side of each of equations (B); *i.e.*, in general the signs of
$$\left. \begin{aligned} \phi(a+h)-\phi(a) \\ \text{and} \qquad \phi(a-h)-\phi(a) \end{aligned} \right\}$$
are the same as that of $\phi''(a)$. Hence if $\phi''(a)$ be *negative* $\phi(a+h)$ and $\phi(a-h)$ are both $< \phi(a)$, and therefore $\phi(a)$ is a

maximum value of $\phi(x)$; while if $\phi''(a)$ be *positive* both $\phi(a+h)$ and $\phi(a-h)$ are $> \phi(a)$, and therefore $\phi(a)$ is a *minimum* value of $\phi(x)$.

But if it should happen that $\phi''(a)$ vanishes, equations (B) are replaced by

$$\left.\begin{aligned}\phi(a+h)-\phi(a)&=\frac{h^3}{3!}\phi'''(a)+\frac{h^4}{4!}\phi''''(a+\theta_2 h)\\ \phi(a-h)-\phi(a)&=-\frac{h^3}{3!}\phi'''(a)+\frac{h^4}{4!}\phi''''(a-\theta'_2 h)\end{aligned}\right\} ;\ \ldots\ldots\text{(c)}$$

and therefore when h is sufficiently small

$$\left.\begin{aligned}\phi(a+h)-\phi(a)\\ \phi(a-h)-\phi(a)\end{aligned}\right\}$$

are of opposite signs, and therefore there cannot be a maximum or minimum value of $\phi(x)$ when $x=a$ unless $\phi'''(a)$ also vanish, in which case the sign of the right side of each equation depends upon that of $\phi''''(a)$. And, as before, if this be negative we have a maximum value and if positive a minimum.

Similarly, if several successive differential coefficients vanish when x is put equal to a, it appears that for a maximum or minimum value it is essential that the first not vanishing should be of an *even order,* and that if that differential coefficient be *negative* when $x=a$ a *maximum* value of $\phi(x)$ is indicated, but if *positive* a *minimum.*

EXAMPLES.

1. Determine for what values of x the function
$$\phi(x)=12x^5-45x^4+40x^3+6$$
acquires maximum or minimum values.

Here $\phi'(x)=60(x^4-3x^3+2x^2).$

Putting this $=0$ we obtain $x=0$, $x=1$, $x=2$.

Again $\phi''(x)=60(4x^3-9x^2+4x).$

If $x=1$, $\phi''(x)$ is negative and therefore we have a maximum value; if $x=2$, $\phi''(x)$ is positive and therefore this value of x gives a minimum value for $\phi(x)$. If $x=0$, $\phi''(x)$ vanishes, so we must proceed further.

Now $\phi'''(x)=60(12x^2-18x+4),$

which does not vanish when $x=0$, so $x=0$ gives neither a maximum nor a minimum.

2. Show that $x=0$ gives a maximum value, and $x=1$ a minimum, for the function $\dfrac{x^3}{3}-\dfrac{x^2}{2}.$

3. Show that $x=0$ gives a maximum and $x=1$ a minimum for
$$\frac{x^5}{5}-\frac{x^4}{4}.$$

4. Show that the expression $\sin^3\theta \cos\theta$ attains a maximum value when
$$\theta=60°.$$

5. Illustrate geometrically the statement of Art. 488 that in general $\phi(x+h)-\phi(x)$ and $\phi(x-h)-\phi(x)$ are of opposite sign.

6. Show that the maximum value of
$$\frac{x^2}{(a^2+x^2)^3} \quad\text{is}\quad \frac{4}{27a^4}.$$

7. If $u=x^m(a-x)^n$, the critical values are
$$x=0, \quad x=a, \quad x=\frac{ma}{m+n}.$$
Examine the several cases arising as m and n are odd or even.

8. If $u=x/\log x$, prove that $x=e$ gives a minimum.

9. If $u=\dfrac{(x+a)(x+b)}{(x-a)(x-b)}$, prove that the maximum and minimum are

respectively $\qquad -\left(\dfrac{\sqrt{a}+\sqrt{b}}{\sqrt{a}-\sqrt{b}}\right)^2$ and $-\left(\dfrac{\sqrt{a}-\sqrt{b}}{\sqrt{a}+\sqrt{b}}\right)^2.$

(Compare Ex. 3, p. 390.)

10. Discuss the maxima and minima values of
$$\cos mx \cos^m(a+x).$$

11. *ABCDEFabcdef* is a right prism upon a regular hexagonal base. The corners B, D, F are cut off by planes through the lines AC, CE, EA meeting in a point V on the axis VN of the prism, and intersecting Bb, Dd, Ff respectively at X, Y, Z. It is plain that the volume of the figure thus formed is the same as that of the original prism with hexagonal ends. For if the axis cut the hexagon $ABCDEF$ in N, the volumes $VNAC$, $XBAC$ are clearly equal. It is required to determine the inclination of the faces forming the trihedral solid angle at V to the axis so that the surface of the figure may be a minimum.*

Let $\qquad NVX=\theta$, side of hexagon $=a$, $Aa=h$.

Then $\qquad\qquad AC=2a\cos 30°=a\sqrt{3}$

and $\qquad\qquad VX=a/\sin\theta.$

Hence $\qquad$ area of rhombus $= VAXC=a^2\sqrt{3}/2\sin\theta.$

* Gregory (*Examples*, page 106) makes the following interesting remark:—
"This is the celebrated problem of the form of the cells of bees. Maraldi was the first who measured the angles of the faces of the terminating solid angle, and he found them to be 109° 28' and 70° 32' respectively. It occurred to Réaumur that this might be the form, which, for the solid content, gives the minimum of surface, and he requested Koenig to examine the question mathematically. That geometer confirmed the conjecture; the result of his calculations agreeing with Maraldi's measurements within 2'. Maclaurin and L'Huillier, by different methods, verified the preceding result, excepting that they showed that the difference of 2' was due to an error in the calculations of Koenig—not to a mistake on the part of the bees."

Again area of $A\dot{a}bX = \dfrac{a}{2}(2h - \frac{1}{2}VX\cos\theta)$

$$= \dfrac{a}{2}(2h - \dfrac{a}{2}\cot\theta).$$

Hence the total area = hexagon $abcdef + 3a(2h - \dfrac{a}{2}\cot\theta) + 3a^2\sqrt{3}/2\sin\theta$.

Differentiating,

$$\dfrac{d(\text{Area})}{d\theta} = \dfrac{3a^2}{2}\left(\dfrac{1}{\sin^2\theta} - \dfrac{\sqrt{3}\cos\theta}{\sin^2\theta}\right) = 0.$$

Hence $\cos\theta = \dfrac{1}{\sqrt{3}}$.

The change of sign is evidently from negative to positive as θ increases through $\cos^{-1}\dfrac{1}{\sqrt{3}}$; hence this angle gives the minimum surface.

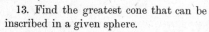

Fig. 123.

12. A person being in a boat a miles from the nearest point of the beach wishes to reach as quickly as possible a point b miles from that point along the shore. The ratio of his rate of walking to his rate of rowing is sec a. Prove that he should land at a distance $b - a\cot a$ from the place to be reached.

13. Find the greatest cone that can be inscribed in a given sphere.

14. Find the cone of least surface which can be circumscribed about a given sphere, and show that it is also the circumscribing cone of minimum volume.

IMPLICIT FUNCTIONS.

489. In the case in which the quantity y, whose maximum and minimum values are the subject of investigation, appears as an implicit function of x, and cannot readily be expressed explicitly, we may proceed as follows:—

Let the connecting relation between x and y be

$$\phi(x, y) = 0, \dots\dots\dots\dots\dots\dots(1)$$

then $\dfrac{\partial\phi}{\partial x} + \dfrac{\partial\phi}{\partial y}\dfrac{dy}{dx} = 0. \dots\dots\dots\dots\dots(2)$

Now in searching for maxima and minima values of y those values of x are critical which make $\dfrac{dy}{dx}$ zero or infinite. Thus we should examine the cases for which $\dfrac{\partial\phi}{\partial x}$, or $\dfrac{\partial\phi}{\partial y}$ change sign.

Taking, for instance, the case of maxima or minima deduced
from the equations

$$\phi(x,\,y)=0 \atop \dfrac{\partial \phi}{\partial x}=0 \Bigg\} ,\quad \dots\dots\dots\dots\dots\dots(3)$$

we can proceed to their discrimination as follows:—

Differentiating equation (2) we have

$$\frac{\partial^2 \phi}{\partial x^2}+\frac{\partial^2 \phi}{\partial x \partial y}\cdot\frac{dy}{dx}+\left(\frac{\partial^2 \phi}{\partial x \partial y}+\frac{\partial^2 \phi}{\partial y^2}\cdot\frac{dy}{dx}\right)\frac{dy}{dx}+\frac{\partial \phi}{\partial y}\cdot\frac{d^2 y}{dx^2}=0,\dots.(4)$$

and, remembering that $\dfrac{dy}{dx}=0$, this reduces to

$$\frac{d^2 y}{dx^2}=-\frac{\dfrac{\partial^2 \phi}{\partial x^2}}{\dfrac{\partial \phi}{\partial y}}.\quad\dots\dots\dots\dots\dots\dots(5)$$

Substituting the values of x and y derived from equations (3)
we can test the sign of $\dfrac{d^2 y}{dx^2}$, and thus discriminate between the
maxima and minima values.

The case in which this test fails, viz., when $\dfrac{\partial^2 \phi}{\partial x^2}=0$ for the
values of x and y deduced by equations (3), is complicated
owing to the complex nature of the general formulae for
$\dfrac{d^3 y}{dx^3}$ and $\dfrac{d^4 y}{dx^4}$.

Ex. Find the maximum and minimum ordinates of the curve
$$x^3+y^3=3axy.$$

Here
$$(x^2-ay)+(y^2-ax)\frac{dy}{dx}=0,\dots\dots\dots\dots\dots\dots(1)$$

and $\dfrac{dy}{dx}=0$ gives
$$x^2=ay.$$

Combining this with the equation to the curve we obtain
$$y^3=2axy\,;$$

i.e.,
$$y=0 \text{ or } y^2=2ax.$$

y=0 gives
$$x=0,$$

whilst $y^2=2ax$ and $x^2=ay$ $\Big\}$ give
$$y^4=4a^3 y,$$

which presents the additional solution
$$y=a\sqrt[3]{4},$$
$$x=a\sqrt[3]{2}.$$

Hence the points at which maxima or minima ordinates may exist have for their co-ordinates $(0, 0)$ and $(a \sqrt[3]{2}, \; a \sqrt[3]{4})$.

Now $\qquad \dfrac{\partial^2 \phi}{\partial x^2} = 6x$ and $\dfrac{\partial \phi}{\partial y} = 3(y^2 - ax)$,

and therefore at the point $\qquad x = a \sqrt[3]{2}$,

$$y = a \sqrt[3]{4},$$

$$\frac{d^2 y}{dx^2} = - \frac{\dfrac{\partial^2 \phi}{\partial x^2}}{\dfrac{\partial \phi}{\partial y}} = - \frac{2x}{y^2 - ax} = \frac{-2a \sqrt[3]{2}}{2a^2 \sqrt[3]{2} - a^2 \sqrt[3]{2}} = - \frac{2}{a},$$

and is negative, and therefore at this point y has a maximum value.

At the point $x = 0$, $y = 0$, the formulae for $\dfrac{dy}{dx}$ and $\dfrac{d^2 y}{dx^2}$ both become indeterminate, and we have to investigate their true values.

Differentiating equation (1) we have

$$2x - 2a \frac{dy}{dx} + 2y \left(\frac{dy}{dx} \right)^2 + (y^2 - ax) \frac{d^2 y}{dx^2} = 0,$$

$$2 + 2 \left(\frac{dy}{dx} \right)^3 + \left(6y \frac{dy}{dx} - 3a \right) \frac{d^2 y}{dx^2} + (y^2 - ax) \frac{d^3 y}{dx^3} = 0.$$

And when x and y both vanish these give

$$\frac{dy}{dx} = 0 \text{ and } \frac{d^2 y}{dx^2} = \frac{2}{3a},$$

showing that the ordinate y has for this point a minimum value.

Several Dependent Variables.

490. Suppose the quantity u, whose maxima and minima values are the subject of investigation, to be a function of n variables x, y, z, etc., but that by virtue of $n-1$ relations between them there is but one variable independent, say x. We may now, from the $n-1$ equations, theoretically find the $n-1$ dependent variables y, z, ... in terms of x, and suppose that by substitution u is expressed as a function of the one independent variable x. The methods of the preceding articles can now be applied. It is often, however, inconvenient, even if possible, actually to eliminate the $n-1$ dependent variables y, z, etc., and it is not necessary that this should be immediately done.

Suppose, for instance, $\qquad u = \phi(x, y, z)$
a function such as the one discussed, x the independent variable, y and z dependent variables connected with x by the relations

$$F_1(x, y, z) = 0,$$
$$F_2(x, y, z) = 0.$$

Then putting $\dfrac{du}{dx}=0$ for a maximum or minimum, we have

$$\frac{du}{dx}=\frac{\partial\phi}{\partial x}+\frac{\partial\phi}{\partial y}\cdot\frac{dy}{dx}+\frac{\partial\phi}{\partial z}\cdot\frac{dz}{dx}=0,\ \ldots\ldots\ldots\ldots(1)$$

$$\frac{\partial F_1}{\partial x}+\frac{\partial F_1}{\partial y}\cdot\frac{dy}{dx}+\frac{\partial F_1}{\partial z}\cdot\frac{dz}{dx}=0,\ \ldots\ldots\ldots\ldots(2)$$

$$\frac{\partial F_2}{\partial x}+\frac{\partial F_2}{\partial y}\cdot\frac{dy}{dx}+\frac{\partial F_2}{\partial z}\cdot\frac{dz}{dx}=0,\ \ldots\ldots\ \ldots\ldots(3)$$

and eliminating $\dfrac{dy}{dx}$ and $\dfrac{dz}{dx}$,

$$\begin{vmatrix} \dfrac{\partial\phi}{\partial x}, & \dfrac{\partial\phi}{\partial y}, & \dfrac{\partial\phi}{\partial z} \\[2ex] \dfrac{\partial F_1}{\partial x}, & \dfrac{\partial F_1}{\partial y}, & \dfrac{\partial F_1}{\partial z} \\[2ex] \dfrac{\partial F_2}{\partial x}, & \dfrac{\partial F_2}{\partial y}, & \dfrac{\partial F_2}{\partial z} \end{vmatrix}=0,\ \ldots\ldots\ldots\ldots\ldots,\ldots(4)$$

an equation in x, y, z which, with $u=\phi(x,\ y,\ z)$, $F_1=0$ and $F_2=0$, will serve to find x, y, z and u.

Again, by differentiating equations (1), (2), (3), and eliminating $\dfrac{dy}{dx},\ \dfrac{dz}{dx},\ \dfrac{d^2y}{dx^2},\ \dfrac{d^2z}{dx^2}$ we may deduce the value of $\dfrac{d^2u}{dx^2}$ and test its sign for the values of x, y, z found.

Ex. A Norman window consists of a rectangle surmounted by a semi-circle. Given the perimeter, show that, when the quantity of light admitted is a maximum, the radius of the semicircle must equal the height of the rectangle.　　　　　[Todhunter's Diff. Calc., p. 214, Ex. 30.]

Let y be the height and $2x$ the breadth of the rectangle, then the area of the window is given by $A=\frac{1}{2}\pi x^2+2xy$,
and this is to be a maximum.

For the perimeter we have

$$P=2y+2x+\pi x=\text{constant}.$$

Choose x to be the independent variable. Then we have, since A is a

maximum,　　　　　$\dfrac{dA}{dx}=0=\pi x+2y+2x\dfrac{dy}{dx}$,

and since P is constant　　$\dfrac{dP}{dx}=0=2\dfrac{dy}{dx}+2+\pi.$

Eliminating $\dfrac{dy}{dx}$ we have

$$\pi x + 2y = x(\pi + 2),$$

or
$$x = y = \frac{P}{\pi + 4},$$

and therefore the radius of the semicircle is equal to the height of the rectangle.

To test whether this result gives a maximum value to A we have

$$\frac{d^2 A}{dx^2} = \pi + 4\frac{dy}{dx} + 2x\frac{d^2 y}{dx^2},$$

and
$$\frac{d^2 P}{dx^2} = 0 = 2\frac{d^2 y}{dx^2};$$

therefore
$$\frac{d^2 A}{dx^2} = \pi + 2(-2 - \pi) = -\pi - 4,$$

and is therefore negative.

Hence the relation found, viz., $x = y$, indicates a *maximum* value of the area.

491. In the solution of such questions as the foregoing it is frequently unnecessary to employ any test for the discrimination between the maxima and minima, since it is often sufficiently obvious from geometrical or other considerations which results give the maxima values and which give the minima.

492. Function of a Function.

Suppose $z = f(x)$, where x is capable of assuming all possible values, and let $y = F(z)$; then it appears that since

$$\frac{dy}{dx} = \frac{dy}{dz} \cdot \frac{dz}{dx} = F'(z)f'(x),$$

the vanishing of either of the factors $f'(x)$ or $F'(z)$ will give $\dfrac{dy}{dx} = 0$, and therefore y may have maxima or minima either for solutions of $F'(z) = 0$ or for such values of x as make $f'(x) = 0$, and which therefore make z a maximum or minimum. Moreover, if z be not capable of assuming all possible values, it may happen that some of the roots of $F'(z) = 0$ are excluded by reason of their not lying within the limits to which z is restricted. Several such problems have been discussed at length in the *Cambridge Mathematical Journal*, vol. III., p. 237.

Ex. 1. To find the maxima and minima values of the perpendicular from the centre of an ellipse upon a tangent.

If r and r' be conjugate semi-diameters, a and b the semi-axes, and p the perpendicular from the centre on the tangent at the point whose radius vector is r, we have

$$r^2 + r'^2 = a^2 + b^2,$$

$$pr' = ab,$$

giving

$$\frac{a^2 b^2}{p^2} = a^2 + b^2 - r^2,$$

Differentiating with respect to r,

$$\frac{a^2 b^2}{p^3} \frac{dp}{dr} = r,$$

and putting

$$\frac{dp}{dr} = 0,$$

we obtain

$$r = 0,$$

a result which is inadmissible, since r is restricted to lie between the limits a and b. It appears therefore at first sight as if the ordinary criteria had failed to determine the true maxima and minima values of r. We should remember, however, that since r is restricted to lie between certain values it will not do for an independent variable, and we should therefore have substituted the value of r from the equation of the curve in terms of θ, which is susceptible of all values and therefore suitable for an independent variable. We should thus have

$$\frac{a^2 b^2}{p^3} \frac{dp}{d\theta} = r \frac{dr}{d\theta},$$

and the vanishing of $\dfrac{dr}{d\theta}$ indicates that the maximum and minimum values of p are to be sought at the same values of θ for which the maximum and minimum values of r occur; i.e., obviously when $r = a$ and when $r = b$. This result was of course apparent ab initio from the form of the relation between p and r.

Ex. 2. The orbits of the earth and Venus being assumed circular and co-planar, to investigate in what position Venus appears brightest.

The brightness of a planet varies directly as the area of its phase, and inversely as the square of the distance of the planet from the earth.

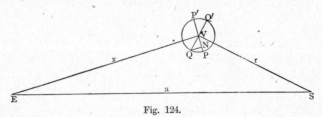

Fig. 124.

Let E and S be the earth and the sun and V the centre of Venus, the plane of the paper being the plane of motion.

Let PVP', QVQ' be diametral planes of the planet, perpendicular to the lines EV and SV, and let ZVZ' be the diameter perpendicular to the plane of motion. Draw QN at right angles to PP'. Let c be the planet's radius and x, a, r the lengths of EV, ES, and SV respectively. The hemispherical portion QPQ' is illuminated by the sun's rays, whilst PQP' is the portion exposed to view from the earth. The illuminated portion visible is therefore bounded by the line $ZQZ'PZ$, whose projection upon the plane $PZP'Z'$ is a crescent-shaped area bounded by a semicircle and a semi-ellipse, the greatest breadth being PN. The area of this crescent is

$$\tfrac{1}{2}\pi c^2 - \tfrac{1}{2}\pi c \cdot c \cos NVQ,$$

and therefore $\qquad \propto 1 - \cos NVQ.$

The brightness therefore

$$\propto \frac{1 - \cos NVQ}{EV^2} \text{ or } \frac{1 + \cos EVS}{EV^2}.$$

Now $\qquad\qquad \cos EVS = \dfrac{x^2 + r^2 - a^2}{2xr},$

whence brightness $\quad \propto \dfrac{(x+r)^2 - a^2}{x^3} \text{ or } \dfrac{1}{x} + \dfrac{2r}{x^2} + \dfrac{r^2 - a^2}{x^3}.$

This expression has its maximum and minimum values,

      (1) when x is a maximum or a minimum, *i.e.*,

          when $\qquad\qquad\qquad\qquad\qquad x = a \pm r\,;$

      (2) when $\qquad\qquad \dfrac{1}{x^2} + \dfrac{4r}{x^3} + \dfrac{3(r^2 - a^2)}{x^4} = 0.$

This second relation gives

$$x^2 + 4rx + 3(r^2 - a^2) = 0,$$

or $\qquad\qquad\qquad x = \sqrt{3a^2 + r^2} - 2r,$

the negative root being inadmissible.

We have now to inquire whether this value of x lies between the greatest and least of the admissible values of x, viz., $a \pm r$.

Now $\qquad\qquad\qquad \sqrt{3a^2 + r^2} - 2r > a - r$

if $\qquad\qquad\qquad\qquad\qquad r < a,$

and $\qquad\qquad\qquad \sqrt{3a^2 + r^2} - 2r < a + r$

if $\qquad\qquad\qquad\qquad\qquad r > \dfrac{a}{4}.$

For the inferior planets, Venus and Mercury, whose mean distances from the sun are respectively $\cdot 7a$ and $\cdot 39a$ roughly, r obviously lies within the prescribed limits. To distinguish between the maxima and minima, we observe that when the earth and planet are in conjunction, *i.e.*, when $x = a - r$, the brightness $= 0$, and is obviously a minimum. Hence

$$x = \sqrt{3a^2 + r^2} - 2r$$

gives a maximum and $x = a + r$ a minimum. It is easy to deduce hence that, for the position of maximum brightness,

$$2 \tan E = \tan \frac{V}{2}.$$

an equation due to Halley, and

$$3a \cos^2 E + 4r \cos E - 4a = 0,$$

which determines the angle E. [See GODFRAY'S ASTRONOMY, 2nd Ed., p. 287.]

493. Other Maxima and Minima ; Singularities.

The accompanying figure (Fig. 125) is intended to illustrate some points with regard to maxima and minima which we have not at present considered.

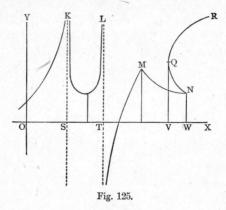

Fig. 125.

At S there is an asymptote parallel to the y-axis. The curve $y = \phi(x)$ approaches the asymptote at each side towards the same extremity. Here $y = \infty$ and $\dfrac{dy}{dx} = \infty$, but $\dfrac{dy}{dx}$ changes sign in crossing the asymptote, and there is an *infinite maximum* ordinate at S.

At T there is another asymptote parallel to the y-axis, but in crossing the asymptote the curve reappears at the opposite extremity and $\dfrac{dy}{dx}$ does not change sign ; there is therefore neither a maximum nor a minimum at T.

At M there is a "*point saillant*" giving a discontinuity in the value of $\dfrac{dy}{dx}$. The ordinate at such a point is a maximum or a minimum. In the case in the figure we have a maximum ordinate.

At R the curve has a "*point d'arrêt*" and a maximum ordinate, though $\dfrac{dy}{dx}$ does not vanish or become infinite.

At N there is a *cusp*, but $\dfrac{dy}{dx}$ is neither zero nor infinite. Yet the ordinate at N is the smallest in its immediate neighbourhood, and therefore a minimum. It is to be noticed, however, that in travelling along the branch MN the value of x does not *pass through* OW, and therefore the ordinary theory does not apply.

At such points as Q, $\dfrac{dy}{dx} = \infty$ and changes sign, and yet obviously the value of y is not a maximum or minimum. As in the last case, it should be observed that in travelling along the branch NQR the value of x does not *pass through* the value OV, but recedes to it from W to V and then increases again.

We notice, however, that this result may be written as $\dfrac{dx}{dy} = 0$, and that $\dfrac{dx}{dy}$ changes sign at Q, indicating a *maximum or minimum value of the abscissa x.*

For further information upon this subject the student is referred to Professor de Morgan's *Diff. and Int. Calculus.*

EXAMPLES.

1. Show algebraically that the greatest value of
$$x(a - x)$$
is $\dfrac{a^2}{4}$, and illustrate the result geometrically.

2. Find algebraically the limits between which the expression
$$ax + \frac{b}{x}$$
must or must not lie for real values of x. Illustrate your result by a sketch of the curve
$$y = ax + \frac{b}{x}.$$

3. Investigate algebraically the maximum and minimum values of the expression
$$\frac{x^2 - 4x + 2}{2x - 7}$$
for real values of x. Illustrate your answer geometrically.

4. Find for what values of x the expression
$$(x - 1)^4(x + 3)^5$$
has maximum or minimum values.

5. Investigate the maximum and minimum values of the expression
$$2x^3 - 21x^2 + 60x + 30.$$

6. Find the minimum ordinate and the point of inflexion on the curve
$$x^3 - axy + b^3 = 0.$$

7. Find the maximum and minimum ordinates of the curve

$$(y - c)^2 = (x - a)^6(x - b).$$

8. Show that the curve $\quad y = xe^x$

has a minimum ordinate where $x = -1$.

9. Show that the values of x for which $e^{x\sin x}$ has maximum or minimum values may be determined graphically as the abscissae of the points of intersection of the straight line

$$y = -x,$$

with the curve of tangents $\quad y = \tan x.$

10. Show that the expression

$$a + (x - b)^{\frac{2}{3}} + (x - b)^{\frac{4}{3}}$$

has a minimum value when $x = b$.

11. Find the minimum value of

$$\frac{a^2}{\sin^2 x} + \frac{b^2}{\cos^2 x}.$$

12. Show that $\quad \sin^p\theta \cos^q\theta$

attains a maximum value when

$$\theta = \tan^{-1}\sqrt{\frac{p}{q}}.$$

13. Show that $\sqrt[e]{e}$ is a maximum value of $\left(\dfrac{1}{x}\right)^x$.

14. Show that the function

$$x \sin x + \cos x + \cos^2 x$$

continually diminishes as x increases from 0 to $\dfrac{\pi}{2}$.

15. If $\quad y = 2x - \tan^{-1}x - \log\{x + \sqrt{1 + x^2}\},$

show that y continually increases as x changes from zero to positive infinity.

16. If $\quad z = \dfrac{a^2}{x} + \dfrac{b^2}{y},$

where $\quad x + y = a,$

show that z has a minimum value when

$$x = \frac{a^2}{a + b},$$

and a maximum when $\quad x = \dfrac{a^2}{a - b}.$

17. Given that $\quad \dfrac{x}{a} + \dfrac{y}{b} = 1,$

show that the maximum value of xy is $\dfrac{ab}{4}$ and that the minimum value of $x^2 + y^2$ is $\dfrac{a^2b^2}{a^2 + b^2}$.

18. Show that the area of the greatest rectangle inscribed in a given ellipse and having its sides parallel to the axes of the ellipse is to that of the ellipse as $2 : \pi$.

19. Show that the maximum and minimum values of

$$x^2 + y^2,$$

where

$$ax^2 + 2hxy + by^2 = 1$$

are given by the roots of the quadratic

$$\left(a - \frac{1}{r^2}\right)\left(b - \frac{1}{r^2}\right) = h^2.$$

Hence find the area of the conic denoted by the first equation.

20. Divide a given number a into two parts, such that the product of the pth power of one and the qth power of the other shall be as great as possible.

21. Show that if a number be divided into two factors, such that the sum of their squares is a minimum, the factors are each equal to the square root of the given number.

22. Into how many equal parts must the number ne be divided so that their continued product may be a maximum; n being a positive integer and e the base of the Napierian Logarithms?

23. What fraction exceeds its pth power by the greatest number possible?

24. Given the length of an arc of a circle, find the radius of the circle when the corresponding segment has a maximum or minimum area. [Pappus Alexandrinus.]

25. The centres of two spheres, radii r_1, r_2, are at the extremities of a straight line of length $2a$, on which a circle is described. Find a point in the circumference from which the greatest amount of spherical surface is visible.

26. In the line joining the centres of two spheres find a point such that the sum of the spherical surfaces visible therefrom may be a maximum. [Educational Times.]

27. AC and BD are parallel straight lines, and AD is drawn. Show how to draw a straight line COE, cutting AD and BD in O and E respectively, so that the sum of the triangles EOD, COA may be a minimum. [Viviani.]

28. A person wishes to divide a triangular field into two equal parts by a straight fence. Show how it is to be done so that the fence may be of the least expense.

29. If four straight rods be freely hinged at their extremities the greatest quadrilateral they can form is inscribable in a circle.

30. A tree in the form of a frustum of a cone is n feet long, and its greater and less diameters are a and b feet respectively. Show that the greatest beam of square section that can be cut out of it is $\dfrac{na}{3(a-b)}$ feet long.

31. If the polar diameter of the earth be to the equatorial as $229 : 230$, show that the greatest angle made by a body falling to the earth with a perpendicular to the surface is about $14' \ 59''$, and that the latitude is $45° \ 7' \ 29''$.

32. The resistance to a steamer's motion in still water varies as the nth power of the velocity. Find the rate at which the steamer must be propelled against a tide running at a knots an hour so as to consume the least amount of fuel in a given journey.

33. Show that the volume of the greatest cylinder which can be inscribed in a cone of height b and semivertical angle a is $\dfrac{4}{27}\pi b^3 \tan^2 a$.

34. Show that the height of the cone of greatest convex surface which can be inscribed in a given sphere is to the radius of the sphere as $4 : 3$.

35. Two particles move uniformly along the axes of x and y with velocities u and v respectively. They are initially at distances a and b respectively from the origin, and the axes are inclined at an angle ω. Show that the least distance between the particles is

$$\frac{(av - bu)\sin \omega}{(u^2 + v^2 - 2uv \cos \omega)^{\frac{1}{2}}}.$$

36. For a maximum or minimum parabola circumscribing a given triangle ABC, show that the sum of the perpendiculars from ABC upon the axis is algebraically zero.

37. In a submarine telegraph cable the speed of signalling varies as $x^2 \log \dfrac{1}{x}$ where x is the ratio of the radius of the core to that of the covering. Show that the greatest speed is attained when this ratio is $1 : \sqrt{e}$.

38. A and B are fixed points and P is a variable point on a fixed line ; show that $\lambda \cdot AP + \mu \cdot BP$ will be a minimum if $\lambda \cos \theta = \mu \cos \phi$, θ and ϕ being the angles which AP and BP make with the fixed line.

39. S is the focus of an ellipse of eccentricity e, and E is a fixed point on the major axis, and P is any point on the curve. Show that when PE is a minimum $SP = \dfrac{SE}{e}$.

40. Find the maximum value of

$$(x - a)^2 (x - b), \quad \begin{cases} (1) \text{ when } a > b, \\ (2) \text{ when } a < b, \end{cases}$$

What happens if $a = b$? Illustrate your answers by diagrams of the curve $\qquad y = (x - a)^2 (x - b)$

in the three different cases. [I. C. S., 1879.]

41. An open tank is to be constructed with a square base and vertical sides so as to contain a given quantity of water. Show that the expense of lining it with lead will be least if the depth is made half of the width.

42. If two variables x and y are connected by the relation $ax^2 + by^2 = ab$, show that the maximum and minimum values of the function $x^2 + y^2 + xy$ will be the values of u given by the equation

$$4(u - a)(u - b) = ab.$$

43. If SP and SQ be two focal distances in an ellipse inclined to each other at the given angle $2a$, find the greatest and least values of the area of the triangle PSQ.

44. SQ is a focal radius vector in a given ellipse inclined at a given angle a to SA, where A is the vertex nearest to the focus S. Find the angle ASP, where SP is another focal radius, such that the area of the triangle PSQ may be a maximum.

45. Find the point P on the parabola $y^2 = 4ax$ such that the perpendicular on the tangent at P from a given point on the axis distant h from the vertex may be the least possible. What is the geometrical meaning of the result ?

46. Find the area and position of the maximum triangle having a given angle which can be inscribed in a given circle, and prove that the area cannot have a minimum value.

47. From a fixed point A on the circumference of a circle of radius c the perpendicular AY is let fall on the tangent at P. Prove that the maximum area of the triangle APY is

$$\tfrac{3}{8} c^2 \sqrt{3}.$$

48. If a parallelogram be inscribed in an ellipse the greatest possible value of its perimeter is equal to twice the diagonal of the rectangle described on the axes.

49. O is a fixed point without a circle, A one of the extremities of the diameter through O, OQQ' a chord through O. Find its position when the area of the triangle QAQ' is a maximum. Does it ever become a minimum ?

50. A length l of wire is cut into two portions which are bent into the shapes of a circle and a square respectively. Show that if the sum of the areas be the least possible the side of the square is double the radius of the circle.

51. Obtain the maximum and minimum values of the volume of a right circular cone whose vertex is at a given point and whose base is a plane section of a given sphere; and point out the difference of the cases of the point being within or without the sphere.

[MATH. TRIPOS, 1876.]

52. Prove that a chord of constant inclination to the arc of a closed curve divides the area most unequally when it is a chord of curvature.

53. When the area of a triangle has a maximum or minimum value and all the parts vary, then

$$\cos A \cdot da + \cos B \cdot db + \cos C \cdot dc = 0. \quad \text{[OXFORD, 1888.]}$$

54. Show that the normal chord to the parabola $y^2 = 4ax$ which cuts off the least arc is normal where $y = \dfrac{\text{Lat. Rect.}}{\sqrt{3}}$ and is inclined to the axis at an angle $\tan^{-1}\dfrac{2}{\sqrt{3}}$.

55. When the product of two perpendicular radii vectores of a curve is a maximum or a minimum, show that they make supplementary angles with the tangents at their extremities.

56. Two perpendicular lines intersect on a parabola, one passing through the focus. Show that the triangle formed by them with the directrix has its least values when the focal distances of the right angle and the vertex of the parabola include an angle of 36° or of 108°.

57. A plane triangle ABC, right-angled at B, and of given perimeter P, revolves either round an axis through A parallel to BC, or round an axis through C parallel to BA, and the solid generated is a maximum; show that the three sides of the triangle are equal to

$$\frac{3P}{8}(-3 + \sqrt{17}), \quad \frac{P}{4}(5 - \sqrt{17}), \quad \frac{P}{8}(7 - \sqrt{17}).$$

[SMITH'S PRIZE, 1878.]

58. Show that when the angle between the tangent to a curve and the radius vector of the point of contact has a maximum or minimum value the radius of curvature at that point is given by

$$\rho = \frac{r^2}{p}.$$

59. Show that the greatest distance which can be saved in a single voyage by sailing along a great circle instead of a parallel of latitude, is

$$a\{2 \sin^{-1}\frac{2}{\pi} + \sqrt{\pi^2 - 4} - \pi\},$$

where a is the earth's radius. [MATH. TRIPOS.]

60. Show how to find the co-ordinates of the points on a curve given in Cartesians at which the curvature is a maximum or a minimum.

CHAPTER XVI.

MAXIMA AND MINIMA—SEVERAL INDEPENDENT VARIABLES.

494. Preliminary Algebraical Lemma.

The binary quadratic $I_2 \equiv ax^2 + 2hxy + by^2$

may be written $\dfrac{1}{a}[(ax+hy)^2 + (ab-h^2)y^2]$,

and therefore retains the same sign as a for all real values of x and y if $ab-h^2$ be positive.

The ternary quadratic

$$I_3 \equiv ax^2 + by^2 + cz^2 + 2fyz + 2gzx + 2hxy$$

may be written

$$\frac{1}{a}[(ax+hy+gz)^2 + (ab-h^2)y^2 + 2(af-gh)yz + (ac-g^2)z^2],$$

and therefore by what has gone before will retain the same sign as a for all real values of x, y, z

if $ab-h^2$ and $(ab-h^2)(ac-g^2) - (af-gh)^2$ be positive,

i.e., if $ab-h^2$ and $a(abc + 2fgh - af^2 - bg^2 - ch^2)$ be positive.

That is to say, I_2 and I_3 will both be positive if

$$a, \quad \begin{vmatrix} a, & h \\ h, & b \end{vmatrix}, \quad \begin{vmatrix} a, & h, & g \\ h, & b, & f \\ g, & f, & c \end{vmatrix}$$

be all positive, and will both be negative if these expressions are alternately negative and positive.

495. These results may be generalized. For the general homogeneous quadratic function of n variables can be thrown into the form

$$p_1(x_1 + a_2x_2 + a_3x_3 + \ldots + a_nx_n)^2$$
$$+ p_2(x_2 + b_3x_3 + \ldots + b_nx_n)^2$$
$$+ p_3(x_3 + \ldots + c_nx_n)^2$$
$$+ \ldots$$
$$+ p_nx_n^2,$$

420

since the number of arbitrary constants at our disposal is the same as the number of coefficients of the original quantic. And it is a known proposition* that the values of $p_1, p_2, ..., p_n$ are

$$p_1 = \Delta_1, \quad p_2 = \frac{\Delta_2}{\Delta_1}, \quad p_3 = \frac{\Delta_3}{\Delta_2}, \quad ..., \quad p_n = \frac{\Delta_n}{\Delta_{n-1}},$$

where Δ_r is the discriminant of the quantic obtained from the original function by putting $x_{r+1}, x_{r+2}, ...,$ etc., all zero.

Now assuming that all the letters involved are real, it is clear that if $\Delta_1, \Delta_2, \Delta_3, ...$ be all positive, we shall have $p_1, p_2, p_3, ..., p_n$ all positive, and therefore the quantic positive; and if $\Delta_1, \Delta_2, \Delta_3, ...$ be alternately negative and positive, $p_1, p_2, p_3, ..., p_n$ will all be negative, and hence the quantic will also be negative.

For an inductive proof of this result the student is referred to a note at the end of Dr Williamson's *Treatise on the Differential Calculus.*

496. To search for Maxima and Minima.

DEF. Let $\phi(x, y, z, ...)$ be any function of several independent variables $x, y, z, ...,$ supposed continuous and finite for all values of these variables in the neighbourhood of their values $a, b, c, ...$ respectively. Then the value of $\phi(a, b, c, ...)$ is said to be a maximum or a minimum value of $\phi(x, y, z, ...)$ according as $\phi(a+h, b+k, c+l, ...)$ is less or greater than $\phi(a, b, c, ...),$ whatever be the relative values of the increments $h, k, l, ...,$ positive or negative, provided they be taken sufficiently small and be finite.

In other words, $\phi(a+h, b+k, c+l, ...) - \phi(a, b, c, ...)$ is to preserve an invariable sign for all finite values of $h, k, l,$ etc., lying between zero and certain small limits, positive or negative.

To find $a, b, c, ...$ the values of $x, y, z, ...$ which will make $\phi(a, b, ...)$ answer to the above definition we expand by the extended form of Taylor's theorem (Art. 178)

$$\phi(x+h, y+k, ...) - \phi(x, y, ...)$$

$$= h\frac{\partial \phi}{\partial x} + k\frac{\partial \phi}{\partial y} + ... + \text{terms of the second and higher orders.}$$

Now by taking $h, k, l, ...$ sufficiently small, the first degree terms can be made to govern the sign of the right-hand side, and therefore of the left side also, of the above equation; therefore by changing the sign of $h, k, l, ...$ the sign of the left-hand member would be changed. Hence as a first condition

---

* Burnside and Panton, *Theory of Equations,* p. 401.

for a maximum or minimum value we must have

$$h\frac{\partial\phi}{\partial x}+k\frac{\partial\phi}{\partial y}+l\frac{\partial\phi}{\partial z}+\ldots=0,$$

and therefore as these arbitrary increments are independent of each other, we must have

$$\frac{\partial\phi}{\partial x}=0, \quad \frac{\partial\phi}{\partial y}=0, \quad \frac{\partial\phi}{\partial z}=0, \text{etc.,} \ldots\ldots\ldots\ldots(1)$$

If there be n independent variables, we have thus obtained n simultaneous equations which serve by their solution to find the admissible values of x, y, z, ... for which maxima and minima values may exist.

The above equations therefore form *essential* conditions for the existence of maxima and minima, but we shall see that they are not in themselves *sufficient*, and we shall have to employ a further test for their discrimination.

We shall now consider the cases of two and of three independent variables separately.

Let one system of values of x, y, z, ... satisfying equations (1) be a, b, c, ... respectively.

497. Case I. Two Independent Variables. The Lagrange-Condition.

Let us put r, s, t for the values of $\dfrac{\partial^2\phi}{\partial x^2}, \dfrac{\partial^2\phi}{\partial x\partial y}, \dfrac{\partial^2\phi}{\partial y^2}$ when $x=a$ and $y=b$, then

$$\phi(a+h,\,b+k)-\phi(a,\,b)=\frac{1}{2!}(rh^2+2shk+tk^2)+R_3$$

where R_3 consists of terms of the third and higher orders of small quantities, and by taking h and k sufficiently small the second degree terms now can be made to govern the sign of the right-hand side and therefore of the left also. And if these terms be of permanent sign for all such values of h and k we shall have a maximum or minimum for $\phi(x,\,y,\,\ldots)$ according as that sign is negative or positive.

By our Lemma (Art. 494) the condition for an invariable sign is that $rt-s^2$ shall be positive, and the sign will be that of r, and if $rt-s^2$ be positive, it is clear that r and t must have the same sign.

Thus, if $rt - s^2$ be positive, we have a maximum or minimum according as r and t are both negative or both positive.

This condition was first pointed out by Lagrange (*Turin Memoirs*), and is known as " Lagrange's Condition."

If $rt < s^2$, we get neither a maximum nor a minimum.

If however $rt = s^2$, the quadratic terms

$$rh^2 + 2shk + tk^2 \text{ become } \frac{1}{r}(hr + ks)^2$$

and are therefore of the same sign as r or t unless

$$\frac{h}{k} = -\frac{s}{r} = \beta, \text{ say.}$$

In this case we must consider terms of higher degree in the expansion of $\phi(a+h, b+k) - \phi(a, b)$. The cubic terms must vanish collectively when $\frac{h}{k} = \beta$; otherwise, by changing the signs of both h and k we could change the sign of $\phi(a+h, b+k) - \phi(a, b)$. And the biquadratic terms must collectively be of the same sign as r and t when $\frac{h}{k} = \beta$.

498. In the case in which r, s, t are each of them zero, the quadratic terms are altogether absent, and the cubic terms would change sign with h and k, and therefore all the differential coefficients of the third order must vanish separately when $x = a$ and $y = b$ and the biquadratic terms must be such that they retain the same sign for all sufficiently small values of h, k.

Ex. Let

$$u = xy + \frac{a^3}{x} + \frac{a^3}{y},$$

$$\left. \begin{array}{l} \dfrac{\partial u}{\partial x} = y - \dfrac{a^3}{x^2} = 0 \\[2mm] \dfrac{\partial u}{\partial y} = x - \dfrac{a^3}{y^2} = 0 \end{array} \right\}, \text{ giving } x = y = a.$$

Hence

$$\frac{\partial^2 u}{\partial x^2} = \frac{2a^3}{x^3} = 2, \qquad \frac{\partial^2 u}{\partial x \partial y} = 1, \qquad \frac{\partial^2 u}{\partial y^2} = \frac{2a^3}{y^3} = 2.$$

So r and t are positive when $x = y = a$,

and

$$\left| \begin{array}{cc} r, & s \\ s, & t \end{array} \right| = 2 \cdot 2 - 1 = 3$$

and is positive ; and therefore there is a minimum value of u, viz.,

$$u = 3a^2.$$

499. Geometrical Explanation.

Let the reader imagine that the plane of xy is the horizontal plane at the sea level, and that $z = \phi(x, y)$ is the equation of the surface of a mountainous tract of country in which there are isolated hills, mountain chains, valleys, lakes and mountain passes. Let a map be constructed showing the various contour lines of the hills, lakes, etc., at different altitudes. Corresponding to an isolated hill or a lake these contour lines will form closed curves, dwindling to a point at the top of an isolated hill or at the deepest point of a lake. At a saddle-shaped mountain pass the contour lines at the highest point of the pass will intersect and form a node while, corresponding to the ridge of a chain of mountains of uniform height or the bottom of a V-shaped depression of uniform depth in a lake, the closed contour line degenerates into a single curved terminated line. Again, at a bar across a valley, as at a mountain pass, the contour lines form a node at the highest point of the bar.

Now at all these several places the tangent plane to the country is horizontal and the preliminary conditions $\dfrac{\partial \phi}{\partial x} = 0$, $\dfrac{\partial \phi}{\partial y} = 0$ are satisfied (Art. 496).

At the top of an isolated hill we have a true maximum value of z; $rt - s^2$ is positive whilst r and t are both negative.

At the deepest point of a lake we have a true minimum; $rt - s^2$ is positive whilst r and t are both positive.

At a mountain pass $rt - s^2$ is negative, and although the traveller over the pass arrives at a maximum height in the direction in which he travels, yet if he diverge from the path either to right or left he at once begins to ascend to higher ground. This therefore is not a point of maximum height on the surface. The same is true at the highest point of a bar separating two depressed regions.

If $rt = s^2$ then in the direction of $hr + ks = 0$ the tangents to the contour lines through that point coincide. Further investigation is now necessary. If the contour lines open out and separate immediately after their contact, there is neither a maximum nor a minimum; but if they dwindle down to a single line all along their length, we have a row of what may be called maxima or minima. This is the case of a line along the ridge of a mountain chain of uniform height or along the bottom of a **V**-shaped depression of uniform depth; and a person travelling along such a line will move continually at a constant distance above or below the sea level. (See Greenhill's *Diff. and Int. Calc.*)

500. The effect of the variation in sign of $rt - s^2$ will be more easily understood by the student of solid geometry. The equation giving the principal radii of curvature at any point is

$$(rt - s^2)\rho^2 + k\{t(1 + p^2) + r(1 + q^2) - 2pqs\}\rho + k^4 = 0,$$

where $\qquad k^2 = 1 + p^2 + q^2, \quad p = \dfrac{\partial z}{\partial x}, \quad q = \dfrac{\partial z}{\partial y}.$*

Hence the principal radii of curvature are of the same or of opposite sign according as $rt - s^2$ is positive or negative; and one of them is infinite when $rt - s^2 = 0$. In the latter case the corresponding line of curvature has either an inflexional or an undulatory point.

501. A ridge of Maxima or Minima.

Suppose that $\dfrac{\partial \phi}{\partial x}$ and $\dfrac{\partial \phi}{\partial y}$ contain a common factor v.

Let $\qquad \dfrac{\partial \phi}{\partial x} = vw_1, \qquad \dfrac{\partial \phi}{\partial y} = vw_2,$

Then $\qquad r = \dfrac{\partial v}{\partial x}w_1 + v\dfrac{\partial w_1}{\partial x},$

$\qquad s = \dfrac{\partial v}{\partial y}w_1 + v\dfrac{\partial w_1}{\partial y},$ and also $= \dfrac{\partial v}{\partial x}w_2 + v\dfrac{\partial w_2}{\partial x},$

$\qquad t = \dfrac{\partial v}{\partial y}w_2 + v\dfrac{\partial w_2}{\partial y}.$

So that for the values of x and y satisfying $v = 0$ we have

$$rt - s^2 = w_1\dfrac{\partial v}{\partial x} \cdot w_2\dfrac{\partial v}{\partial y} - \left(w_1\dfrac{\partial v}{\partial y}\right)\left(w_2\dfrac{\partial v}{\partial x}\right) = 0.$$

Suppose we solve $v = 0$ and find $y = f(x)$. Substituting this in $z = \phi(x, y)$ we have z a function of x only and

$$\frac{dz}{dx} = \frac{\partial \phi}{\partial x} + \frac{\partial \phi}{\partial y}\frac{dy}{dx}$$

which vanishes for such values as satisfy $v = 0$, and therefore make $\qquad \dfrac{\partial \phi}{\partial x} = \dfrac{\partial \phi}{\partial y} = 0.$

Thus along a curve line on the surface, whose projection on the plane of xy is $v = 0$, z is constant.

* Smith's *Solid Geometry*, p. 218.

This is the case of a locus of maxima or minima such, for instance, as would be produced by the revolution round the z-axis of any closed curve. The definition of maxima and minima according to this view needs a slight modification, and we must suppose a maximum value to be one which is *not less* than and a minimum to be one which is *not greater* than any other value which is immediately contiguous to it.[*]

Ex. Consider the Anchor Ring or Tore formed by the revolution of a circle of radius b about a straight line in its own plane at a distance a from the centre. Taking the axis of revolution for the z-axis and the plane through the centre perpendicular to the z-axis for the plane of xy, the equation is
$$z^2 = b^2 - a^2 - x^2 - y^2 + 2a\sqrt{x^2 + y^2}.$$

Here
$$z\frac{\partial z}{\partial x} = -x + \frac{ax}{\sqrt{x^2 + y^2}},$$
$$z\frac{\partial z}{\partial y} = -y + \frac{ay}{\sqrt{x^2 + y^2}}.$$

The vanishing of the common factor $1 - \dfrac{a}{\sqrt{x^2 + y^2}}$ gives both $\dfrac{\partial z}{\partial x}$ and $\dfrac{\partial z}{\partial y} = 0$, and the cylinder $x^2 + y^2 = a^2$ cuts the surface along the ridge formed by points which are all at the same distance b from the plane of xy and at greater distance from that plane than any other points of the surface which do not lie in that circular ridge.

502. Case II. Three Independent Variables.

Let a set of the values of x, y, z determined from the equations
$$\frac{\partial \phi}{\partial x} = \frac{\partial \phi}{\partial y} = \frac{\partial \phi}{\partial z} = 0$$

be a, b, c, as explained in Art. 496. Let the corresponding values of
$$\frac{\partial^2 \phi}{\partial x^2}, \quad \frac{\partial^2 \phi}{\partial y^2}, \quad \frac{\partial^2 \phi}{\partial z^2}, \quad \frac{\partial^2 \phi}{\partial y \partial z}, \quad \frac{\partial^2 \phi}{\partial z \partial x}, \quad \frac{\partial^2 \phi}{\partial x \partial y}$$

be called A, B, C, F, G, H. Then we have
$$\phi(a+h, b+k, c+l) - \phi(a, b, c)$$
$$= \frac{1}{2!}(Ah^2 + Bk^2 + Cl^2 + 2Fkl + 2Glh + 2Hhk) + R_3,$$

where R_3 consists of terms of the third and higher orders of small quantities, and by taking $h, k,$ and l sufficiently small the second degree terms can be made to govern the sign of the right-hand side and therefore of the left also. If this group of terms form an expression of permanent sign for all such values

[*] See *Français Annales de Gergonne*, vol. III.   Gregory's *Examples*, p. 110.

of h, k, and l, we shall have a maximum or minimum value according as that sign is negative or positive. Hence by our Lemma, Art. 494, if the expressions

$$A, \quad \begin{vmatrix} A, & H \\ H, & B \end{vmatrix}, \quad \begin{vmatrix} A, & H, & G \\ H, & B, & F \\ G, & F, & C \end{vmatrix}$$

be all positive, we shall have a minimum value of $\phi(x, y, z)$, and if they be alternately negative and positive we shall have a maximum, whilst if these conditions are not satisfied we shall in general have neither a maximum nor a minimum.

503. Similarly we might proceed by aid of the generalization in Art. 495 to consider the case of several independent variables. And according to that article we shall have a minimum when all the discriminants are positive and a maximum if they are alternately negative and positive.

504. **Several Independent Variables. Lagrange's Method of Undetermined Multipliers.**[*]

Let $u = \phi(x_1, x_2, ..., x_n)$, a function of n variables, which we shall suppose connected by m equations

$$f_1(x_1, x_2, ..., x_n) = 0, \; f_2(x_1, x_2, ..., x_n) = 0 ..., \; f_m(x_1, x_2, ..., x_n) = 0,$$

so that only $n - m$ of the variables are independent.

Suppose the m dependent variables to have been eliminated between the equation $u = \phi(x_1, x_2, ..., x_n)$ and the m equations of condition. The values or the remaining variables which give maxima and minima can then be found as in Art. 496.

To avoid the absolute elimination we may make use of undetermined multipliers as follows:—

When u is a maximum or minimum

$$\left. \begin{aligned} du &= \frac{\partial u}{\partial x_1}dx_1 + \frac{\partial u}{\partial x_2}dx_2 + \frac{\partial u}{\partial x_3}dx_3 + ... + \frac{\partial u}{\partial x_n}dx_n = 0. \\ \text{Also} \quad df_1 &= \frac{\partial f_1}{\partial x_1}dx_1 + \frac{\partial f_1}{\partial x_2}dx_2 + \frac{\partial f_1}{\partial x_3}dx_3 + ... + \frac{\partial f_1}{\partial x_n}dx_n = 0, \\ df_2 &= \frac{\partial f_2}{\partial x_1}dx_1 + \frac{\partial f_2}{\partial x_2}dx_2 + \frac{\partial f_2}{\partial x_3}dx_3 + ... + \frac{\partial f_2}{\partial x_n}dx_n = 0, \\ &\quad\quad\quad\quad \text{etc.,} \\ df_m &= \frac{\partial f_m}{\partial x_1}dx_1 + \frac{\partial f_m}{dx_2}dx_2 + \frac{\partial f_m}{dx_3}dx_3 + ... + \frac{\partial f_m}{dx_n}dx_n = 0. \end{aligned} \right\} ......(1)$$

[*] *Mécanique Analytique*, vol. I.

Multiplying these lines respectively by $1, \lambda_1, \lambda_2, \ldots, \lambda_m$ and adding, we get a result which may be written

$$P_1 dx_1 + P_2 dx_2 + P_3 dx_3 + \ldots + P_n dx_n = 0 \ldots \ldots \ldots (2)$$

where
$$P_r = \frac{\partial u}{\partial x_r} + \lambda_1 \frac{\partial f_1}{\partial x_r} + \lambda_2 \frac{\partial f_2}{\partial x_r} + \ldots + \lambda_m \frac{\partial f_m}{\partial x_r}.$$

The m quantities $\lambda_1, \lambda_2, \ldots, \lambda_m$ are at our choice.

Let us choose them so as to satisfy the m linear equations

$$P_1 = P_2 = P_3 = \ldots = P_m = 0.$$

The above equation is now reduced to

$$P_{m+1} dx_{m+1} + P_{m+2} dx_{m+2} + \ldots + P_n dx_n = 0.$$

It is indifferent which $n-m$ of the n variables are regarded as independent. Let them be $x_{m+1}, x_{m+2}, \ldots, x_n$. Then since the $n-m$ quantities $dx_{m+1}, dx_{m+2}, \ldots, dx_n$ are all independent their coefficients must be separately zero.

Thus we obtain the additional $n-m$ equations

$$P_{m+1} = P_{m+2} = \ldots = P_n = 0.$$

Thus the $m+n$ equations

$$f_1 = f_2 = f_3 = \ldots = f_m = 0,$$
and $$P_1 = P_2 = P_3 = \ldots = P_n = 0,$$

determine the m multipliers $\lambda_1, \lambda_2, \ldots, \lambda_m$ and values of the n variables $x_1, x_2, \ldots, x_n$ for which maxima and minima values of u are possible.

505. If u be a homogeneous function of degree p, and $f_1, f_2, f_3, \ldots, f_m$ be capable of being put into the forms $u_a = A$, $u_b = B, u_c = C, \ldots, u_k = K$; u_a, u_b, etc., being homogeneous expressions of degrees a, b, etc., and A, B, etc. constants, there is a very useful relation between the quantities λ. Multiplying the n equations of which $P_r = 0$ is a type by $x_1, x_2, \ldots, x_n$ and adding, we have by Euler's theorem on homogeneous functions

$$pu + \lambda_1 a A + \lambda_2 b B + \lambda_3 c C + \ldots + \lambda_m k K = 0.$$

Ex. Let us investigate the maximum and minimum radii vectores of the section of the "surface of elasticity" [*]

$$(x^2 + y^2 + z^2)^2 = a^2 x^2 + b^2 y^2 + c^2 z^2$$

made by the plane $\quad lx + my + nz = 0.$

We must make $\quad r^2 = x^2 + y^2 + z^2$ a max. or min.

[*] Gregory's *Examples*, p. 120, and Fresnel, *Mémoires de l'Institut*, vol. VII.

Then $$xdx+ydy+zdz=0 \dots \dots \dots (1)$$
$$a^2xdx+b^2ydy+c^2zdz=0 \dots \dots \dots (2)$$
$$ldx+mdy+ndz=0 \dots \dots \dots (3)$$

Whence multiplying (2) and (3) by λ_1 and λ_2 and adding, we have by Art. 504
$$x+\lambda_1 a^2 x+\lambda_2 l=0 \dots \dots \dots (4)$$
$$y+\lambda_1 b^2 y+\lambda_2 m=0 \dots \dots \dots (5)$$
$$z+\lambda_1 c^2 z+\lambda_2 n=0 \dots \dots \dots (6)$$

Multiplying by x, y, z, respectively and adding,
$$r^2+\lambda_1 r^4=0 \quad \text{or} \quad \lambda_1=-\frac{1}{r^2}.$$

$\therefore$
$$x\left(1-\frac{a^2}{r^2}\right)+\lambda_2 l=0 \quad \text{or} \quad x=\frac{\lambda_2 l r^2}{a^2-r^2}$$

and two similar equations.

Whence multiplying by l, m, and n and adding,
$$\frac{l^2}{a^2-r^2}+\frac{m^2}{b^2-r^2}+\frac{n^2}{c^2-r^2}=0,$$

a quadratic which gives the values of r required.

EXAMPLES.

1. Discuss the maxima or minima values of u in the following cases :—

(a) $u=x^3y^2(1-x-y)$.

(β) $u=x^4+y^4-2x^2+4xy-2y^2$.

(γ) $u=2a^2xy-3ax^2y-ay^3+x^3y+xy^3$.

(δ) $u=axy^2z^3-x^2y^2z^3-xy^3z^3-xy^2z^4$.

(ϵ) $u=\sin x \sin y \sin(x+y)$.

(ζ) $u=x^2y^2-5x^2-8xy-5y^2$.

(η) $u=x^3+y^3-3axy$.

2. Find the minimum value of
$$x^2+y^2+z^2,$$
having given $$ax+by+cz=p.$$

3. Find the maximum value of
$$x^m y^n z^p$$
with condition $$x+y+z=a.$$

4. In a plane triangle find the maximum value of
$$\cos A \cos B \cos C.$$

5. Find a plane triangle such that
$$\sin^m A \sin^n B \sin^p C$$
has a maximum value.

6. Divide a number n into three parts x, y, z such that
$$ayz + bzx + cxy$$
shall have a maximum or minimum value and determine which it is.

7. Find the maximum or minimum values of
$$x^2/a^4 + y^2/b^4 + z^2/c^4$$
when $\quad lx + my + nz = 0$ and $x^2/a^2 + y^2/b^2 + z^2/c^2 = 1.$ [OXFORD, 1888.]

8. Inscribe in an ellipsoid the maximum rectangular parallelopiped.

9. Given $a^x b^y c^z = A$, find the maximum value of
$$(x+1)(y+1)(z+1).$$
Interpret the result.   [WARING.]

10. Required the rectangular parallelopiped of given volume and least surface.

11. Find the minimum value of $x^2 + y^2 + z^2$
with the conditions $ax + by + cz = a'x + b'y + c'z = 1.$

12. Find the maxima and minima of $x^2 + y^2 + z^2$
subject to the following conditions :—

(1) $ax^2 + by^2 + cz^2 = 1.$

(2) $ax^2 + by^2 + cz^2 + 2fyz + 2gzx + 2hxy = 1.$

(3) $\begin{cases} \quad ax^2 + by^2 + cz^2 = 1 \\ \text{and} \quad lx + my + nz = 0. \end{cases}$

(4) $\begin{cases} \quad ax^2 + by^2 + cz^2 + 2fyz + 2gzx + 2hxy = 1 \\ \text{and} \quad lx + my + nz = 0. \end{cases}$

13. Find the maximum or minimum of $ax^p + by^q + cz^r$
with the condition $\qquad x^l + y^m + z^n = k.$

14. Find the maximum value of
$$xyz/(a+x)(x+y)(y+z)(z+b).$$ [LAGRANGE.]

15. Find the minimum value of
$$x^2 + y^2 + z^2 + w^2 + \ldots$$
with condition $\qquad ax + by + cz + dw + \ldots = k.$

16. Show that the point within a triangle for which the sum of the squares of its perpendicular distances from the sides is least is the centre of the Cosine-Circle.

17. Find a point within a triangle such that the sum of the squares on its distances from the three angles is a minimum.

18. Find a point within a triangle such that the sum of the distances from the angular points may be a minimum.   [FERMAT.]

19. Find the triangular pyramid of given base and altitude which has the least surface.   [GREGORY'S EXAMPLES.]

20. Find the minimum value of the continued product of the perpendiculars drawn from a point upon the faces of a given polyhedron. [Coll. Exam.]

21. If a be a maximum or a minimum value of $f(x, y, z)$ for points which lie on $F(x, y, z) = 0$, then the surfaces $f(x, y, z) = a$ and $F(x, y, z) = 0$ will touch. [Coll. Exam.]

22. Find the maximum and minimum values of ρ where
$$rx^2 + 2sxy + ty^2 = k/\rho,$$
having given that
$$(1 + p^2)x^2 + 2pqxy + (1 + q^2)y^2 = 1.$$

23. If there are p tops of mountains on the earth and q bottoms of lakes and seas, prove that there must be $p - 1$ passes, or places where a level surface drawn through the point cuts off two elevated regions which meet at that point; and also $q - 1$ bars, or places where the level surface cuts off two depressed regions which meet at that point. Show also that there must be at least two summits higher than any pass, and two bottoms lower than any bar. [Math. Tripos, 1870.]

24. A framework crossed or uncrossed is formed of two unequal rods joined together at their ends by two equal rods; prove that the distance between the middle points of either pair of rods is a maximum when the unequal rods are parallel and a minimum when the equal rods are parallel; unless the two unequal rods are together less than the two equal rods, in which case the unequal rods are parallel in both the maximum and minimum positions. [Math. Tripos, 1875.]

25. If u be a function of n independent variables $x_1, x_2, \ldots, x_n$, prove that, in order that u may have maximum or minimum values, the roots of the equation

$$\begin{vmatrix} U_1 - z, & u_{12}, & \ldots, & u_{1n} \\ u_{12}, & U_2 - z, & \ldots, & u_{2n} \\ \cdots\cdots\cdots\cdots\cdots\cdots \\ u_{1n}, & u_{2n}, & \ldots, & U_n - z \end{vmatrix} = 0$$

must all be of the same sign; U_r, u_{rs} denoting the particular values of $\dfrac{\partial^2 u}{\partial x_r^2}, \dfrac{\partial^2 u}{\partial x_r \partial x_s}$, for certain values of $x_1, x_2, \ldots, x_n$ which make

$$\frac{\partial u}{\partial x_1}, \frac{\partial u}{\partial x_2}, \ldots, \frac{\partial u}{\partial x_n} = 0. \qquad \text{[Math. Tripos, 1873.]}$$

CHAPTER XVII.

ELIMINATION.

506. Construction of a Differential Equation.

It has been seen that the equation

$$f(x,\ y,\ a) = 0 \dots\dots\dots\dots\dots\dots (1)$$

is representative of a certain family of curves, for each individual of which the constant a receives a particular and definite value, the same for the same curve, but different for different curves of the family.

Problems sometimes occur in which it is necessary to treat of the whole family of curves together, as for instance in finding the family of curves which intersect each curve of the first system at right angles. And it is manifest that for such operations the letter a ought not to appear as a constant in the functions operated upon, otherwise we should be treating one individual curve of the system instead of the whole collectively.

Now the process of differentiation can be easily applied to get rid of a. For by differentiation with regard to x, we have

$$\frac{\partial f}{\partial x} + \frac{\partial f}{\partial y}\frac{dy}{dx} = 0, \dots\dots\dots\dots\dots\dots (2)$$

and a may be eliminated between these two equations, if indeed it has not already disappeared. There will now result an equation between

$$x,\ y,\ \text{and}\ \frac{dy}{dx},$$

which may be called the Differential Equation of the family of curves.

432

For example, consider the family of straight lines obtained by giving special values to the arbitrary constant m in the equation

$$y = mx.$$

Differentiating, $\qquad \dfrac{dy}{dx} = m,$

and therefore $\qquad y = x\dfrac{dy}{dx},$

a differential equation which is true for each member of the family since the m has been eliminated.

It is clear that the m would have disappeared at once upon differentiation if we had written the equation of the line

$$\frac{y}{x} = m ;$$

for, differentiating, we have $\qquad \dfrac{x\dfrac{dy}{dx} - y}{x^2} = 0,$

or $\qquad y = x\dfrac{dy}{dx}$

as before.

This is then the differential equation of all straight lines passing through the origin and expresses the geometrical fact that the *direction of the straight line is the same as that of the vector from the origin* at all points of the same line.

507. Again, suppose the representative equation of the family of curves to be

$$f(x, y, a, b) = 0,$$

containing two arbitrary constants a, b whose values particularize the several members of the family.

Now a single differentiation with respect to x will either cause one of the constants to disappear or will result in a relation between

$$x, y, \frac{dy}{dx}, a \text{ and } b.$$

From this relation and the original equation of the curve one of the two arbitrary constants may be eliminated, say a. Then we have a result of the form

$$F\left(x, y, \frac{dy}{dx}, b\right) = 0.$$

If we again differentiate with respect to x, we shall either cause the b to disappear or shall be able to eliminate b

between the result and the last equation, thus obtaining a differential equation of the second order between

$$x, \ y, \ \frac{dy}{dx}, \ \text{and} \ \frac{d^2y}{dx^2}$$

Thus if a function with one independent variable contains one arbitrary constant, the result of eliminating it is a differential equation of the first order. If it contain two arbitrary constants, the result is a differential equation of the second order. And our argument is general; so that to eliminate n arbitrary constants we shall have to proceed to n differentiations, and the result is a differential equation connecting

$$x, \ y, \ \frac{dy}{dx}, \ ..., \ \frac{d^ny}{dx^n},$$

and is therefore of the nth order.

Again, the final result is independent of the order and of the manner in which the eliminations are effected.

For suppose the arbitrary constants to be

$$a_1, \ a_2, \ ..., \ a_n,$$

and let any particular values be assigned to these constants. Then we have made choice of some particular curve of the system. Next take any value of x; at the points thus determined,

$$y, \ \frac{dy}{dx}, \ \frac{d^2y}{dx^2}, \ ..., \ \frac{d^ny}{dx^n}$$

have each definite values dependent upon the chosen values of

$$x, \ a_1, \ a_2, \ ..., \ a_n,$$

thus fixing the inclination of the tangent to the axis of x, the measure of curvature, and peculiarities of shape of a higher order at the point in question. These peculiarities of shape intrinsically belong to the chosen curve, and cannot be dependent upon any particular algebraic process which it may be found necessary to employ in obtaining a numerical measure of them, but must depend solely upon the geometrical character of the curve. Hence, if for the whole family any general algebraic identity be discovered connecting these peculiarities, in which none of the particularizing constants are present, and which is therefore true at any point of any member of the family, it must amount to a statement of some geometrical property characteristic of the family, and be independent of the method of its discovery. And in obtaining the n differential coefficients of y with regard to x we have in all $n+1$ equations, including that of the original curve, with n arbitrary constants to eliminate, leaving one single relation between

$$x, \ y, \ \frac{dy}{dx}, \ \cdots, \ \frac{d^n y}{dx^n}.$$

Ex. 1. Form the general differential equation of all straight lines.
The general equation of a straight line is

$$y = mx + c.$$

Hence $\qquad\qquad y_1 = m,$ ....(1)
and $\qquad\qquad y_2 = 0.$ ....(2)

Equation (2) evidently then is the general differential equation sought.

Its geometrical interpretation is clearly that the *curvature vanishes* at every point of each member of the family.

Ex. 2. Eliminate a and c from the equation

$$x^2 + y^2 = 2ax + c.$$

Differentiating, $\qquad\qquad x + yy_1 = a.$
Differentiating again, $\qquad 1 + y_1^2 + yy_2 = 0.$

This is the differential equation of all circles whose centres lie on the x-axis.

Ex. 3. Eliminate a, b, and c from the equation

$$(x-a)^2 + (y-b)^2 = c^2$$

and thus form the general differential equation of all circles.

We may write this equation

$$x^2 + y^2 = 2ax + 2by + c^2 - a^2 - b^2.$$

Differentiating three times we have the results

$$x + yy_1 = a + by_1,$$
$$1 + y_1^2 + yy_2 = by_2,$$
$$3y_1 y_2 + yy_3 = by_3,$$

Eliminating b between the last two results

$$(3y_1 y_2 + yy_3)y_2 = (1 + y_1^2 + yy_2)y_3,$$

or $\qquad\qquad (1 + y_1^2)y_3 = 3y_1 y_2^2.$

Referring to the result of Ex. 38, p. 110, the geometrical meaning of this equation is plainly that the *aberrancy of curvature vanishes* at any point of any circle.

Ex. 4. To eliminate the constants from the equation of the general conic.
Let the conic be

$$ax^2 + 2hxy + by^2 + 2gx + 2fy + c = 0.$$

We have by differentiating

$$ax + h(xy_1 + y) + byy_1 + g + fy_1 = 0 \dots\dots\dots\dots\dots(1)$$

$$a + h(xy_2 + 2y_1) + b(yy_2 + y_1^2) + fy_2 = 0 \dots\dots\dots\dots\dots(2)$$

$$h(xy_3 + 3y_2) + b(yy_3 + 3y_1y_2) + fy_3 = 0 \dots\dots\dots\dots\dots(3)$$

$$h(xy_4 + 4y_3) + b(yy_4 + 4y_1y_3 + 3y_2^2) + fy_4 = 0 \dots\dots\dots\dots\dots(4)$$

$$h(xy_5 + 5y_4) + b(yy_5 + 5y_1y_4 + 10y_2y_3) + fy_5 = 0 \dots\dots\dots\dots\dots(5)$$

From the last three equations

$$\begin{vmatrix} xy_3 + 3y_2, & yy_3 + 3y_1y_2 & , y_3 \\ xy_4 + 4y_3, & yy_4 + 4y_1y_3 + 3y_2^2 & , y_4 \\ xy_5 + 5y_4, & yy_5 + 5y_1y_4 + 10y_2y_3, & y_5 \end{vmatrix} = 0,$$

which immediately reduces to

$$\begin{vmatrix} 3y_2, & 0 & , y_3 \\ 4y_3, & 3y_2, & y_4 \\ 5y_4, & 10y_3, & y_5 \end{vmatrix} = 0,$$

or

$$9y_2^2 y_5 - 45y_2 y_3 y_4 + 40y_3^3 = 0.$$

This general differential equation of all conics was discovered by Monge. Dr. Boole, in his *Differential Equations*, p. 20, remarked : " But here our powers of geometrical interpretation fail, and results such as this can scarcely be otherwise useful than as a registry of integrable forms." A remarkable interpretation which calls for notice has, however, been recently offered by Mr. A. Mukhopadhyay, who has observed that the expression for the radius of curvature of the locus of the centre of the conic of five pointic contact with any curve (called the centre of aberrancy) contains as a factor the left-hand member of Monge's equation, and this differential equation therefore expresses that the "*radius of curvature of the 'curve of aberrancy' vanishes* for any point of any conic."[*]

EXAMPLES.

1. Eliminate a from the equation

$$y^2 = 4ax.$$

2. Eliminate a and b from the equation

$$\frac{x^2}{a^2} + \frac{y^2}{b^2} = 1.$$

3. Eliminate a and b from

$$r = a + b \cos \theta.$$

4. Form the general differential equation of all parabolas whose axes are parallel to the axis of y.

5. Eliminate a and b from the equation

$$y = ae^{nx} + be^{-nx}.$$

6. Eliminate a and b from the equation

$$y = a \sin(nx + b).$$

[*] *Journal of the Asiatic Society of Bengal*, vol. LVIII. Part I.

508. Elimination of Functions of Known Form.

We have already met with examples of elimination of various functions of known form from given equations by means of differentiation. For example, we found that if

$$y = \tan^{-1}x,$$

the function $\tan^{-1}$ was eliminated by simply differentiating, giving the result

$$(1+x^2)y_1 = 1.$$

And again, from the equation

$$y = \sin m(\sin^{-1}x)$$

we eliminated the circular and inverse functions sin and $\sin^{-1}$, obtaining the differential equation

$$(1-x^2)y_2 = xy_1 - m^2y. \quad \text{(Art. 122.)}$$

These were both made use of when series in ascending powers of x were required for $\tan^{-1}x$ and $\sin m(\sin^{-1}x)$ respectively. And it was seen that such differential equations are frequently useful in the expansion of certain classes of functions. But the chief interest in the processes by which, by differentiation and elimination, the differential equation is formed from its primitive equation rests in the light which they throw upon the converse problem of obtaining the primitive equation of the typical member when the differential equation of the family is given. This problem presents itself in numberless investigations and is the subject of special consideration in works on Differential Equations.

Ex. 1. Eliminate the constant a and the logarithmic function from
$$y = a \log x.$$

Here
$$y_1 = \frac{a}{x}.$$

and
$$xy_1 = a.$$

Differentiating again
$$y_1 + xy_2 = 0.$$

Ex. 2. Eliminate a, and the exponential and inverse circular functions from
$$y = ae^{mx}\sin^{-1}x.$$

Here
$$y_1 = ame^{mx}\sin^{-1}x + ae^{mx}\frac{1}{\sqrt{1-x^2}}$$

and
$$y_2 = am^2e^{mx}\sin^{-1}x + 2ame^{mx}\frac{1}{\sqrt{1-x^2}} + ae^{mx}\frac{x}{(1-x^2)^{\frac{3}{2}}},$$

i.e., $$y_2 = m^2y + 2m(y_1 - my) + \frac{x}{1-x^2}(y_1 - my)$$

or $$(1-x^2)y_2 = \{2m(1-x^2) + x\}y_1 - m^2y - mxy + m^2x^2y.$$

EXAMPLES.

1. From the equation $\qquad y = x^2 \log x$
eliminate the logarithmic function.

2. Given $\qquad\qquad\qquad y = e^{a\,\tan^{-1}x},$
eliminate the exponential and inverse functions.

3. Given the equation $\qquad y = \cos(\log x),$
eliminate the circular and logarithmic functions.

509. Genesis of Partial Differential Equations.

When more than one independent variable enters into our primitive equations, partial differential coefficients occur upon differentiation. A differential equation containing partial differential coefficients is styled a "partial differential equation" in distinction from an "ordinary differential equation" in which there is but one independent variable.

In Chapter VI. we proved Euler's Theorem, that if

$$u = x^n f\left(\frac{y}{x}, \frac{z}{x}, \ldots\right),$$

we have $$x\frac{\partial u}{\partial x} + y\frac{\partial u}{\partial y} + z\frac{\partial u}{\partial z} + \ldots = nu,$$

thus eliminating a function of perfectly arbitrary form.

We shall give other examples of elimination of arbitrary functions of unknown form obtaining as a final result in each case a partial differential equation.

When only three variables x, y, z occur two being independent, it is usual to take z for the dependent variable, and to use the abbreviations p, q, r, s, t to denote the partial differential coefficients

$$\frac{\partial z}{\partial x}, \frac{\partial z}{\partial y}, \frac{\partial^2 z}{\partial x^2}, \frac{\partial^2 z}{\partial x \partial y}, \frac{\partial^2 z}{\partial y^2} \text{ respectively. (Art. 170.)}$$

Ex. 1. Eliminate the arbitrary function ϕ from the equation
$$z = \phi(ax + by).$$
Here $$p = a\phi'(ax + by),$$
$$q = b\phi'(ax + by),$$
$\therefore$ $$bp - aq = 0,$$
the partial differential equation required.

Ex. 2. Eliminate the arbitrary functions ϕ and ψ from the equation

$$z = x\phi\left(\frac{y}{x}\right) + y\psi(x).$$

Here

$$p = \phi\left(\frac{y}{x}\right) - \frac{y}{x}\phi'\left(\frac{y}{x}\right) + y\psi'(x),$$

$$q = \phi'\left(\frac{y}{x}\right) + \psi(x),$$

$$s = -\frac{y}{x^2}\phi''\left(\frac{y}{x}\right) + \psi'(x),$$

$$t = \frac{1}{x}\phi''\left(\frac{y}{x}\right).$$

Hence $z - px - qy = -xy\psi'(x).$

Also $xs + yt = x\psi'(x),$

$\therefore$ $z - px - qy + xys + y^2t = 0,$

a partial differential equation of the second order.

EXAMPLES.

1. If $z = \phi(y + ax) + \psi(y - ax),$

prove $r - a^2t = 0.$

2. If $z = (x + y)\phi(x^2 - y^2),$

prove $z = py + qx.$

3. If $x = f(y) + \phi(z),$

prove $ps - qr = 0.$

4. If $z = x\phi(ax + by) + y\psi(ax + by),$

prove $b^2r - 2abs + a^2t = 0.$

510. PROP. *If u and v be explicit functions of x and y, and if u be a function of v, then will*

$$\frac{\partial u}{\partial x} \cdot \frac{\partial v}{\partial y} - \frac{\partial u}{\partial y} \cdot \frac{\partial v}{\partial x} = 0;$$

and conversely, if this relation be identically satisfied, u will be a function of v.[*]

For if $u = F(v),$

we have $\dfrac{\partial u}{\partial x} = F'(v)\dfrac{\partial v}{\partial x},$

and $\dfrac{\partial u}{\partial y} = F'(v)\dfrac{\partial v}{\partial y},$

[*] Boole, *Differential Equations*, p. 24.

and therefore eliminating $F'(v)$,

$$\frac{\partial u}{\partial x} \cdot \frac{\partial v}{\partial y} - \frac{\partial u}{\partial y} \cdot \frac{\partial v}{\partial x} = 0.$$

Conversely, suppose this condition satisfied, then will u be a function of v.

For since u and v are known functions of x and y, we may eliminate one of these letters, say y. Then, unless x is simultaneously eliminated, we obtain a relation of the form

$$u = f(v,\ x).$$

Now

$$\frac{\partial u}{\partial x} = \frac{\partial f}{\partial v} \cdot \frac{\partial v}{\partial x} + \frac{\partial f}{\partial x},$$

$$\frac{\partial u}{\partial y} = \frac{\partial f}{\partial v} \cdot \frac{\partial v}{\partial y},$$

$$\therefore \qquad \frac{\partial u}{\partial x} \cdot \frac{\partial v}{\partial y} - \frac{\partial u}{\partial y} \cdot \frac{\partial v}{\partial x} = \frac{\partial f}{\partial x} \cdot \frac{\partial v}{\partial y}.$$

Hence

$$\frac{\partial f}{\partial x} \cdot \frac{\partial v}{\partial y} = 0.$$

i.e., either

$$\frac{\partial v}{\partial y} = 0, \text{ or } \frac{\partial f}{\partial x} = 0.$$

If $\frac{\partial f}{\partial x} = 0$, $f(v,\ x)$ is independent of x, and therefore u is a function of v. And $\frac{\partial v}{\partial y}$ cannot in general vanish, since v involves usually both x and y.

If, however, v be a function of x alone, $\frac{\partial v}{\partial y} = 0$. If also u be a function of v, u is a function of x alone, and $\frac{\partial u}{\partial y} = 0$; hence in this case the relation

$$\frac{\partial u}{\partial x} \cdot \frac{\partial v}{\partial y} - \frac{\partial u}{\partial y} \cdot \frac{\partial v}{\partial x} = 0$$

is satisfied. And conversely, if this relation be identically satisfied, and if $\frac{\partial v}{\partial y} = 0$, we must have

$$\frac{\partial u}{\partial y} \cdot \frac{\partial v}{\partial x} = 0;$$

and therefore u must be independent of y, since we cannot assume v independent of x as well as of y. Hence, as u and

v are both functions of the same variable, it is obvious that by eliminating it we can express u as a function of v.

EXAMPLES.

1. If $\qquad u=\dfrac{x+y}{1-xy}$ and $v=\dfrac{x(1-y^2)+y(1-x^2)}{(1+x^2)(1+y^2)}$,

prove that $\qquad\qquad u_x v_y = u_y v_x,$

and interpret this result.

2. If $\quad u=x\sqrt{1-y^2}+y\sqrt{1-x^2}$ and $v=xy-\sqrt{1-x^2}\sqrt{1-y^2}$,

prove that u is a function of v.

3. If u and v be explicit functions of three variables x, y, z, and if u be a function of v, prove that

$$\begin{vmatrix} u_x, & u_y, & u_z \\ v_x, & v_y, & v_z \\ p, & q, & -1 \end{vmatrix} = 0.$$

511. Next suppose u a known function of x, y, and z, and that $\phi(u)$ is an arbitrary function of u. We shall show how to eliminate the arbitrary function $\phi(u)$ from an equation of the form

$$f\{x,\ y,\ z,\ \phi(u)\} = 0. \qquad\qquad\qquad(1)$$

Supposing x and y to be the independent variables, we have by differentiating

$$\left.\begin{aligned} \frac{\partial f}{\partial x}+p\frac{\partial f}{\partial z}+\frac{\partial f}{\partial u}\left(\frac{\partial u}{\partial x}+p\frac{\partial u}{\partial z}\right)=0 \\[2mm] \frac{\partial f}{\partial y}+q\frac{\partial f}{\partial z}+\frac{\partial f}{\partial u}\left(\frac{\partial u}{\partial y}+q\frac{\partial u}{\partial z}\right)=0 \end{aligned}\right\} \qquad(2)$$

Hence, eliminating $\dfrac{\partial f}{\partial u}$,

$$\begin{vmatrix} \dfrac{\partial f}{\partial x}+p\dfrac{\partial f}{\partial z}, & \dfrac{\partial u}{\partial x}+p\dfrac{\partial u}{\partial z} \\[3mm] \dfrac{\partial f}{\partial y}+q\dfrac{\partial f}{\partial z}, & \dfrac{\partial u}{\partial y}+q\dfrac{\partial u}{\partial z} \end{vmatrix} = 0, \qquad\qquad(3)$$

an equation containing x, y, z, p, q and $\phi(u)$; $\phi'(u)$ disappearing on the elimination of $\dfrac{\partial f}{\partial u}$. Hence, if $\phi(u)$ be eliminated between equations (1) and (3), we shall obtain a partial differential equation of the first order between x, y, z, p and q.

512. Suppose u_1 and u_2 known functions of x, y, and z, and $\phi_1(u_1)$, $\phi_2(u_2)$ arbitrary functions of u_1 and u_2. We shall now show how the two arbitrary functions $\phi_1(u_1)$ and $\phi_2(u_2)$ may be eliminated from an equation of the form

$$f\{x,\ y,\ z,\ \phi_1(u_1),\ \phi_2(u_2)\} = 0.$$

If we form the equations

$$f_x = 0,\ f_y = 0,$$

we introduce the two new functions

$$\phi_1'(u_1),\ \phi_2'(u_2)$$

Proceeding to differentiations of the second order, we have the three additional equations

$$f_{xx} = 0,\ f_{xy} = 0,\ f_{yy} = 0,$$

introducing again two new unknown functions

$$\phi_1''(u_1) \text{ and } \phi_2''(u_2).$$

We now have in all *six* equations with six quantities to eliminate. It is therefore in general necessary to proceed to differentiations of the third order, thereby obtaining the four new equations

$$f_{xxx} = 0,\ f_{xxy} = 0,\ f_{xyy} = 0,\ f_{yyy} = 0,$$

and introducing at the same time the two additional unknown functions

$$\phi_1'''(u_1),\ \phi_2'''(u_2).$$

We now have ten equations with eight unknown functions to eliminate, leaving in general two independent resulting partial differential equations of the third order.

513. Generally, suppose an equation given of the form

$$f\{x,\ y,\ z,\ \dots,\ t,\ \phi_1(u_1),\ \phi_2(u_2),\ \dots,\ \phi_n(u_n)\} = 0,$$

containing $p+1$ variables, of which p are independent, and n arbitrary functions $\phi_1(u_1)$, $\phi_2(u_2) \dots$, $\phi_n(u_n)$ of the n known functions $u_1, u_2, \dots, u_n$; to eliminate the n arbitrary functions. Suppose t the dependent variable; then forming all differential coefficients up to those of the rth order inclusive, we have

(a) $f = 0$;   one equation.

(β) $f_x = 0,\ f_y = 0,\ \dots$; p equations.

(γ) $f_{xx}=0$, $f_{xy}=0$, $f_{xz}=0$, ...; $\qquad \dfrac{p(p+1)}{1\,.\,2}$ equations.

[being the number of homogeneous products of p things of two dimensions]

$$\cdots\cdots\cdots\cdots\cdots\cdots\cdots\cdots\cdots ;$$

(κ) and proceeding to r differentiations;

$$\frac{p(p+1)(p+2)\ldots(p+r-1)}{r!} \text{ equations,}$$

making in all

$$1+p+\frac{p(p+1)}{1\,.\,2}+\ldots+\frac{p(p+1)\ldots(p+r-1)}{r!} \text{ equations,}$$

containing partial differential coefficients up to those of the rth order inclusive.

The sum of this series is the coefficient of x^r in the product of the series for $(1-x)^{-p}$ and $(1-x)^{-1}$

$$= \text{coefficient of } x^r \text{ in } (1-x)^{-(p+1)}$$

$$= \frac{(p+1)(p+2)\ldots(p+r)}{r!} = \frac{(p+r)!}{p!\,r!}.$$

We have therefore thus obtained $\dfrac{(p+r)!}{p!\,r!}$ equations, containing differential coefficients up to those of the rth order.

Moreover, there are $(r+1)n$ functions to eliminate, viz.,

$$\phi_1, \quad \phi_2, \quad \ldots, \quad \phi_n, \qquad \text{originally:}$$

$$\frac{d\phi_1}{du_1}, \frac{d\phi_2}{du_2}, \quad \ldots, \quad \frac{d\phi_n}{du_n}, \quad \begin{cases}\text{introduced among the differ-}\\ \text{entiations of the 1st order;}\end{cases}$$

$$\cdots\cdots\cdots\cdots\cdots\cdots\cdots\cdots$$

and $\quad \dfrac{d^r\phi_1}{du_1{}^r}, \quad \ldots, \quad \dfrac{d^r\phi_n}{du_n{}^r} \quad \begin{cases}\text{introduced at the differenti-}\\ \text{ations of the } r^{\text{th}} \text{ order.}\end{cases}$

Hence, we must in general go on forming all differential coefficients of the primitive function until

$$\frac{(p+r)!}{p!\,r!} \text{ is first greater than } (r+1)n,$$

and there will generally be

$$\frac{(p+r)!}{p!\,r!}-(r+1)n \text{ independent results.}$$

Cor. If there be three variables x, y, and z, we have $p = 2$,

and then $$\frac{(r+2)!}{2 \cdot r!} > n(r+1),$$

and therefore $$r + 2 > 2n,$$

and $$r > 2n - 2.$$

Hence in general it is necessary to proceed to differentiations of the $(2n-1)^{\text{th}}$ order at least, and there will in general be n independent results.

514. The case however in which the n arbitrary functions $\phi_1(u)$, $\phi_2(u)$, ..., $\phi_n(u)$ to be eliminated are all functions of the *same* known function of x, y, z is exceptional.* We now have

$$f\{x, y, z, \phi_1(u), \phi_2(u), ..., \phi_n(u)\} = 0.$$

Proceeding as in Art. 511, equations (2) and (3) are still true,

and we obtain $$\begin{vmatrix} \dfrac{\partial f}{\partial x} + p\dfrac{\partial f}{\partial z}, & \dfrac{\partial u}{\partial x} + p\dfrac{\partial u}{\partial z} \\[2ex] \dfrac{\partial f}{\partial y} + q\dfrac{\partial f}{\partial z}, & \dfrac{\partial u}{\partial y} + q\dfrac{\partial u}{\partial z} \end{vmatrix} = 0,$$

an equation containing

$$x, y, z, p, q, \phi_1(u), \phi_2(u), ..., \phi_n(u),$$

for $\phi_1'(u)$, $\phi_2'(u)$, ..., all disappear as before, on the elimination of $\dfrac{df}{du}$. Treating this equation in like manner, we obtain a third equation, containing

$$x, y, z, p, q, r, s, t, \phi_1(u), ..., \phi_n(u).$$

And the process may be repeated until we have in all $n+1$ equations from which the n arbitrary functions may be eliminated, leaving as result a partial differential equation of the nth order.

EXAMPLES.

1. Eliminate a and b from the equation

$$y = a \sin nx + b \cos nx.$$

2. Eliminate a and b from the equation

$$y = (a + bx)e^{nx}.$$

* See Todhunter's *Diff. Calc.*, Arts. 251-254.

3. Eliminate a and b from the equation
$$xy = ae^x + be^{-x}.$$

4. Eliminate the circular and exponential functions from the equation
$$y = e^x \cos x.$$

5. Eliminate the circular and exponential functions from the equation
$$y = ae^{2x}\cos 3x + be^{2x}\sin 3x.$$

6. Eliminate the circular and exponential functions from the equation
$$y = ae^{mx}\sin nx + be^{mx}\cos nx.$$

7. Eliminate the hyperbolic functions from the equation
$$a \cosh x + b \sinh x = c \cosh y + d \sinh y.$$

8. Eliminate the constants from the equation
$$ax^2 + 2hxy + by^2 = c.$$

9. Eliminate the circular and logarithmic functions from the equation
$$y = \sin \log x.$$

10. Eliminate the circular and logarithmic functions from the equation
$$y = \log \sin x.$$

11. Eliminate a and b from the equation
$$y = a \cos nx + b \sin nx + \frac{\cos mx}{n^2 - m^2}.$$

12. Eliminate a and b from the equation
$$y = a \cos nx + b \sin nx + x \sin nx.$$

13. Eliminate a, b, and c from the equation
$$y = ae^{n_1 x} + be^{n_2 x} + ce^{n_3 x},$$
n_1, n_2, n_3 being the roots of the cubic
$$z^3 + pz^2 + qz + r = 0.$$

14. If $y = Ae^{ax}$ satisfies the linear differential equation
$$\frac{d^n y}{dx^n} + p_1\frac{d^{n-1}y}{dx^{n-1}} + p_2\frac{d^{n-2}y}{dx^{n-2}} + \ldots + p_n = 0,$$
prove that a is one of the roots of the equation
$$z^n + p_1 z^{n-1} + p_2 z^{n-2} + \ldots + p_n = 0.$$

15. Show that for a given primitive equation involving x, y, and n arbitrary constants, there are $\dfrac{n!}{r!(n-r)!}$ differential equations of the rth order ($r < n$), each involving $n - r$ arbitrary constants, but that only $r + 1$ of these equations will be independent.   [BOOLE.]

16. Eliminate a, b, and c from the equation

$$y = (a + bx)e^x + ce^{-x}.$$

17. Eliminate a, b, c, and d from the equation

$$y = (a + bx)\cos nx + (c + dx)\sin nx.$$

18. Eliminate the circular and logarithmic functions from the equation

$$y = A \cos\left\{\frac{n}{b}\log(a + bx)\right\} + B \sin\left\{\frac{n}{b}\log(a + bx)\right\}$$

19. Eliminate the function from the equation

$$z = y \sin^{-1}\frac{x}{y} + \phi(y).$$

20. If

$$z = \frac{x}{a} + \phi(ay - bx),$$

prove

$$ap + bq = 1.$$

21. If

$$z = \phi\{x + \psi(y)\},$$

prove

$$ps - qr = 0.$$

22. If

$$lx + my + nz = F(x^2 + y^2 + z^2),$$

prove

$$(mz - ny)p + (nx - lz)q = ly - mx$$

23. If

$$\frac{y - b}{z - c} = F\left(\frac{x - a}{z - c}\right),$$

prove

$$(a - x)p + (b - y)q = c - z.$$

24. If

$$z = e^{\frac{y}{a}}\phi(x - y),$$

prove

$$p + q = \frac{z}{a}.$$

25. If

$$z = x\phi\left(\frac{y}{x}\right) + \psi\left(\frac{y}{x}\right),$$

show that

$$x^2 r + 2xys + y^2 t = 0.$$

26. Given

$$z = F(y - mx) + f(y - nx),$$

prove

$$r + (m + n)s + mnt = 0.$$

27. Given

$$z = xF(ax + by + cz) + yf(ax + by + cz),$$

prove

$$(b + cq)^2 r - 2(b + cq)(a + cp)s + (a + cp)^2 t = 0.$$

28. Given

$$\frac{1}{z} - \frac{1}{x} = f\left(\frac{1}{y} - \frac{1}{x}\right),$$

show that

$$x^2\frac{\partial z}{\partial x} + y^2\frac{\partial z}{\partial y} = z^2.$$

29. X and Y are functions of x and y. Show that the result of eliminating t between the equations

$$\frac{d^2x}{dt^2} = X, \quad \frac{d^2y}{dt^2} = Y$$

is

$$2X = \frac{d}{dx}\left\{ \frac{Y - X\dfrac{dy}{dx}}{\dfrac{d^2y}{dx^2}} \right\}.$$

30. If

$$u = xyz F(x^2 + y^2 + z^2),$$

show that $(y-z)\dfrac{\partial u}{\partial x} + (z-x)\dfrac{\partial u}{\partial y} + (x-y)\dfrac{\partial u}{\partial z} + \dfrac{(y-z)(z-x)(x-y)u}{xyz} = 0.$

31. If

$$u = F(x^2 + y^2 + z^2)f(xy + yz + zx),$$

prove that $(y-z)\dfrac{\partial u}{\partial x} + (z-x)\dfrac{\partial u}{\partial y} + (x-y)\dfrac{\partial u}{\partial z} = 0.$

32. If

$$z = x^m F\left(\frac{y}{x}\right) + x^n f\left(\frac{y}{x}\right),$$

show that

$$x^2\frac{\partial^2 z}{\partial x^2} + 2xy\frac{\partial^2 z}{\partial x\partial y} + y^2\frac{\partial^2 z}{\partial y^2} - (m+n-1)\left(x\frac{\partial z}{\partial x} + y\frac{\partial z}{\partial y}\right) + mnz = 0.$$

33. Show that the result of eliminating the n arbitrary functions from the equation

$$z = x^{p_1}f_1\left(\frac{y}{x}\right) + x^{p_2}f_2\left(\frac{y}{x}\right) + \ldots + x^{p_n}f_n\left(\frac{y}{x}\right)$$

may be written

$$\begin{vmatrix} z, & 1, & 1, & \ldots, & 1 \\ \Delta z, & p_1, & p_2, & \ldots, & p_n \\ \Delta^2 z, & p_1^2, & p_2^2, & \ldots, & p_n^2 \\ \hdotsfor{5} \\ \Delta^n z, & p_1^n, & p_2^n, & \ldots, & p_n^n \end{vmatrix} = 0.$$

where Δ represents the operative symbol $x\dfrac{d}{dx} + y\dfrac{d}{dy}$.

34. If

$$\phi(u^2 - x^2, \ u^2 - y^2, \ u^2 - z^2) = 0,$$

show that

$$\frac{1}{x}\frac{\partial u}{\partial x} + \frac{1}{y}\frac{\partial u}{\partial y} + \frac{1}{z}\frac{\partial u}{\partial z} = \frac{1}{u}.$$

35. If

$$\phi\{S^{\frac{3}{2}}(u-x), \ S^{\frac{3}{2}}(u-y), \ S^{\frac{3}{2}}(u-z)\} = 0$$

where

$$S = x + y + z + u,$$

show that $(S-x)\dfrac{\partial u}{\partial x} + (S-y)\dfrac{\partial u}{\partial y} + (S-z)\dfrac{\partial u}{\partial z} = S - u.$ [LAGRANGE.]

36. If
$$\phi\left(\frac{x^a}{u^d},\ \frac{y^b}{u^d},\ \frac{z^c}{u^d}\right) = 0,$$

show that
$$\frac{x}{a}\frac{\partial u}{\partial x} + \frac{y}{b}\frac{\partial u}{\partial y} + \frac{z}{c}\frac{\partial u}{\partial z} = \frac{u}{d}.$$

37. Eliminate the arbitrary functions from the equation
$$z = f\left(\frac{y}{x}\right)F(xy).$$

CHAPTER XVIII.

EXPANSIONS.

(CONTINUED FROM CHAPTER V.)

THEOREMS OF ARBOGAST, LAGRANGE, LAPLACE, AND BURMANN.

515. Arbogast's Rule.

Arbogast has given in his *Calcul des Derivations* (Strasburg, 1800) a useful method for the expansion of

$$\phi(a_0 + a_1 x + a_2 x^2 + \ldots)$$

in a series of ascending powers of x, ϕ being any arbitrary function.

Taylor's theorem at once gives

$$\phi(a_0 + a_1 x + a_2 x^2 + a_3 x^3 + \ldots)$$

$$= \phi(a_0) + \frac{\phi'(a_0)}{\underline{1}}(a_1 x + a_2 x^2 + a_3 x^3 + a_4 x^4 + \ldots)$$

$$+ \frac{\phi''(a_0)}{\underline{2}}(a_1 x + a_2 x^2 + a_3 x^3 + \ldots)^2$$

$$+ \frac{\phi'''(a_0)}{\underline{3}}(a_1 x + a_2 x^2 + a_3 x^3 + \ldots)^3$$

$$+ \frac{\phi''''(a_0)}{\underline{4}}(a_1 x + a_2 x^2 + \ldots)^4$$

$$+ \ldots\ldots\ldots\ldots\ldots\ldots\ldots ;$$

or, expanding the several powers of this polynomial increment which occur, and arranging in powers of x, we have

$$\phi(a_0 + a_1 x + a_2 x^2 + \ldots)$$

$$= \phi(a_0) + x[\phi'(a_0) . a_1]$$

$$+ x^2\left[\phi'(a_0) . a_2 + \phi''(a_0) . \frac{a_1^2}{2}\right]$$

$$+ x^3\left[\phi'(a_0) . a_3 + \phi''(a_0) . a_1 . a_2 + \phi'''(a_0)\frac{a_1^3}{2.3}\right]$$

$$+ x^4\left[\phi'(a_0) . a_4 + \phi''(a_0) . a_1 . a_3 + \phi''(a_0)\frac{a_2^2}{2}\right.$$

$$\left. + \phi'''(a_0)\frac{a_1^2 a_2}{2} + \phi''''(a_0)\frac{a_1^4}{2.3.4}\right]$$

$$+ \ldots\ldots\ldots\ldots\ldots\ldots\ldots\ldots\ldots\ldots\ldots\ldots\ldots$$

Upon examination, it will appear that each of these co-efficients may be formed from the preceding one by differentiating each term with regard to the last letter contained and integrating with regard to the next letter, and then differentiating with regard to the letter next before the last and integrating with regard to the last.

Professor Cayley (*Messenger of Math.*, vol. V.) called this the "rule of the last and the last but one."

I am indebted to Mr. A. E. Joliffe for the following elegant and convenient form of the theorem.

If
$$\phi\left(a_0 + a_1 x + a_2\frac{x^2}{2!} + a_3\frac{x^3}{3!} + \ldots\right)$$

be expanded in the form,

$$A_0 + A_1 x + A_2\frac{x^2}{2!} + A_3\frac{x^3}{3!} + \ldots$$

the coefficients A_1, A_2, A_3, ... can be successively calculated by the formula,

$$A_{r+1} = \left(a_1\frac{\partial}{\partial a_0} + a_2\frac{\partial}{\partial a_1} + a_3\frac{\partial}{\partial a_2} + \ldots\right)A_r.$$

To demonstrate this let

$$a_1\frac{\partial}{\partial a_0} + a_2\frac{\partial}{\partial a_1} + a_3\frac{\partial}{\partial a_2} + \ldots \equiv \Delta,$$

then $\quad \Delta\phi\left(a_0 + a_1 x + a_2 \dfrac{x^2}{2!} + \dots\right)$

$$= \left(a_1 + a_2 x + a_3 \dfrac{x^2}{2!} + \dots\right)\phi'(a_0 + \dots)$$

$$= \dfrac{d}{dx}\phi(a_0 + \dots).$$

Hence $\quad \Delta A_0 + \Delta A_1 . x + \Delta A_2 \dfrac{x^2}{2!} + \Delta A_3 \dfrac{x^3}{3!} + \dots$

$$\equiv A_1 + A_2 x + A_3 \dfrac{x^2}{2!} + A_4 \dfrac{x^3}{3!} + \dots$$

whence $\qquad\qquad A_{r+1} = \Delta A_r.$

Now $\qquad A_0 = \phi(a_0);$

hence $\qquad A_1 = a_1 \phi'(a_0),$

$$A_2 = a_1^2 \phi''(a_0) + a_2 \phi'(a_0),$$

$$A_3 = a_1^3 \phi'''(a_0) + 3 a_1 a_2 \phi''(a_0) + a_3 \phi'(a_0),$$

$$\text{etc.}$$

516. Maclaurin's theorem gives a method of expanding z in powers of x whenever the limiting values of z, $\dfrac{dz}{dx}$, $\dfrac{d^2z}{dx^2}$, ...,

when $x = 0$, can be found. It is therefore specially adapted for the case in which z is expressed explicitly in terms of x. But in the case of the fundamental relation between z and x being implicit, the evaluation of high differential coefficients is often tedious and difficult, and it is therefore advantageous to make use of theorems specially constructed to meet the requirements of this case. We therefore proceed to the investigation of Lagrange's and Laplace's Theorems.

517. **Lagrange's Theorem.**

Suppose z to be a function of x and y defined by the equation $\qquad z = y + x\phi(z),$ ....(1) and let u be any function of z, say $f(z)$; it is required to expand u in a series of powers of x.

Maclaurin's theorem gives

$$u = u_0 + x\left(\frac{\partial u}{\partial x}\right)_0 + \frac{x^2}{2!}\left(\frac{\partial^2 u}{\partial x^2}\right)_0 + \frac{x^3}{3!}\left(\frac{\partial^3 u}{\partial x^3}\right)_0 + \dots,$$

where $\left(\dfrac{\partial u}{\partial x}\right)_0$, $\left(\dfrac{\partial^2 u}{\partial x^2}\right)_0$, ... indicate that x is to be made zero after the differentiations indicated are completed. The values of these expressions may all be calculated by successive differentiation, but the process may be much simplified, as we now proceed to show.

It will be clear that

$$\frac{\partial}{\partial y}\left[F(u)\frac{\partial u}{\partial x}\right] = \frac{\partial}{\partial x}\left[F(u)\frac{\partial u}{\partial y}\right], \dots\dots\dots(2)$$

where u is any function of x and y; for each side is equal to

$$F'(u)\cdot\frac{\partial u}{\partial x}\cdot\frac{\partial u}{\partial y} + F(u)\frac{\partial^2 u}{\partial x \partial y}.$$

Differentiating equation (1) with regard to x and y, we

obtain
$$\frac{\partial z}{\partial x} = \phi(z) + x\phi'(z)\frac{\partial z}{\partial x}\Bigg\}$$

and
$$\frac{\partial z}{\partial y} = \quad 1 + x\phi'(z)\frac{\partial z}{\partial y}\Bigg\}.$$

Giving
$$\frac{\partial z}{\partial x} = \phi(z)/\{1 - x\phi'(z)\}, \dots\dots\dots(3)$$

$$\frac{\partial z}{\partial y} = \quad 1/\{1 - x\phi'(z)\}, \dots\dots\dots(4)$$

whence
$$\frac{\partial z}{\partial x} = \phi(z)\frac{\partial z}{\partial y}. \dots\dots\dots\dots(5)$$

If now u be any function of z, we have

$$\frac{\partial u}{\partial x} = \frac{du}{dz}\cdot\frac{\partial z}{\partial x},$$

and
$$\frac{\partial u}{\partial y} = \frac{du}{dz}\cdot\frac{\partial z}{\partial y},$$

whence equation (5) becomes

$$\frac{\partial u}{\partial x} = \phi(z)\frac{\partial u}{\partial y}. \dots\dots\dots\dots(6)$$

We shall in a similar manner change the independent variable from x to y for each of the remaining expressions

$$\frac{\partial^2 u}{\partial x^2}, \quad \frac{\partial^3 u}{\partial x^3}, \quad \dots.$$

Thus we have $\dfrac{\partial^2 u}{\partial x^2} = \dfrac{\partial}{\partial x}\left[\phi(z)\dfrac{\partial u}{\partial y}\right] = \dfrac{\partial}{\partial y}\left[\phi(z)\dfrac{\partial u}{\partial x}\right],$

remembering that u is a function of z, and therefore, conversely, z a function of u, and applying equation (2). Hence, substituting the value of $\dfrac{\partial u}{\partial x}$ from equation (6),

$$\frac{\partial^2 u}{\partial x^2} = \frac{\partial}{\partial y}\left[\{\phi(z)\}^2 \frac{\partial u}{\partial y}\right]. \quad\text{..........................(7)}$$

Differentiating again,

$$\begin{aligned}
\frac{\partial^3 u}{\partial x^3} &= \frac{\partial}{\partial x}\,\frac{\partial}{\partial y}\left[\{\phi(z)\}^2 \frac{\partial u}{\partial y}\right] \\
&= \frac{\partial}{\partial y}\,\frac{\partial}{\partial x}\left[\{\phi(z)\}^2 \frac{\partial u}{\partial y}\right] \\
&= \frac{\partial}{\partial y}\,\frac{\partial}{\partial y}\left[\{\phi(z)\}^2 \frac{\partial u}{\partial x}\right], \\
&= \frac{\partial^2}{\partial y^2}\left[\{\phi(z)\}^3 \frac{\partial u}{\partial y}\right]. \quad\text{.................(8)}
\end{aligned}$$

The general law indicated by equations (6), (7), (8), viz.,

$$\frac{\partial^n u}{\partial x^n} = \frac{\partial^{n-1}}{\partial y^{n-1}}\left[\{\phi(z)\}^n \frac{\partial u}{\partial y}\right], \quad\text{...................(9)}$$

may easily be proved by induction. For differentiating equation (9) with respect to x,

$$\begin{aligned}
\frac{\partial^{n+1} u}{\partial x^{n+1}} &= \frac{\partial}{\partial x}\,\frac{\partial^{n-1}}{\partial y^{n-1}}\left[\{\phi(z)\}^n \frac{\partial u}{\partial y}\right] \\
&= \frac{\partial^{n-1}}{\partial y^{n-1}}\,\frac{\partial}{\partial x}\left[\{\phi(z)\}^n \frac{\partial u}{\partial y}\right] \\
&= \frac{\partial^{n-1}}{\partial y^{n-1}}\,\frac{\partial}{\partial y}\left[\{\phi(z)\}^n \frac{\partial u}{\partial x}\right] \\
&= \frac{\partial^n}{\partial y^n}\left[\{\phi(z)\}^{n+1} \frac{\partial u}{\partial y}\right],
\end{aligned}$$

whence $\dfrac{\partial^{n+1} u}{\partial x^{n+1}}$ follows the same law of formation as $\dfrac{\partial^n u}{\partial x^n}$; but equations (6), (7), (8) established the form for the special cases $n=1$, $n=2$, $n=3$, and hence the form holds universally.

In finding $\left(\dfrac{\partial u}{\partial x}\right)_0$, $\left(\dfrac{\partial^2 u}{\partial x^2}\right)_0$, ..., x is to be put $=0$ *after* the differentiations are performed, but as all these differential coefficients are transformed into differentiations taken with regard to y, which is independent of x, it is permissible to make $x=0$ *before* effecting the differentiation with regard to y, and we shall therefore be able to write $z=y$ and $\frac{\partial u}{\partial y}=f'(y)$; and then equation (9) gives

$$\left(\frac{\partial^n u}{\partial x^n}\right)_0=\frac{d^{n-1}}{dy^{n-1}}[\{\phi(y)\}^n f'(y)],$$

and the development of u or $f(z)$ by Maclaurin's theorem, viz.,

$$f(z)=u_0+x\left(\frac{\partial u}{\partial x}\right)_0+\frac{x^2}{2!}\left(\frac{\partial^2 u}{\partial x^2}\right)_0+\cdots,$$

becomes

$$f(z)=f(y)+x\phi(y)f'(y)+\frac{x^2}{2!}\frac{d}{dy}[\{\phi(y)\}^2 f'(y)]+\cdots$$
$$+\frac{x^n}{n!}\frac{d^{n-1}}{dy^{n-1}}[\{\phi(y)\}^n f'(y)]+\cdots.$$

Ex. Given $$z=y+\frac{x}{2}(z^2-1),\quad\ldots\ldots\ldots\ldots\ldots\ldots(1)$$

to expand z in powers of x.

Here $f(z)=z$ and $\phi(z)=\frac{1}{2}(z^2-1)$,

and therefore $\dfrac{d^{n-1}}{dy^{n-1}}[(\phi y)^n f'y]=\dfrac{1}{2^n}\dfrac{d^{n-1}}{dy^{n-1}}(y^2-1)^n,$

and Lagrange's theorem gives

$$z=y+\frac{x}{2}(y^2-1)+\left(\frac{x}{2}\right)^2\frac{1}{2!}\frac{d}{dy}(y^2-1)^2+\cdots+\left(\frac{x}{2}\right)^n\frac{1}{n!}\frac{d^{n-1}(y^2-1)^n}{dy^{n-1}}+\cdots.\quad(2)$$

From this result we may deduce an important expansion, viz., that of

$$(1-2yx+x^2)^{-\frac{1}{2}}.$$

From Equation (1) $$z=\frac{1}{x}-\frac{1}{x}\sqrt{1-2xy+x^2},\quad\ldots\ldots\ldots\ldots\ldots(3)$$

the negative sign being adopted, since when $x=0$ we are to have $z=y$.

Differentiating the right-hand sides of (2) and (3) with regard to y, we have

$$(1-2yx+x^2)^{-\frac{1}{2}}=1+\frac{x}{2}\frac{d}{dy}(y^2-1)+\frac{x^2}{2!}\frac{1}{2^2}\frac{d^2(y^2-1)^2}{dy^2}+\cdots+\frac{x^n}{n!}\frac{1}{2^n}\frac{d^n(y^2-1)^n}{dy^n}+\cdots.$$

The coefficients P_0, P_1, P_2, ... of the several powers of x in this expansion are called Laplace's Coefficients. We thus have established

$$P_n=\frac{1}{2^n n!}\frac{d^n(y^2-1)^n}{dy^n}.$$

518. Laplace's Generalization of Lagrange's Theorem.

The result of the preceding article is due to Lagrange.[*] The proof is however due to Laplace, who has thrown the

[*] *Mémoires de Berlin*, 1768.

same theorem into a more general form, which is easily deducible from the foregoing.

Suppose that instead of equation (1) of the preceding article we had

$$z = F\{y + x\phi(z)\}, \quad\text{...........................(1)}$$

and that it is required to expand any function of z, say $f(z)$, in ascending powers of x.

If we write $\qquad y + x\phi(z) = t,$

we have $\qquad z = F(t),$

and therefore $\qquad t = y + x\phi[F(t)]. \quad\text{.........................(2)}$

Hence we have to develop $f(z)$ or $f[F(t)]$ in powers of x from equation (2), which is therefore an obvious case of Lagrange's theorem, the complex functions $f\{F(t)\}$ and $\phi\{F(t)\}$ taking the place of the simple functions $f(z)$ and $\phi(z)$ in the above result. We therefore obtain

$$f(z) = f\{F(y)\} + x\phi\{F(y)\}\frac{df\{F(y)\}}{dy} + \frac{x^2}{2!}\frac{d}{dy}\left[\overline{\phi\{F(y)\}}|^2\frac{df\{F(y)\}}{dy}\right]$$

$$+ \ldots + \frac{x^n}{n!}\frac{d^{n-1}}{dy^{n-1}}\left[\overline{\phi\{F(y)\}}|^n\frac{df\{F(y)\}}{dy}\right] + \ldots.$$

519. Burmann's Theorem.

Burmann has given a series of very general form for expanding any function of z, say $f(z)$, in powers of any other function of z, $F(z)$. This like Laplace's result includes Lagrange's series as a particular case, and admits of easy deduction from the original series.

Lagrange's series may be written

$$f(z) = f(a) + \sum_{r=1}^{r=\infty}\frac{A_r x^r}{r!}, \quad\text{..........................(1)}$$

where $\qquad z = a + x\phi(z), \quad\text{...........................(2)}$

and $\qquad A_r = \left[\frac{d^{r-1}}{dz^{r-1}}\{(\phi z)^r f'z\}\right]_{z=a}. \quad\text{................(3)}$

Put $\qquad x = \left(\frac{z-a}{\phi(z)}\right) = F(z).$

It is clear then that $z = a$ is a solution of the equation $F(z) = 0$; also the form of $\phi(z)$ is $\dfrac{z-a}{F(z)}$.

Thus equation (1) becomes

$$f(z) = f(a) + \sum_{r=1}^{r=\infty} \frac{B_r (Fz)^r}{r!},$$

where

$$B_r = \left[\frac{d^{r-1}}{dz^{r-1}} \left\{ \left(\frac{z-a}{Fz} \right)^r f'z \right\} \right]_{z=a}.$$

This is Burmann's result.

Ex. To expand e^z in powers of $\dfrac{z}{e^z}$.　　　　　　[COLL. EXAM. 1879.]

Here　　　　　　$f(z) = e^z$, $F(z) = \dfrac{z}{e^z}$, and $a = 0$.

Hence　　　　　$\phi(z) = e^z$.

∴　　　　　　$B_r = \left[\dfrac{d^{r-1}}{dz^{r-1}} e^{(r+1)z} \right]_{z=0} = (r+1)^{r-1}.$

Hence Burmann's theorem gives

$$e^z = 1 + \sum_{r=1}^{r=\infty} \frac{(r+1)^{r-1}}{r!} (ze^{-z})^r,$$

or　　　　$e^z = 1 + (ze^{-z}) + \frac{3}{2!}(ze^{-z})^2 + \frac{4^2}{3!}(ze^{-z})^3 + \frac{5^3}{4!}(ze^{-z})^4 + \dots.$

520. We have not attempted to give any test for the convergency of the series of the present chapter, and the investigation for the form of the remainder after n terms, corresponding to Arts. 130 to 136, has been omitted as beyond the scope of the present work. For further information the student is referred to *Leçons de Calcul Différentiel*, par M. l'Abbé Moigno (18me Leçon); Liouville's *Journal*, vol. XI.; Bertrand, *Calcul Différentiel*, livre Second, chapitre III.

EXAMPLES.

1. If　　　　　　　$z^3 - az + b = 0$

i.e.,　　　　　　　$z = \dfrac{b}{a} + \dfrac{1}{a} z^3,$

prove that one of the roots is

$$z = \frac{b}{a} \left(1 + \frac{b^2}{a^3} + 3\frac{b^4}{a^6} + 12\frac{b^6}{a^9} + 55\frac{b^8}{a^{12}} + \dots \right).$$　　　[PEACOCK.]

2. If
$$z = a + bz^n,$$

prove $z = a\left\{1 + a^{n-1}b + 2na^{2n-2}\dfrac{b^2}{2!} + 3n(3n-1)a^{3n-3}\dfrac{b^3}{3!} + \ldots\right\}.$

[Gregory.]

3. If
$$z = 1 + ca^z,$$

then $z = 1 + a \cdot \dfrac{c}{1} + 2 \log a \dfrac{a^2c^2}{2!} + 3^2(\log a)^2\dfrac{a^3c^3}{3!} + \ldots.$

[Gregory.]

4. If
$$z = a + x \log z,$$

then $z = a + \log a \cdot x + \dfrac{2 \log a}{a}\dfrac{x^2}{2!} + \dfrac{3 \log a}{a^2}(2 - \log a)\dfrac{x^3}{3!}$

$$+ \dfrac{4 \log a}{a^3}(6 - 9\,\overline{\log a}|^2 + 2\,\overline{\log a}|^3)\dfrac{x^4}{4!} + \ldots.$$

[Gregory.]

5. If
$$z = a + b(z^n + cz^r),$$

prove
$$z = a + (a^n + ca^r)\dfrac{b}{1} + \{2na^{2n-1} + 2c(n+r)a^{n+r-1} + c^2 2ra^{2r-1}\}\dfrac{b^2}{1 \cdot 2} + \ldots.$$

[Gregory.]

6. If
$$u = a + e \sin u,$$

prove $u = a + e \sin a + \dfrac{e^2}{2!}\dfrac{d}{da}(\sin^2 a) + \dfrac{e^3}{3!}\dfrac{d^2}{da^2}(\sin^3 a) + \ldots.$

[Laplace.]

7. If
$$z = a + \dfrac{x}{z},$$

prove $z^{-k} = a^{-k} - xka^{-k-2} + \dfrac{x^2}{2!}k(k+3)a^{-k-4} - \dfrac{x^3}{3!}k(k+4)(k+5)a^{-k-6} + \ldots.$

By putting $a = 2$, deduce

$$\left(\dfrac{2}{1 + \sqrt{1+x}}\right)^k = 1 - \dfrac{k}{1}\dfrac{x}{4} + \dfrac{k(k+3)}{1 \cdot 2}\left(\dfrac{x}{4}\right)^2 - \ldots.$$

[Bertrand.]

8. If
$$cx^2 - bx + a = 0 \quad \text{or} \quad x = \dfrac{a}{b} + \dfrac{c}{b} \cdot x^2,$$

prove (1) $x = \dfrac{a}{b} + \dfrac{a^2c}{b^3} + \dfrac{4a^3c^2}{2b^5} + \dfrac{5 \cdot 6}{2 \cdot 3} \cdot \dfrac{a^4c^3}{b^7} + \ldots.$

[Peacock.]

(2) $\dfrac{x^2}{2} = \dfrac{a^2}{2b^2} + \dfrac{a^3c}{b^4} + \dfrac{5}{2} \cdot \dfrac{a^4c^2}{b^6} + \dfrac{7 \cdot 6}{2 \cdot 3} \cdot \dfrac{a^5c^3}{b^8} + \ldots.$

(3) $\log x = \log \dfrac{a}{b} + \dfrac{ac}{b^2} + \dfrac{3}{2} \cdot \dfrac{a^2c^2}{b^4} + \dfrac{5 \cdot 4}{2 \cdot 3} \cdot \dfrac{a^3c^3}{b^6} + \ldots.$

[Bertrand.]

9. If
$$1 - x + ax = 0,$$
prove by Lagrange's theorem
$$x^n = 1 + na + \frac{n(n+1)}{1 \cdot 2}a^2 + \cdots,$$

$$e^{1-\frac{1}{x}} = 1 + a + \frac{a^2}{1 \cdot 2} + \frac{a^3}{1 \cdot 2 \cdot 3} + \cdots,$$

$$\sin\left(1 - \frac{1}{x}\right) = a - \frac{a^3}{3!} + \frac{a^5}{5!} - \cdots.$$
[PEACOCK.]

10. If
$$1 - x + e^x = 0,$$
prove
$$x^n = 1 + ne + \frac{n(n+1)}{1 \cdot 2}e^2 + \frac{n(n^2 + 3n + 5)}{3!}e^3 + \cdots,$$

$$e^x = e\left\{1 + \frac{2e}{2!} + \frac{3^2 e^2}{3!} + \frac{4^3 e^3}{4!} + \frac{5^4 e^4}{5!} + \cdots\right\}.$$
[PEACOCK.]

11. Given
$$x^{m+1} + ax - b = 0,$$
prove
$$x = \frac{b}{a} - \frac{b^{m+1}}{a^{m+2}} + \frac{2m+2}{1 \cdot 2} \cdot \frac{b^{2m+1}}{a^{2m+3}} - \frac{(3m+2)(3m+3)}{3!} \frac{b^{3m+1}}{a^{3m+4}} + \cdots.$$

Apply this to show that one of the roots of
$$x^5 + 4x + 2 = 0 \text{ is } x = -\cdot4928\ldots$$
correct to four places of decimals.   [BERTRAND.]

12. If
$$y = \log(z + x \sin y),$$
prove
$$e^y = z + \sin(\log z)\frac{x}{1} + \frac{\sin \log z^2}{z}\frac{x^2}{2!}$$

$$+ \frac{3\sin(\log z)}{4z^2}\{8 - 9\sin(\log z) - 2\sin(\log z^2) + 3\sin(\log z^3)\}\frac{x^3}{3!} + \cdots.$$
[GREGORY.]

13. If
$$y = e^{z + x \cos y},$$
prove
$$y = e^z + e^z \cos e^z \frac{x}{1} + e^z \cos e^z (\cos e^z - 2 \sin e^z \cdot e^z)\frac{x^2}{2!} + \cdots.$$

14. Having given that u is a function of x such that
$$u + h\frac{du}{dx} + \frac{h^2}{2!}\frac{d^2u}{dx^2} + \cdots = 0,$$
prove that
$$h = vu + \left(v\frac{d}{dx}\right)v \cdot \frac{u^2}{2!} + \left(v\frac{d}{dx}\right)^2 v \cdot \frac{u^3}{3!} + \cdots$$
where
$$\frac{dx}{du} = -v.$$
[PAOLI, ELEMENTI D'ALGEBRA.]

15. Apply Burmann's theorem to develop x in powers of

$$\frac{2x}{1+x^2}.$$

16. Expand e^{az} in powers of ze^{bz} by Burmann's theorem.

[BERTRAND.]

17. If $\phi(x)$ be any function of x which can be expanded in powers of e^x, prove (by aid of Ex. 16)

$\phi(x+a)$

$$= \phi(x) + a\phi'(x+b) + \frac{a(a-2b)}{1\cdot2}\phi''(x+2b) + \frac{a(a-3b)^2}{3!}\phi'''(x+3b) + \dots.$$

For example

$$(x+a)^m = x^m + ma(x+b)^{m-1} + \frac{m(m-1)}{1\cdot2}a(a-2b)(x+2b)^{m-2} + \dots.$$

[ABEL.]

18. If $\phi^{-1}(x)$ be the inverse function of $\phi(x)$, and $\phi(x)$ vanish with x, prove

$$\phi^{-1}(x) = x\left[\frac{x}{\phi(x)}\right]_0 + \frac{x^2}{2!}\left[\frac{d}{dx}\frac{x^2}{\{\phi(x)\}^2}\right]_0 + \frac{x^3}{3!}\left[\frac{d^2}{dx^2}\frac{x^3}{\{\phi(x)\}^3}\right]_0 + \dots.$$

CHAPTER XIX.

CHANGE OF THE INDEPENDENT VARIABLE.

521. If there be an expression involving two variables x and y and containing the differential coefficients $\dfrac{dy}{dx}, \dfrac{d^2y}{dx^2}, \ldots$, it is sometimes desirable to change the independent variable from x to some third variable t, of which x is a known function. This change may be effected as follows:—

It has been shown in Art. 41 that

$$\frac{dy}{dx} = \frac{\dfrac{dy}{dt}}{\dfrac{dx}{dt}}.$$

The operation $\dfrac{d}{dx}$ is therefore equivalent to the operation

$$\frac{1}{\dfrac{dx}{dt}} \cdot \frac{d}{dt}.$$

For instance,

$$\frac{d^2y}{dx^2} = \frac{1}{\dfrac{dx}{dt}} \frac{d}{dt}\left[\frac{\dfrac{dy}{dt}}{\dfrac{dx}{dt}}\right] = \frac{\dfrac{d^2y}{dt^2}\cdot\dfrac{dx}{dt} - \dfrac{d^2x}{dt^2}\cdot\dfrac{dy}{dt}}{\left(\dfrac{dx}{dt}\right)^3}.$$

Similarly

$$\frac{d^3y}{dx^3} = \frac{1}{\dfrac{dx}{dt}} \frac{d}{dt}\left[\frac{\dfrac{d^2y}{dt^2}\dfrac{dx}{dt} - \dfrac{d^2x}{dt^2}\dfrac{dy}{dt}}{\left(\dfrac{dx}{dt}\right)^3}\right]$$

$$= \frac{\left(\dfrac{d^3y}{dt^3}\dfrac{dx}{dt} - \dfrac{d^3x}{dt^3}\dfrac{dy}{dt}\right)\left(\dfrac{dx}{dt}\right)^3 - \left(\dfrac{d^2y}{dt^2}\dfrac{dx}{dt} - \dfrac{d^2x}{dt^2}\dfrac{dy}{dt}\right)3\left(\dfrac{dx}{dt}\right)^2\dfrac{d^2x}{dt^2}}{\left(\dfrac{dx}{dt}\right)^7}$$

$$= \frac{\left(\dfrac{d^3y}{dt^3}\dfrac{dx}{dt} - \dfrac{d^3x}{dt^3}\dfrac{dy}{dt}\right)\dfrac{dx}{dt} - 3\left(\dfrac{d^2y}{dt^2}\dfrac{dx}{dt} - \dfrac{d^2x}{dt^2}\dfrac{dy}{dt}\right)\dfrac{d^2x}{dt^2}}{\left(\dfrac{dx}{dt}\right)^5},$$

and similarly for differential coefficients of a higher order.

Also, x being a known function of t, all the expressions

$$\frac{dx}{dt}, \quad \frac{d^2x}{dt^2}, \quad \frac{d^3x}{dt^3}, \quad \cdots$$

are known functions of t, and therefore the desired transformation can be performed.

522. If we wish to make y the independent variable instead of x, we have at once, by putting $t=y$,

$$\frac{dy}{dt} = 1, \quad \frac{d^2y}{dt^2} = 0, \quad \frac{d^3y}{dt^3} = 0, \text{ etc.,}$$

and therefore

$$\frac{dy}{dx} = \frac{1}{\dfrac{dx}{dy}},$$

$$\frac{d^2y}{dx^2} = -\frac{\dfrac{d^2x}{dy^2}}{\left(\dfrac{dx}{dy}\right)^3},$$

$$\frac{d^3y}{dx^3} = -\frac{\dfrac{d^3x}{dy^3}\cdot\dfrac{dx}{dy} - 3\left(\dfrac{d^2x}{dy^2}\right)^2}{\left(\dfrac{dx}{dy}\right)^5},$$

formulae which may of course also be obtained directly.

523. Differential equations may often be simplified by such substitutions, as in the following examples:—

(1) Change the independent variable from x to θ in the equation

$$(1 - x^2)\frac{d^2y}{dx^2} - x\frac{dy}{dx} + y = 0,$$

having given $x = \cos\theta$.

Here $\qquad$ $\dfrac{dx}{d\theta} = -\sin\theta,$

and therefore $\qquad$ $\dfrac{dy}{dx} = -\dfrac{1}{\sin\theta}\dfrac{dy}{d\theta},$

and $\qquad$ $\dfrac{d^2y}{dx^2} = -\dfrac{1}{\sin\theta}\dfrac{d}{d\theta}\left(-\dfrac{1}{\sin\theta}\dfrac{dy}{d\theta}\right)$

$$= \dfrac{1}{\sin\theta}\dfrac{\sin\theta\dfrac{d^2y}{d\theta^2} - \cos\theta\dfrac{dy}{d\theta}}{\sin^2\theta}.$$

Hence the given equation becomes

$$(1-\cos^2\theta)\dfrac{\sin\theta\dfrac{d^2y}{d\theta^2} - \cos\theta\dfrac{dy}{d\theta}}{\sin^3\theta} + \cos\theta\cdot\dfrac{1}{\sin\theta}\dfrac{dy}{d\theta} + y = 0,$$

and reduces to $\qquad$ $\dfrac{d^2y}{d\theta^2} + y = 0.$

(2) Change the equation $\dfrac{d^2y}{dx^2} - \left(\dfrac{dy}{dx}\right)^2 - y\left(\dfrac{dy}{dx}\right)^3 = 0$

so that y may be considered the independent variable instead of x.

Here we have $\qquad$ $-\dfrac{\dfrac{d^2x}{dy^2}}{\left(\dfrac{dx}{dy}\right)^3} - \dfrac{1}{\left(\dfrac{dx}{dy}\right)^2} - \dfrac{y}{\left(\dfrac{dx}{dy}\right)^3} = 0,$

or $\qquad$ $\dfrac{d^2x}{dy^2} + \dfrac{dx}{dy} + y = 0.$

EXAMPLES.

1. Show that the equation

$$(1+ax^2)\dfrac{d^2y}{dx^2} + ax\dfrac{dy}{dx} \pm q^2 y = 0$$

may be reduced to the form $\qquad$ $\dfrac{d^2y}{dt^2} \pm q^2 y = 0$

by putting $\qquad$ $\dfrac{dx}{dt} = \sqrt{1+ax^2}.$

2. Show that the equation $\qquad$ $\dfrac{d^2x}{ds^2} = a$

may be written in the form $\dfrac{d^2s}{dx^2} + a\left(\dfrac{ds}{dx}\right)^3 = 0.$

524. The Operator $x\dfrac{d}{dx}$.

A transformation which renders peculiar service in reducing a certain class of linear differential equations to a form in which all the coefficients are constants, arises from putting

$$x = e^t.$$

In this case

$$\frac{dx}{dt} = e^t,$$

and therefore

$$x\frac{dy}{dx} = \frac{dy}{dt}.$$

It is obvious therefore that the operators $x\dfrac{d}{dx}$ and $\dfrac{d}{dt}$ are equivalent. Let D stand for $\dfrac{d}{dt}$. Then we have

$$x\frac{d}{dx}\left(x^{n-1}\frac{d^{n-1}y}{dx^{n-1}}\right) = x^n\frac{d^n y}{dx^n} + (n-1)x^{n-1}\frac{d^{n-1}y}{dx^{n-1}},$$

or

$$x^n\frac{d^n y}{dx^n} = \left(x\frac{d}{dx} - n + 1\right)x^{n-1}\frac{d^{n-1}y}{dx^{n-1}},$$

which we may write

$$x^n\frac{d^n y}{dx^n} = (D - n + 1)x^{n-1}\frac{d^{n-1}y}{dx^{n-1}}.$$

Now putting n in succession $= 2, 3, 4, \ldots$, we have

$$x^2\frac{d^2 y}{dx^2} = (D-1)x\frac{dy}{dx},$$

$$x^3\frac{d^3 y}{dx^3} = (D-2)x^2\frac{d^2 y}{dx^2},$$

$$x^4\frac{d^4 y}{dx^4} = (D-3)x^3\frac{d^3 y}{dx^3},$$

etc.

Hence, generally, we have

$$x^n\frac{d^n y}{dx^n} \equiv (D-n+1)(D-n+2)\ldots(D-1)Dy,$$

or reversing the order of the operations,

$$\equiv D(D-1)(D-2)\ldots(D-n+1)y.$$

Ex. The differential equation

$$x^3\frac{d^3 y}{dx^3} + 2x^2\frac{d^2 y}{dx^2} + 3x\frac{dy}{dx} + 4y = 0.$$

reduces at once to

$$D(D-1)(D-2)y + 2D(D-1)y + 3Dy + 4y = 0,$$

or

$$D^3 y - D^2 y + 3Dy + 4y = 0,$$

by putting $x = e^t$.

525. Transformation to Polars, and vice versa.

It often happens that a result in Cartesians is much simplified on reduction to Polars, or *vice versa*.

In such cases we have

$$x = r\cos\theta,$$

$$y = r\sin\theta.$$

Suppose θ to be the independent Polar Variable, then

$$\frac{dy}{dx} = \frac{\dfrac{dy}{d\theta}}{\dfrac{dx}{d\theta}} = \frac{\dfrac{dr}{d\theta}\sin\theta + r\cos\theta}{\dfrac{dr}{d\theta}\cos\theta - r\sin\theta}.$$

Similarly,
$$\frac{d^2y}{dx^2} = \frac{1}{\dfrac{dx}{d\theta}}\frac{d}{d\theta}\left[\frac{\dfrac{dr}{d\theta}\sin\theta + r\cos\theta}{\dfrac{dr}{d\theta}\cos\theta - r\sin\theta}\right],$$

which easily simplifies down to

$$\frac{r^2 + 2\left(\dfrac{dr}{d\theta}\right)^2 - r\dfrac{d^2r}{d\theta^2}}{\left(\cos\theta\dfrac{dr}{d\theta} - r\sin\theta\right)^3}.$$

526. Suppose x and y to be expressed in terms of some third variable t, then it is easy to show that

$$x\frac{dx}{dt} + y\frac{dy}{dt} = r\frac{dr}{dt}, \quad\dotfill(1)$$

$$x\frac{dy}{dt} - y\frac{dx}{dt} = r^2\frac{d\theta}{dt}, \quad\dotfill(2)$$

and therefore $\quad \left(\dfrac{dx}{dt}\right)^2 + \left(\dfrac{dy}{dt}\right)^2 = \left(\dfrac{dr}{dt}\right)^2 + r^2\left(\dfrac{d\theta}{dt}\right)^2 \dotfill(3)$

Equation (1) is at once obvious by differentiating the equation $\qquad\qquad x^2 + y^2 = r^2$ with regard to t.

To prove (2). Let O be the pole of the curve whose equation is obtained by the elimination of t between the expressions for x and y. Let P be a point on the curve whose co-ordinates are (x, y) or (r, θ), Q an adjacent point whose co-ordinates are by Taylor's theorem

$$\left.\begin{array}{c} x+\dfrac{dx}{dt}\delta t \\[2mm] y+\dfrac{dy}{dt}\delta t \end{array}\right\}, \text{ or in Polars} \quad \left.\begin{array}{c} r+\dfrac{dr}{dt}\delta t \\[2mm] \theta+\dfrac{d\theta}{dt}\delta t \end{array}\right\}.$$

The Cartesian and Polar expressions for the area of the triangle OPQ, when δt is very small, are equivalent. Hence

$$\tfrac{1}{2}\left[x\left(y+\dfrac{dy}{dt}\delta t\right)-y\left(x+\dfrac{dx}{dt}\delta t\right)\right] = \tfrac{1}{2}r\left(r+\dfrac{dr}{dt}\delta t\right)\sin\left(\dfrac{d\theta}{dt}\delta t\right),$$

which gives in the limit

$$x\dfrac{dy}{dt}-y\dfrac{dx}{dt}=r^2\dfrac{d\theta}{dt}.$$

Formula (3) obviously represents the equivalence of the two expressions for $\left(\dfrac{ds}{dt}\right)^2$. Arts. 200 and 201.

All these formulae may of course be established otherwise.

Ex. Transform to Cartesians the formula

$$t=\dfrac{r}{\sqrt{1+r^2\left(\dfrac{d\theta}{dr}\right)^2}}.$$

This we may write as

$$t=\dfrac{r\dfrac{dr}{dt}}{\sqrt{\left(\dfrac{dr}{dt}\right)^2+r^2\left(\dfrac{d\theta}{dt}\right)^2}}=\dfrac{x\dfrac{dx}{dt}+y\dfrac{dy}{dt}}{\sqrt{\left(\dfrac{dx}{dt}\right)^2+\left(\dfrac{dy}{dt}\right)^2}}=\dfrac{x+y\dfrac{dy}{dx}}{\sqrt{1+\left(\dfrac{dy}{dx}\right)^2}}.$$

527. Two Independent Variables.

We shall now consider the case in which there are two independent variables x and y.

Let $\qquad U=f(x, y),$ ....(1)

Suppose $\qquad \left.\begin{array}{c} x=\phi_1(u, v) \\ y=\phi_2(u, v) \end{array}\right\},$ ....(2)

be the proposed transformation; then we have

$$\left.\begin{array}{l} \dfrac{\partial U}{\partial u}=\dfrac{\partial U}{\partial x}\cdot\dfrac{\partial x}{\partial u}+\dfrac{\partial U}{\partial y}\cdot\dfrac{\partial y}{\partial u} \\[3mm] \dfrac{\partial U}{\partial v}=\dfrac{\partial U}{\partial x}\cdot\dfrac{\partial x}{\partial v}+\dfrac{\partial U}{\partial y}\cdot\dfrac{\partial y}{\partial v} \end{array}\right\} \quad \dots\dots\dots\dots\dots(3)$$

These equations may be solved for $\dfrac{\partial U}{\partial x}, \dfrac{\partial U}{\partial y}$, giving

$$\frac{\partial U}{\partial x} = \frac{\dfrac{\partial U}{\partial u} \cdot \dfrac{\partial y}{\partial v} - \dfrac{\partial U}{\partial v} \cdot \dfrac{\partial y}{\partial u}}{\dfrac{\partial x}{\partial u} \cdot \dfrac{\partial y}{\partial v} - \dfrac{\partial x}{\partial v} \cdot \dfrac{\partial y}{\partial u}},$$

and

$$\frac{\partial U}{\partial y} = \frac{\dfrac{\partial U}{\partial v} \cdot \dfrac{\partial x}{\partial u} - \dfrac{\partial U}{\partial u} \cdot \dfrac{\partial x}{\partial v}}{\dfrac{\partial x}{\partial u} \cdot \dfrac{\partial y}{\partial v} - \dfrac{\partial x}{\partial v} \cdot \dfrac{\partial y}{\partial u}}.$$

If, however, we could solve equations (2) for u and v in terms of x and y so as to express them thus,

$$\left. \begin{array}{l} u = F_1(x, y) \\ v = F_2(x, y) \end{array} \right\}, \dotfill (4)$$

we can find $\dfrac{\partial u}{\partial x}, \dfrac{\partial u}{\partial y}, \dfrac{\partial v}{\partial x}, \dfrac{\partial v}{\partial y}$, and substitute in the formulae

$$\left. \begin{array}{l} \dfrac{\partial U}{\partial x} = \dfrac{\partial U}{\partial u} \cdot \dfrac{\partial u}{\partial x} + \dfrac{\partial U}{\partial v} \cdot \dfrac{\partial v}{\partial x} \\[2mm] \dfrac{\partial U}{\partial y} = \dfrac{\partial U}{\partial u} \cdot \dfrac{\partial u}{\partial y} + \dfrac{\partial U}{\partial v} \cdot \dfrac{\partial v}{\partial y} \end{array} \right\} \dotfill (5)$$

528. The differential coefficients on the right-hand sides of the equations of the preceding article are all partial. For instance, in finding the value of $\dfrac{\partial x}{\partial u}$ from equations (2), v is treated as a constant, while in finding $\dfrac{\partial u}{\partial x}$ from equations (4), y is treated as a constant. The student should therefore guard carefully against any such assumption as that $\dfrac{\partial x}{\partial u} \cdot \dfrac{\partial u}{\partial x} = 1$. For the truth of this equation was proved in Art. 55 on the assumption of a relation between u and x and no other variable, but this is not the case now considered.

529. The case of transformation from the Cartesian to the polar form deserves special notice.

Here $x = r \cos \theta$, $r = \sqrt{x^2 + y^2}$,

          $y = r \sin \theta$, $\theta = \tan^{-1} \dfrac{y}{x}$,

$$\frac{\partial x}{\partial r} = \cos\theta = \frac{x}{r}, \qquad \frac{\partial r}{\partial x} = \frac{x}{\sqrt{x^2+y^2}} = \cos\theta,$$

$$\frac{\partial y}{\partial r} = \sin\theta = \frac{y}{r}, \qquad \frac{\partial r}{\partial y} = \frac{y}{\sqrt{x^2+y^2}} = \sin\theta,$$

$$\frac{\partial x}{\partial \theta} = -r\sin\theta = -y, \qquad \frac{\partial \theta}{\partial x} = -\frac{y}{x^2+y^2} = -\frac{\sin\theta}{r},$$

$$\frac{\partial y}{\partial \theta} = r\cos\theta = x, \qquad \frac{\partial \theta}{\partial y} = \frac{x}{x^2+y^2} = \frac{\cos\theta}{r}.$$

Now
$$\frac{\partial V}{\partial x} = \frac{\partial V}{\partial r}\cdot\frac{\partial r}{\partial x} + \frac{\partial V}{\partial \theta}\cdot\frac{\partial \theta}{\partial x} = \cos\theta\frac{\partial V}{\partial r} - \frac{\sin\theta}{r}\cdot\frac{\partial V}{\partial \theta},$$

$$\frac{\partial V}{\partial y} = \frac{\partial V}{\partial r}\cdot\frac{\partial r}{\partial y} + \frac{\partial V}{\partial \theta}\cdot\frac{\partial \theta}{\partial y} = \sin\theta\frac{\partial V}{\partial r} + \frac{\cos\theta}{r}\cdot\frac{\partial V}{\partial \theta}.$$

$$\frac{\partial V}{\partial r} = \frac{\partial V}{\partial x}\cdot\frac{\partial x}{\partial r} + \frac{\partial V}{\partial y}\cdot\frac{\partial y}{\partial r} = \frac{x}{r}\cdot\frac{\partial V}{\partial x} + \frac{y}{r}\cdot\frac{\partial V}{\partial y},$$

$$\frac{\partial V}{\partial \theta} = \frac{\partial V}{\partial x}\cdot\frac{\partial x}{\partial \theta} + \frac{\partial V}{\partial y}\cdot\frac{\partial y}{\partial \theta} = -y\frac{\partial V}{\partial x} + x\frac{\partial V}{\partial y}.$$

Hence we have the following equivalence of Polar and Cartesian operations :—

$$\left.\begin{array}{l}\dfrac{\partial}{\partial x} \equiv \cos\theta\dfrac{\partial}{\partial r} - \dfrac{\sin\theta}{r}\dfrac{\partial}{\partial \theta},\\[2mm] \dfrac{\partial}{\partial y} \equiv \sin\theta\dfrac{\partial}{\partial r} + \dfrac{\cos\theta}{r}\dfrac{\partial}{\partial \theta},\end{array}\right\}$$

while

and either of these operators may be obtained from the other by changing θ into $\frac{\pi}{2} - \theta$.

Also
$$\left.\begin{array}{l}r\dfrac{\partial}{\partial r} \equiv x\dfrac{\partial}{\partial x} + y\dfrac{\partial}{\partial y},\\[2mm] \dfrac{\partial}{\partial \theta} \equiv x\dfrac{\partial}{\partial y} - y\dfrac{\partial}{\partial x}.\end{array}\right\}$$

and

530. It will be noticed here that

$$\frac{\partial r}{\partial x}\cdot\frac{\partial x}{\partial r} = \cos^2\theta,$$

$$\frac{\partial r}{\partial y}\cdot\frac{\partial y}{\partial r} = \sin^2\theta,$$

$$\frac{\partial x}{\partial \theta} \cdot \frac{\partial \theta}{\partial x} = \sin^2\theta,$$

$$\frac{\partial y}{\partial \theta} \cdot \frac{\partial \theta}{\partial y} = \cos^2\theta,$$

thus bearing out the observations of Art. 528 that such products are not of the kind contemplated in Art. 55, and whose values are unity.

531. To transform $\dfrac{\partial^2 V}{\partial x^2}$ and $\dfrac{\partial^2 V}{\partial y^2}$ to Polar Co-ordinates.

We have $\dfrac{\partial^2 V}{\partial x^2} = \left(\dfrac{\partial}{\partial x}\right)^2 V = \left(\cos\theta \dfrac{\partial}{\partial r} - \dfrac{\sin\theta}{r}\dfrac{\partial}{\partial\theta}\right)^2 V$

$$= \cos\theta\frac{\partial}{\partial r}\left[\cos\theta\frac{\partial V}{\partial r} - \frac{\sin\theta}{r}\frac{\partial V}{\partial\theta}\right] - \frac{\sin\theta}{r}\frac{\partial}{\partial\theta}\left[\cos\theta\frac{\partial V}{\partial r} - \frac{\sin\theta}{r}\frac{\partial V}{\partial\theta}\right]$$

$$= \cos^2\theta\frac{\partial^2 V}{\partial r^2} - 2\frac{\sin\theta\cos\theta}{r}\frac{\partial^2 V}{\partial r\partial\theta} + \frac{\sin^2\theta}{r^2}\frac{\partial^2 V}{\partial\theta^2}$$

$$+ \frac{\sin^2\theta}{r}\frac{\partial V}{\partial r} + \frac{2\sin\theta\cos\theta}{r^2}\frac{\partial V}{\partial\theta}.$$

And $\dfrac{\partial^2 V}{\partial y^2} = \left(\dfrac{\partial}{\partial y}\right)^2 V = \left(\sin\theta\dfrac{\partial}{\partial r} + \dfrac{\cos\theta}{r}\dfrac{\partial}{\partial\theta}\right)^2 V$

$$= \sin\theta\frac{\partial}{\partial r}\left[\sin\theta\frac{\partial V}{\partial r} + \frac{\cos\theta}{r}\frac{\partial V}{\partial\theta}\right] + \frac{\cos\theta}{r}\frac{\partial}{\partial\theta}\left[\sin\theta\frac{\partial V}{\partial r} + \frac{\cos\theta}{r}\frac{\partial V}{\partial\theta}\right]$$

$$= \sin^2\theta\frac{\partial^2 V}{\partial r^2} + \frac{2\sin\theta\cos\theta}{r}\frac{\partial^2 V}{\partial r\partial\theta} + \frac{\cos^2\theta}{r^2}\frac{\partial^2 V}{\partial\theta^2}$$

$$+ \frac{\cos^2\theta}{r}\frac{\partial V}{\partial r} - \frac{2\sin\theta\cos\theta}{r^2}\frac{\partial V}{\partial\theta}.$$

532. **Transformation of** $\nabla^2 V$.

By addition we have

$$\frac{\partial^2 V}{\partial x^2} + \frac{\partial^2 V}{\partial y^2} = \frac{\partial^2 V}{\partial r^2} + \frac{1}{r}\frac{\partial V}{\partial r} + \frac{1}{r^2}\frac{\partial^2 V}{\partial\theta^2}.$$

It is easy to deduce from this result the corresponding transformation of the expression

$$\nabla^2 V \equiv \frac{\partial^2 V}{\partial x^2} + \frac{\partial^2 V}{\partial y^2} + \frac{\partial^2 V}{\partial z^2}$$

to polar co-ordinates, the operator ∇^2 standing for

$$\frac{\partial^2}{\partial x^2} + \frac{\partial^2}{\partial y^2} + \frac{\partial^2}{\partial z^2}.$$

The transformation formulae are now

$$\left.\begin{array}{l} x = r\sin\theta\cos\phi \\ y = r\sin\theta\sin\phi \\ z = r\cos\theta \end{array}\right\}.$$

Let $\qquad r\sin\theta = u,$

then $\qquad x = u\cos\phi,$

$$y = u\sin\phi,$$

and by the preceding article

$$\frac{\partial^2 V}{\partial x^2} + \frac{\partial^2 V}{\partial y^2} = \frac{\partial^2 V}{\partial u^2} + \frac{1}{u}\frac{\partial V}{\partial u} + \frac{1}{u^2}\frac{\partial^2 V}{\partial \phi^2}.$$

Adding $\dfrac{\partial^2 V}{\partial z^2},$ $\qquad \nabla^2 V = \dfrac{\partial^2 V}{\partial u^2} + \dfrac{\partial^2 V}{\partial z^2} + \dfrac{1}{u}\dfrac{\partial V}{\partial u} + \dfrac{1}{u^2}\dfrac{\partial^2 V}{\partial \phi^2}.$

The quantities u, ϕ, z are often termed Cylindric Co-ordinates.

Again by the preceding article, since

$$z = r\cos\theta,$$

$$u = r\sin\theta,$$

$$\frac{\partial^2 V}{\partial u^2} + \frac{\partial^2 V}{\partial z^2} = \frac{\partial^2 V}{\partial r^2} + \frac{1}{r}\frac{\partial V}{\partial r} + \frac{1}{r^2}\frac{\partial^2 V}{\partial \theta^2},$$

and $\qquad \dfrac{\partial V}{\partial u} = \sin\theta\dfrac{\partial V}{\partial r} + \dfrac{\cos\theta}{r}\dfrac{\partial V}{\partial \theta}.$ (Art. 530.)

Hence $\qquad \dfrac{1}{u}\dfrac{\partial V}{\partial u} = \dfrac{1}{r}\dfrac{\partial V}{\partial r} + \dfrac{\cot\theta}{r^2}\dfrac{\partial V}{\partial \theta},$

wherefore

$$\nabla^2 V \equiv \frac{\partial^2 V}{\partial r^2} + \frac{2}{r}\frac{\partial V}{\partial r} + \frac{1}{r^2}\frac{\partial^2 V}{\partial \theta^2} + \frac{\cot\theta}{r^2}\frac{\partial V}{\partial \theta} + \frac{1}{r^2\sin^2\theta}\frac{\partial^2 V}{\partial \phi^2}.$$

These transformations derive their interest from the frequency with which the equation $\nabla^2 V = 0$ occurs in various problems in the higher branches of physics.   (See Art. 189.)

533. Orthogonal Transformation of $\nabla^2 V$.

If we transform the expression

$$\frac{\partial^2 V}{\partial x^2} + \frac{\partial^2 V}{\partial y^2} + \frac{\partial^2 V}{\partial z^2}$$

by changing to any other set of axes $O\xi$, $O\eta$, $O\zeta$ mutually at right angles, retaining the same origin, it becomes

$$\frac{\partial^2 V}{\partial \xi^2} + \frac{\partial^2 V}{\partial \eta^2} + \frac{\partial^2 V}{\partial \zeta^2}.$$

For let the scheme of the orthogonal transformation of co-ordinates be that shown in the margin. Then it is shown in books on solid geometry that

	ξ	η	ζ
x	l_1	m_1	n_1
y	l_2	m_2	n_2
z	l_3	m_3	n_3

$$l_1{}^2 + m_1{}^2 + n_1{}^2 = 1, \text{ etc.,}$$
$$l_1{}^2 + l_2{}^2 + l_3{}^2 = 1, \text{ etc.,}$$
$$l_1 m_1 + l_2 m_2 + l_3 m_3 = 0, \text{ etc.,}$$
$$l_1 l_2 + m_1 m_2 + n_1 n_2 = 0, \text{ etc.}$$

Now
$$\xi = l_1 x + l_2 y + l_3 z,$$
$$\eta = m_1 x + m_2 y + m_3 z,$$
$$\zeta = n_1 x + n_2 y + n_3 z,$$

and
$$\frac{\partial V}{\partial x} = \frac{\partial V}{\partial \xi}\frac{\partial \xi}{\partial x} + \frac{\partial V}{\partial \eta}\frac{\partial \eta}{\partial x} + \frac{\partial V}{\partial \zeta}\frac{\partial \zeta}{\partial x}$$
$$= l_1 \frac{\partial V}{\partial \xi} + m_1 \frac{\partial V}{\partial \eta} + n_1 \frac{\partial V}{\partial \zeta}.$$

And similarly

$$\frac{\partial^2 V}{\partial x^2} = \frac{\partial}{\partial x}\frac{\partial V}{\partial x} = \left(l_1 \frac{\partial}{\partial \xi} + m_1 \frac{\partial}{\partial \eta} + n_1 \frac{\partial}{\partial \zeta}\right)\left(l_1 \frac{\partial V}{\partial \xi} + m_1 \frac{\partial V}{\partial \eta} + n_1 \frac{\partial V}{\partial \zeta}\right)$$

$$= l_1{}^2 \frac{\partial^2 V}{\partial \xi^2} + m_1{}^2 \frac{\partial^2 V}{\partial \eta^2} + n_1{}^2 \frac{\partial^2 V}{\partial \zeta^2} + 2m_1 n_1 \frac{\partial^2 V}{\partial \eta \partial \zeta}$$

$$+ 2n_1 l_1 \frac{\partial^2 V}{\partial \zeta \partial \xi} + 2l_1 m_1 \frac{\partial^2 V}{\partial \xi \partial \eta}.$$

Similarly

$$\frac{\partial^2 V}{\partial y^2} = l_2{}^2 \frac{\partial^2 V}{\partial \xi^2} + \text{etc.,}$$

$$\frac{\partial^2 V}{\partial z^2} = l_3{}^2 \frac{\partial^2 V}{\partial \xi^2} + \text{etc.}$$

Whence by addition

$$\frac{\partial^2 V}{\partial x^2} + \frac{\partial^2 V}{\partial y^2} + \frac{\partial^2 V}{\partial z^2} = \frac{\partial^2 V}{\partial \xi^2} + \frac{\partial^2 V}{\partial \eta^2} + \frac{\partial^2 V}{\partial \zeta^2}.$$

and the form is therefore unaltered by the transformation.

EXAMPLES.

1. Change the independent variable from x to z in the equation

$$(1 - x^2)\frac{d^2y}{dx^2} = x\frac{dy}{dx} - n^2y,$$

where $\qquad x = \sin z.$

2. Show that the form of the equation

$$x^2\frac{d^2y}{dx^2} + x\frac{dy}{dx} + y = 0$$

remains unchanged if we substitute $\dfrac{1}{z}$ for x.

3. Show that the equation

$$x^2\frac{d^2y}{dx^2} + x\frac{dy}{dx} + y = 0$$

becomes $\qquad \dfrac{d^2y}{dz^2} + y = 0$

by substituting e^z for x.

4. Transform the equation

$$\sin^2 2z\frac{d^2y}{dz^2} + \sin 4z\frac{dy}{dz} + 4y = 0$$

by putting $\qquad \tan z = e^x.$

5. Transform the equation

$$(a + bx)^2\frac{d^2y}{dx^2} + A(a + bx)\frac{dy}{dx} + By = f(x)$$

by putting $\qquad a + bx = e^z$

6. Transform the equation

$$(1 + x^2)^2\frac{d^2y}{dx^2} + 2x(1 + x^2)\frac{dy}{dx} + y = 0$$

into one in which z is the independent variable, given $x = \tan z$.

7. Transform the Cartesian formula

$$p = \frac{x\dfrac{dy}{dx} - y}{\sqrt{1 + \left(\dfrac{dy}{dx}\right)^2}}$$

to polars.

8. Transform the polar formula

$$\tan \phi = \frac{r d\theta}{dr}$$

to Cartesians.

9. Transform the formula

$$\rho = \frac{\left\{1 + \left(\dfrac{dy}{dx}\right)^2\right\}^{\frac{3}{2}}}{\dfrac{d^2y}{dx^2}}$$

into polar co-ordinates

10. Given

$$x = a(\theta + \sin\ \theta),$$
$$y = a(1 - \cos\ \theta),$$

prove

$$\frac{d^2y}{dx^2} = \frac{1}{4a}\sec^4\frac{\theta}{2}.$$

11. Transform $\dfrac{d^2y}{dx^2}$ to the new variables u and v, taking u as independent variable, given $x = v^{-1}$, $y = uv$.   [OXFORD, 1888.]

12. If V be a function of r alone, where

$$r^2 = x^2 + y^2,$$

show that

$$\frac{\partial^2 V}{\partial x^2} + \frac{\partial^2 V}{\partial y^2} = \frac{d^2 V}{dr^2} + \frac{1}{r}\frac{dV}{dr}.$$

13. If V be a function of r alone, where

$$r^2 = x^2 + y^2 + z^2,$$

show that

$$\frac{\partial^2 V}{\partial x^2} + \frac{\partial^2 V}{\partial y^2} + \frac{\partial^2 V}{\partial z^2} = \frac{d^2 V}{dr^2} + \frac{2}{r}\frac{dV}{dr}.$$

14. Generally, if V be a function of r alone, where

$$r^2 = x_1^2 + x_2^2 + \ldots + x_n^2,$$

show that

$$\frac{\partial^2 V}{\partial x_1^2} + \frac{\partial^2 V}{\partial x_2^2} + \frac{\partial^2 V}{\partial x_3^2} + \ldots + \frac{\partial^2 V}{\partial x_n^2} = \frac{d^2 V}{dr^2} + \frac{n-1}{r}\frac{dV}{dr}.$$

15. If

$$x = e^v\sec u, \quad y = e^v\tan u,$$

and ϕ is a function of x and y, show that

$$\cos u\left(\frac{\partial^2\phi}{\partial u\partial v} - \frac{\partial\phi}{\partial u}\right) = xy\left(\frac{\partial^2\phi}{\partial x^2} + \frac{\partial^2\phi}{\partial y^2}\right) + (x^2 + y^2)\frac{\partial^2\phi}{\partial x\partial y}.$$

[OXFORD, 1889.]

16. In transforming any function u of x, y, z from Cartesians to polars by the formulae $x = r \sin\ \theta \cos\ \phi,$

$$y = r \sin\ \theta \sin\ \phi,$$
$$z = r \cos\ \theta,$$

prove (α) $\dfrac{\partial x}{\partial r} = \dfrac{\partial r}{\partial x}$,

(β) $\dfrac{\partial x}{\partial\theta} = r^2\dfrac{\partial\theta}{\partial x}$, (γ) $\quad \dfrac{\partial x}{\partial \phi}\dfrac{\partial \phi}{\partial x} + \dfrac{\partial y}{\partial \phi}\dfrac{\partial \phi}{\partial y} = 1,$

(δ) $\quad \left(\dfrac{\partial u}{\partial x}\right)^2 + \left(\dfrac{\partial u}{\partial y}\right)^2 + \left(\dfrac{\partial u}{\partial z}\right)^2 = \left(\dfrac{\partial u}{\partial r}\right)^2 + \left(\dfrac{1}{r}\dfrac{\partial u}{\partial \theta}\right)^2 + \left(\dfrac{1}{r \sin \theta}\dfrac{\partial u}{\partial \phi}\right)^2.$

17. If V be a function of two independent variables x and y which are connected with two other variables r and θ by the equations

$$F_1(x,\ y,\ r,\ \theta) = 0,$$
$$F_2(x,\ y,\ r,\ \theta) = 0,$$

show how to express $\dfrac{\partial V}{\partial x}$ and $\dfrac{\partial V}{\partial y}$ in terms of $\dfrac{\partial V}{\partial r}$ and $\dfrac{\partial V}{\partial \theta}$.

18. If in the differential equation

$$x^n \dfrac{d^n y}{dx^n} + A_1 x^{n-1}\dfrac{d^{n-1}y}{dx^{n-1}} + \dots + A_{n-1}x\dfrac{dy}{dx} + A_n = 0$$

the independent variable be changed to θ, where $x = e^\theta$, show that all the coefficients in the transformed equation are constants.

19. Show that by putting $x^2 = s$ and $y^2 = t$ the equation

$$Axy\left(\dfrac{dy}{dx}\right)^2 + (x^2 - Ay^2 - B)\dfrac{dy}{dx} - xy = 0$$

is reduced to $\qquad t = s\dfrac{dt}{ds} - \dfrac{B\dfrac{dt}{ds}}{A\dfrac{dt}{ds} + 1}.$

20. Transform the equation

$$\dfrac{d}{dx}\left\{(1 - x^2)\dfrac{dP}{dx}\right\} + n(n+1)P = 0$$

by putting $\qquad x = \cos \theta.$

21. If $\qquad x^2 + z^2 = 1,$

show that the equation $\dfrac{d}{dx}\left\{(1 - x^2)\dfrac{dP}{dx}\right\} + n(n+1)P = 0$

becomes $\qquad z(z^2 - 1)\dfrac{d^2 P}{dz^2} + (2z^2 - 1)\dfrac{dP}{dz} - n(n+1)zP = 0.$

22. If $\qquad x = \tfrac{1}{2}\left(z + \dfrac{1}{z}\right),$

show that the equation $\dfrac{d}{dx}\left\{(1 - x^2)\dfrac{dP}{dx}\right\} + n(n+1)P = 0$

becomes $\qquad z^2(z^2 - 1)\dfrac{d^2 P}{dz^2} + 2z^3\dfrac{dP}{dz} - n(n+1)(z^2 - 1)P = 0.$

23. If
$$x = r \cos \theta \Big\}, \text{ and } r = e^z,$$
$$y = r \sin \theta \Big\}$$

prove
$$x^2 \frac{\partial^2 u}{\partial x^2} + 2xy \frac{\partial^2 u}{\partial x \partial y} + y^2 \frac{\partial^2 u}{\partial y^2} = r \frac{\partial}{\partial r} \Big(r \frac{\partial}{\partial r} - 1 \Big) u = \frac{\partial}{\partial z} \Big(\frac{\partial}{\partial z} - 1 \Big) u,$$

and
$$x^2 \frac{\partial^2 u}{\partial y^2} - 2xy \frac{\partial^2 u}{\partial x \partial y} + y^2 \frac{\partial^2 u}{\partial x^2} = \frac{\partial^2 u}{\partial \theta^2} + r \frac{\partial u}{\partial r} = \frac{\partial^2 u}{\partial \theta^2} + \frac{\partial u}{\partial z}.$$

24. If $\quad x + y = 2e^\theta \cos \phi, \text{ and } x - y = 2\sqrt{-1}\, e^\theta \sin \phi,$

show that
$$\frac{\partial^2 V}{\partial \theta^2} + \frac{\partial^2 V}{\partial \phi^2} = 4xy \frac{\partial^2 V}{\partial x \partial y}. \qquad \text{[OXFORD.]}$$

25. Prove that, if $\quad x = r \sin \theta \cos \phi,$
$$y = r \sin \theta \sin \phi,$$
$$z = r \cos \theta,$$
$$\frac{\partial^2 V}{\partial x^2} + \frac{\partial^2 V}{\partial y^2} + \frac{\partial^2 V}{\partial z^2} = 0$$

transforms into
$$\frac{\partial}{\partial r} \Big(r^2 \sin \theta \frac{\partial V}{\partial r} \Big) + \frac{\partial}{\partial \theta} \Big(\sin \theta \frac{\partial V}{\partial \theta} \Big) + \frac{\partial}{\partial \phi} \Big(\frac{1}{\sin \theta} \frac{\partial V}{\partial \phi} \Big) = 0,$$

and also into $\quad r \frac{\partial^2 (Vr)}{\partial r^2} + \frac{\partial}{\partial \mu} \Big\{ (1 - \mu^2) \frac{\partial V}{\partial \mu} \Big\} + \frac{1}{1 - \mu^2} \frac{\partial^2 V}{\partial \phi^2} = 0,$

where $\quad \mu = \cos \theta.$

26. Transform $P \dfrac{d^2 y}{dx^2} + Q \dfrac{dy}{dx}$, where P and Q are functions of x only

so that t may be the independent variable, where $\dfrac{dx}{dt} = \sqrt{P}.$

27. Transform the equation
$$ry^2 - 2sxy + tx^2 = px + qy - z$$
by putting $\qquad x = u \cos v \Big\}.$
$$y = u \sin v \Big\}$$

28. If z be a function of x and y, and Z be written for $px + qy - z$, prove that if p and q be taken as independent variables,

$$\frac{\partial Z}{\partial p} = x, \quad \frac{\partial Z}{\partial q} = y, \quad \frac{\partial^2 Z}{\partial p^2} = \frac{t}{rt - s^2}, \quad \frac{\partial^2 Z}{\partial p \partial q} = -\frac{s}{rt - s^2}, \quad \frac{\partial^2 Z}{\partial q^2} = \frac{r}{rt - s^2}.$$

29. Show that
$$x^3 \frac{\partial^3 u}{\partial x^3} + 3x^2 y \frac{\partial^3 u}{\partial x^2 \partial y} + 3xy^2 \frac{\partial^3 u}{\partial x \partial y^2} + y^3 \frac{\partial^3 u}{\partial y^3} = \Delta(\Delta - 1)(\Delta - 2)u,$$

where Δ represents the operative symbol $x \dfrac{d}{dx} + y \dfrac{d}{dy}$ or $r \dfrac{d}{dr}$ in polars.

30. Prove generally that if $x = e^\theta$ and $y = e^\phi$,

$$x^n\frac{\partial^n u}{\partial x^n} + nx^{n-1}y\frac{\partial^n u}{\partial x^{n-1}\partial y} + \ldots + y^n\frac{\partial^n u}{\partial y^n} = \Delta(\Delta - 1)(\Delta - 2)\ldots(\Delta - n + 1)u,$$

where
$$\Delta \equiv \frac{\partial}{\partial\theta} + \frac{\partial}{\partial\phi}.$$

31. If
$$x = e^\theta, \quad y = e^\phi,$$

transform the expression

$$e^{2\theta}\frac{\partial^2 V}{\partial x^2} + e^{2\phi}\frac{\partial^2 V}{\partial y^2} + e^\theta\frac{\partial V}{\partial x} + e^\phi\frac{\partial V}{\partial y}.$$

32. If
$$u + \iota v = f(x + \iota y),$$

where x and y are independent and u, v, x, y are all real, prove that

$$\frac{\partial^2 V}{\partial x^2} + \frac{\partial^2 V}{\partial y^2} = \left(\frac{\partial^2 V}{\partial u^2} + \frac{\partial^2 V}{\partial v^2}\right)f'(x + \iota y)f'(x - \iota y).$$

Hence establish that if $x = r\cos\theta$, $y = r\sin\theta$,

then
$$\frac{\partial^2 V}{\partial x^2} + \frac{\partial^2 V}{\partial y^2} = \frac{\partial^2 V}{\partial r^2} + \frac{1}{r}\frac{\partial V}{\partial r} + \frac{1}{r^2}\frac{\partial^2 V}{\partial\theta^2}.$$ [Oxford, 1888.]

33. Transform the equation

$$\frac{\partial^2 u}{\partial x^2} + \frac{\partial^2 u}{\partial y^2} + k^2 u = 0$$

to polar co-ordinates.

34. Show by a change of rectangular axes that

$$a\frac{\partial^2 V}{\partial x^2} + b\frac{\partial^2 V}{\partial y^2} + c\frac{\partial^2 V}{\partial z^2} + 2f\frac{\partial^2 V}{\partial y\partial z} + 2g\frac{\partial^2 V}{\partial z\partial x} + 2h\frac{\partial^2 V}{\partial x\partial y}$$

may be transformed to $A\dfrac{\partial^2 V}{\partial x^2} + B\dfrac{\partial^2 V}{\partial y^2} + C\dfrac{\partial^2 V}{\partial z^2}$.

35. Under what condition can

$$\begin{aligned} a_1\frac{\partial V}{\partial x} + b_1\frac{\partial V}{\partial y} \\ a_2\frac{\partial V}{\partial x} + b_2\frac{\partial V}{\partial y} \end{aligned}\Bigg\}$$

by a rectangular transformation be reduced to the forms $A\dfrac{\partial V}{\partial x}$, $B\dfrac{\partial V}{\partial y}$ respectively ?

36. If $u = f(x, y)$, $x^2 = \xi\eta$ and $y^2 = \dfrac{\xi}{\eta}$, change the independent variables to ξ, η in the equation

$$x^2\frac{\partial^2 u}{\partial x^2} - 2xy\frac{\partial^2 u}{\partial x\partial y} + y^2\frac{\partial^2 u}{\partial y^2} + 2y\frac{\partial u}{\partial y} = 0.$$

37. If x, y be the rectangular, r, θ the polar co-ordinates of the same point, prove

$$\frac{\partial^2 u}{\partial x^2} \cdot \frac{\partial^2 u}{\partial y^2} - \left(\frac{\partial^2 u}{\partial x \partial y}\right)^2 = \frac{1}{r^2}\frac{\partial^2 u}{\partial r^2} \cdot \frac{\partial^2 u}{\partial \theta^2} + \frac{1}{r}\frac{\partial u}{\partial r}\frac{\partial^2 u}{\partial r^2} - \frac{1}{r^2}\left(\frac{\partial^2 u}{\partial r \partial \theta} - \frac{1}{r}\frac{\partial u}{\partial \theta}\right)^2.$$

38. The position of a point in a plane is defined by the length r of the tangent from it to a fixed circle of radius a and the inclination θ of the tangent to a fixed line. Show that the continuity equation

$$\frac{\partial^2 \phi}{\partial x^2} + \frac{\partial^2 \phi}{\partial y^2} = 0$$

transforms into

$$\frac{\partial^2 \phi}{\partial r^2} + \frac{1}{r}\frac{\partial \phi}{\partial r} + \frac{1}{r^2}\frac{\partial^2 \phi}{\partial \theta^2} + \frac{a^2}{r^2}\left(\frac{\partial^2 \phi}{\partial r^2} - \frac{1}{r}\frac{\partial \phi}{\partial r}\right) - \frac{a}{r^2}\left(2\frac{\partial^2 \phi}{\partial r \partial \theta} - \frac{1}{r}\frac{\partial \phi}{\partial \theta}\right) = 0.$$

39. Prove that

$$\frac{\partial^2 V}{\partial x_1^2} + \frac{\partial^2 V}{\partial x_2^2} + \frac{\partial^2 V}{\partial x_3^2} + \dots + \frac{\partial^2 V}{\partial x_n^2}$$

$$= \frac{1}{W}\left\{\frac{\partial}{\partial r}\left(W\frac{\partial V}{\partial r}\right) + \frac{\partial}{\partial \theta_1}\left(\frac{W}{u_1}\frac{\partial V}{\partial \theta_1}\right) + \frac{\partial}{\partial \theta_2}\left(\frac{W}{u_2}\frac{\partial V}{\partial \theta_2}\right) + \dots + \frac{\partial}{\partial \theta_{n-1}}\left(\frac{W}{u_{n-1}}\frac{\partial V}{\partial \theta_{n-1}}\right)\right\}$$

where $x_1 = r \sin\theta_1 \sin\theta_2 \dots \sin\theta_{n-1}$, $\quad u_1 = r^2$,

$\qquad x_2 = r \sin\theta_1 \sin\theta_2 \dots \cos\theta_{n-1}$, $\quad u_2 = r^2\sin^2\theta_1$,

$\qquad x_3 = r \sin\theta_1 \sin\theta_2 \dots \cos\theta_{n-2}$, $\quad u_3 = r^2\sin^2\theta_1\sin^2\theta_2$,

$$\dots\dots\dots\dots\dots\dots\dots \qquad \dots\dots\dots\dots\dots$$

$\qquad x_{n-1} = r \sin\theta_1 \cos\theta_2$, $\qquad\qquad \dots\dots\dots\dots\dots$

$\qquad x_n = r \cos\theta_1$, $\qquad\qquad u_{n-1} = r^2\sin^2\theta_1\sin^2\theta_2 \dots \sin^2\theta_{n-2}$,

and $\quad W = r^{n-1}\sin^{n-2}\theta_1\sin^{n-3}\theta_2 \dots \sin\theta_{n-2}$. $\qquad$ [MATH. TRIPOS, 1889.]

40. If $\qquad\qquad \rho_1 = f_1(x, y, z)$,

$$\rho_2 = f_2(x, y, z),$$

$$\rho_3 = f_3(x, y, z),$$

show how to change the independent variables from x, y, z to ρ_1, ρ_2, ρ_3 in any partial differentials.

If ρ_1, ρ_2, ρ_3 be a system of orthogonal surfaces show that the expression $\qquad\qquad \dfrac{\partial^2 V}{\partial x^2} + \dfrac{\partial^2 V}{\partial y^2} + \dfrac{\partial^2 V}{\partial z^2}$

transforms into

$$h_1 h_2 h_3 \left\{\frac{\partial}{\partial \rho_1}\left(\frac{h_1}{h_2 h_3}\frac{\partial V}{\partial \rho_1}\right) + \frac{\partial}{\partial \rho_2}\left(\frac{h_2}{h_3 h_1}\frac{\partial V}{\partial \rho_2}\right) + \frac{\partial}{\partial \rho_3}\left(\frac{h_3}{h_1 h_2}\frac{\partial V}{\partial \rho_3}\right)\right\}$$

where $\qquad\qquad h_1^2 = \left(\dfrac{\partial \rho_1}{\partial x}\right)^2 + \left(\dfrac{\partial \rho_1}{\partial y}\right)^2 + \left(\dfrac{\partial \rho_1}{\partial z}\right)^2$,

$$\text{etc.} \qquad\qquad \text{[MATH. TRIPOS, 1875.]}$$

CHAPTER XX.

MISCELLANEOUS THEOREMS.

JACOBIANS.

534. Definition. Notation.

If $u_1, u_2, ..., u_n$ be n functions of the n variables $x_1, x_2, x_3, ...,$ x_n, the determinant

$$\begin{vmatrix} \dfrac{\partial u_1}{\partial x_1}, & \dfrac{\partial u_1}{\partial x_2}, & \dfrac{\partial u_1}{\partial x_3}, & \cdots, & \dfrac{\partial u_1}{\partial x_n} \\[2ex] \dfrac{\partial u_2}{\partial x_1}, & \dfrac{\partial u_2}{\partial x_2}, & \cdots\cdots\cdots, & & \dfrac{\partial u_2}{\partial x_n} \\[2ex] \cdots\cdots\cdots\cdots\cdots\cdots\cdots \\[1ex] \dfrac{\partial u_n}{\partial x_1}, & \dfrac{\partial u_n}{\partial x_2}, & \cdots\cdots\cdots, & & \dfrac{\partial u_n}{\partial x_n} \end{vmatrix}$$

has been called by Dr. Salmon the Jacobian of $u_1, u_2, ..., u_n$, with regard to $x_1, x_2, ..., x_n$.[*]

This determinant is often denoted by

$$\frac{\partial(u_1, u_2, ..., u_n)}{\partial(x_1, x_2, ..., x_n)}, \quad J(u_1, u_2, ..., u_n),$$

or shortly J, when there can be no doubt as to the variables referred to.

535. The Jacobian of Three Curves.

If $u = 0$, $v = 0$, $w = 0$ be the equations of three curves in any homogeneous co-ordinates, it has been shown that the polar lines of x, y, z with regard to these curves are respectively

$$Xu_x + Yu_y + Zu_z = 0,$$
$$Xv_x + Yv_y + Zv_z = 0,$$
$$Xw_x + Yw_y + Zw_z = 0.$$

[*] Salmon, *Higher Algebra*, p. 78 and p. 292.

477

These three lines are concurrent if

$$J \equiv \begin{vmatrix} u_x, & u_y, & u_z \\ v_x, & v_y, & v_z \\ w_x, & w_y, & w_z \end{vmatrix} = 0.$$

Thus the vanishing of the Jacobian of three curves indicates the locus of a point whose *three polar lines are concurrent*.

Ex. Show that the Jacobian of three circles gives their orthotomic circle.

536. Prop. *If any set of homogeneous equations be satisfied by a common system of variables, the equation $J=0$ is also satisfied by the same system, and if the degrees are the same, the equations $\dfrac{\partial J}{\partial x}=0, \dfrac{\partial J}{\partial y}=0,\dots$ will also be satisfied by the same system.*

For if $u=0$, $v=0$, $w=0$, ... be the equations, of degrees p, q, r, ... respectively, and x, y, z, ... the variables, Euler's theorem on homogeneous functions gives

$$xu_x + yu_y + zu_z + \dots = pu,$$
$$xv_x + yv_y + \quad \dots = qv,$$
$$xw_x + yw_y + \quad \dots = rw,$$
$$\text{etc.,}$$

and solving for x we obtain

$$xJ = puU + qvV + rwW + \dots, \quad \dots\dots\dots\dots(1)$$

where U, V, W, ... are the co-factors of J corresponding to $u_x, v_x, w_x, \dots$. Hence if any system of variables can be found to make $u=v=w=\dots=0$ simultaneously, that system will also make $J=0$.

Again, differentiating equation (1) of the last article we have

$$x\frac{\partial J}{\partial x} + J = p\left(u_x U + u\frac{\partial U}{\partial x}\right) + \dots = pu_x U + qv_x V + \dots,$$

when $u = v = \dots = 0.$

Hence if the expressions u, v, ... were all of the same degree, we should have $p=q=\dots=n$ say, and

$$x\frac{\partial J}{\partial x} + J = nJ,$$

and therefore for such a set of variables as simultaneously satisfy the equations $u=0$, $v=0$, $w=0$, ... we have $\dfrac{\partial J}{\partial x}=0.$*

---

* The method of proof adopted is given by Dr. Salmon, *Higher Algebra*, p. 78.

Similarly, $\qquad \dfrac{\partial J}{\partial y} = 0,\ \dfrac{\partial J}{\partial z} = 0,$ etc.

537. If then the curves $u = 0,\ v = 0,\ w = 0$ have a common point, the curve $J = 0$ *will go through that point*, and further, if the curves be of like degree, we shall have

$$\frac{\partial J}{\partial x} = \frac{\partial J}{\partial y} = \frac{\partial J}{\partial z} = 0,$$

so that $J = 0$ will have a *double point there*.

538. Since the equation

$$\begin{vmatrix} u_x, & u_y, & u_z \\ v_x, & v_y, & v_z \\ w_x, & w_y, & w_z \end{vmatrix} = 0.$$

is satisfied when $u_x = u_y = u_z = 0$, it goes through all *the multiple points on the curve* $u = 0$. Similarly, it passes through all the multiple points on any of the curves of the families $u = a,\ v = b$ $w = c$ for any values of $a,\ b,\ c$.

539. **The Hessian.**

The Jacobian of the first differential coefficients $u_x,\ u_y,\ u_z$ of any function u is

$$\begin{vmatrix} u_{xx}, & u_{xy}, & u_{xz} \\ u_{xy}, & u_{yy}, & u_{yz} \\ u_{xz}, & u_{yz}, & u_{zz} \end{vmatrix}$$

and has been called the Hessian (Art. 311).

540. Prop. *If J be the Jacobian of the system $u,\ v$ with regard to $x,\ y$ and J' the Jacobian of $x,\ y$ with regard to $u,\ v$, then will* $\qquad JJ' = 1.$

Let $\qquad u = f(x,\ y)$ and $v = F(x,\ y),$

and suppose these solved for x and y, giving

$$x = \phi(u,\ v) \text{ and } y = \psi(u,\ v),$$

we then have

$$\left. \begin{aligned} 1 &= \frac{\partial u}{\partial x}\frac{\partial x}{\partial u} + \frac{\partial u}{\partial y}\frac{\partial y}{\partial u} \\ 0 &= \frac{\partial u}{\partial x}\frac{\partial x}{\partial v} + \frac{\partial u}{\partial y}\frac{\partial y}{\partial v} \end{aligned} \right\},$$

$$\left. \begin{aligned} 0 &= \frac{\partial v}{\partial x}\frac{\partial x}{\partial u} + \frac{\partial v}{\partial y}\frac{\partial y}{\partial u} \\ 1 &= \frac{\partial v}{\partial x}\frac{\partial x}{\partial v} + \frac{\partial v}{\partial y}\frac{\partial y}{\partial v} \end{aligned} \right\}.$$

Also
$$JJ' = \begin{vmatrix} \dfrac{\partial u}{\partial x}, & \dfrac{\partial u}{\partial y} \\[2mm] \dfrac{\partial v}{\partial x}, & \dfrac{\partial v}{\partial y} \end{vmatrix} \times \begin{vmatrix} \dfrac{\partial x}{\partial u}, & \dfrac{\partial y}{\partial u} \\[2mm] \dfrac{\partial x}{\partial v}, & \dfrac{\partial y}{\partial v} \end{vmatrix}$$

$$= \begin{vmatrix} \dfrac{\partial u}{\partial x}\dfrac{\partial x}{\partial u} + \dfrac{\partial u}{\partial y}\dfrac{\partial y}{\partial u}, & \dfrac{\partial u}{\partial x}\dfrac{\partial x}{\partial v} + \dfrac{\partial u}{\partial y}\dfrac{\partial y}{\partial v} \\[3mm] \dfrac{\partial v}{\partial x}\dfrac{\partial x}{\partial u} + \dfrac{\partial v}{\partial y}\dfrac{\partial y}{\partial u}, & \dfrac{\partial v}{\partial x}\dfrac{\partial x}{\partial v} + \dfrac{\partial v}{\partial y}\dfrac{\partial y}{\partial v} \end{vmatrix}$$

$$= \begin{vmatrix} 1, & 0 \\ 0, & 1 \end{vmatrix} = 1.$$

In the same way the theorem admits of proof if there be more functions and more variables than two.

This theorem may be written

$$\frac{\partial(u, v, \ldots)}{\partial(x, y, \ldots)} \times \frac{\partial(x, y, \ldots)}{\partial(u, v, \ldots)} = 1.$$

541. Prop. *If U, V are functions of u and v, where u and v are themselves functions of x and y, we shall have*

$$\frac{\partial(U, V)}{\partial(x, y)} = \frac{\partial(U, V)}{\partial(u, v)} \cdot \frac{\partial(u, v)}{\partial(x, y)}.$$

For let $\quad U = f(u, v), \quad V = F(u, v),$

$$u = \phi(x, y), \quad v = \psi(x, y).$$

Now
$$\frac{\partial U}{\partial x} = \frac{\partial U}{\partial u}\frac{\partial u}{\partial x} + \frac{\partial U}{\partial v}\frac{\partial v}{\partial x},$$

$$\frac{\partial U}{\partial y} = \frac{\partial U}{\partial u}\frac{\partial u}{\partial y} + \frac{\partial U}{\partial v}\frac{\partial v}{\partial y},$$

$$\frac{\partial V}{\partial x} = \frac{\partial V}{\partial u}\frac{\partial u}{\partial x} + \frac{\partial V}{\partial v}\frac{\partial v}{\partial x},$$

$$\frac{\partial V}{\partial y} = \frac{\partial V}{\partial u}\frac{\partial u}{\partial y} + \frac{\partial V}{\partial v}\frac{\partial v}{\partial y},$$

and $\dfrac{\partial(U, V)}{\partial(u, v)} \times \dfrac{\partial(u, v)}{\partial(x, y)}$

$$= \begin{vmatrix} \dfrac{\partial U}{\partial u}, & \dfrac{\partial U}{\partial v} \\[2mm] \dfrac{\partial V}{\partial u}, & \dfrac{\partial V}{\partial v} \end{vmatrix} \times \begin{vmatrix} \dfrac{\partial u}{\partial x}, & \dfrac{\partial v}{\partial x} \\[2mm] \dfrac{\partial u}{\partial y}, & \dfrac{\partial v}{\partial y} \end{vmatrix}$$

$$= \begin{vmatrix} \dfrac{\partial U}{\partial u}\dfrac{\partial u}{\partial x} + \dfrac{\partial U}{\partial v}\dfrac{\partial v}{\partial x}, & \dfrac{\partial U}{\partial u}\dfrac{\partial u}{\partial y} + \dfrac{\partial U}{\partial v}\dfrac{\partial v}{\partial y} \\[2ex] \dfrac{\partial V}{\partial u}\dfrac{\partial u}{\partial x} + \dfrac{\partial V}{\partial v}\dfrac{\partial v}{\partial x}, & \dfrac{\partial V}{\partial u}\dfrac{\partial u}{\partial y} + \dfrac{\partial V}{\partial v}\dfrac{\partial v}{\partial y} \end{vmatrix}$$

$$= \begin{vmatrix} \dfrac{\partial U}{\partial x}, & \dfrac{\partial U}{\partial y} \\[2ex] \dfrac{\partial V}{\partial x}, & \dfrac{\partial V}{\partial y} \end{vmatrix} = \dfrac{\partial(U,\ V)}{\partial(x,\ y)},$$

and the same method of proof applies if there are several functions and the same number of variables.

542. The above propositions exhibit the curious analogy pointed out by Jacobi between these determinants and ordinary differential coefficients.

543. PROP. *If u, v be connected implicitly with the independent variables x, y by the relations*

$$f_1(x,\ y,\ u,\ v) = 0,$$
$$f_2(x,\ y,\ u,\ v) = 0,$$

we shall have
$$\dfrac{\partial(f_1, f_2)}{\partial(x,\ y)} = \dfrac{\partial(f_1, f_2)}{\partial(u,\ v)} \cdot \dfrac{\partial(u,\ v)}{\partial(x,\ y)}.$$

For
$$\dfrac{\partial f_1}{\partial x} + \dfrac{\partial f_1}{\partial u}\dfrac{\partial u}{\partial x} + \dfrac{\partial f_1}{\partial v}\dfrac{\partial v}{\partial x} = 0,$$

$$\dfrac{\partial f_1}{\partial y} + \dfrac{\partial f_1}{\partial u}\dfrac{\partial u}{\partial y} + \dfrac{\partial f_1}{\partial v}\dfrac{\partial v}{\partial y} = 0,$$

$$\dfrac{\partial f_2}{\partial x} + \dfrac{\partial f_2}{\partial u}\dfrac{\partial u}{\partial x} + \dfrac{\partial f_2}{\partial v}\dfrac{\partial v}{\partial x} = 0,$$

$$\dfrac{\partial f_2}{\partial y} + \dfrac{\partial f_2}{\partial u}\dfrac{\partial u}{\partial y} + \dfrac{\partial f_2}{\partial v}\dfrac{\partial v}{\partial y} = 0.$$

Hence
$$\dfrac{\partial(f_1, f_2)}{\partial(u,\ v)} \cdot \dfrac{\partial(u,\ v)}{\partial(x,\ y)}$$

$$= \begin{vmatrix} \dfrac{\partial f_1}{\partial u}\dfrac{\partial u}{\partial x} + \dfrac{\partial f_1}{\partial v}\dfrac{\partial v}{\partial x}, & \dfrac{\partial f_1}{\partial u}\dfrac{\partial u}{\partial y} + \dfrac{\partial f_1}{\partial v}\dfrac{\partial v}{\partial y} \\[2ex] \dfrac{\partial f_2}{\partial u}\dfrac{\partial u}{\partial x} + \dfrac{\partial f_2}{\partial v}\dfrac{\partial v}{\partial x}, & \dfrac{\partial f_2}{\partial u}\dfrac{\partial u}{\partial y} + \dfrac{\partial f_2}{\partial v}\dfrac{\partial v}{\partial y} \end{vmatrix}$$

$$= \begin{vmatrix} -\dfrac{\partial f_1}{\partial x}, & -\dfrac{\partial f_1}{\partial y} \\[2ex] -\dfrac{\partial f_2}{\partial x}, & -\dfrac{\partial f_2}{\partial y} \end{vmatrix} = \dfrac{\partial(f_1, f_2)}{\partial(x,\ y)}.$$

544. If there had been three independent relations with six variables u, v, w; x, y, z; it is plain that we should in a similar manner obtain

$$\frac{\partial(f_1, f_2, f_3)}{\partial(u, v, w)} \cdot \frac{\partial(u, v, w)}{\partial(x, y, z)} = \begin{vmatrix} -\dfrac{\partial f_1}{\partial x}, & -\dfrac{\partial f_1}{\partial y}, & -\dfrac{\partial f_1}{\partial z} \\[2mm] -\dfrac{\partial f_2}{\partial x}, & -\dfrac{\partial f_2}{\partial y}, & -\dfrac{\partial f_2}{\partial z} \\[2mm] -\dfrac{\partial f_3}{\partial x}, & -\dfrac{\partial f_3}{\partial y}, & -\dfrac{\partial f_3}{\partial z} \end{vmatrix} = (-1)^3 \frac{\partial(f_1, f_2, f_3)}{\partial(x, y, z)}.$$

And in general, if there be n independent relations

$$f_1 = 0, \; f_2 = 0, \; \ldots, \; f_n = 0$$

involving $2n$ variables $u_1, u_2, \ldots, u_n$ and $x_1, x_2, \ldots, x_n$, then

$$\frac{\partial(f_1, f_2, \ldots, f_n)}{\partial(x_1, x_2, \ldots, x_n)} = (-1)^n \frac{\partial(f_1, f_2, \ldots, f_n)}{\partial(u_1, u_2, \ldots, u_n)} \cdot \frac{\partial(u_1, u_2, \ldots, u_n)}{\partial(x_1, x_2, \ldots, x_n)}.$$

545. Covariant. Definition.

Let f be any quantic from which another function ϕ is derived in any manner, involving the constants and variables of the first. Let the variables of f and ϕ be changed by any linear transformation, the functions becoming F and Φ. Then if it be found that the function derived from F by the same process by which ϕ was derived from f is merely Φ multiplied by some power of the modulus of transformation, ϕ is said to be a Covariant of f. If none of the variables enter into ϕ, then ϕ is called an Invariant.

546. PROP. *The Jacobian of a system of functions u, v, w is a covariant of the system.*

Let the transformation scheme be that shown in the margin, so that

	x_1	y_1	z_1
x	l_1	m_1	n_1
y	l_2	m_2	n_2
z	l_3	m_3	n_3

$$x = l_1 x_1 + m_1 y_1 + n_1 z_1,$$
etc.

Then
$$\frac{\partial u}{\partial x_1} = \frac{\partial u}{\partial x} \cdot l_1 + \frac{\partial u}{\partial y} \cdot l_2 + \frac{\partial u}{\partial z} \cdot l_3,$$
etc.

Hence the Jacobian of the transformed system is

$$J_1 \equiv \begin{vmatrix} u_{x_1}, & u_{y_1}, & u_{z_1}, \\ v_{x_1}, & v_{y_1}, & v_{z_1}, \\ w_{x_1}, & w_{y_1}, & w_{z_1}, \end{vmatrix} = \begin{vmatrix} u_x, & u_y, & u_z \\ v_x, & v_y, & v_z \\ w_x, & w_y, & w_z \end{vmatrix} \times \begin{vmatrix} l_1, & l_2, & l_3 \\ m_1, & m_2, & m_3 \\ n_1, & n_2, & n_3 \end{vmatrix},$$

(by the rule of multiplication of determinants)
$$= J \times \mu,$$
where J is the Jacobian of the original system and μ the transformation-modulus.

547. PROP. *Let* $u_1, u_2, \ldots, u_n$ *be a set of functions of* n *independent variables* $x_1, x_2, \ldots, x_n$. *Then if these functions are not each independent, but if some relation exists among them which is identically satisfied when their values are substituted, their Jacobian*
$$J \equiv \frac{\partial(u_1, u_2, \ldots, u_n)}{\partial(x_1, x_2, \ldots, x_n)}$$
will vanish identically. Also conversely, if J *is identically zero, some relation must subsist amongst the several functions.*

This result has already been established in the case of two functions of two variables in Art. 510.

Consider the case of three functions u_1, u_2, u_3. Let the relation subsisting among them be
$$f(u_1, u_2, u_3) = 0.$$
Then, for all values of the variables,
$$\frac{\partial f}{\partial u_1}\frac{\partial u_1}{\partial x_1} + \frac{\partial f}{\partial u_2}\frac{\partial u_2}{\partial x_1} + \frac{\partial f}{\partial u_3}\frac{\partial u_3}{\partial x_1} = 0,$$
$$\frac{\partial f}{\partial u_1}\frac{\partial u_1}{\partial x_2} + \frac{\partial f}{\partial u_2}\frac{\partial u_2}{\partial x_2} + \frac{\partial f}{\partial u_3}\frac{\partial u_3}{\partial x_2} = 0,$$
$$\frac{\partial f}{\partial u_1}\frac{\partial u_1}{\partial x_3} + \frac{\partial f}{\partial u_2}\frac{\partial u_2}{\partial x_3} + \frac{\partial f}{\partial u_3}\frac{\partial u_3}{\partial x_3} = 0.$$

Hence eliminating $\dfrac{\partial f}{\partial u_1}, \dfrac{\partial f}{\partial u_2}, \dfrac{\partial f}{\partial u_3}$, we have

$$\begin{vmatrix} \dfrac{\partial u_1}{\partial x_1}, & \dfrac{\partial u_2}{\partial x_1}, & \dfrac{\partial u_3}{\partial x_1} \\ \dfrac{\partial u_1}{\partial x_2}, & \dfrac{\partial u_2}{\partial x_2}, & \dfrac{\partial u_3}{\partial x_2} \\ \dfrac{\partial u_1}{\partial x_3}, & \dfrac{\partial u_2}{\partial x_3}, & \dfrac{\partial u_3}{\partial x_3} \end{vmatrix} = 0$$

identically satisfied, *i.e.*, $\dfrac{\partial(u_1, u_2, u_3)}{\partial(x_1, x_2, x_3)} \equiv 0.$

548. Conversely, let $\dfrac{\partial(u_1, u_2, u_3)}{\partial(x_1, x_2, x_3)} \equiv 0.$

Between the equations connecting the u's and the remaining variables eliminate two of the latter (say x_1 and x_2), and we obtain a relation between u_1, u_2, u_3, x_3, say

$$u_3 = F(u_1, u_2, x_3). \quad \dots\dots\dots\dots\dots\dots\dots(A)$$

Now,
$$\frac{\partial(u_1, u_2, u_3)}{\partial(x_1, x_2, x_3)} = \frac{\partial(u_1, u_2, F)}{\partial(u_1, u_2, x_3)} \cdot \frac{\partial(u_1, u_2, x_3)}{\partial(x_1, x_2, x_3)}$$

$$= \begin{vmatrix} 1, & 0, & 0 \\ 0, & 1, & 0 \\ \dfrac{\partial F}{\partial u_1}, & \dfrac{\partial F}{\partial u_2}, & \dfrac{\partial F}{\partial x_3} \end{vmatrix} \times \begin{vmatrix} \dfrac{\partial u_1}{\partial x_1}, & \dfrac{\partial u_1}{\partial x_2}, & \dfrac{\partial u_1}{\partial x_3} \\ \dfrac{\partial u_2}{\partial x_1}, & \dfrac{\partial u_2}{\partial x_2}, & \dfrac{\partial u_2}{\partial x_3} \\ 0, & 0, & 1 \end{vmatrix},$$

for in forming the first determinant we are regarding u_1, u_2, x_3, as independent variables, and in the second x_1, x_2, x_3.

Therefore
$$\frac{\partial(u_1, u_2, u_3)}{\partial(x_1, x_2, x_3)} = \frac{\partial F}{\partial x_3} \times \frac{\partial(u_1, u_2)}{\partial(x_1, x_2)}.$$

Now the left-hand side by hypothesis vanishes, hence either

$$(1) \qquad \frac{\partial F}{\partial x_3} = 0,$$

or
$$(2) \quad \frac{\partial(u_1, u_2)}{\partial(x_1, x_2)} = 0.$$

In the first case F is independent of x_3, hence the quantity x_3 has not appeared in equation (A) after the elimination of x_1 and x_2, and therefore a relation between u_1, u_2, u_3 has been established.

In the second case, viz., $\dfrac{\partial(u_1, u_2)}{\partial(x_1, x_2)} = 0$,

no differential coefficients with regard to x_3 occur, and therefore x_3 may be regarded as a constant. Hence by Art. 510 there is some relation between u_1 and u_2, which may however involve x_3 as a constant. Let it be

$$f(u_1, u_2, x_3) = 0.$$

If x_3 be eliminated between this equation and (A), there will result a relation between u_1, u_2, u_3.

By proceeding in similar manner the proof may be extended to any number of functions of the same number of variables. See Forsyth's *Differential Equations*, Art. 9.

Some Important Operative Symbols.

549. The Operator ϑ.

It has been shown in Art. 524 that the operator $x\dfrac{d}{dx}$ becomes $\dfrac{d}{dt}$ by the change in the variable $x = e^t$. Let this operator be denoted by the symbol ϑ.

The fundamental properties of this symbol are

$$(1) \qquad \vartheta^n x^a = a^n x^a,$$

$$(2) \qquad \phi(\vartheta)x^a = \phi(a)x^a,$$

$$(3) \ x^n\left(\frac{d}{dx}\right)^n u = \vartheta(\vartheta-1)(\vartheta-2)\ldots(\vartheta-n+1)u,$$

$$(4) \qquad \phi(\vartheta)x^n u = x^n \phi(\vartheta+n)u.$$

(1) The first of these is obvious—

For
$$\vartheta x^a = x\frac{d}{dx}x^a = ax^a,$$

$$\vartheta^2 x^a = \vartheta a x^a = a^2 x^a,$$

$$\text{etc.} \qquad \text{etc.}$$

$$\vartheta^n x^a = a^n x^a,$$

where n is any positive integer.

For negative indices—

Let
$$\vartheta^{-1}x^a = y,$$

therefore
$$\vartheta y = x^a = \vartheta\frac{x^a}{a},$$

so that
$$\vartheta^{-1}x^a = a^{-1}x^a,$$

supposing that no constants are added in the inverse operation.

Hence also
$$\vartheta^{-n}x^a = a^{-n}x^a,$$

so that the law (1) is true for any integral index.

(2) If $\phi(z)$ be any function of z, which is capable of expansion in integral powers of z, $\Sigma A_n z^n$, say,

$$\phi(\vartheta)x^a = \Sigma A_n \vartheta^n x^a$$

$$= \Sigma A_n a^n x^a$$

$$= \phi(a)x^a.$$

(3) The third law has been established in Art. 524.

(4) To prove the fourth—

Let $\qquad\qquad\qquad x = e^t,$

and let $\qquad\qquad u \equiv F(x) = F(e^t);$

then

$$\phi(\vartheta)x^n u = \phi\left(\frac{d}{dt}\right)e^{nt}F(e^t),$$

$$= e^{nt}\phi\left(\frac{d}{dt}+n\right)F(e^t), \quad \text{(Art. 101)}$$

$$= x^n\phi(\vartheta+n)u.$$

Ex. 1. Prove

$$\left(\frac{d}{dx}\right)^m x^{m+r}\left(\frac{d}{dx}\right)^r x^{-m}\left(\frac{d}{dx}\right)^{n-r}\phi(x) = x^r\left(\frac{d}{dx}\right)^{m+n}\phi(x).$$

[MATH. TRIPOS, 1878.]

Let $\qquad\qquad\qquad \left(\frac{d}{dx}\right)^{n-r}\phi(x) = \psi(x).$

We then have to prove

$$x^m\left(\frac{d}{dx}\right)^m x^m . x^r\left(\frac{d}{dx}\right)^r . x^{-m}\psi(x) = x^{m+r}\left(\frac{d}{dx}\right)^{m+r}\psi(x).$$

And the left side

$$= \vartheta(\vartheta-1)...(\vartheta-m+1)x^m\vartheta(\vartheta-1)...(\vartheta-r+1)x^{-m}\psi(x)$$

$$= \vartheta(\vartheta-1)...(\vartheta-m+1)(\vartheta-m)(\vartheta-m-1)...(\vartheta-m-r+1)\psi(x)$$

$$= x^{m+r}\left(\frac{d}{dx}\right)^{m+r}\psi(x).$$

This solution and another of the same result are given in the *Solutions of Senate House Problems and Riders* for 1878.

Ex. 2. Prove $\qquad\left(x^{1-m}\frac{d}{dx}x^m\right)x^a = (a+m)x^a,$

and that any number of operators

$$\left(x^{1-m}\frac{d}{dx}x^m\right), \qquad \left(x^{1-n}\frac{d}{dx}x^n\right), ...$$

are convertible with regard to order.   [PROC. LOND. MATH. SOC. VOL. VIII.]

Ex. 3. Prove $\left(\frac{d}{dx}\right)^n x^{n+\frac{1}{2}}\left(\frac{d}{dx}\right)^{n+1}\phi(x^{\frac{1}{2}}) = \frac{1}{2^{2n+1}}\phi^{2n+1}(x^{\frac{1}{2}}).$

[SOLUTIONS S. H. PROBLEMS, 1878.]

550. The Operations E and Δ.

The operator $e^{\frac{d}{dx}}$, which when applied to $\phi(x)$ changes x to $x+1$ (Art. 116), is often denoted by E, so that

$$Eu_x = u_{x+1}.$$

Let $\qquad\qquad \Delta u_x = u_{x+1} - u_x = Eu_x - u_x = (E-1)u_x.$

Then the operators E, Δ, $e^{\frac{d}{dx}}$ are connected thus—

$$E = 1 + \Delta = e^{\frac{d}{dx}}.$$

It will be clear from considerations analogous to those of Art. 89 that the operative symbols E and Δ like $D \left(\text{or } \dfrac{d}{dx} \right)$ are distributive, commutative with regard to constants and each other, and obey an index law the same in form as that of algebraical quantities. Hence theorems hold good for these symbols analogous to corresponding theorems for algebraic symbols of quantity.

551. Secondary Form of Maclaurin's Theorem.

It will be evident that the value of $\left(\dfrac{d}{dx} \right)^p x^q$, when $x = 0$, is $p!$ or zero, according as p is equal or unequal to q.

Hence, if $f(z)$ and $F(z)$ are functions both capable of expansion in positive integral powers of z as $\Sigma a_n z^n$, say, and $\Sigma b_m z^m$ respectively, we shall have

$$\left[f\left(\frac{d}{dx} \right) F(x) \right]_{x=0} = \Sigma a_n b_n n!,$$

and therefore

$$= \left[F\left(\frac{d}{dx} \right) f(x) \right]_{x=0}.$$

This theorem may be written

$$f\left(\frac{d}{d0} \right) F(0) = F\left(\frac{d}{d0} \right) f(0).$$

Now, Maclaurin's theorem may be written as

$$F(x) = F(0) + x \frac{d}{d0} F(0) + \frac{x^2}{2!} \frac{d^2}{d0^2} F(0) + \frac{x^3}{3!} \frac{d^3}{d0^3} F(0) + \cdots,$$

and therefore may be transformed by the above result into

$$F(x) = F(0) + x F\left(\frac{d}{d0} \right)(0) + \frac{x^2}{2!} F\left(\frac{d}{d0} \right)(0^2) + \frac{x^3}{3!} F\left(\frac{d}{d0} \right)(0^3) + \cdots,$$

which Dr. Boole * calls the secondary form of Maclaurin's theorem, and writes

$$F(x) = F(D)e^{0 \cdot x}.$$

EXAMPLES.

1. $\Delta^n u_x = (E-1)^n u_x = \left[E^n - nE^{n-1} + \dfrac{n(n-1)}{1 \cdot 2} E^{n-2} - \ldots + (-1)^n \right] u_x,$

$\qquad = u_{x+n} - n u_{x+n-1} + \dfrac{n(n-1)}{1 \cdot 2} u_{x+n-2} - \ldots + (-1)^n u_x,$

*Finite Differences, p. 22.

2.
$$-\frac{du}{dx} = \frac{d}{dx}u = \log(1+\Delta)u \quad [\text{for } e^D = 1+\Delta]$$

$$= \Delta u - \frac{\Delta^2 u}{2} + \frac{\Delta^3 u}{3} - \dots.$$

Similarly $\dfrac{1}{r!}\dfrac{d^r u}{dx^r} = [\log(1+\Delta)]^r u = \dfrac{\Delta^r u}{r!} - {}_rP_1\dfrac{\Delta^{r+1}u}{(r+1)!} + {}_{r+1}P_2\dfrac{\Delta^{r+2}u}{(r+2)!} - \dots.$

(See Ex. 11, p. 80.)

3. Prove $\Delta^p x^m = (x+p)^m - p(x+p-1)^m + \dfrac{p(p-1)}{1\cdot 2}(x+p-2)^m - \dots.$

4. Prove $F(e^x) = F(1) + F(E)0 \cdot x + F(E)0^2 \cdot \dfrac{x^2}{1\cdot 2} + \dots = F(E)e^{0 \cdot x}.$

[HERSCHEL'S THEOREM.]

5. Deduce the secondary form of Maclaurin's Theorem from Herschel's Theorem.

552. Many other curious results may be established by means of these operators.

For example,

$$\frac{1}{e^z - 1} = -\frac{1}{2} + \frac{1}{z} + B_1\frac{z}{2!} - B_3\frac{z^3}{4!} + B_5\frac{z^5}{6!} - \dots.$$

and writing for z the operator hD we have

$$\frac{1}{E^h - 1} \equiv (hD)^{-1} - \frac{1}{2} + \frac{B_1}{2!}hD - \frac{B_3}{4!}(hD)^3 + \frac{B_5}{6!}(hD)^5 - \dots,$$

and therefore $1 + E^h + E^{2h} + \dots + E^{(n-1)h} \equiv \dfrac{E^{nh}-1}{E^h-1}$

$$\equiv \left[(hD)^{-1} - \frac{1}{2} + \frac{B_1}{2!}hD - \frac{B_3}{4!}(hD)^3 + \dots\right](E^{nh}-1).$$

Applying each side to the function $\phi'(x)$ we obtain

$$\phi'(x) + \phi'(x+h) + \phi'(x+2h) + \dots + \phi'\{x+(n-1)h\}$$

$$\equiv (E^{nh}-1)\left[\frac{1}{h}\phi(x) - \frac{1}{2}\phi'(x) + \frac{B_1}{2!}h\phi''(x) - \frac{B_3}{4!}h^3\phi''''(x) + \dots\right]$$

$$\equiv \frac{1}{h}[\phi(x+nh) - \phi(x)] - \frac{1}{2}[\phi'(x+nh) - \phi'(x)]$$

$$+ \sum_{r=1}^{r=\infty}(-1)^{r-1}\frac{B_{2r-1}}{(2r)!}h^{2r-1}[\phi^{2r}(x+nh) - \phi^{2r}(x)],$$

or $\phi(x+nh) - \phi(x) \equiv h[\frac{1}{2}\phi'(x) + \phi'(x+h) + \dots + \phi'\{x+(n-1)h\} + \frac{1}{2}\phi'(x+nh)]$

$$+ \sum_{r=1}^{r=\infty}(-1)^r B_{2r-1}\frac{h^{2r}}{(2r)!}[\phi^{2r}(x+nh) - \phi^{2r}(x)]. \qquad [\text{POISSON.}]$$

553. Various trigonometrical identities may be used to establish similar results.

Ex. Taking the identity

$$\cos\theta - \cos 2\theta + \cos 3\theta - \dots \text{ to } \infty = \tfrac{1}{2},$$

we have $\quad (e^{\iota\theta} + e^{-\iota\theta}) - (e^{2\iota\theta} + e^{-2\iota\theta}) + (e^{3\iota\theta} + e^{-3\iota\theta}) - \dots = 1.$

Writing for $e^{t\theta}$ the operator $e^{h\frac{d}{dx}}$ or E^h we get

$$(E^h + E^{-h}) - (E^{2h} + E^{-2h}) + (E^{3h} + E^{-3h}) - \ldots \equiv 1,$$

and applying this operator to $\phi(x)$ we obtain

$$\phi x = \phi(x+h) - \phi(x+2h) + \phi(x+3h) - \ldots$$
$$+ \phi(x-h) - \phi(x-2h) + \phi(x-3h) - \ldots. \qquad \text{[Gregory.]}$$

554. The expansion of e^z in powers of ze^{-z} by Burmann's Theorem (Ex. Art. 519), may be applied to establish a remarkable result due to Murphy, as follows :—

Dividing by e^z we have

$$1 \equiv e^{-z} + \frac{(2z)}{2!}e^{-2z} + \frac{(3z)^2}{3!}e^{-3z} + \frac{(4z)^3}{4!}e^{-4z} + \ldots.$$

Replacing z by $h\dfrac{d}{dx}$ we have the corresponding operative analogue

$$1 \equiv e^{-h\frac{d}{dx}} + \frac{\left(2h\frac{d}{dx}\right)}{2!}e^{-2h\frac{d}{dx}} + \frac{\left(3h\frac{d}{dx}\right)^2}{3!}e^{-3h\frac{d}{dx}} + \ldots,$$

and applying each side to the function $f(x)$ we obtain

$$f(x) = f(x-h) + \frac{2h}{1.2}f'(x-2h) + \frac{(3h)^2}{1.2.3}f''(x-3h) + \text{etc.}$$

Examples.

1. Establish the series

$$\frac{\pi}{2}h\frac{d}{dx}\phi(x) = \phi(x+h) - \frac{1}{3^2}\phi(x+3h) + \frac{1}{5^2}\phi(x+5h) - \ldots$$
$$- \phi(x-h) + \frac{1}{3^2}\phi(x-3h) - \frac{1}{5^2}\phi(x-5h) + \ldots.$$

[Francais and Gregory.]

2. Prove that $[\phi(x+h) - \phi(x-h)] - \frac{1}{2}[\phi(x+2h) - \phi(x-2h)]$
$$+ \frac{1}{3}[\phi(x+3h) - \phi(x-3h)] - \ldots = h\phi'(x).$$

[Gregory.]

3. Prove that $\dfrac{1}{1^3}\{\phi(x+h) + \phi(x-h)\} - \dfrac{1}{3^3}\{\phi(x+3h) + \phi(x-3h)\}$
$$+ \frac{1}{5^3}\{\phi(x+5h) + \phi(x-5h)\} - \ldots = \frac{\pi^3}{16}\phi(x) + \frac{\pi}{4}h^2\phi''(x).$$

4. Prove that if a be not an integer

$$\frac{\pi}{2}\frac{f(x+ah) - f(x-ah)}{\sin a\pi} = \frac{f(x+h) - f(x-h)}{1^2 - a^2} - 2\frac{f(x+2h) - f(x-2h)}{2^2 - a^2}$$
$$+ 3\frac{f(x+3h) - f(x-3h)}{3^2 - a^2} - \text{etc.}$$

5. If a curve whose equation is $f(x, y)=0$ be subjected to a simple translation in its own plane, its equation becomes

$$e^{a\frac{\partial}{\partial x}+b\frac{\partial}{\partial y}}f(x, y)=0\ ;$$

and if the curve be turned round the origin through an angle ω, the equation becomes

$$e^{\omega\left(x\frac{\partial}{\partial y}-y\frac{\partial}{\partial x}\right)}f(x, y)=0.$$

If both these operations be performed, is the order of the operation indifferent? [CARMICHAEL.]

TAYLOR'S THEOREM. CAUCHY'S METHOD OF PROOF.

555. The following line of argument is adopted by Cauchy in establishing Taylor's series.

556. If any function of z, $f(z)$, be continuous and finite between two given values of z, say $z=x$ and $z=x+h$, and if $f'(z)$ does not vanish or become infinite between those limits, it follows that $f'(z)$ must be continuously of one sign, and therefore $f(z)$ continually increasing or continually decreasing between these values. Hence $f(x+h)-f(x)$ cannot vanish.

557. We shall next establish the result that

$$\frac{F(x+h)-F(x)}{f(x+h)-f(x)}=\frac{F'(x+\theta h)}{f'(x+\theta h)},$$

supposing that

(a) $F(z)$ and $f(z)$ and their first differential coefficients are finite and continuous between the values x and $x+h$ of the variable z;

(b) that one of the two $F''(z)$, $f'(z)$ (say the latter) does not vanish anywhere between these limits.

Let

$$\frac{F(x+h)-F(x)}{f(x+h)-f(x)}\equiv R,$$

which is therefore a function of x and h. It has been shown that the denominator does not vanish, hence

$$F(x+h)-F(x)-R\{f(x+h)-f(x)\}=0\ldots\ldots\ldots\ldots(1)$$

Let

$$\phi(z)\equiv F(z)-F(x)-R\{f(z)-f(x)\},$$

therefore

$$\phi'(z)=F'(z)-Rf'(z).$$

Now, ϕ and ϕ' are finite and continuous between the specified values of z; and $\phi(x+h)=0$ by equation (1), also

$\phi(x)=0$. Hence $\phi'(x+\theta h)=0$, where θ is some positive proper fraction (Art. 126), therefore

$$R=\frac{F'(x+\theta h)}{f'(x+\theta h)}.$$

Thus

$$\frac{F(x+h)-F(x)}{f(x+h)-f(x)}=\frac{F'(x+\theta h)}{f'(x+\theta h)}$$

under the circumstances specified.

(If $F'(z)$ instead of $f'(z)$ had been the one whose value did not vanish in the given interval, we should have obtained the same result by similarly treating the reciprocal fraction.)

558. If we add the extra conditions that all the differential coefficients of $f(z)$ and $F(z)$ up to the nth inclusive are finite and continuous; also that one of the two of each order does not pass through the value zero between the given values of z, we have the following series of equalities :—

$$\frac{F(x+h)-F(x)}{f(x+h)-f(x)}=\frac{F'(x+\theta_1 h)}{f'(x+\theta_1 h)},$$

$$\frac{F'(x+\theta_1 h)-F'(x)}{f'(x+\theta_1 h)-f'(x)}=\frac{F''(x+\theta_2 h)}{f''(x+\theta_2 h)},$$

$$\text{etc.} \qquad\qquad \text{etc.}$$

$$\frac{F^{n-1}(x+\theta_{n-1}h)-F^{n-1}(x)}{f^{n-1}(x+\theta_{n-1}h)-f^{n-1}(x)}=\frac{F^{n}(x+\theta h)}{f^{n}(x+\theta h)},$$

where $\theta_1, \theta_2, \theta_3, \ldots, \theta_{n-1}, \theta$ are all positive proper fractions in diminishing order.

559. In any case in which $x=0$,

and

$$F(0)=F'(0)=\ldots=F^{n-1}(0)=0, \ldots\ldots\ldots\ldots(A)$$

and

$$f(0)=f'(0)=\ldots=f^{n-1}(0)=0, \ldots\ldots\ldots\ldots(B)$$

we thus have

$$\frac{F(h)}{f(h)}=\frac{F^{n}(\theta h)}{f^{n}(\theta h)}, \ldots\ldots\ldots\ldots\ldots(C)$$

where θ is some positive proper fraction.

560. Let $\phi(a+z)$ and all its differential coefficients up to the nth inclusive be finite and continuous between the values $z=0$ and $z=h$, and let

$$F(z)\equiv\phi(a+z)-\phi(a)-z\phi'(a)-\ldots-\frac{z^{n-1}}{(n-1)!}\phi^{n-1}(a),\ldots(D)$$

then equations (A) are all satisfied.

And if we put $f(z)=z^n$, equations (B) are satisfied. Also all the imposed conditions as to the continuity of $F(z), f(z)$ and their first n differential coefficients are satisfied, and no differential coefficient of $f(z)$ up to the nth vanishes for a value of z intermediate between $z=0$ and $z=h$.

Hence equation (C) is applicable; and since

$$F^n(z)=\phi^n(a+z), \text{ and } f^n(z)=n!,$$

it becomes

$$F(h)=\frac{h^n}{n!}\phi^n(a+\theta h).$$

Therefore by equation (D)

$$\phi(a+h)=\phi(a)+h\phi'(a)+\ldots+\frac{h^{n-1}}{(n-1)!}\phi^{n-1}(a)+\frac{h^n}{n!}\phi^n(a+\theta h),$$

the result of Art. 130.

ROULETTES, ETC.

561. DEF. When a curve rolls upon another which is fixed, as in the case of the description of the Trochoid family, any point P carried by the rolling curve traces out a curve which is called its roulette.

562. Geometrical Construction of Normal.

As in Art. 393 the join of P to the point of contact is the normal at P to the roulette.

563. A Special Case.

If the curve
$$r=f(\theta) \dots\dots\dots\dots\dots\dots\dots\dots\dots(1)$$

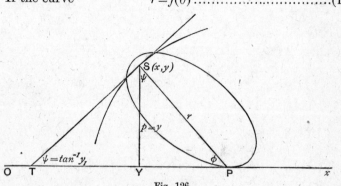

Fig. 126.

be rolling along a straight line, the locus of the pole can be found as follows:—

Taking the given straight line as the x-axis, the radius

vector of the point of contact is the normal of the roulette, and therefore, if x, y be the co-ordinates of the tracing point,

$$r = y\sqrt{1 + y_1^2}. \quad\ldots\ldots\ldots\ldots\ldots\ldots\ldots\ldots(2)$$

Also y is the perpendicular from the pole upon the tangent;

hence

$$\frac{1}{y^2} = \frac{1}{r^2} + \frac{1}{r^4}\left(\frac{dr}{d\theta}\right)^2. \quad\ldots\ldots\ldots\ldots\ldots\ldots(3)$$

If r and θ be eliminated between these three equations, the differential equation of the roulette will result.

Ex. The curve whose polar equation is $r^m \cos m\theta = a^m$ rolls on a fixed straight line. Taking this line as the x-axis show that the roulette of

the pole is $\qquad dx = \left\{\left(\frac{y}{a}\right)^{\frac{2m}{1-m}} - 1\right\}^{-\frac{1}{2}} dy.$

Examine the cases $m = \frac{1}{2}$, $m = 2$. [FRENET.]

564. Curvature of a Roulette.

The radius of curvature of the roulette may be obtained as follows :—

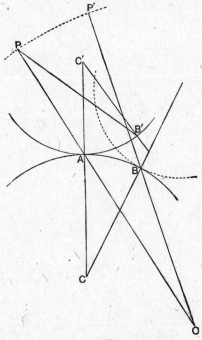

Fig. 127.

Let A be the point of contact, B an adjacent point on the

fixed curve, B' the point of the rolling curve which will come
into contact with B; P and P' the two points on the roulette
corresponding to contact at A and B respectively, so that
$PA, P'B$ are contiguous normals to the roulette; let them meet
in O, say, and let $PO = R$, and $AP = r$, so that $AO = R - r$.
Let C and C' be the centres of curvature of the fixed and
rolling curves respectively at A, and ρ_1 and ρ_2 the radii of
curvature. Then, when $C'B'$ comes into line with CB, PB'
will come into line with BO.

Thus the angle turned through is either of the angles
between $C'B'$ and CB or between PB' and OB. Thus

$$A\hat{C}B + A\hat{C'}B' = A\hat{O}B + APB'.$$

Now, $$ACB = \frac{ds}{\rho_1}, \quad AC'B' = \frac{ds}{\rho_2},$$

and if $PAC' = \phi$, the perpendiculars on BO and PB' from A
are both $ds \cos \phi$ to first order infinitesimals, hence

$$A\hat{O}B = \frac{ds \cos \phi}{R - r}, \text{ and } A\hat{P}B' = \frac{ds \cos \phi}{r}.$$

Hence $$\frac{1}{\rho_1} + \frac{1}{\rho_2} = \frac{\cos \phi}{R - r} + \frac{\cos \phi}{r}.$$

565. Curvature of Envelope of a Carried Curve.

If any curve rolling in one plane upon a second curve carry
a third curve rigidly attached to the first, the radius of
curvature of the envelope of the carried curve may be readily
found in a manner similar to that of the last article.

Let XY, $X'Y'$ be two contiguous positions of the carried
curve, A the point of contact, B an adjacent point on the fixed
curve, B' the point of the rolling curve which will come into
contact with B; AQ, $B'Q''$ the shortest distances from the
points A and B' to the carried curve, meeting in P the centre
of curvature of the carried curve corresponding to the point
Q. Then $Q''B'$ turns into the position $Q'B$ as XY comes into
the position $X'Y'$. Then since the motion of Q is perpendicular to AQ, the locus QQ' is the envelope of the carried
curve. Let $Q'B$ intersect QA in O.

Let $AQ=r$, $QP=\rho$, $QO=R$, the radius of curvature required, the other letters remaining the same as in the last

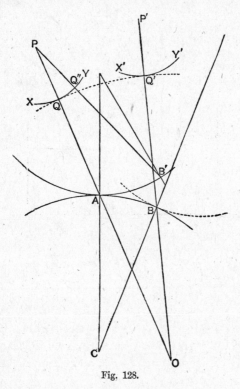

Fig. 128.

article. Then $AP=r+\rho$, $AO=R-r$, and exactly as before we have

$$\frac{1}{\rho_1}+\frac{1}{\rho_2}=\frac{\cos\phi}{r+\rho}+\frac{\cos\phi}{R-r}.$$

If the curve XY be concave to A we must of course change the sign of ρ.

When the curve XY reduces to a point, ρ vanishes and we have the result of the preceding article.

When the curve XY is a straight line we have

$$R=r+\frac{\rho_1\rho_2}{\rho_1+\rho_2}\cos\phi.$$

When the carried curve XY is a straight line, the rolling

curve a circle of radius a, and the fixed curve a straight line, we have

$$\rho_1 = \infty, \quad \rho = \infty, \quad \rho_2 = a,$$

and

$$R = r + a \cos \phi.$$

566. PROP. *A plane lamina has traced upon it two given curves, and moves so that these curves pass each through a fixed point. To find the envelope of a carried straight line.*

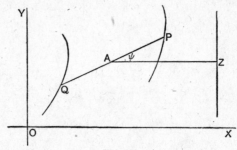

Fig. 129.

Let $y = f_1(x)$, $y = f_2(x)$ be the equations of the curves referred to a pair of axes OX, OY fixed in the lamina; P, Q the fixed points; $PQ = 2a$; (x_1, y_1), (x_2, y_2) the co-ordinates of P, Q; and let the y-axis be supposed to have been chosen parallel to the carried line, whose equation we may therefore take as $x = h$. Let A be the mid-point of PQ, and let PQ make an angle ψ with the x-axis, and let p be the perpendicular from A on the carried line.

Then

$$y_1 - y_2 = 2a \sin \psi,$$

and

$$x_1 = h - p + a \cos \psi,$$

$$x_2 = h - p - a \cos \psi.$$

Hence the tangential polar equation of the envelope is

$$2a \sin \psi = f_1(h - p + a \cos \psi) - f_2(h - p - a \cos \psi).$$

Ex. 1. If the slots be straight, say

$$\left. \begin{array}{l} y = Ax + B \\ y = Cx + D \end{array} \right\},$$

the result is of the form $\qquad p = \lambda + \mu \cos \psi + \nu \sin \psi,$

where λ, μ, ν are constants; so that the locus of the foot of the perpendicular on the carried line is a limaçon, and the envelope being its first negative pedal is therefore a circle. (See Art. 375.)

Ex. 2. Suppose one slot elliptical and the other slot along the major axis, the distance between the pegs being the semi-minor axis. Show that the envelope of any line parallel to the minor axis is one of two circles, and that the minor axis itself passes through one of two fixed points.

567. PROP. *If two curves fixed in a given lamina touch two straight lines fixed in space, it is required to find the envelope of any straight line carried by the lamina.*

We shall consider the case when the fixed straight lines are at right angles. The general case is exactly similar.

Let OX, OY be the fixed straight lines; S an origin fixed in the lamina; FG the carried line; SR the perpendicular upon $FG = h$, a constant. Let OF, the perpendicular upon FG, be p, and let p make an angle α with OX. Let $F\widehat{G}X = \psi$.

The tangential-polar equations of the two curves fixed in the lamina may be written in the forms

$$p_1 = f_1(\alpha), \quad p_2 = f_2(\alpha),$$

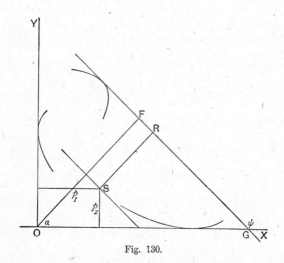

Fig. 130.

where p_1 and p_2 are the co-ordinates of S referred to OX and OY, and

$$p = h + f_1(\alpha)\cos\alpha + f_2(\alpha)\sin\alpha.$$

Also

$$\alpha = \psi - \frac{\pi}{2}.$$

Thus

$$p = h + f_1\left(\psi - \frac{\pi}{2}\right)\cos\left(\psi - \frac{\pi}{2}\right) + f_2\left(\psi - \frac{\pi}{2}\right)\sin\left(\psi - \frac{\pi}{2}\right)$$

or $$p = h + f_1\left(\psi - \frac{\pi}{2}\right)\sin\psi - f_2\left(\psi - \frac{\pi}{2}\right)\cos\psi.$$

This is the tangential polar equation of the envelope of the carried line.

EXAMPLES.

1. A parabola touches two fixed lines at right angles. Apply the above method to show that the envelope of a line perpendicular to the axis is a circle. Also that the envelope of the axis is the first negative pedal of a certain Cotes's spiral.

2. Supposing the guiding curves to be a circle and a parabola whose focus is the centre of the circle, and the two fixed lines at right angles, show that any line at right angles to the axis of the parabola envelopes a parabola.

568. PROP. *Given three straight lines traced upon a lamina, and that two of them are made to touch two given curves. To find the envelope of the third.*

Let the three lines form a triangle ABC whose sides BC, CA, AB make angles ψ_1, ψ_2, ψ respectively with a given straight line. Let $p = f_1(\psi)$, $p = f_2(\psi)$ be the tangential polar equations of the envelopes of BC and CA.

Then $$\left.\begin{array}{l} \psi_1 = \psi + a \\ \psi_2 = \psi + \beta \end{array}\right\},$$

a and β being constants known in terms of the angles of the triangle. Also, if p_1, p_2, p be the perpendiculars from any fixed origin on the three given straight lines

$$a p_1 + b p_2 + c p = 2\Delta,$$

therefore the tangential polar equation of the envelope is

$$c p = 2\Delta - a f_1(\psi + a) - b f_2(\psi + \beta).$$

569. Since $\rho = p + \dfrac{d^2 p}{d\psi^2}$, and $a\dfrac{d^2 p_1}{d\psi_1{}^2} + b\dfrac{d^2 p_2}{d\psi_2{}^2} + c\dfrac{d^2 p}{d\psi^2} = 0$,

we have by addition $a\rho_1 + b\rho_2 + c\rho = 2\Delta.$

Ex. 1. It follows at once that if ρ_1 and ρ_2 are constants ρ is also constant. Hence if two of the sides of the moving triangle envelope circles the third side also envelopes a circle.

Ex. 2. Similarly if two of the sides touch respectively $p = \lambda \psi + \mu$, $p = \lambda' \psi + \mu'$, the third will also touch a curve of the form $p = \lambda'' \psi + \mu''$. These are the involutes of three concentric circles.

Ex. 3. If two sides touch equiangular spirals with a common pole, the third side will touch an equiangular spiral with the same pole.

Ex. 4. If two sides touch concentric epi- or hypo-cycloids, the third side will touch a parallel to an epi- or hypo-cycloid.

570. Many interesting results in this part of the subject will be found in Dr. Besant's "*Notes on Roulettes and Glisettes*," to which the reader is referred for further information.

Note on Bernoulli's and Euler's Numbers.

571. Bernoulli's numbers have been already defined in Art. 148 as the coefficients $B_1, B_3, B_5, B_7, \dots$ occurring in the expansion

$$\frac{x}{2} \frac{e^x + 1}{e^x - 1} = 1 + B_1 \frac{x^2}{2!} - B_3 \frac{x^4}{4!} + B_5 \frac{x^6}{6!} - B_7 \frac{x^8}{8!} + \dots,$$

and the values of several of them were there obtained.

It may save the student some trouble to remark that many writers denote the same coefficients by the notation

$$B_1, \ B_2, \ B_3, \ B_4, \ \dots,$$

with *consecutive* numbers as suffixes, but the present notation with odd numbers for suffixes is for some reasons more convenient.

It was shown in Art. 149 and Examples 26-32, page 109, that many important expansions involve these numbers in the coefficients.

Thus if we write the expansion of $\tan x$ as

$$\tan x = S_1 \frac{x}{1!} + S_3 \frac{x^3}{3!} + S_5 \frac{x^5}{5!} + \dots,$$

then by Art. 149,

$$S_{2n-1} = B_{2n-1} \frac{2^{2n}(2^{2n} - 1)}{2n}.$$

The numbers $S_1, S_3, S_5, \dots$ we shall refer to as "prepared Bernoullians."

572. Euler's Numbers.

The coefficients S_2, S_4, S_6, ... occurring in the expansion

$$\sec x = 1 + S_2 \frac{x^2}{2!} + S_4 \frac{x^4}{4!} + S_6 \frac{x^6}{6!} + \ldots,$$

are called Euler's Numbers.

By division of unity by the expansion of $\cos x$ in powers of x, or otherwise, we may show that

$$S_2 = 1, \quad S_4 = 5, \quad S_6 = 61, \quad S_8 = 1385, \text{ etc.}$$

573. We may therefore write

$$\sec x + \tan x = 1 + S_1 \frac{x}{1!} + S_2 \frac{x^2}{2!} + S_3 \frac{x^3}{3!} + S_4 \frac{x^4}{4!} + \ldots, \ldots \ldots (1)$$

where S_{2n} is the nth Eulerian number (sometimes denoted by E_{2n}) and S_{2n-1} is the nth " prepared Bernoullian " number

$$\frac{2^{2n}(2^{2n}-1)}{2n} B_{2n-1}.$$

Taking logarithms we have

$$\log\left(1 + S_1 \frac{x}{1!} + S_2 \frac{x^2}{2!} + S_3 \frac{x^3}{3!} + \ldots\right) = \log(\sec x + \tan x)$$

$$= \log \tan\left(\frac{\pi}{4} + \frac{x}{2}\right)$$

$$= \text{gd}^{-1} x$$

$$= \int \sec x \, dx$$

$$= x + S_2 \frac{x^3}{3!} + S_4 \frac{x^5}{5!} + \ldots.$$

Differentiating and equating coefficients we obtain (whether p be even or odd)

$$S_{p+1} = S_p + \frac{p(p-1)}{1 \cdot 2} S_{p-2} S_2 + \frac{p(p-1)(p-2)(p-3)}{1 \cdot 2 \cdot 3 \cdot 4} S_{p-4} S_4 + \ldots (2)$$

This series expresses :

(1) Any Bernoullian (prepared) in terms of lower Eulerians (p even).

(2) Any Eulerian in terms of lower Eulerians and prepared Bernoullians (p odd).

It is easy to thus obtain

$$S_1 = 1, \qquad S_6 = 61,$$
$$S_2 = 1, \qquad S_7 = 272,$$
$$S_3 = 2, \qquad S_8 = 1385,$$
$$S_4 = 5, \qquad S_9 = 7936,$$
$$S_5 = 16, \qquad \text{etc.}$$

Giving

$$E_2 = 1, \quad E_4 = 5, \quad E_6 = 61, \quad E_8 = 1385, \quad \text{etc.}$$

and $B_1 = \frac{1}{6}, \quad B_3 = \frac{1}{30}, \quad B_5 = \frac{1}{42}, \quad B_7 = \frac{1}{30}, \qquad B_9 = \frac{5}{66},$ etc.

574. By expressing $1 - \sin x$ in factors, and taking its logarithmic differential coefficient we obtain

$$\sec x + \tan x = \frac{4}{\pi - 2x} - \frac{4}{3\pi + 2x} + \frac{4}{5\pi - 2x} - \frac{4}{7\pi + 2x}$$
$$+ \frac{4}{9\pi - 2x} - \frac{4}{11\pi + 2x} + \dots,$$

so that $\left(x \text{ lying between } \pm \dfrac{\pi}{2} \right)$

$$\sec x + \tan x = \frac{4}{\pi}\left[1 + \frac{2}{\pi}x + \frac{2^2}{\pi^2}x^2 + \dots + \frac{2^n}{\pi^n}x^n + \dots \right]$$
$$- \frac{4}{3\pi}\left[1 - \frac{2}{3\pi}x + \frac{2^2}{3^2\pi^2}x^2 - \dots + \frac{2^n}{3^n\pi^n}(-1)^n x^n + \dots \right]$$
$$+ \text{etc.}$$

which gives by equating coefficients

$$S_n = \frac{2^{n+2} n!}{\pi^{n+1}}\left\{ 1 + \left(-\frac{1}{3}\right)^{n+1} + \left(\frac{1}{5}\right)^{n+1} + \left(-\frac{1}{7}\right)^{n+1} + \left(\frac{1}{9}\right)^{n+1} + \dots \right\} \quad (3)$$

The special cases, $n = 1, 2, 3, 4, 5, \dots$, give the well-known results,

$$1 - \frac{1}{3} + \frac{1}{5} - \frac{1}{7} + \dots = \frac{\pi}{4},$$

$$1 + \frac{1}{3^2} + \frac{1}{5^2} + \frac{1}{7^2} + \dots = \frac{\pi^2}{8},$$

$$1 - \frac{1}{3^3} + \frac{1}{5^3} - \frac{1}{7^3} + \dots = \frac{\pi^3}{32} \quad \text{(Tchebechef)},$$

$$1 + \frac{1}{3^4} + \frac{1}{5^4} + \frac{1}{7^4} + \dots = \frac{\pi^4}{96},$$

$$1 - \frac{1}{3^5} + \frac{1}{5^5} - \frac{1}{7^5} + \dots = \frac{5\pi^5}{1536} \quad \text{(Tchebechef)},$$

and generally when n is even $(=2m)$,

$$E_{2m} = \frac{2(2m)!}{\left(\frac{\pi}{2}\right)^{2m+1}} \left\{ 1 - \frac{1}{3^{2m+1}} + \frac{1}{5^{2m+1}} - \frac{1}{7^{2m+1}} + \dots \right\}, \quad \dots\dots\dots(4)$$

and when n is odd $(=2m-1)$,

$$B_{2m-1} = \frac{2m}{2^{2m}(2^{2m}-1)} \frac{(2m-1)! 2^{2m+1}}{\pi^{2m}} \left\{ 1 + \frac{1}{3^{2m}} + \frac{1}{5^{2m}} + \frac{1}{7^{2m}} + \dots \right\}$$

$$= \frac{2(2m)!}{(2\pi)^{2m}} \left\{ 1 + \frac{1}{2^{2m}} + \frac{1}{3^{2m}} + \frac{1}{4^{2m}} + \dots \right\}, \quad \dots\dots\dots\dots(5)$$

thus establishing *together* these well-known expressions for E_{2m} and B_{2m-1}.

575. Putting $y = \sec x + \tan x = 1 + S_1 \dfrac{x}{1!} + S_2 \dfrac{x^2}{2!} + \dots$

we have $\qquad\qquad\qquad y \cos x = 1 + \sin x.$

Differentiating n times and putting $x = 0$ and $(y_n)_{x=0} = S_n$, we obtain

$$S_n - \frac{n(n-1)}{1.2} S_{n-2} + \frac{n(n-1)(n-2)(n-3)}{1.2.3.4} S_{n-4} - \dots$$

$$+ \cos\frac{n\pi}{2} = \sin\frac{n\pi}{2}, \dots\dots(6)$$

which if n be even gives the Eulerians, and if n be odd gives the prepared Bernoullians. In the latter case putting $n = 2m - 1$, we have

$$S_{2m-1} = \frac{(2m-1)(2m-2)}{1.2} S_{2m-3}$$

$$- \frac{(2m-1)(2m-2)(2m-3)(2m-4)}{1.2.3.4} S_{2m-5} + \dots$$

$$+ \sin(2m-1)\frac{\pi}{2}, \dots\dots\dots\dots\dots(7)$$

an equation which seems much easier to use for calculating purposes than Demoivre's form given in Ex. 25, page 109, since all the coefficients S_1, S_3, etc., are integers.

We thus successively obtain

$S_1 = 1,$

$S_3 = 3S_1 - 1 = 2,$

$S_5 = 10S_3 - 5S_1 + 1 = 16,$

$S_7 = 21S_5 - 35S_3 + 7S_1 - 1 = 272,$

$S_9 = 36S_7 - 126S_5 + 84S_3 - 9S_1 + 1 = 7936,$

$S_{11} = 55S_9 - 330S_7 + 462S_5 - 165S_3 + 11S_1 - 1 = 353792,$

etc.,

whence

$B_1 = \frac{1}{6}, \quad B_3 = \frac{1}{30}, \quad B_5 = \frac{1}{42}, \quad B_7 = \frac{1}{30}, \quad B_9 = \frac{5}{66}, \quad B_{11} = \frac{691}{2730},$ etc.

576. Other formulae may be used for the calculation of Bernoulli's numbers. But it seems unlikely that any more than those calculated by Prof. Adams (Art. 149) will ever be required. The student may refer for further information to Boole, *Finite Differences*, Chapter VI.; Scherk (Crelle, t. IV).

MISCELLANEOUS EXAMPLES.

1. Sum the infinite series

$\quad (a) \quad \dfrac{1}{1^2 + x^2} + \dfrac{1}{2^2 + x^2} + \dfrac{1}{3^2 + x^2} + \dfrac{1}{4^2 + x^2} + \cdots,$

$\quad (b) \quad \dfrac{1}{1^2 + x^2} + \dfrac{1}{3^2 + x^2} + \dfrac{1}{5^2 + x^2} + \cdots,$

and evaluate the results when $x = 0$.

2. Prove that if $J_n(x)$ is the Bessel's function of the nth order,

$$\frac{d^m}{dx^m}\{x^{-\frac{n}{2}}J_n(\sqrt{x})\} = (-\tfrac{1}{2})^m x^{-\frac{m+n}{2}} J_{m+n}(\sqrt{x}).$$

[MATH TRIPOS, 1889.]

3. If $\qquad y = (a^3 + x^3)^{-1},$

prove that

$$3a^2(a\sqrt{3})^{n+1}y_n = (-1)^n n! \sin^{n+1}\theta \left\{ \operatorname{cosec}^{n+1}\left(\theta + \frac{\pi}{6}\right) + 2^{n+2}\sin\left(\overline{n+1}\,\theta - \frac{\pi}{6}\right) \right\},$$

where $\qquad x + a = a\sqrt{3} \sin\left(\theta + \dfrac{\pi}{6}\right) \Big/ \sin\theta.$

[PROF. ANGLIN.]

4. If
$$y = (a^4 + a^2 x^2 + x^4)^{-1},$$

prove that $2a^{n+4}\sin^{n+2}\dfrac{\pi}{3}y_n$

$$= (-1)^n n!\left\{\sin^{n+1}\theta\,\sin\left(\overline{n+1}\,\theta + \frac{\pi}{3}\right) + \sin^{n+1}\phi\,\sin\left(\overline{n+1}\,\phi - \frac{\pi}{3}\right)\right\},$$

where $\qquad x = a\,\cos\left(\theta + \dfrac{\pi}{6}\right)\text{cosec }\theta = a\,\cos\left(\phi - \dfrac{\pi}{6}\right)\text{cosec }\phi.$

[Prof. Anglin.]

5. Prove that

$$\frac{d^n}{dx^n}\left(\frac{\sin x}{x}\right) = \left[P\sin\left(x + \frac{n\pi}{2}\right) + Q\cos\left(x + \frac{n\pi}{2}\right)\right]\Big/ x^{n+1},$$

where $\quad P = x^n - n(n-1)x^{n-2} + n(n-1)(n-2)(n-3)x^{n-4} - \ldots,$

and $\qquad Q = nx^{n-1} - n(n-1)(n-2)x^{n-3} + \ldots.$ [London, 1891.]

Prove also

$$\frac{d^n}{dx^n}\left(\frac{\cos x}{x}\right) = \left[P\cos\left(x + \frac{n\pi}{2}\right) - Q\sin\left(x + \frac{n\pi}{2}\right)\right]\Big/ x^{n+1}.$$

6. Prove that

$$\frac{d^n}{dx^n}\left(\frac{e^{ax}\sin bx}{x}\right) = e^{ax}[P\sin(bx + n\phi) + Q\cos(bx + n\phi)]/x^{n+1},$$

where $\quad P = (rx)^n - n(rx)^{n-1}\cos\phi + n(n-1)(rx)^{n-2}\cos 2\phi - \ldots,$

$\qquad Q = \qquad n(rx)^{n-1}\sin\phi - n(n-1)(rx)^{n-2}\sin 2\phi + \ldots,$

$\qquad r^2 = a^2 + b^2,$ and $\tan\phi = b/a.$ [Prof. Anglin.]

7. Show that if $f(x+h)$ be expanded by Taylor's Theorem and then h be put equal to $-x$, the sum of the first $n+1$ terms may be expressed as

$$(-1)^n\frac{x^{n+1}}{n!}\frac{d^n}{dx^n}\left[\frac{f(x)}{x}\right].$$

8. If
$$y = \frac{\sin x}{x} \text{ and } z = \frac{\cos x}{x},$$

then $\qquad\qquad (-1)^n x^{n+1}(y_n\sin x + z_n\cos x)/n!$

and $\qquad\qquad (-1)^n x^{n+1}(z_n\sin x - y_n\cos x)/n!$

are the sums of $\dfrac{2n+3+(-1)^n}{4}$ and $\dfrac{2n+1-(-1)^n}{4}$ terms respectively

of the series for $\cos x$ and $\sin x$.

Show also that the limiting forms, when $n = \infty$, of $(-1)^n x^{n+1} y_n/n!$ and $(-1)^n x^{n+1}z_n/n!$ are respectively zero and unity.

9. If $\qquad e^x \sin x = \sum\limits_{r=1}^{r=\infty} a_r x^r$ and $e^x \cos x = 1 + \sum\limits_{r=1}^{r=\infty} b_r x^r$,

prove the following results :—

(1) $b_n - \dfrac{b_{n-1}}{1!} + \dfrac{b_{n-2}}{2!} - \ldots + (-1)^{n-1} \dfrac{b_1}{(n-1)!} = 2 \sin \dfrac{n\pi}{4} \sin \dfrac{3n\pi}{4} \Big/ n!$;

(2) $a_n + \dfrac{a_{n-1}}{1!} + \dfrac{a_{n-2}}{2!} + \ldots + \qquad \dfrac{a_1}{(n-1)!} = 5^{\frac{n}{2}} \sin(n \tan^{-1} \tfrac{1}{2}) / n!$;

(3) $a_n + a_{n-1}b_1 + a_{n-2}b_2 + \ldots + b_n \qquad = 2^{\frac{n}{2}} \Big(\cos \dfrac{n\pi}{4} \cdot 2^{n-1} \sin \dfrac{n\pi}{4} \Big) n!$;

(4) $2^{n-1} n_1 a_1 - 2^{n-2} n_2 a_2 + 2^{n-3} n_3 a_3 - \ldots + (-1)^{n-1} n_n a_n$

$$= (-1)^{n-1} 2^{\frac{n}{2}} \sin \dfrac{3n\pi}{4},$$

where $\qquad n_r = n(n-1)\ldots(n-r+1).$ $\qquad$ [PROF. ANGLIN.]

10. Prove that

(i.) $\operatorname{vers}^{-1} x / \sqrt{2x}$

$$= 1 + \dfrac{1}{3 \cdot 4} x + \dfrac{1 \cdot 3}{5 \cdot 4^2} \dfrac{x^2}{2!} + \dfrac{1 \cdot 3 \cdot 5}{7 \cdot 4^3} \dfrac{x^3}{3!} + \ldots + \dfrac{1 \cdot 3 \ldots (2n-1)}{(2n+1)4^n} \dfrac{x^n}{n!} + \ldots ,$$

(ii.) $(\operatorname{vers}^{-1} x)^2 / 2$

$$= x + \dfrac{1}{3} \dfrac{x^2}{2} + \dfrac{1 \cdot 2}{3 \cdot 5} \dfrac{x^3}{3} + \dfrac{1 \cdot 2 \cdot 3}{3 \cdot 5 \cdot 7} \dfrac{x^4}{4} + \ldots + \dfrac{1 \cdot 2 \ldots (n-1)}{3 \cdot 5 \ldots (2n-1)} \dfrac{x^n}{n} + \ldots .$$

$\qquad\qquad$ [PROF. ANGLIN.]

11. Establish the results

(a) $\dfrac{\theta}{\cos \theta} = \sin \theta + \dfrac{2}{3} \sin^3 \theta + \dfrac{2 \cdot 4}{3 \cdot 5} \sin^5 \theta + \dfrac{2 \cdot 4 \cdot 6}{3 \cdot 5 \cdot 7} \sin^7 \theta + \ldots ,$

$\qquad\qquad$ [PFAFF.]

(b) $\dfrac{\operatorname{gd}^{-1}\theta}{\sin \theta} = 1 + \dfrac{\tan^2 \theta}{3} - \dfrac{2}{3} \dfrac{\tan^4 \theta}{5} + \dfrac{2 \cdot 4}{3 \cdot 5} \dfrac{\tan^6 \theta}{7} - \ldots .$

$\qquad\qquad$ [PROF. ANGLIN.]

12. Prove that for all values of x from 0 to π inclusive

$$\dfrac{\pi}{8} x(\pi - x) = \dfrac{\sin x}{1^3} + \dfrac{\sin 3x}{3^3} + \dfrac{\sin 5x}{5^3} + \ldots .$$

What is the sum of the series for values of x between π and 2π?

$\qquad\qquad$ [LONDON, 1891.]

13. Establish the results

(a) $\dfrac{\pi}{2} = 1 + \dfrac{1}{3} + \dfrac{1 \cdot 2}{3 \cdot 5} + \dfrac{1 \cdot 2 \cdot 3}{3 \cdot 5 \cdot 7} + \ldots ,$

(b) $\dfrac{2\pi}{3\sqrt{3}} = 1 + \dfrac{1}{3} \cdot \dfrac{1}{2} + \dfrac{1 \cdot 2}{3 \cdot 5} \cdot \dfrac{1}{2^2} + \dfrac{1 \cdot 2 \cdot 3}{3 \cdot 5 \cdot 7} \cdot \dfrac{1}{2^3} + \ldots ,$

(c) $\quad \dfrac{\pi^2}{9} = 1 + \dfrac{1}{2} \cdot \dfrac{1}{3}\Big(\dfrac{1}{2}\Big) + \dfrac{1}{3} \cdot \dfrac{1 \cdot 2}{3 \cdot 5}\Big(\dfrac{1}{2}\Big)^2 + \dfrac{1}{4} \cdot \dfrac{1 \cdot 2 \cdot 3}{3 \cdot 5 \cdot 7}\Big(\dfrac{1}{2}\Big)^3 + \ldots$

(d) $\quad \dfrac{\pi^3}{32} = \dfrac{1}{1^3} - \dfrac{1}{3^3} + \dfrac{1}{5^3} - \dfrac{1}{7^3} + \ldots$

14. If $\quad x\dfrac{d^2u}{dx^2} + \dfrac{du}{dx} - u = 0, \quad \text{and} \quad x\dfrac{d^2v}{dx^2} + \dfrac{dv}{dx} + v = 0,$

prove that the product uv satisfies the differential equation

$$x^2\dfrac{d^4y}{dx^4} + 5x\dfrac{d^3y}{dx^3} + 4\dfrac{d^2y}{dx^2} + 4y = 0.$$

Hence show that the product of the series

$$1 + \dfrac{x}{1^2} + \dfrac{x^2}{(1 \cdot 2)^2} + \dfrac{x^3}{(1 \cdot 2 \cdot 3)^2} + \ldots,$$

$$1 - \dfrac{x}{1^2} + \dfrac{x^2}{(1 \cdot 2)^2} - \dfrac{x^3}{(1 \cdot 2 \cdot 3)^2} + \ldots$$

is equal to $\quad 1 - \dfrac{x^2}{1^2 \cdot 2!} + \dfrac{x^4}{(1 \cdot 2)^2 \cdot 4!} - \dfrac{x^6}{(1 \cdot 2 \cdot 3)^2 \cdot 6!} + \ldots$

[London, 1891.]

15. Prove that $\quad e^{-ax^2\frac{d}{dx}}f(x) = f\Big(\dfrac{x}{1+ax}\Big).$

[Coll. Exam.]

16. Evaluate the expressions

$$\Big(x \tan\dfrac{1}{x}\Big)^{x^2} \quad \text{and} \quad \dfrac{d}{dx}\Big(\dfrac{ax^2 + bx + c}{ex + f}\Big),$$

when $x = \infty$.

[London.]

17. If $\quad y = \sin(m \cos^{-1}\sqrt{x}),$

prove that $\quad Lt_{x=0}\dfrac{y_{n+1}}{y_n} = \dfrac{4n^2 - m^2}{4n + 2}.$

[Oxford, 1889.]

18. Show that if m, n, p, q be positive integers, the limiting value, when $x = y = z = a$ of the fraction,

$$\dfrac{x^m(y^n - z^n) + y^m(z^n - x^n) + z^m(x^n - y^n)}{x^p(y^q - z^q) + y^p(z^q - x^q) + z^p(x^q - y^q)},$$

is $\quad \dfrac{mn(m-n)}{pq(p-q)}a^{m+n-p-q}.$

[Math. Tripos, 1882.]

19. Find $\quad Lt_{x=0}\Big[\dfrac{1}{x} - \dfrac{1 \cdot 2 \cdot 3 \ldots n}{x(x+1)(x+2)\ldots(x+n)}\Big].$

[London, 1891.]

20. If $u = \phi(H_n)$, where H_n is a homogeneous function of x and y of the nth degree, show that

$$x^2\dfrac{\partial^2 u}{\partial x^2} + 2xy\dfrac{\partial^2 u}{\partial x \partial y} + y^2\dfrac{\partial^2 u}{\partial y^2} = n^2\dfrac{F(F'^2 - FF'')}{F'^3} - n\dfrac{F}{F'},$$

where the function $F \equiv \phi^{-1}(u)$.

21. Prove

$$\begin{vmatrix} \dfrac{\partial}{\partial x_1}, & \dfrac{\partial}{\partial x_2}, & \dfrac{\partial}{\partial x_3}, & \dots, & \dfrac{\partial}{\partial x_n} \\ \dfrac{\partial}{\partial x_n}, & \dfrac{\partial}{\partial x_1}, & \dfrac{\partial}{\partial x_2}, & \dots, & \dfrac{\partial}{\partial x_{n-1}} \\ \dfrac{\partial}{\partial x_{n-1}}, & \dfrac{\partial}{\partial x_n}, & \dfrac{\partial}{\partial x_1}, & \dots, & \dfrac{\partial}{\partial x_{n-2}} \\ \hdotsfor{5} \\ \dfrac{\partial}{\partial x_2}, & \dfrac{\partial}{\partial x_3}, & \dfrac{\partial}{\partial x_4}, & \dots, & \dfrac{\partial}{\partial x_1} \end{vmatrix} \begin{vmatrix} x_1, & x_2, & x_3, & \dots, & x_n \\ x_n, & x_1, & x_2, & \dots, & x_{n-1} \\ x_{n-1}, & x_n, & x_1, & \dots, & x_{n-2} \\ \hdotsfor{5} \\ x_2, & x_3, & x_4, & \dots, & x_1 \end{vmatrix} = n^n.$$

[OXFORD, 1890.]

22. If

$$e^u = \begin{vmatrix} x_1, & x_2, & x_3, & \dots, & x_n \\ x_n, & x_1, & x_2, & \dots, & x_{n-1} \\ x_{n-1}, & x_n, & x_1, & \dots, & x_{n-2} \\ \hdotsfor{5} \\ x_2, & x_3, & x_4, & \dots, & x_1 \end{vmatrix},$$

prove that

$$\frac{\partial^r u}{\partial x_1{}^r} + \frac{\partial^r u}{\partial x_2{}^r} + \frac{\partial^r u}{\partial x_3{}^r} + \dots + \frac{\partial^r u}{\partial x_n{}^r} = (-1)^{r-1} n(r-1)! / (x_1 + x_2 + \dots + x_n)^r,$$

provided that r is not a multiple of n.

23. Prove that the maxima and minima values of the fraction

$$\frac{ax^2 + by^2 + c + 2hxy + 2gx + 2fy}{a'x^2 + b'y^2 + c' + 2h'xy + 2g'x + 2f'y}$$

are given by the roots of the equation

$$\begin{vmatrix} a - a'u, & h - h'u, & g - g'u \\ h - h'u, & b - b'u, & f - f'u \\ g - g'u, & f - f'u, & c - c'u \end{vmatrix} = 0.$$

[LONDON.]

24. Show that if a triangle of minimum area be circumscribed about an ellipse, the normals at the points of contact meet in a point, and find the equation of its locus.   [LONDON, 1891.]

25. If g, γ, c are real quantities, the fraction $\dfrac{x^2 + y^2 + 2gx + c}{x^2 + y^2 + 2\gamma x + c}$ has two critical values or none according as c is positive or negative, and interpret the result geometrically.   [OXFORD, 1890.]

26. Find the maximum area of a triangle which is such that the sum of the squares of the distances of the angular points from the centroid is constant.   [OXFORD, 1890.]

27. From a point P on an ellipse PS, PH are drawn to the foci and produced to meet the ellipse in Q and R; PN is the ordinate of P. Show that when P moves up to one extremity of the major axis, ultimately $QR : PN = 4e : (1 - e^2)$.   [MATH. TRIPOS, 1882.]

28. *A*, *B* are two given points and *KL* a given straight line, find a point *O* such that if *OC* be drawn perpendicular to *KL*, the sum of *OA*, *OB*, *OC* may be the least possible. [COLL. EXAM.]

29. Given the volume of a paraboloid of revolution bounded by a plane perpendicular to the axis, find the maximum sphere that can be inscribed in it. [COLL. EXAM.]

30. *PP′* is a double ordinate of an ellipse, and from *P′* is drawn a perpendicular *P′Q* on the tangent at *P*. Find the positions of *P* for which the square of the area *PQP′* is a maximum, and show that the value is really a maximum. [OXFORD, 1889.]

31. With the foci of an ellipse as centres two fixed circles are described so as not to intersect the ellipse in real points ; show that the point on the perimeter of the latter at which the two circles subtend equal angles is that for which the sum of the four tangents from it to the circles is a maximum. [OXFORD, 1888.]

32. If the equations of two curves are given in rectangular co-ordinates, show how to find the points on the first curve the normals at which will touch the second, and determine how many such points there are. [MATH. TRIPOS, 1885.]

33. Prove that for any constant value of μ the family of curves
$$\cosh x \, \mathrm{cosec} \, y - \mu \cot y = \text{constant}$$
cut the family $\mu \coth x - \mathrm{cosech} \, x \cos y = \text{constant}$
at right angles. [LONDON, 1890.]

34. In the curve whose equation is
$$xy^2 - y = x^3 + 2x^2 + x + b$$
the hyperbolic asymptotes are defined by the equations
$$y = x \quad + 1 + \frac{1}{2x},$$
$$y = -x - 1 - \frac{1}{2x}.$$
[HIND.]

35. The equation of a curve is
$$y^2(x^2 - y^2) - 2ax(x + 2y)(x - y) - a^2(x + y)^2 + 2a^4 = 0 \; ;$$
show that the parabolic asymptote is
$$(y - a)^2 = 2a(x - a),$$
and find on which side of the asymptote $x = y$ the corresponding branch lies. [MATH. TRIPOS, 1882.]

36. If the equation of the curve be
$$x^n \phi\!\left(\frac{y}{x}\right) + x^{n-1} \psi\!\left(\frac{y}{x}\right) + x^{n-2} \chi\!\left(\frac{y}{x}\right) + \ldots = 0$$
where the equation $\phi(z) = 0$ has two roots equal to μ, and μ is not a root of $\psi(z) = 0$, show that there are a doubly infinite number of

parabolas meeting the curve in three points at infinity, and a singly infinite number meeting it in four points at infinity, and satisfying the condition of indefinite approach, and that the general equation of the latter is

$$(y - \mu x)^2 \phi''(\mu) + \tfrac{2}{3}(y - \mu x)\{3\psi'(\mu) - \phi'''(\mu)\psi(\mu)/\phi''(\mu)\} + 2\psi(\mu)x = c,$$

where c is a constant. [MATH. TRIPOS, 1891.]

37. Prove that when a curve is defined as the envelope of a line $lx + my = 1$ moving subject to the condition $\phi(l, m) = 0$ the line is an asymptote approached by the curve at one end, but on both sides when the values of l, m are those given by the equations

$$\left(l\frac{\partial}{\partial l} + m\frac{\partial}{\partial m}\right)\phi = 0,$$

and

$$\left(l\frac{\partial}{\partial l} + m\frac{\partial}{\partial m}\right)^2 \phi = 0,$$ [MATH. TRIPOS, 1888.]

38. For any plane curve prove that

$$\frac{1}{\rho^3} = \frac{d^2x}{ds^2} \cdot \frac{d^3y}{ds^3} - \frac{d^2y}{ds^2} \cdot \frac{d^3x}{ds^3}.$$ [COLL. EXAM. 1876.]

39. If the square of the radius vector be a rational integral function of the curvature of odd degree, then the perpendicular on the tangent is one of even degree. [MATH. TRIPOS, 1882.]

40. Prove that if in the equation of any polar curve we put

$$c^{n-1}r' = r^n \text{ and } \theta' = n\theta,$$

the new curve will cut the radii vectores at the same angle ϕ as the old curve; and that if ρ, ρ' be corresponding radii of curvature

$$\frac{nr'}{\rho'} - \frac{r}{\rho} = (n - 1)\sin \phi.$$ [LONDON, 1887.]

41. Show that the centre of curvature at any point of an ellipse is the pole of the tangent at the point with respect to the confocal hyperbola which passes through that point.

42. From E the centre of curvature at any point P of an ellipse, two other normals, EQ, ER are drawn. Prove that the locus of the point of intersection of QR with the normal at P is an ellipse, and that the line QR always touches the curve $(x/a)^{\frac{2}{3}} + (y/b)^{\frac{2}{3}} = 1$.

[MATH. TRIPOS.]

43. Show that as we pass along a curve the tangent turns round more quickly than the radius vector, when $\log p$ changes its value more rapidly than $\log r$. Prove that in all curves for which these lines turn round with equal speed the radius of curvature is proportional to either r or r^3: and hence show that these curves must be of one of the forms given by $r = ce^{n\theta}$ or $r^2\sin 2\theta = c$.

[MATH. TRIPOS, 1888.]

44. The envelope of a family of equilateral hyperbolas is a lemniscate if a vertex lie on the circle $r = c\cos\theta$ and the pole be the centre.

[COLL. EXAM.]

45. Find the equation to the envelope of a circle which rolls on an ellipse; prove that the area between the two enveloping curves, formed by the circle rolling on the inside and outside of the ellipse respectively is twice the rectangle formed by the perimeter of the ellipse and the diameter of the circle. [COLL. EXAM.]

46. A three-cusped hypocycloid moves without rotation in its own plane and always passes through a fixed point. Show that the tangent to the hypocycloid which is at right angles to the tangent at the fixed point envelopes another three-cusped hypocycloid, and determine its magnitude and position. [MATH. TRIPOS, 1891.]

47. Prove that the envelope of the latera recta of all parabolas inscribed in the same triangle is a three-cusped hypocycloid.

[MATH. TRIPOS, 1887.]

48. Show that the axes of the conic of closest contact at any point of the curve whose intrinsic equation is

$$(s-a)^2\psi = b^2,$$

are equally inclined to the tangent and normal at the point.

[MATH. TRIPOS, 1887.]

49. Show that the equation of the conic of closest contact with the curve $y = f(x)$ at the point whose abscissa is (x, y) is

$$\begin{vmatrix} X^2 - x^2, & 2(XY-xy), & Y^2 - y^2, & 2(X-x), & 2(Y-y) \\ x, & y + xy_1, & yy_1, & 1, & y_1 \\ 1, & 2y_1 + xy_2, & y_1^2 + yy_2, & 0, & y_2 \\ 0, & 3y_2 + xy_3, & 3y_1y_2 + yy_3, & 0, & y_3 \\ 0, & 4y_3 + xy_4, & 4y_1y_3 + 3y_2^2 + yy_4, & 0, & y_4 \end{vmatrix} = 0.$$

50. Show that the locus of the centre of the conic of closest contact to the curve $y^3 = x^2$ is

$$32y^3 = 5x^2,$$

[MATH. TRIPOS, 1891.]

51. Find the equation of the conic of closest contact at the point (x, y) of the curve $y = x^n$.

Show that the centre of aberrancy is at the point

$$\left(2\frac{n+1}{2n-1}x, \ -2\frac{n+1}{n-2}y\right),$$

and show that its locus is similar to the original curve.

52. If p and q be positive integers such that q is not greater than p, and $f(z)$ any function of z which is continuous and finite, as also its differential coefficients up to the nth inclusive, between the values x and $x+h$ of the variable z, show that the remainder after n terms of

the expansion of $f(x+h)$ in powers of h may be written

$$R = \frac{q!\,(p-q)!}{(n-1)!\,(p+1)!}\,\frac{(1-\theta)^{n-q-1}}{\theta^{p-q}}h^n f^n(x+\theta h),$$

θ being a positive proper fraction.

Deduce the forms of Schlömilch and Roche, Lagrange and Cauchy.

[MÉMOIRES DE L'ACADÉMIE ... DE MONTPELLIER.*]

53. Show that $\sin(n+1)\dfrac{\pi}{2}$ is the limiting value of $\dfrac{d^n}{dx^n}\left(\dfrac{x}{\sin^{-1}x}\right)^{n+1}$ when x is zero.

[OXFORD, 1889.]

54. Show that one of the roots of the equation

$$z^3 - 2z^2 + z - 4b^2 = 0$$

may be expanded in the form

$$1 + 2b\left\{1 - b + \frac{5b^2}{2!} - \frac{6\cdot8}{3!}b^3 + \frac{7\cdot9\cdot11}{4!}b^4 - \dots\right\}.$$

[OXFORD, 1888.]

55. Prove that

$$\cos ax = 1 - ax\sin bx - \frac{a(a-2b)}{2!}x^2\cos 2bx + \frac{a(a-3b)^2}{3!}x^3\sin 3bx$$

$$+ \frac{a(a-4b)^3}{4!}x^4\cos 4bx - \dots.$$

[MATH. TRIPOS, 1891.]

56. If

$$\frac{\partial^2 z}{\partial x^2} + 2xy^2\frac{\partial z}{\partial x} + 2(y-y^3)\frac{\partial z}{\partial y} + x^2y^2z = 0,$$

then

$$\frac{\partial^2 z}{\partial u^2} + 2uv^2\frac{\partial z}{\partial u} + 2(v-v^3)\frac{\partial z}{\partial v} + u^2v^2z = 0,$$

where

$$u = xy, \quad v = \frac{1}{y}.$$

[COLL. EXAM.]

57. If the co-ordinates x and y be transformed orthogonally to ξ, η and V be any function of x, y, then will

$$\frac{\partial^2 V}{\partial x^2}\cdot\frac{\partial^2 V}{\partial y^2} - \left(\frac{\partial^2 V}{\partial x\partial y}\right)^2 = \frac{\partial^2 V}{\partial\xi^2}\cdot\frac{\partial^2 V}{\partial\eta^2} - \left(\frac{\partial^2 V}{\partial\xi\partial\eta}\right)^2.$$

58. A curve PQ rolls on a straight line Ox, and P is the point of contact. If C be the centre of curvature corresponding to P, and CT the tangent to the locus of C meet Ox in T, prove

$$\tan CTx = \frac{\rho_1}{\rho},$$

where $\rho = CP$ and ρ_1 is the corresponding radius of curvature of the evolute of the rolling curve.

* See Todhunter, *Diff. Calc.*, p. 404.

Hence show that if for the rolling curve

$$\rho = \phi(s),$$

then the locus of the centre of curvature of the point of contact will be
$$y = \phi(x).$$

59. If an equiangular spiral roll along a straight line, show that the loci of the pole and of the centre of curvature of the point of contact are the same straight line.

60. If a catenary roll along a straight line its directrix always passes through a fixed point.

61. If any of the class of curves

$$r^m = a^m \sin m\theta$$

roll along a straight line, the radius of curvature of the path of the pole
$$= \frac{m+1}{m} r.$$

Examine the special cases
$$m = -2, \ -\tfrac{1}{2}, \ \tfrac{1}{2}, \ 1, \ 2.$$

62. The curve $r^m = a^m \sin m\theta$ rolls along a straight line. Show that the intrinsic equation to the evolute of the locus of the pole is

$$s^m = a^m \left(1 + \frac{1}{m}\right)^m \sin \psi.$$

[COLL. EXAM.]

63. If the curve $r = b \sin \dfrac{b}{a} \theta$ roll upon an ellipse whose axes are $2a$, $2b$, and if the pole coincide originally with the extremity of the major axis, it will always lie on the major axis.

64. The equation of a curve is given in the form $f(r_1, r_2) = 0$, where r_1, r_2 are the lengths of the normals OP, OQ drawn from any point O on the curve to two fixed curves. The perpendiculars drawn from the centres of curvature at the points P and Q of the fixed curves, at right angles to the normals at P and Q respectively, meet the normal at O in N_1 and N_2. Prove that the radius of curvature σ of the locus of O is given by

$$\left(\sin \alpha \frac{\partial}{\partial r_1} - \sin \beta \frac{\partial}{\partial r_2}\right)^2 f = \frac{\partial f}{\partial r_1} \cos \alpha \left(\frac{1}{ON_1} - \frac{1}{\sigma}\right) + \frac{\partial f}{\partial r_2} \cos \beta \left(\frac{1}{ON_2} - \frac{1}{\sigma}\right),$$

where α, β are the angles which the normal at O makes with OP, OQ respectively and the differentiations on the left-hand side only affect f.

[MATH. TRIPOS, 1888.]

ANSWERS TO THE EXAMPLES.

CHAPTER I.
PAGE 7.

1. (i.) ∞ ; (ii.) $\dfrac{1}{a}$; (iii.) ∞. 　　4. $\pm\dfrac{b}{a}$. 　　7. $3a^2$.

2. (i.) $\frac{1}{2}$; (ii.) 2. 　　　　　5. $\frac{1}{2}$. 　　　8. (i.) $\dfrac{b}{a}$; (ii.) $\dfrac{a}{b}$.

3. ∞. 　　　　　　　　　6. a. 　　　9. $\frac{1}{2}$.

PAGE 17.

11. ·0027 of an inch.

CHAPTER II.
PAGE 22.

1. $Xx + Yy = c^2$. 　　3. $Y - y = y(X - x)$. 　　5. $\cos^2 x(Y - y) = X - x$.

2. $\dfrac{Xx}{a^2} + \dfrac{Yy}{b^2} = 1$. 　　4. $x(Y - y) = X - x$. 　　6. $(1 + x^2)(Y - y) = X - x$.

PAGE 24.

1. $\sec^2 x$. 　　2. $\dfrac{1}{1 + x^2}$. 　　3. $-\dfrac{\cos x}{\sin^2 x}$. 　　4. $-\dfrac{1}{x\sqrt{x^2 - 1}}$.

PAGE 27.

1. $3x^2$. 　　　　4. e^x. 　　　　7. $\dfrac{1}{x}a^{\log x}\log_e a$. 　10. $\dfrac{2}{\sin 2x}$.

2. $\sqrt{\dfrac{a}{x}}$. 　　　5. $\dfrac{e^{\sqrt{x}}}{2\sqrt{x}}$. 　　8. $\dfrac{3x^2}{1 + x^6}$. 　　11. $x^x(\log_e x + 1)$.

3. $\dfrac{x}{\sqrt{a^2 + x^2}}$. 　6. $a^{\sin x}\cos x \log_e a$. 　9. $-\tan x$.

12. $x^{\sin x}\left\{\cos x \cdot \log x + \dfrac{\sin x}{x}\right\}$. 　　14. $\dfrac{(\sin x)^{\sqrt{x}}}{\sqrt{x}}(\log\sqrt{\sin x} + x\cot x)$.

13. $(\sin x)^x\{\log\sin x + x\cot x\}$. 　　17. $(0, 0)$ and $\left(2a, -\dfrac{4a^3}{3b^2}\right)$.

18. $\left(\pm\dfrac{a^2}{\sqrt{a^2 + b^2}}, \pm\dfrac{b^2}{\sqrt{a^2 + b^2}}\right)$.

PAGE 37.

1. (i.) $\log \sin x + x \cot x$.

(ii.) $\dfrac{a^2 - 2x^2}{\sqrt{a^2 - x^2}}$.

(iii.) $\dfrac{c}{x} e^{\frac{x}{c}}\left(1 - \dfrac{c}{x}\right)$.

(iv.) $\dfrac{-a^3}{x^2\sqrt{a^2 - x^2}}$.

(v.) $a^{\frac{1 + \sin x}{2}} \cos x \cdot \log_e a$.

(vi.) $e^{\sqrt{u}} \dfrac{x}{\sqrt{u}} \cot v\, (\sin w)^w (\log \sin w + w \cot w)$.

CHAPTER III.

PAGE 51.

1. $\dfrac{1}{2\sqrt{x}}$.

2. $-\frac{1}{2} x^{-\frac{3}{2}}$.

3. $\dfrac{b}{c}$.

4. $1 - \dfrac{1}{x^2}$.

5. $\cosh x$.

6. $\sinh x$.

7. $(bx^{\frac{3}{2}} - 5a)/4c_x^4/x^9$.

8. $b \cos(a + bx)$.

9. $bnx^{n-1}\cos(a + bx^n)$.

10. $\dfrac{\cos\sqrt{x}}{2\sqrt{x}}$.

11. $\dfrac{\cos x}{2\sqrt{\sin x}}$.

12. $\dfrac{\cos\sqrt{x}}{4\sqrt{x \sin\sqrt{x}}}$.

13. $pqx^{q-1}\cos x^q \sin^{p-1}x^q$.

14. $\dfrac{2x}{\sqrt{1 - x^4}}$.

15. $\dfrac{\pi}{\sqrt{1 - x^2}}$.

16. $\dfrac{1}{x[1 + (\log x)^2]}$.

17. $\dfrac{\pi}{180}\cos x°$.

18. $\log x + 1$.

19. $\dfrac{e^x}{x}\log(ex^x)$.

20. $\cos e^x \cdot e^x \cdot \log x + \dfrac{\sin e^x}{x}$.

21. $\dfrac{\log\sqrt{\cot x}}{\cosh x} - \dfrac{2\tan^{-1}e^x}{\sin 2x}$.

22. $(x + a)^{m-1}(x + b)^{n-1}[(m+n)x + mb + na]$.

23. $\dfrac{x^2 + 2x - 2}{(x + 1)^2}$.

24. $\dfrac{1}{n}(a + x)^{\frac{1-n}{n}}$.

25. $\dfrac{2x}{n}(a^2 + x^2)^{\frac{1-n}{n}}$.

26. $\dfrac{\sinh x}{2\sqrt{\cosh x}}$.

27. $\tanh x$.

28. $\operatorname{sech} 2x$.

29. $\dfrac{2}{\sqrt{2 - x^2}}$.

30. $-\dfrac{2\operatorname{cosec} 2x}{\sqrt{2\log \cot x} - (\log \cot x)^2}$.

31. $\dfrac{\cos x}{1 + \sin^2 x}$.

32. $-\dfrac{1}{1 + x^2}$.

33. $-\dfrac{1}{x\sqrt{x^2 - 1}}$.

34. $\dfrac{x^2 - 2x^{\frac{3}{2}} - 2x^{\frac{1}{2}} + 1}{2x^{\frac{1}{2}}(1 + x)(1 + x^2)}$.

35. $\sin^{m-1}x \cos^{n-1}x(m\cos^2 x - n\sin^2 x)$.

36. $\dfrac{(\sin^{-1}x)^{m-1}(\cos^{-1}x)^{n-1}}{\sqrt{1 - x^2}}(m\cos^{-1}x - n\sin^{-1}x)$.

37. $\cos(e^x\log x)e^x\log\left(xe^{\frac{1}{x}}\right)\sqrt{1 - (\log x)^2} - \sin(e^x\log x)\dfrac{\log x^{\frac{1}{x}}}{\sqrt{1 - (\log x)^2}}$.

38. $-\dfrac{1}{(1 - x)^{\frac{1}{2}}(1 + x)^{\frac{3}{2}}}$.

39. $-\dfrac{3x + x^3}{(1 + x^2)^{\frac{3}{2}}}$.

40. $\dfrac{x^4 - 2a^2x^2 + 4a^4}{(x^2 - a^2)^{\frac{3}{2}}(x^2 - 4a^2)^{\frac{1}{2}}}$.

41. $-\dfrac{2 + 2x - x^2}{2(1 - x)^{\frac{1}{2}}(1 + x + x^2)^{\frac{3}{2}}}$.

42. $\dfrac{2(1-x^2)}{1+x^2+x^4}$.

46. $\dfrac{ab}{a^2+x^2\left(\tan^{-1}\dfrac{x}{a}\right)^2}\left\{\tan^{-1}\dfrac{x}{a}+\dfrac{ax}{a^2+x^2}\right\}$.

43. $\log\left(\dfrac{e^{\frac{1}{x}}}{a}\right)$.

47. $\dfrac{\cos^{-1}x-x\sqrt{1-x^2}}{(1-x^2)^{\frac{3}{2}}}$.

44. $\dfrac{2}{\sqrt{1-x^2}}$.

48. $\dfrac{a\sin(a\,\operatorname{cosec}^{-1}x)}{x\sqrt{x^2-1}}$.

45. $\left(\dfrac{x}{n}\right)^{nx}\left\{n\left(\log\dfrac{ex}{n}\right)^2+\dfrac{1}{x}\right\}$.

49. $-\dfrac{\sqrt{b^2-a^2}}{b+a\cos x}$.

50. $2e^{\tan^{-1}x}\left\{\dfrac{\log\sec x^3}{1+x^2}+3x^2\tan x^3\right\}$.

51. $e^{ax}\left\{a\cos(b\tan^{-1}x)-\dfrac{b}{1+x^2}\sin(b\tan^{-1}x)\right\}$.

52. $\dfrac{xa^{cx}(2+cx\log_e a)}{1+a^{2cx}x^4}$.

60. $\dfrac{2}{\sqrt{x}(1+4x)}$

53. $\dfrac{x\log_a e\,\sin(\log_a\sqrt{a^2+x^2})}{(a^2+x^2)\cos^2(\log_a\sqrt{a^2+x^2})}$.

61. $\dfrac{x^2-1}{x^2-4}$.

54. $\dfrac{2}{1-x^4}$.

62. $10^x\cdot 10^{10^x}(\log_e 10)^2$.

55. $\dfrac{6}{1-x^4}$.

63. $e^x\cdot e^{e^x}$

56. $\dfrac{1}{x\log x}$.

64. $e^{x^x}\cdot x^x(\log x+1)$.

57. $\dfrac{1}{x\log x\log^2 x\log^3 x\ldots\log^{n-1}x}$.

65. $x^{e^x}\cdot e^x\left\{\log x+\dfrac{1}{x}\right\}$.

58. $\dfrac{1}{a+b\cos x}$.

66. $x^{x^x}\cdot x^x\left\{(\log x)^2+\log x+\dfrac{1}{x}\right\}$.

59. $\dfrac{1}{\sqrt{1-x^2}}-\dfrac{1}{2\sqrt{x-x^2}}$.

67. $x^x\log ex-x^{\frac{1}{x}-2}\log\dfrac{x}{e}$.

68. $(\sin x)^{\cos x}\left(\dfrac{\cos^2 x}{\sin x}-\sin x\log\sin x\right)-(\cos x)^{\sin x}\left(\dfrac{\sin^2 x}{\cos x}-\cos x\log\cos x\right)$.

69. $-(\cot x)^{\cot x}\operatorname{cosec}^2 x\log e\cot x-(\coth x)^{\coth x}\operatorname{cosech}^2 x\log e\coth x$.

70. $\dfrac{\sqrt{x}}{1+x^{\frac{3}{2}}}\dfrac{a^{cx}x^{\sin x}}{1+a^{2cx}x^2\sin x}\log\left(a^c x^{\cos x}\cdot e^{\frac{\sin x}{x}}\right)+\tan^{-1}(a^{cx}x^{\sin x})\dfrac{1-2x^{\frac{3}{2}}}{2x^{\frac{1}{2}}(1+x^{\frac{3}{2}})^2}$

71. $\dfrac{1}{\sqrt{1-e^{2\tan^{-1}x}}}\cdot\dfrac{e^{\tan^{-1}x}}{1+x^2}$.

72. $\dfrac{\left(\sin\dfrac{m}{x}+\cos\dfrac{m}{x}\right)\left(1-\sin\dfrac{m}{x}+\cos\dfrac{m}{x}\right)\dfrac{m}{x^2}}{2\sqrt{\left(1+\cos\dfrac{m}{x}\right)\left(1-\sin\dfrac{m}{x}\right)}}$.

73. $\dfrac{\sqrt{1-x^2}-2\sqrt{x}}{4\sqrt{x}\sqrt{1-x^2}\sqrt{\sqrt{x}+\cos^{-1}x}(1+\sqrt{x}+\cos^{-1}x)}$.

2 K 2

74. $y\left[2xe^{x^2}\cos e^{x^2}\log\dfrac{1+\sqrt{x}}{1+2\sqrt{x}}-\dfrac{\sin e^{x^2}}{2\sqrt{x}(1+\sqrt{x})(1+2\sqrt{x})}\right].$

75. $-y\cot x(1+2\operatorname{cosec}^2 x\log\cos x).$ 76. $-y\left\{\dfrac{\log\cot^{-1}x}{x^2}+\dfrac{1}{x(1+x^2)\cot^{-1}x}\right\}$

77. $\left(1+\dfrac{1}{x}\right)^x\left\{\log\dfrac{x+1}{x}-\dfrac{1}{x+1}\right\}+x^{\frac{1}{x}-1}\{x+1-\log x\}.$

78. $\dfrac{b}{a}\dfrac{x^2+y^2-ay}{(x^2+y^2)\sec^2\frac{y}{b}-bx}.$ 85. $\dfrac{y^2}{x-xy\log x}.$

79. $\cos x\cos 2x\cos^2 y e^{\cos^2 x}.$ 86. $\dfrac{y\log y}{x\log x}\dfrac{1+x\log x\log y}{1-x\log y}.$

80. $-\dfrac{ax+hy}{hx+by}.$ 87. $\dfrac{y\{(a+bx)y-bx^2\}}{x(y-x)(a+bx)}.$

81. $\dfrac{n}{2x}\left(\dfrac{a}{a+bx^n}\right)^{\frac{1}{2}}.$ 88. $-\dfrac{ax+hy+g}{hx+by+f}.$

82. $\dfrac{y\tan x+\log\sin y}{\log\cos x-x\cot y}.$ 89. $\dfrac{y}{x}.$

83. $x(3+2\tan\log x+\tan^2\log x).$ 90. $\dfrac{6x^2(1+y^2)\tan x^3\cdot e^{\tan^{-1}y}}{1+y^2-\log\sec^2 x^3\cdot e^{\tan^{-1}y}}.$

84. $\dfrac{y(x-y)}{x(x+y)}.$ 91. $\dfrac{\log_{10}e}{2x^2}.$

92. $\dfrac{(1+a^2\cos^2 bx)(x^2+ax+a^2)^{n-1}\left[n(2x+a)\log\cot\dfrac{x}{2}-\operatorname{cosec}x(x^2+ax+a^2)\right]}{-ab\sin bx}.$

93. $\dfrac{ab}{a^2+b^2}\left(a^2\cot\dfrac{x}{2}-b^2\tan\dfrac{x}{2}\right).$ 94. $x^{\sin^{-1}x}\left(\log x+\dfrac{\sqrt{1-x^2}}{x}\sin^{-1}x\right).$

95. $\tfrac{1}{2}.$ 96. $\dfrac{1}{x^4}\dfrac{\sqrt{1+x^2}+\sqrt{1-x^2}}{\sqrt{1+x^2}-\sqrt{1-x^2}}.$ 97. $\dfrac{2}{x}.$ 98. $-\tfrac{1}{2}.$ 99. $1.$

100. $2\dfrac{n(1+x^2)\tan^{-1}x\log\tan^{-1}x+x}{(1+x^2)\tan^{-1}x(\sqrt{x}\cos\sqrt{x}-3\sin\sqrt{x})}x^{\frac{2n+3}{2}}.$

110. $\dfrac{e^{-xz}}{4z^3+x^2}\left[\dfrac{8z^4+5x^5}{2xz\sqrt{x^2z-1}}-(5z^4+4x^5)\sec^{-1}x\sqrt{z}\right].$

121. $A_r=m(m-1)\ldots(m-r+1).$

123. $\dfrac{q+1}{pq-1}x^{\frac{2-q(p-1)}{pq-1}}$ (assuming $pq>1$).

CHAPTER IV.

PAGE 63.

2. $\dfrac{3}{4}\sin\left(x+\dfrac{n\pi}{2}\right)-\dfrac{3^n}{4}\sin\left(3x+\dfrac{n\pi}{2}\right).$

3. $-\dfrac{1}{32}\left\{6^n\cos\left(6x+\dfrac{n\pi}{2}\right)-6\cdot 4^n\cos\left(4x+\dfrac{n\pi}{2}\right)+15\cdot 2^n\cos\left(2x+\dfrac{n\pi}{2}\right)\right\}.$

4. $-\dfrac{1}{16}\left\{5^n\cos\left(5x+\dfrac{n\pi}{2}\right)+3^n\cos\left(3x+\dfrac{n\pi}{2}\right)-2\cos\left(x+\dfrac{n\pi}{2}\right)\right\}.$

5. $\dfrac{1}{128}\left\{8^n\cos\left(8x+\dfrac{n\pi}{2}\right)-4.4^n\cos\left(4x+\dfrac{n\pi}{2}\right)\right\}.$

6. $\dfrac{1}{4}\left\{2^n\sin\left(2x+\dfrac{n\pi}{2}\right)+4^n\sin\left(4x+\dfrac{n\pi}{2}\right)-6^n\sin\left(6x+\dfrac{n\pi}{2}\right)\right\}.$

7. $e^{2x}.2^{n-1}.\left\{1+2^{\frac{n}{2}}\cos\left(2x+\dfrac{n\pi}{4}\right)\right\}.$

8. $\dfrac{e^{ax}}{4}\left[3(a^2+b^2)^{\frac{n}{2}}\sin\left(bx+n\tan^{-1}\dfrac{b}{a}\right)-(a^2+9b^2)^{\frac{n}{2}}\sin\left(3bx+n\tan^{-1}\dfrac{3b}{a}\right)\right].$

9. $-\dfrac{e^{3x}}{16}\left[(34)^{\frac{n}{2}}\cos\left(5x+n\tan^{-1}\dfrac{5}{3}\right)+(18)^{\frac{n}{2}}\cos\left(3x+\dfrac{n\pi}{4}\right)-2(10)^{\frac{n}{2}}\cos\left(x+n\tan^{-1}\dfrac{1}{3}\right)\right].$

PAGE 64.

1. $\dfrac{(-1)^n n!}{a-b}\left\{\dfrac{a}{(x-a)^{n+1}}-\dfrac{b}{(x-b)^{n+1}}\right\}.$

2. $\dfrac{(-1)^n n!}{7}\left\{\dfrac{1}{(x-3)^{n+1}}-\dfrac{3^{n+1}}{(3x-2)^{n+1}}\right\}.$

3. $\dfrac{(-1)^n n!}{2a}\left\{\dfrac{1}{(x-a)^{n+1}}-\dfrac{1}{(x+a)^{n+1}}\right\}.$

4. $(-1)^{n-1}n!\left[\dfrac{(n+2)(n+1)}{2(x-1)^{n+3}}+\dfrac{3(n+1)}{(x-1)^{n+2}}+\dfrac{4}{(x-1)^{n+1}}-\dfrac{4}{(x-2)^{n+1}}\right].$

PAGE 65.

1. $\dfrac{(-1)^n n!}{a^{n+2}}\sin(n+1)\theta\sin^{n+1}\theta$, where $x=a\cot\theta$.

2. $\dfrac{(-1)^{n-1}(n-1)!}{a^n}\sin n\theta\sin^n\theta$, where $x=a\cot\theta$.

3. $(-1)^n n!\cos(n+1)\theta\sin^{n+1}\theta/a^{n+1}$, where $x=a\cot\theta$.

4. $\dfrac{(n-1)!}{2}\left\{\dfrac{(-1)^{n-1}}{(a+x)^n}+\dfrac{1}{(a-x)^n}\right\}.$

5. $\dfrac{(-1)^n n!}{4a^3}\left[\dfrac{1}{(x-a)^{n+1}}-\dfrac{1}{(x+a)^{n+1}}-\dfrac{2}{a^{n+1}}\sin(n+1)\theta\sin^{n+1}\theta\right]$, where $x=a\cot\theta$.

6. $\dfrac{(-1)^n n!}{a^2-b^2}\left[\dfrac{\sin(n+1)\theta\sin^{n+1}\theta}{b^{n+2}}-\dfrac{\sin(n+1)\phi\sin^{n+1}\phi}{a^{n+2}}\right],$

    where $x=b\cot\theta=a\cot\phi.$

7. $2(-1)^{n-1}(n-1)!\sin n\theta\sin^n\theta$, where $x=\cot\theta$.

8. $(-1)^{n-1}(n-2)!\sin^{n-1}\theta\cos\theta\cos n\theta\{n\tan\theta-\tan n\theta\}$, where $x=\cot\theta$.

9. $(-1)^{n-1}(n-1)!\sin n\theta\sin^n\theta\operatorname{cosec}^n a$, where $\cot\theta=x\operatorname{cosec}a-\cot a$.

10. $(-1)^n n!\left\{\dfrac{1}{(x-1)^{n+1}}+\sec^{n+2}\dfrac{2\pi}{6}\sin(n+1)\theta\sin^{n+1}\theta\right\},$

    where $x=\cos\left(\theta+\dfrac{\pi}{6}\right)\operatorname{cosec}\theta.$

11. $\dfrac{(-1)^n}{2a}\left(\dfrac{2}{a\sqrt{3}}\right)^{n+2}n!\{\sin(n+1)\theta\sin^{n+1}\theta-\sin(n+1)\phi\sin^{n+1}\phi\},$

    where $x=\dfrac{a}{\sin\theta}\cos\left(\theta-\dfrac{\pi}{6}\right)=\dfrac{a}{\sin\phi}\cos\left(\phi+\dfrac{\pi}{6}\right).$

12. $(-1)^n n! \left\{ \sin(n+1)\theta \sin^{n+1}\theta + \sec^{n+2}\dfrac{2\pi}{6}\sin(n+1)\phi \sin^{n+1}\phi \right\}$,

where $\qquad x = \cot\theta = \dfrac{1}{\sin\phi}\cos\left(\phi+\dfrac{\pi}{6}\right)$.

PAGE 69.

1. $y_n = a^{n-2}e^{ax}\{a^2x^2 + 2nax + n(n-1)\}$.

2. $y_n = a^{n-2}\left\{ a^2x^2\sin\left(ax+\dfrac{n\pi}{2}\right) + 2nax\sin\left(ax+\dfrac{\overline{n-1}\pi}{2}\right) \right.$

$$\left. + n(n-1)\sin\left(ax+\dfrac{\overline{n-2}\,\pi}{2}\right) \right\}.$$

3. $y_n = e^z\left\{ z^n + \dfrac{n_1^2 z^{n-1}}{1!} + \dfrac{n_2^2 z^{n-2}}{2!} + \dfrac{n_3^2 z^{n-3}}{3!} + \ldots + \dfrac{n_n^2}{n!} \right\}$,

where $\quad z = x\log_e a$ and $n_r = n(n-1)\ldots(n-r+1)$.

4. $y_n = \displaystyle\sum_{r=0}^{r=n} \dfrac{(n!)^2}{(r!)^2(n-r)!}(a^2+b^2)^{\frac{r}{2}}x^r e^{ax}\sin\left(bx+r\tan^{-1}\dfrac{b}{a}\right)$.

PAGE 74.

1. $y_2 = \dfrac{2(1-3x^4)}{(1+x^4)^2}$.   2. $y_3 = \dfrac{2}{x}$.   3. $y_3 = a^2 e^{ax}(ax+3)$.

4. $\begin{cases} \text{If } r < n, \ y_r = n(n-1)\ldots(n-r+1)x^{n-r}. \\ \text{If } r = n, \ y_r = n!. \\ \text{If } r > n, \ y_r = 0. \end{cases}$ 13. $y_n = a^{n+2}x^2 e^{ax}$.

19. $y_n = \dfrac{(-1)^n n!}{(a-b)}\left\{ \dfrac{a^2}{(x-a)^{n+1}} - \dfrac{b^2}{(x-b)^{n+1}} \right\}$.

20. $y_n = (-1)^{n-1}n!\left\{ \dfrac{(n+2)(n+1)}{2(x-1)^{n+3}} + \dfrac{n+1}{(x-1)^{n+2}} + \dfrac{1}{(x-1)^{n+1}} - \dfrac{1}{(x-2)^{n+1}} \right\}$.

21. If m be even

$$y_n = (-1)^n\dfrac{n!}{ma^{m-1}}\left[\{(x-a)^{-n-1} - (x+a)^{-n-1}\} + 2\sum_{r=1}^{r=\frac{m}{2}-1} \dfrac{\cos\left(\dfrac{2r\pi}{m}+\overline{n+1}\phi_r\right)}{\left(x^2-2ax\cos\dfrac{2r\pi}{m}+a^2\right)^{\frac{n+1}{2}}} \right]$$

where $\qquad \cot\phi_r + \cot\dfrac{2r\pi}{m} = \dfrac{x}{a}\operatorname{cosec}\dfrac{2r\pi}{m}$,

and if m be odd

$$y_n = (-1)^n\dfrac{n!}{ma^{m-1}}\left[(x-a)^{-n-1} + 2\sum_{r=1}^{r=\frac{m-1}{2}} \dfrac{\cos\left(\dfrac{2r\pi}{m}+\overline{n+1}\phi_r\right)}{\left(x^2-2ax\cos\dfrac{2r\pi}{m}+a^2\right)^{\frac{n+1}{2}}} \right].$$

22. $y_n = n!\left(\log x + 1 + \dfrac{1}{2} + \dfrac{1}{3} + \ldots + \dfrac{1}{n}\right)$.

37. $(2x)^n\sin\left(x^2+n\dfrac{\pi}{2}\right) + n(n-1)(2x)^{n-2}\sin\left(x^2+\dfrac{n-1}{2}\pi\right)$

$$+ \dfrac{n(n-1)(n-2)(n-3)}{1.2}(2x)^{n-4}\sin\left(x^2+\dfrac{n-2}{2}\pi\right) + \ldots,$$

and the same series with cosines written for sines.

CHAPTER V.

PAGE 80.

7. $\sum \dfrac{(3^n-3)\{1-(-1)^n\}}{8n!}x^n$ and $\sum \dfrac{(3^n+3)\{1+(-1)^n\}}{8n!}x^n$.

9. $x^3+x^4+\dfrac{x^5}{2}\ldots$

10. (a) $\tan^{-1}\dfrac{p-qx}{q+px}=\tan^{-1}\dfrac{p}{q}-\tan^{-1}x=$ etc.

   (b) $\tan^{-1}\dfrac{\sqrt{1+x^2}-1}{x}=\tfrac{1}{2}\tan^{-1}x=$ etc.

   (c) $\sin^{-1}\dfrac{2x}{1+x^2}=2\tan^{-1}x=$ etc.

   (d) $\cos^{-1}\dfrac{x-x^{-1}}{x+x^{-1}}=2\cot^{-1}x=\pi-2\tan^{-1}x=$ etc.

PAGE 85.

3. $2\left(x+\dfrac{x^5}{5}+\dfrac{x^9}{9}+\ldots\right).$

4. Double the series in 3.

5. Treble the series in 3.

6. $\tan^{-1}\dfrac{x}{\sqrt{1-x^2}}=\sin^{-1}x=$ etc.

7. $\sec^{-1}\dfrac{1}{1-2x^2}=2\sin^{-1}x=$ etc.

8. $\sinh^{-1}(3x+4x^3)=3\sinh^{-1}x=$ etc.

9. Expression $=\tfrac{1}{2}\sin^{-1}x^2=$ etc.

PAGE 106.

11. $1+nx+\dfrac{n^2x^2}{2!}+\dfrac{n(n^2-1^2)}{3!}x^3+\dfrac{n^2(n^2-2^2)}{4!}x^4+\dfrac{n(n^2-1^2)(n^2-3^2)}{5!}x^5+\ldots$

12. The relation between three consecutive coefficients is
$$2(n+1)a_{n+1}=3a_n+(2n-1)a_{n-1}.$$

13. $y=\dfrac{\pi}{4}+\dfrac{a}{2}x+\dfrac{2b-a^2}{4}x^2+\dfrac{a^3-6ab}{12}x^3\ldots$

33. $mx-\dfrac{m(m-1)(m-2)}{3!}x^3+\dfrac{m(m-1)(m-2)(m-3)(m-4)}{5!}x^5-\ldots$

CHAPTER VI.

PAGE 133.

6. (1) $\dfrac{dy}{dx}=\dfrac{1+4xz}{1-2z},\ \dfrac{dz}{dx}=\dfrac{1+2x}{1-2z}.$ (2) $\dfrac{dx}{dy}=\dfrac{1-2z}{1+4xz},\ \dfrac{dz}{dy}=\dfrac{1+2x}{1+4xz}.$

   (3) $\dfrac{dx}{dz}=\dfrac{1-2z}{1+2x},\ \dfrac{dy}{dz}=\dfrac{1+4xz}{1+2x}.$

7. $p=-\dfrac{a^3}{x^2y},\quad q=-\dfrac{a^3}{xy^2},\quad r=\dfrac{2a^3}{x^3y},\quad s=\dfrac{a^3}{x^2y^2},\quad t=\dfrac{2a^3}{xy^3}.$

PAGE 137.

2. (a) $-\dfrac{ax+hy}{hx+by}$.   (β) $-\dfrac{4x^3-5a^2y}{4y^3-5a^2x}$.   ($\gamma$) $\dfrac{y\tan x+\log\sin y}{\log\cos x-x\cot y}$.

(δ) $-\dfrac{y^x\log y+yx^{y-1}-(x+y)^{x+y}\log e(x+y)}{x^y\log x+xy^{x-1}-(x+y)^{x+y}\log e(x+y)}$.

(ϵ) $-\dfrac{x^{y-1}y^{x+1}+x^y\cdot y^x\log y-\dfrac{\cos y}{x}x^{\cos y}-y^{\log x}\cdot\dfrac{\log y}{x}}{x^{y+1}y^{x-1}+x^y\cdot y^x\log x+x^{\cos y}\log x\cdot\sin y-\dfrac{\log x}{y}y^{\log x}}$.

6. $\dfrac{\partial V}{\partial u}=\dfrac{\dfrac{\partial V}{\partial x}\cdot\dfrac{\partial v}{\partial y}-\dfrac{\partial V}{\partial y}\cdot\dfrac{\partial v}{\partial x}}{\dfrac{\partial u}{\partial x}\cdot\dfrac{\partial v}{\partial y}-\dfrac{\partial u}{\partial y}\cdot\dfrac{\partial v}{\partial x}}$.

14. $\begin{cases}\dfrac{\partial z}{\partial x}=-\dfrac{c^n x^{n-1}}{a^n z^{n-1}}.\\[2mm]\dfrac{\partial^2 x}{\partial y\partial z}=-(n-1)\dfrac{a^{2n}}{b^n c^n}\dfrac{(yz)^{n-1}}{x^{2n-1}}.\\[2mm]\dfrac{dy}{dx}=\dfrac{b}{a}\dfrac{\left(\dfrac{x}{a}\right)^{n-1}+\left(\dfrac{z}{c}\right)^{n-1}}{\left(\dfrac{y}{b}\right)^{n-1}-\left(\dfrac{z}{c}\right)^{n-1}}.\end{cases}$

12. $\dfrac{dy}{dz}=\dfrac{\sin z}{\cos y}\cdot\dfrac{c-b\cos z}{c-b\sin y}$.

18. $\dfrac{a^2 b^2}{c}\dfrac{x^2+y^2}{(a^2x^2+b^2y^2)^{\frac{3}{2}}}$.

CHAPTER VII.

PAGE 147.

Ex. 1.   *Tangents.*

(1) $Xx+Yy=c^2$.   (4) $Y-y=\sinh\dfrac{x}{c}(X-x)$.

(2) $Yy=2a(X+x)$.   (5) $X(2xy+y^2)+Y(x^2+2xy)=3a^3$.

(3) $\dfrac{X}{x}+\dfrac{Y}{y}=2$.   (6) $Y-y=\cot x(X-x)$.

(7.) $X(x^2-ay)+Y(y^2-ax)=axy$.

(8.) $X\{2x(x^2+y^2)-a^2x\}+Y\{2y(x^2+y^2)+a^2y\}=a^2(x^2-y^2)$.

Normals.

(1) $\dfrac{X}{x}=\dfrac{Y}{y}$.   (2) $\dfrac{X-x}{2a}+\dfrac{Y-y}{y}=0$, etc.

2. $\begin{cases}\text{Tangents are }\ Y=\pm\dfrac{3\sqrt{3}}{8}X-\dfrac{a}{8}.\\[2mm]\text{Normals are }\ Y=\mp\dfrac{8\sqrt{3}}{9}X+\dfrac{41}{36}a.\end{cases}$

4. (a) $\begin{cases}\text{Parallel at points of intersection with}\ \ \ \ \ \ ax+hy=0.\\ \text{Perpendicular at points of intersection with}\ \ hx+by=0.\end{cases}$

(β) Parallel at $\left(-\dfrac{a}{\sqrt[3]{2}},\ \dfrac{3a\sqrt[3]{2}}{2}\right)$; perpendicular where $x=0$.

(γ) $\begin{cases} \text{Parallel at} \quad \left(\dfrac{4a}{3}, \ \dfrac{2\sqrt[3]{4}}{3}a \right). \\ \text{Perpendicular at } (0, 0), \ (2a, 0). \end{cases}$

5. (a) $\begin{cases} \text{Tangent, } \dfrac{x \cos \theta}{a} + \dfrac{y \sin \theta}{b} = 1. \\ \text{Normal, } ax \sec \theta - by \ \mathrm{cosec} \ \theta = a^2 - b^2. \end{cases}$

(β) $\begin{cases} \text{Tangent, } x \sin \dfrac{\theta}{2} - y \cos \dfrac{\theta}{2} = a\theta \sin \dfrac{\theta}{2}. \\ \text{Normal, } x \cos \dfrac{\theta}{2} + y \sin \dfrac{\theta}{2} = a\theta \cos \dfrac{\theta}{2} + 2a \sin \dfrac{\theta}{2}. \end{cases}$

(γ) $\begin{cases} \text{Tangent, } x \sin \dfrac{A+B}{2B}\theta - y \cos \dfrac{A+B}{2B}\theta = (A+B)\sin \dfrac{A-B}{2B}\theta. \\ \text{Normal, } x \cos \dfrac{A+B}{2B}\theta + y \sin \dfrac{A+B}{2B}\theta = (A-B)\cos \dfrac{A-B}{2B}\theta. \end{cases}$

6. $\begin{cases} \text{For an ellipse,} \qquad\qquad r^2 = a^2\cos^2\theta + b^2\sin^2\theta. \\ \text{For a rectangular hyperbola, } r^2 = a^2\cos 2\theta. \end{cases}$

7. $\dfrac{1}{a} - \dfrac{1}{b} = \dfrac{1}{a'} - \dfrac{1}{b'}$, *i.e.*, they must be confocal.

9. The axes are tangents at the origin. Also at the point $(2^{\frac{1}{3}}a, \ 2^{\frac{2}{3}}a)$ the tangents to the parabolas make angles $\tan^{-1}2^{\frac{4}{3}}, \ \tan^{-1}2^{-\frac{2}{3}}$ respectively with the tangent to the Folium.

PAGE 149.

(a) $ax = \pm by.$ (β) $x = 0$ and $y = 0.$ (γ) $ax = \pm y\sqrt{b^2 - a^2}.$

PAGE 152.

1. $\dfrac{c^4}{\sqrt{x^6 + y^6}}.$ 8. Area $= \frac{1}{2}\sqrt[3]{a^4xy}.$ 9. $n = -2; \ n = 1.$

PAGE 177.

Ex. 18. $p^2 = 9a^2(r^2 - a^2)/(r^2 + 15a^2).$

CHAPTER VIII.

PAGE 191.

1. $x + y = \dfrac{2a}{3}.$ 6. $x = 2a.$ 11. $x = a, \ y = a, \ x = y.$

2. $x + y = 0.$ 7. $x + y + a = 0.$ 12. $x = \pm a.$

3. $x + y = 0.$ 8. $x = 0, \ y = 0, \ x + y = 0.$ 13. $x = 0.$

4. $y = 0.$ 9. $y = 0.$ 14. $x = a.$

5. $x = 0.$ 10. $x = \pm a.$ 15. $x = \pm 1, \ y = x.$

16. $x = 0, \ y = \pm\left(x + \dfrac{m}{2}\right).$ 20. $x - 2y = 0, \ x + 2y = \pm 2.$

17. $x + 2y = 0, \ x + y = 1, \ x - y = -1.$ 21. $x + y = \pm 2\sqrt{2}, \ x + 2y + 2 = 0.$

18. $x = 0, \ x - y = 0, \ x - y + 1 = 0.$ 22. $y = 3x - 2a, \ x + 3y = \pm a.$

19. $y = 0, \ x = y, \ x = y \pm 1.$

PAGE 192.

1. $x^3 - 6x^2y + 11xy^2 - 6y^3 = x.$ 3. $\dfrac{x^2}{a^2} + \dfrac{y^2}{b^2} = 1.$

5. $\left(\dfrac{a}{a'} + \dfrac{b}{b'} - 1\right)\left(\dfrac{x}{a} + \dfrac{y}{b} - 1\right)\dfrac{xy}{ab} = \dfrac{x}{a'} + \dfrac{y}{b'} - 1.$

6. $bxy(x^2 - y^2) = a(a^2 - b^2)(x^2 + y^2 - a^2).$

PAGE 198.

1. $x = \pm a,\ y = x.$ Above.

2. $\begin{cases} y = x + a,\ y = -x - a,\ x = a. \\ \text{In the first quadrant above the first.} \quad \text{In the fourth quadrant below} \\ \quad\quad \text{the second.} \end{cases}$

PAGE 205.

1. $\theta = 0.$ 2. $r \sin\theta = a.$

3. $nr \sin\left(\theta - \dfrac{k\pi}{n}\right) = a \sec k\pi,$ where k is any integer.

4. $r \sin\theta = a.$ 5. $r \cos\theta = 2a.$ 6. $\theta = \dfrac{\pi}{2},\ r \sin\theta = \dfrac{a}{2}.$

7. $r \sin\left(\theta - \dfrac{k\pi}{n}\right) = \dfrac{b}{n},$ where k is any integer.

8. $n\theta = k\pi,$ where k is any integer.

PAGE 206.

1. (i.) $x = y.$ (ii.) $x = y,\ x + y = 0.$

4. $x = \pm a,\ x - y + a = 0,\ x - y = \dfrac{a}{2},\ x + y + \dfrac{a}{2} = 0.$

5. $x = 2y - 14a,\ x = 3y + 13a,\ x - y = a,\ x - y = 2a.$ 6. $x \pm y\sqrt{2} = \pm\frac{3}{2}.$

8. $r \sin\theta = a,\ r \cos\theta = -2a/(2n+1)\pi.$

9. $r \sin\theta = a,\ r \cos\theta = 2ae^{\frac{2n+1}{2}\pi}/(2n+1)\pi.$ 13. $x + y + a = 0.$

18. (i.) $y = 0,\ x - y - a = 0,\ x + y + a = 0.$

     (ii.) $\left(x \pm y + \dfrac{3a}{8}\right)^2 = \dfrac{ax}{4} + \dfrac{a^2}{16}.$

19. $(x^2 - y^2)^2 = Ax$ or $r^3 = a^3\dfrac{\cos\theta}{\cos^2 2\theta}.$ 22. $(x^2 - y^2)^2 - 4y^2 + y = 0.$

20. $2y^2(x^2 - y^2) = 3a^3x.$ 23. $x = \pm a,\ y = b,\ y = c.$

21. $(x - y)^2(x + y - 1)^2 - (x + y)^2 = 0.$ 28. $2y - 9c = 0,\ y + 2x + \dfrac{c}{2} = 0.$

30. Linear asymptotes $y = x + 1,\ y = x - 2.$

     Parabolic asymptotes $(y - x + \frac{1}{2})^2 + 2x + \frac{1}{4} = 0.$

CHAPTER IX.

PAGE 219.

8. Concave.   12. $x = 7$ and $x = 1.$

6. A single ramphoid cusp.

8. A node at $(1, 2)$. Directions of tangents $y = \pm x$.

9. (a) Single keratoid cusp at $(1, -1)$.

    (b) Two single keratoid cusps at $(\frac{1}{2}, \frac{1}{2})$, $(-\frac{1}{2}, -\frac{1}{2})$.

    (c) A single keratoid cusp at $(-a, a)$.

10. There is a triple point at which the tangents are parallel to the lines
$$y = 0, \quad y = \pm x\sqrt{2}.$$

1. (a) $y = 0$. (β) $ax = by$. (γ) $y = \pm x$. (δ) $x = 0$, $y = 0$.

6. $x = a$ and $x = 2a$.   9. $\theta = \pm \sin^{-1}\sqrt{\frac{2}{5}}$.

30. There is a single keratoid cusp and also a third branch having an inflexion at the origin, the latter touching the y-axis. The shape of the curve resembles the letter R.

31. The origin is a triple point, one branch touching the x-axis and the others inclined to it at angles whose tangents are $\pm\sqrt{\dfrac{a}{b}}$.

32. The form of the curve is that of the "Staffordshire Knot."
The nodes are situated at $(a, 0)$, $(-a, 0)$, $(0, -a)$ and the values of $\dfrac{dy}{dx}$ are respectively $\pm\sqrt{\frac{4}{3}}$, $\pm\sqrt{\frac{4}{3}}$, $\pm\sqrt{\frac{2}{3}}$.

33. $\begin{cases} \text{At } (0, a), \ \tan\psi = \pm\dfrac{2}{\sqrt{3}}. \\ \text{At } (a, 0), \ \tan\psi = \pm\sqrt{\frac{2}{3}}. \\ \text{At } (2a, a), \ \tan\psi = \pm\dfrac{2}{\sqrt{3}}. \end{cases}$ 35. At $x = 2$, $y = 2$ we have $\dfrac{dy}{dx} = \pm 1/2\sqrt{2}$.

36. At the origin and at $(a\sqrt{2}, 0)$.

37. Two keratoid cusps at $(0, \pm 1)$; two nodes at $(\pm\sqrt{2}, 0)$.
Four conjugate points at $(\pm\sqrt{\frac{2}{3}}, \pm\sqrt{\frac{1}{3}})$.

38. Three nodes at $(0, 0)$ and $(1, \pm 1)$.

CHAPTER X.

1. $\rho = a$; $\rho = a\cos\psi$; $\rho = 3a\sec^4\psi\sin\psi$; $\rho = a\sec\psi$.

2. $\rho = 2(a+x)^{\frac{3}{2}}/a^{\frac{1}{2}}$; $\rho = y^2/c$.   4. $\rho = (a^2\sin^2\theta + b^2\cos^2\theta)^{\frac{3}{2}}/ab$.

1. $\rho = 2r^{\frac{3}{2}}/a^{\frac{1}{2}}$; $\rho = a/2$; $\rho = a^m/(m+1)r^{m-1}$.

2. $\rho = a(\theta^2 + 1)^{\frac{3}{2}}/\theta^4$.

1. Infinite.   2. $\rho = -3a\sqrt{2}/2$ or $15a\sqrt{5}/14$.

5. If $y = a\theta$, $\rho = -a(1 + \sin^2\theta)^{\frac{3}{2}}/\cos\theta$; $\bar{x}/a = 1 - 2\cos\theta + 2\sec\theta$
$$\bar{y}/a = \theta - \tan\theta - \tan\theta\sin^2\theta.$$

22. The radii of curvature are respectively

$$a(\cosh \beta - \cos a)^{\frac{3}{2}}/\sin\ a\ (2\cosh \beta - \cos a)(\cosh \beta + \cos a)^{\frac{1}{2}}.$$

and $a(\cosh \beta - \cos a)^{\frac{3}{2}}/\sinh \beta(\cosh \beta - 2\cos a)(\cosh \beta + \cos a)^{\frac{1}{2}}.$

24. $e^{2\mu\lambda} = 1 + \lambda^2.$

CHAPTER XI.

PAGE 296.

2. $256y^3 + 27x^4 = 0.$

3. $\dfrac{a^4}{x^2} + \dfrac{b^4}{y^2} = \dfrac{c^4}{a^2}.$

4. $y + \frac{1}{2}g\dfrac{x^2}{u^2} = \dfrac{u^2}{2g}.$

5. $\begin{cases}(1)\ 4x^3 + 27ay^2 = 0. \\ (2)\ y^2 = 4h(a + h - x).\end{cases}$

6. $y^2 + 4a(x - 2a) = 0.$

7. Two straight lines.

8. A parabola touching the axes

9. A hyperbola.

PAGE 302.

1. $\begin{cases}(1)\ \sqrt{x} + \sqrt{y} = \sqrt{k}. \\ (2)\ x^{\frac{n}{n+1}} + y^{\frac{n}{n+1}} = k^{\frac{n}{n+1}}. \\ (3)\ x^m y^n = \dfrac{m^m n^n}{(m+n)^{m+n}} k^{m+n}.\end{cases}$

2. $\begin{cases}(1)\ x^{\frac{2}{3}} + y^{\frac{2}{3}} = k^{\frac{2}{3}}. \\ (2)\ x^{\frac{2}{5}} + y^{\frac{2}{5}} = k^{\frac{2}{5}}. \\ (3)\ x^{\frac{2m}{m+2}} + y^{\frac{2m}{m+2}} = k^{\frac{2m}{m+2}}. \\ (4)\ 2xy = k^2.\end{cases}$

3. $\begin{cases}(1)\ x^{\frac{1}{3}} + y^{\frac{1}{3}} = k^{\frac{1}{3}}. \\ (2)\ x^{\frac{m}{2m+1}} + y^{\frac{m}{2m+1}} = k^{\frac{m}{2m+1}}. \\ (3)\ 16xy = k^2.\end{cases}$

PAGE 308.

1. $27ay^2 = 4(x - 2a)^3.$

3. $x^{\frac{2}{3}} + y^{\frac{2}{3}} = a^{\frac{2}{3}}.$

6. $r^2 = a^2\cos^2\theta + 6^2\sin^2\theta.$

12. $x^{\frac{4}{5}} + y^{\frac{4}{5}} = a^{\frac{4}{5}}.$

16. $y^2(x + 16a)^2 + 4\{6y^2 - (2a - x)^2\}\{y^2 - 3a(2a - x)\} = 0.$

37. A parabola with the given point for focus.

39. $a^p b^q p^p q^q = (p + q)^{p+q} k^{p+q}.$ 40. A conic.

CHAPTER XIV.

PAGE 376.

1. $\log_b a.$	5. 4.	9. $\frac{1}{2}.$	13. 1.	17. $\frac{13}{60}.$	21. $\infty.$
2. $\frac{3}{5}.$	6. 4.	10. $\frac{3}{2}.$	14. 1.	18. $-\frac{2}{3}.$	22. 1.
3. $\frac{m}{n}.$	7. 2.	11. $\frac{2}{3}.$	15. $\frac{1}{15}.$	19. $\frac{1}{2}.$	23. $e^{-\frac{1}{6}}.$
4. $\frac{1}{n}.$	8. 1.	12. $\frac{1}{6}.$	16. $-\frac{11}{6}.$	20. 1.	24. 0.

25. $e^{-1}.$ 26. $e^{\frac{1}{2}}.$

PAGE 384.

1. 2.

2. $\frac{1}{5}$.

3. 2.

4. $\frac{1}{2}$.

5. $-\dfrac{1}{a}$.

6. 4.

7. $m - \dfrac{4m^3}{3}$.

8. $\dfrac{1}{\sqrt{e}}$.

9. e.

10. 1.

11. $\begin{cases} \text{If } n > m, \ \infty. \\ \quad n = m, \ \dfrac{A}{a}. \\ \quad n < m, \ 0. \end{cases}$

12. 1.

13. e^a.

14. e^2.

15. e^2.

16. $a_1 a_2 a_3 \dots a_n$.

17. -1.

18. 0.

19. b, 0.

20. $\frac{1}{2}$.

21. $-a$.

22. $\frac{1}{3}$.

23. 0.

24. $\sqrt{a}$.

25. 1.

26. $\frac{1}{18}$.

27. $-\dfrac{e}{2}$.

28. $-\frac{7}{16}e$.

29. 0.

30. $-\dfrac{n(n-1)}{2!}a^{n-2}$.

31. 1.

33. $\frac{1}{2}(1 \pm \sqrt{-3})$.

34. 0 or ∞.

35. $\pm \dfrac{b}{\sqrt{a^2 - b^2}}$.

36. 0 or ± 1.

39. $\frac{4}{15}$.

44. $e^{-\frac{a^2}{2b^2}}$.

45. 1, $b^{x-1}(b \cos bx - \sin bx)\cos^2 bx$.

46. $-\frac{3}{2}$.

47. $\dfrac{1}{\sqrt{2a}}$.

48. 1.

CHAPTER XV.

PAGE 390.

9. The height is three times the semi-axis to which the base is perpendicular.

12. $\dfrac{c^2}{\sqrt{2ab}}$.

14. The centroid of the triangle.

20. If a and b are the sides the maximum area $= \frac{1}{2}(a+b)^2$.

21. $\begin{cases} \text{A maximum when the chords coincide with the transverse axis and latus rectum.} \\ \text{A minimum when the chords are equally inclined to the transverse axis.} \end{cases}$

PAGE 396.

5. Maximum value $= 34$, minimum $= 33$.

8. $x = -2, -1, 1, 2$ give maxima and minima alternately.

9. At $x = 1$ $y =$ maximum,
   $x = 3$ $y =$ minimum.
   At $x = 2$ and $x = 4$ there are points of contrary flexure.

10. At $x = 2$ $y =$ minimum.
    At $x = \frac{4}{3}$ $y =$ maximum.

19. Half the triangle formed by the chord and the tangents at its extremities, or three-fourths of the area of the segment.

PAGE 405.

13. Its height $= \frac{4}{3}$ of the radius.

PAGE 413.

2. It cannot lie between $\pm 2\sqrt{ab}$.

4. $x = -\frac{7}{9}$ gives a maximum, $x = 1$ gives a minimum.

5. $x = 2$ gives a maximum, $x = 5$ a minimum.

6. Minimum ordinate at $x = \dfrac{b}{\sqrt[3]{2}}$. A point of inflexion at $(-b, 0)$.

7. $\begin{cases} \text{At } x = a,\ y = c. \\ \text{At } x = \dfrac{a+6b}{7},\ y = c \pm 6^3\left(\dfrac{a-b}{7}\right)^{\frac{7}{2}},\ a \text{ being supposed greater than } b. \end{cases}$

11. $(a+b)^2$.

20. $\dfrac{ap}{p+q},\ \dfrac{aq}{p+q}$.

22. n parts. Continued product $= e^n$.

23. $\dfrac{1}{\sqrt[p-1]{p}}$.

24. $\begin{cases} \text{A maximum when the segment is a semicircle.} \\ \text{A minimum when the radius is infinite.} \end{cases}$

25. The distances of the point from the extremities of the line are

$$\frac{2ar_1}{\sqrt{r_1{}^2 + r_2{}^2}}, \qquad \frac{2ar_2}{\sqrt{r_1{}^2 + r_2{}^2}}.$$

26. The point divides the line of centres in the ratio $r_1{}^{\frac{2}{3}} : r_2{}^{\frac{2}{3}}$, r_1 and r_2 being the radii.

27. $AO : AD = 1 : \sqrt{2}$.

28. If A be the smallest angle and b, c the adjacent sides, the distance of each end of the fence from $A = \sqrt{\dfrac{bc}{2}}$, and the length of the fence $= \sqrt{2bc}\, \sin\dfrac{A}{2}$.

32. $\dfrac{n+1}{n} a$ knots an hour.

40. $\begin{cases} a > b,\ \text{maximum if } x = \dfrac{a+2b}{3}. \\ a < b,\ \text{maximum if } x = a. \\ a = b,\ \text{gives a point of inflexion.} \end{cases}$

43. $\begin{cases} \text{If } \cos a \text{ be } > e,\ \text{Greatest} = \dfrac{l^2 \sin a \cos a}{(1 - e\cos a)^2}.\ \text{Least} = \dfrac{l^2 \sin a \cos a}{(1 + e\cos a)^2}. \\ \text{If } \cos a \text{ be } < e,\ \text{the above values are both minima, and there are two} \\ \qquad \text{maxima each equal to } \dfrac{l^2 \cot a}{1 - e^2}. \end{cases}$

44. The tangent at P must be parallel to SQ.

45. $\begin{cases} \text{If } h < 2a,\ P \text{ is at the vertex.} \\ \text{If } h > 2a,\ \text{the abscissa of } P \text{ is } h - 2a,\ \text{and the perpendicular is there-} \\ \qquad \text{fore the normal at } P. \end{cases}$

46. Maximum area $= 4r^2 \sin a \cos^3 a$, where r is the radius of the circle and $2a$ the given angle.

49. $\sin AOQ = \dfrac{CA}{CO\sqrt{2}}$, C being the centre.

CHAPTER XVI.

PAGE 429.

1. (a) Maximum when $x=\frac{1}{2}$, $y=\frac{1}{3}$.

   (β) Minima when $x=\pm\sqrt{2}$, $y=\mp\sqrt{2}$.

   (γ) Maxima when $x=\left.\dfrac{a}{2}\right\}$, and when $x=\left.\dfrac{3a}{2}\right\}$ and

    $y=\dfrac{a}{2}\Big\}$ $\qquad\qquad y=-\dfrac{a}{2}\Big\}$

    minima when $x=\left.\dfrac{a}{2}\right\}$, and when $x=\left.\dfrac{3a}{2}\right\}$.

    $y=-\dfrac{a}{2}\Big\}$ $\qquad\qquad y=\dfrac{a}{2}\Big\}$

   (δ) Maximum value $=108a^7/7^7$.

   (ϵ) A maximum when $x=y=\dfrac{\pi}{3}$.

   (ζ) $x=y=0$ gives a maximum.

   (η) $x=y=a$ gives a maximum or minimum according as a is negative or positive.

2. Minimum value $=p^2/(a^2+b^2+c^2)$.

3. Maximum value $=m^m n^n p^p a^{m+n+p}/(m+n+p)^{m+n+p}$.

4. Maximum value $=\frac{1}{8}$.

5. A maximum when $\tan A/m=\tan B/n=\tan C/p$.

6. A maximum value given by
$$\begin{vmatrix} 0, & c, & b, & \dfrac{2u}{n} \\[2mm] c, & 0, & a, & \dfrac{2u}{n} \\[2mm] b, & a, & 0, & \dfrac{2u}{n} \\[2mm] 1, & 1, & 1, & n \end{vmatrix}=0,$$

assuming that a, b, c are such that a triangle could be constructed with these sides.

7. The results are the roots of the quadratic
$$l^2 a^4/(1-a^2 u)+m^2 b^4/(1-b^2 u)+n^2 c^4/(1-c^2 u)=0.$$

8. Volume $=8abc/3\sqrt{3}$.

9. $\{\log(Aabc)\}^3/\log a^3 \cdot \log b^3 \cdot \log c^3$.

10. If a^3 be the given volume the parallelopiped is a cube of surface $6a^2$.

11. The root of
$$\begin{vmatrix} u, & 1, & 1 \\ 1, & \Sigma a^2, & \Sigma aa' \\ 1, & \Sigma aa', & \Sigma a'^2 \end{vmatrix}=0.$$

12. The solutions are respectively the roots of

   (1) $\left(\dfrac{1}{a}-u\right)\left(\dfrac{1}{b}-u\right)\left(\dfrac{1}{c}-u\right)=0.$

(2)
$$\begin{vmatrix} a-\dfrac{1}{u}, & h, & g \\[2mm] h, & b-\dfrac{1}{u}, & f \\[2mm] g, & f, & c-\dfrac{1}{u} \end{vmatrix} = 0.$$

(3) $l^2 \Big/ \Big(a-\dfrac{1}{u}\Big) + m^2 \Big/ \Big(b-\dfrac{1}{u}\Big) + n^2 \Big/ \Big(c-\dfrac{1}{u}\Big) = 0.$

(4)
$$\begin{vmatrix} a-\dfrac{1}{u}, & h, & g, & l \\[2mm] h, & b-\dfrac{1}{u}, & f, & m \\[2mm] g, & f, & c-\dfrac{1}{u}, & n \\[2mm] l, & m, & n, & 0 \end{vmatrix} = 0.$$

13. The values of x, y, z are given by

$$\frac{x_{p-l}}{l/pa} = \frac{y^{q-m}}{m/qb} = \frac{z^{r-n}}{n/rc}.$$

14. a, x, y, z, b are to be in geometrical progression and the maximum value is $(a^{\frac{1}{4}} + b^{\frac{1}{4}})^{-4}$.

15. $u = k^2/(a^2 + b^2 + c^2 + \ldots)$.

17. The centroid.

18. It is such that each side subtends an angle of $120°$ there.

19. The faces should be equally inclined to the base.

20. $\Big(\dfrac{3V}{n}\Big)^n \Big/ (A_1 A_2 A_3 \ldots A_n)$ when V is the volume and A_1, $A_2 \ldots A_n$ the n faces.

22. They are the roots of

$$\frac{k^2}{\rho^2}(1+p^2+q^2) - \frac{k}{\rho}\{(1+q^2)r - 2pqs + (1+p^2)t\} + rt - s^2 = 0.$$

CHAPTER XVII.

Page 436.

1. $2xy_1 = y.$

3. $\dfrac{d^2 r}{d\theta^2}\tan\theta = \dfrac{dr}{d\theta}.$

5. $y_2 - n^2 y = 0.$

2. $x(y_1{}^2 + yy_2) = yy_1.$

4. $y_3 = 0.$

6. $y_2 + n^2 y = 0.$

Page 437.

1. $xy_1 = x^2 + 2y.$

2. $(1+x^2)y_1 = ay.$

3. $x^2 y_2 + xy_1 + y = 0.$

Page 444.

1. $y_2 + n^2 y = 0.$

4. $y_2 - 2y_1 + 2y = 0.$

2. $y_2 - 2ny_1 + n^2 y = 0.$

5. $y_2 - 4y_1 + 13y = 0.$

3. $xy_2 + 2y_1 - xy = 0.$

6. $y_2 - 2my_1 + (m^2 + n^2)y = 0.$

7. $(y_3 + y_1^3 - y_1)(y_1^2 - 1) = 3y_1 y_2^2.$

8. $y_3(y - xy_1) + 3xy_2^2 = 0.$

9. $x^2 y_2 + xy_1 + y = 0.$

10. $y_2 + y_1^2 + 1 = 0.$

11. $y_2 + n^2 y = \cos mx.$

19. $p = y/(y^2 - x^2)^{\frac{1}{2}}.$

12. $y_2 + n^2 y = 2n \cos nx.$

13. $y_3 + py_2 + qy_1 + ry = 0.$

16. $y_3 - y_2 - y_1 + y = 0.$

17. $y_4 + 2n^2 y_2 + n^4 y = 0.$

18. $(a + bx)^2 y_2 + b(a + bx)y_1 + n^2 y = 0.$

37. $(x^2 r - y^2 t)z + (z - px - qy)(px - qy) = 0.$

CHAPTER XVIII.

PAGE 459.

15.
$$x = \frac{1}{2}\left(\frac{2x}{1+x^2}\right) + \frac{1}{2 \cdot 4}\left(\frac{2x}{1+x^2}\right)^3 + \frac{1 \cdot 3}{2 \cdot 4 \cdot 6}\left(\frac{2x}{1+x^2}\right)^5 + \ldots,$$

which is true between 1 and -1. If $x > 1$ the series stands for $\frac{1}{x}$.

16. $e^{az} = 1 + a(ze^{bz}) + a(a - 2b)\dfrac{(ze^{bz})^2}{2!} + a(a - 3b)^2\dfrac{(ze^{bz})^3}{3!} + \ldots.$

CHAPTER XIX.

PAGE 471.

1. $\dfrac{d^2 y}{dz^2} + n^2 y = 0.$

4. $\dfrac{d^2 y}{dx^2} + y = 0.$

5. $b^2\dfrac{d^2 y}{dz^2} + (Ab - b^2)\dfrac{dy}{dz} + By = f\left(\dfrac{e^z - a}{b}\right).$

6. $\dfrac{d^2 y}{dz^2} + y = 0.$

7. $\dfrac{1}{p^2} = u^2 + \left(\dfrac{du}{d\theta}\right)^2.$

8. $\tan \phi = \dfrac{x\dfrac{dy}{dx} - y}{x + y\dfrac{dy}{dx}}.$

11. $2uv^3 + 4v^4\left(\dfrac{dv}{du}\right)^{-1} - v^5\dfrac{d^2 v}{du^2}\left(\dfrac{dv}{du}\right)^{-3}.$

20. $\dfrac{d^2 P}{d\theta^2} + \cot \theta \dfrac{dP}{d\theta} + n(n+1)P = 0.$

26. $\dfrac{d^2 y}{dt^2} + \dfrac{1}{\sqrt{P}}\left(Q - \dfrac{1}{2}\dfrac{dP}{dx}\right)\dfrac{dy}{dt}.$

27. $\dfrac{d^2 z}{dv^2} + z = 0.$

31. $\dfrac{\partial^2 V}{\partial \theta^2} + \dfrac{\partial^2 V}{\partial \phi^2}.$

35. $a_1 a_2 + b_1 b_2 = 0.$

37. $2\eta\dfrac{\partial^2 u}{\partial \eta^2} + \dfrac{\partial u}{\partial \eta} = 0.$

WORKS ON
HIGHER PURE MATHEMATICS.

A TREATISE ON DIFFERENTIAL EQUATIONS. By
A. R. FORSYTH, F.R.S. Fourth Edition. 8vo. 17s. net.

ORDINARY DIFFERENTIAL EQUATIONS. By PROF.
JAMES M. PAGE, M.A., Ph.D. Crown 8vo. 6s. 6d.

A SHORT COURSE ON DIFFERENTIAL EQUATIONS.
By PROF. DONALD F. CAMPBELL, Ph.D. Crown 8vo.
4s. net.

THE MODERN THEORY OF EQUATIONS. By F.
CAJORI. Extra Crown 8vo. 10s. net.

AN ELEMENTARY TREATISE ON THE THEORY OF
EQUATIONS. By ISAAC TODHUNTER, F.R.S. Crown
8vo. 8s. 6d.

ELLIPTIC FUNCTIONS. By A. C. DIXON, M.A. Globe
8vo. 5s.

APPLICATIONS OF ELLIPTIC FUNCTIONS. By SIR
A. G. GREENHILL, F.R.S. 8vo. 14s.

TREATISE ON BESSEL FUNCTIONS. By PROF. A.
GRAY and PROF. G. B. MATHEWS. 8vo. 14s. net.

LONDON : MACMILLAN & CO., LTD.